Differential Equations

STABILITY, OSCILLATIONS, TIME LAGS

MATHEMATICS IN SCIENCE AND ENGINEERING

A SERIES OF MONOGRAPHS AND TEXTBOOKS

Edited by Richard Bellman

1. TRACY Y. THOMAS. Concepts from Tensor Analysis and Differential Geometry. Second Edition. 1965
2. TRACY Y. THOMAS. Plastic Flow and Fracture in Solids. 1961
3. RUTHERFORD ARIS. The Optimal Design of Chemical Reactors: A Study in Dynamic Programming. 1961
4. JOSEPH LA SALLE and SOLOMON LEFSCHETZ. Stability by Liapunov's Direct Method with Applications. 1961
5. GEORGE LEITMANN (ed.). Optimization Techniques: With Applications to Aerospace Systems. 1962
6. RICHARD BELLMAN and KENNETH L. COOKE. Differential-Difference Equations. 1963
7. FRANK A. HAIGHT. Mathematical Theories of Traffic Flow. 1963
8. F. V. ATKINSON. Discrete and Continuous Boundary Problems. 1964
9. A. JEFFREY and T. TANIUTI. Non-Linear Wave Propagation: With Applications to Physics and Magnetohydrodynamics. 1964
10. JULIUS T. TOU. Optimum Design of Digital Control Systems. 1963
11. HARLEY FLANDERS. Differential Forms: With Applications to the Physical Sciences. 1963
12. SANFORD M. ROBERTS. Dynamic Programming in Chemical Engineering and Process Control. 1964
13. SOLOMON LEFSCHETZ. Stability of Nonlinear Control Systems. 1965
14. DIMITRIS N. CHORAFAS. Systems and Simulation. 1965
15. A. A. PERVOZVANSKII. Random Processes in Nonlinear Control Systems. 1965
16. MARSHALL C. PEASE, III. Methods of Matrix Algebra. 1965
17. V. E. BENEŠ. Mathematical Theory of Connecting Networks and Telephone Traffic. 1965
18. WILLIAM F. AMES. Nonlinear Partial Differential Equations in Engineering. 1965

MATHEMATICS IN SCIENCE AND ENGINEERING

19. J. Aczél. Lectures on Functional Equations and Their Applications. 1965

20. R. E. Murphy. Adaptive Processes in Economic Systems. 1965

21. S. E. Dreyfus. Dynamic Programming and the Calculus of Variations. 1965

22. A. A. Fel'dbaum. Optimal Control Systems. 1965

23. A. Halanay. Differential Equations: Stability, Oscillations, Time Lags. 1965

In preparation

Dimitris N. Chorafas. Control Systems Functions and Programming Approaches

David Sworder. Optimal Adaptive Control Systems

Namik Oğuztöreli. Time Lag Control Processes

Milton Ash. Optimal Shutdown Control in Nuclear Reactors

Differential Equations

STABILITY, OSCILLATIONS, TIME LAGS

A. Halanay

BUCHAREST UNIVERSITY
INSTITUTE OF MATHEMATICS
ACADEMY OF THE SOCIALIST REPUBLIC OF RUMANIA

1966

ACADEMIC PRESS New York and London

ACADEMIC PRESS INC.
111 Fifth Avenue, New York, New York 10003

United Kingdom Edition published by
ACADEMIC PRESS INC. (LONDON) LTD.
Berkeley Square House, London W.1

LIBRARY OF CONGRESS CATALOG CARD NUMBER: 65-25005

PRINTED IN THE UNITED STATES OF AMERICA

DIFFERENTIAL EQUATIONS:
STABILITY, OSCILLATIONS, TIME LAGS

THIS BOOK WAS ORIGINALLY PUBLISHED AS:
TEORIA CALITATIVA A ECUATIILOR DIFERENTIALE. STABILITATEA DUPA LIAPUNOV.
OSCILATII. SISTEME CU ARGUMENT INTIRZIAT
EDITURA ACADEMIEI REPUBLICII POPULARE
ROMINE, BUCHAREST, 1963

Preface to the English Edition

When it was proposed that an English version of my book on stability and oscillation in differential and differential-difference equations be published, my first intention was to modify it substantially. Indeed, although the Rumanian original appeared in 1963, most of it was written in 1961. In the meantime, progress which deserved to be reported was achieved in all the fields covered in the book. Many remarkable works appeared in the United States. However, the desire not to delay the appearance of this book too much finally prompted me to renounce the initial plan and to content myself with making extensive changes only in the last chapter on systems with time lag. In this chapter, only Sections 1, 2, 5, 13–16 (Sections 1, 2, 4, 11–15 in the Rumanian edition) remain unchanged; the other paragraphs are either newly introduced or completely transformed. Also, Section 11 of Chapter III was completely rewritten. In the new version of Chapter IV the results concerning stability of linear systems with constant coefficients are deduced from the general theory of linear systems with periodic coefficients. Since the book of N. N. Krasovskii on stability theory is now available in English, Appendix III of the Rumanian edition was not included.

Throughout the text a number of misprints and oversights in the Rumanian edition were corrected. Some new titles (89–109), considerably fewer than would have been necessary had my original plan been carried out, were added to the Bibliography. The notations are not always those currently used in the American literature, but this will not create difficulties in reading because all the notation is explained, and the sense will be clear from the context.

I wish to express here my gratitude and warmest thanks to Dr. R. Bellman for his keen interest in this book and for the tiring work he kindly undertook to check the entire translation and to improve it. It is for me a great privilege and pleasure to have this book published in his very interesting and useful series, which in the short time since its inception has won unanimous acceptance.

A. HALANAY

December, 1965
Bucharest

Preface to the Rumanian Edition

The qualitative theory of differential equations is in a process of continuous development, reflected in the great number of books and papers dedicated to it. It is well known that the beginning of the qualitative theory of differential equations is directly connected with the classical works of Poincaré, Lyapunov, and Birkhoff on problems of ordinary and celestial mechanics. From these origins, stability theory, the mathematical theory of oscillations with small parameters, and the general theory of dynamic systems have been developed. The great upsurge, circa 1930, of the qualitative theory of differential equations in the USSR began, on the one hand, with the study, at the Aviation Institute in Kazan, of problems of stability theory with applications in aircraft stability research, and on the other hand, in Moscow, as a consequence of the observations of A. A. Andronov of the useful role played by the theory of periodic solutions of nonlinear equations in explaining some phenomena of radiotechniques. It is the period marked, for example, by the renowned book on the theory of oscillations by A. A. Andronov, Haikin, and Witt, and the well-known book on nonlinear mechanics by Krylov and Bogoliubov.

From 1930 on at Moscow University, a seminar was held on the qualitative theory of differential equations with particular emphasis on fundamental theoretical problems. The results of the first seminar appeared in the two editions of V. V. Nemytzki and V. V. Stepanov's monograph, "The Qualitative Theory of Differential Equations." Wide circulation of this book led to the growth of research in this area.

In the last ten to fifteen years, stability theory and the theory of periodic solutions (to which is added the problem of almost periodic solutions) have been given a new impulse because they represent essential parts of the mathematical apparatus of modern control theory.

A characteristic feature of the development of the qualitative theory of differential equations is the fact that, in solving its problems, a most varied mathematical apparatus is used: topology and functional analysis, linear algebra, and the theory of functions of a complex variable.

Taking into account the great variety of problems, the choice of material for a book devoted to the qualitative theory of differential equations is a difficult task. The author was guided in his selection by the idea of a systematic and consistent exposition of both stability theory (relying in the first place on the method of Lyapunov's function) and oscillation theory, including the theory of small parameter systems. In this exposition emphasis is placed on general theorems, on that development of the theory which clarifies ideas and methods. A chapter related to the stability theory of control systems is included, in which stress is also placed on the most general theorems, and particularly on the presentation of the essential contributions of V. M. Popov, corresponding member of the Academy of the Socialist Republic of Rumania. The last chapter takes up once again the problems of the stability and oscillation theories within the framework of delayed systems. In recent years, these problems have occupied an important place in the attention of mathematicians as well as of those working in the field of applications. In the whole work a series of results obtained in the Socialist Republic of Rumania are included; the last chapter particularly represents a systematic and improved exposition of the author's results in the theory of delayed systems.

The Notes at the end of each chapter are intended to indicate the sources which were consulted when writing this book or those whose ideas are developed in the work. A few exceptions have been made such as mentioning some fundamental ideas not included in the book since they required too extended a development. The Bibliography is not complete, even in the limited sense mentioned above.

THE AUTHOR

Contents

Introduction

CHAPTER 1

Stability Theory

CHAPTER 2

Absolute Stability of Nonlinear Control Systems

CHAPTER 3

Theory of Oscillations

CHAPTER 4

Systems with Time Lag

Appendix

Differential Equations

STABILITY, OSCILLATIONS, TIME LAGS

Introduction

The foundations of the qualitative theory of differential equations are the general theorems of existence, uniqueness, and continuous dependence of the initial conditions and parameters. Therefore, we shall begin by recalling these general theorems and establishing on this occasion some lemmas which will be encountered often in the following pages. The notation most frequently used will be described.

I.1. Vector Representation of Systems of Differential Equations

Let us consider a system of differential equations of the form

$$\frac{dx_i}{dt} = f_i(t, x_1, \dots, x_n) \qquad (i - 1, 2, \dots, n).$$

We shall denote by x the column vector

$$\begin{pmatrix} x_1 \\ \vdots \\ x_n \end{pmatrix}.$$

Ordinarily we shall use the Euclidean norm $|x| = \sqrt{x_1^2 + \cdots + x_n^2}$. In some cases it is also convenient to employ the equivalent norms

$$|x| = |x_1| + |x_2| + \cdots + |x_n| \quad \text{or} \quad |x| = \max_{i=1,2,\cdots,n} |x_i|;$$

when using these norms we shall mention it explicitly.

The derivative of the vector $x(t)$ is, by definition, the vector

$$\begin{pmatrix} \frac{dx_1}{dt} \\ \vdots \\ \frac{dx_n}{dt} \end{pmatrix}.$$

This is not merely a formal definition; it coincides with $\lim_{t\to t_0} [x(t) - x(t_0)]/(t - t_0)$ the limit being defined by means of the norm introduced above. The integral of the vector $x(t)$ on $[a, b]$ is also, by definition, the vector

$$\begin{pmatrix} \int_a^b x_1(t)dt \\ \vdots \\ \int_a^b x_n(t)dt \end{pmatrix}.$$

This, too, is not a formal definition; one may obtain it by defining the integral in the usual way with the aid of the Riemann sums.

Very often we will use the evaluation

$$\left| \int_a^b x(t)dt \right| \leqslant \int_a^b |x(t)|\, dt.$$

We have

$$\left| \int_a^b x(t)dt \right| = \left\{ \left(\int_a^b x_1(t)dt \right)^2 + \left(\int_a^b x_2(t)dt \right)^2 + \cdots + \left(\int_a^b x_n(t)dt \right)^2 \right\}^{1/2}.$$

We denote

$$J_k = \int_a^b x_k(t)dt, \qquad b_k = \frac{J_k}{\sqrt{\sum_l J_l^2}}.$$

Then

$$\sum_k b_k J_k = \frac{\sum_k J_k^2}{\sqrt{\sum_l J_l^2}} = \sqrt{\sum_k J_k^2} = \left| \int_a^b x(t)dt \right|.$$

On the other hand,

$$\sum_k b_k J_k = \sum_k b_k \int_a^b x_k(t)dt = \int_a^b \sum_k b_k x_k(t)dt \leqslant \int_a^b \sqrt{\sum_k b_k^2} \sqrt{\sum_k x_k^2(t)}\, dt.$$

Since $\sum_k b_k^2 = 1$,

$$\sum_k b_k J_k \leqslant \int_a^b \sqrt{\sum_k x_k^2(t)}\, dt = \int_a^b |x(t)|\, dt$$

which proves the above inequality.

I.2. The Existence Theorem

In the vectorial notations introduced above, the system of differential equations will be written

$$\frac{dx}{dt} = f(t, x). \tag{1}$$

We shall assume in what follows that f is continuous in a domain $D \subset R^{n+1}$.

Definition. *A function φ defined and continuous on an interval I of the real axis (with values in R^n) is called an ϵ-solution of system* (1) *on I if:*

(a) $(t, \varphi(t)) \in D$ for $t \in I$.

(b) *φ has a continuous derivative on I with the exception at most of a finite number of points from I.*

(c) $|(d\varphi/dt) - f[t, \varphi(t)]| \leqslant \epsilon$, *in those points where $d\varphi/dt$ exists and is continuous.*

Lemma I.1. *Let $D : |t - t_0| \leqslant a, |x - x_0| \leqslant b, M = \max|f(t, x)|$, $\alpha = \min(a, b/M)$. Then for any $\epsilon > 0$ there exists a ϵ-solution of system* (1) *in $|t - t_0| \leqslant \alpha$ such that $\varphi(t_0) = x_0$.*

Proof. Since f is continuous on the compact set D, it is uniformly continuous; hence for $\epsilon > 0$, there exists a $\delta(\epsilon) > 0$ such that $|f(t, x) - f(\tilde{t}, \tilde{x})| \leqslant \epsilon$ for $(t, x) \subset D$, $(\tilde{t}, \tilde{x}) \in D$, $|t - \tilde{t}| \leqslant \delta(\epsilon)$, $|x - \tilde{x}| \leqslant \delta(\epsilon)$. Let us consider a division of the interval $[t_0, t_0 + \alpha]$ by means of points $t_0 < t_1 < t_2 \cdots < t_n = t_0 + \alpha$ such that

$$\max|t_k - t_{k-1}| \leqslant \min\left(\delta(\epsilon), \frac{\delta(\epsilon)}{M}\right).$$

We define the function φ on $[t_0, t_0 + \alpha]$ through the relations $\varphi(t_0) = x_0$, $\varphi(t) = \varphi(t_{k-1}) + f[t_{k-1}, \varphi(t_{k-1})](t - t_{k-1})$ for $t_{k-1} < t \leqslant t_k$. The function thus defined is continuous, differentiable in the interior of intervals (t_k, t_{k+1}). In addition, $|\varphi(t) - \varphi(\tilde{t})| \leqslant M|t - \tilde{t}|$. For $t \in (t_{k-1}, t_k)$ it follows that $t - t_{k-1} < \delta(\epsilon)$ and $|\varphi(t) - \varphi(t_{k-1})| \leqslant \delta(\epsilon)$. Hence

$$\left|\frac{d\varphi}{dt} - f[t, \varphi(t)]\right| = |f[t_{k-1}, \varphi(t_{k-1})] - f[t, \varphi(t)]| < \epsilon,$$

and therefore φ is a ϵ-solution. The ϵ-solution is constructed in the same way in the interval $[t_0 - \alpha, t_0]$.

Theorem I.1. *Let* $D : |t-t_0| \leqslant a, |x-x_0| \leqslant b, M = \max_D |f(t, x)|$, $\alpha = \min(a, b/M)$. *Then there exists in* $|t - t_0| \leqslant \alpha$ *a solution* φ *of system* (1) *with* $\varphi(t_0) = x_0$.

Proof. Let $\epsilon_n > 0$, $\epsilon_{n+1} < \epsilon_n$, $\lim_{n\to\infty} \epsilon_n = 0$; for each ϵ_n there exists, on the basis of Lemma I.1, an ϵ_n-solution φ_n defined on $|t-t_0| \leqslant \alpha$ and such that $\varphi_n(t_0) = x_0$; in addition, $|\varphi_n(t) - \varphi_n(\tilde{t})| \leqslant M|t - \tilde{t}|$. It follows that the functions φ_n are uniformly bounded and equally continuous on $|t - t_0| \leqslant \alpha$; hence on the basis of the theorem of Arzelà (Ascoli), there exists a subsequence φ_{n_k} uniformly convergent on $|t - t_0| \leqslant \alpha$ toward a function φ. This function is continuous, and, in addition, $|\varphi(t) - \varphi(\tilde{t})| \leqslant M|t - \tilde{t}|$.

Let $\Delta_n(t) = (d\varphi_n/dt) - f[t, \varphi_n(t)]$ in the points in which φ_n is differentiable and $\Delta_n(t) = 0$ in the points in which φ_n is not differentiable. We have

$$\varphi_n(t) = x_0 + \int_{t_0}^{t} [f(s, \varphi_n(s)) + \Delta_n(s)]ds \qquad \Delta_n(t)| \leqslant \epsilon_n .$$

Since $f[t, \varphi_{n_k}(t)]$ converges uniformly in $|t - t_0| \leqslant \alpha$ to $f[t, \varphi(t)]$ and Δ_{n_k} tends uniformly to zero, it is possible to pass to the limit under the integration sign, and it follows that

$$\varphi(t) = \alpha_0 + \int_{t_0}^{t} f[s, \varphi(s)]ds.$$

Since f is continuous, it follows that φ is differentiable in $|t - t_0| \leqslant \alpha$ and $\dot{\varphi}(t) = f[t, \varphi(t)]$. The theorem is thus proved.

I.3. Differential Inequalities

Before passing to further theorems of uniqueness and continuous dependence of the initial conditions, we shall establish some lemmas which are interesting in themselves.

Lemma I.2. *Let* φ *be a real function defined for* $t_0 \leqslant t < t_0 + \alpha$; *we denote*

$$D_{-}\varphi(t) = \liminf_{h\to 0} \frac{\varphi(t + h) - \varphi(t)}{h}.$$

Let φ *and* ψ *be continuous in* $[t_0, t_0 + \alpha)$ *and with the properties*:

(a) $\varphi(t_0) < \psi(t_0)$.

(b) $D_{-}\varphi(t) < f[t, \varphi(t)]$, $D_{-}\psi(t) \geqslant f[t, \psi(t)]$, *for* $t \in [t_0, t_0 + \alpha)$. *Then* $\varphi(t) < \psi(t)$ *on* $[t_0, t_0 + \alpha)$.

Proof. Let us consider the set of values t from $[t_0, t_0 + \alpha)$, where $\varphi(t) \geqslant \psi(t)$; this set does not contain t_0 in conformity with the hypothesis. If it is not void, let ξ be its lower bound.

We have $\varphi(\xi) = \psi(\xi)$, hence $D_{-}\varphi(\xi) < f[\xi, \varphi(\xi)] = f[\xi, \psi(\xi)] \leqslant D_{-}\psi(\xi)$. Therefore it follows that there exists an interval $t_0 \leqslant t < \xi$ such that

$$\frac{\varphi(t) - \varphi(\xi)}{t - \xi} < \frac{\psi(t) - \psi(\xi)}{t - \xi}.$$

Hence

$$\varphi(t) - \varphi(\xi) > \psi(t) - \psi(\xi),$$

and thus $\varphi(t) > \psi(t)$, which comes into contradiction with the definition of ξ as lower bound. The set considered is therefore void and the lemma is proved.

Lemma I.3. *Let f be continuous for $|t - t_0| \leqslant a$, $|y - y_0| \leqslant b$. Let $M = \max|f(t, y)|$, $\alpha = \min(a, b/M)$, $\beta < \alpha$. Then there exists a solution $y(t)$ of the equation $y' = f(t, y)$ defined in $[t_0, t_0 + \beta]$ such that $y(t_0) = y_0$ and with the property that if $z(t)$ is a solution of the equation with $z(t_0) = y_0$ it follows that $z(t) \leqslant y(t)$ on $[t_0, t_0 + \beta]$.*

Proof. There exists an $\epsilon_0 > 0$ such that if $0 \leqslant \epsilon < \epsilon_0$, the equation $y' = f(t, y) + \epsilon$ admits a solution in $[t_0, t_0 + \beta]$. Let $\epsilon_n > 0$, $\epsilon_{n+1} < \epsilon_n < \epsilon_0$, $\lim_{n\to\infty} \epsilon_n = 0$, and y_n be a monotone-decreasing sequence tending to y_0. If $y_n(t)$ is the solution of the equation $y' = f(t, y) + \epsilon_n$, with $y_n(t_0) = y_n$, it follows on the ground of Lemma I.2 that $z(t) < y_{n+1}(t) < y_n(t)$ in $[t_0, t_0 + \beta]$.

It follows that for any $t \in [t_0, t_0 + \beta]$ we have

$$\lim_{n\to\infty} y_n(t) = y(t);$$

hence

$$\lim_{n\to\infty} [f(t, y_n(t)) + \epsilon_n] = f(t, y(t)),$$

and thus

$$y_n'(t) \to f(t, y(t)).$$

Since the sequence $y_n(t)$ is monotone-decreasing, the functions $y_n(t)$ are uniformly bounded; since the sequence $y_n'(t)$ of the derivates is uniformly bounded, the functions $y_n(t)$ are equicontinuous. But then, on the ground of Arzelà's theorem, the sequence $y_n(t)$ is uniformly convergent in $[t_0, t_0 + \beta]$, and $y(t)$ is a solution of the equation $y' = f(t, y)$.

Since $y_n \to y_0$, it follows that $y(t_0) = y_0$. Let $z(t)$ be a solution with

$z(t_0) = y_0$. We have for all n, on the ground of Lemma I.2, $z(t) < y_n(t)$ for $t \in [t_0, t_0 + \beta]$. For $n \to \infty$, we get $z(t) \leqslant y(t)$ in $[t_0, t_0 + \beta]$, and the lemma is proved.

Lemma I.4. *Let f be continuous for $|t - t_0| \leqslant a$, $|y - y_0| \leqslant b$, $M = \max |f(t, y)|$, $\alpha = \min(a, b/M)$, $y(t)$ the solution whose existence is asserted by Lemma* I.3, *and $\omega(t)$ a differentiable function on $[t_0, t_0 + \beta]$ such that $\omega'(t) \leqslant f[t, \omega(t)]$, $\omega(t_0) \leqslant y(t_0)$. Then $\omega(t) \leqslant y(t)$ in $[t_0, t_0 + \beta]$.*

Proof. Let $\epsilon_n > 0$, $\epsilon_{n+1} < \epsilon_n$, $\lim_{n\to\infty} \epsilon_n = 0$, and let y_n be a monotonically decreasing sequence tending toward $y(t_0)$. We have

$$\omega'(t) \leqslant f[t, \omega(t)] < f[t, \omega(t)] + \epsilon_n \qquad \omega(t_0) \leqslant y(t_0) < y_n;$$

hence on the ground of Lemma I.2, $\omega(t) < y_n(t)$ in $[t_0, t_0 + \beta)$. Therefore for $n \to \infty$ it follows that $\omega(t) \leqslant y(t)$ in $[t_0, t_0 + \beta]$.

Lemma I.5. *The equation*

$$y' = a(t)y + b(t).$$

where $a(t)$ and $b(t)$ are continuous on $|t - t_0| \leqslant \alpha$, has in this interval the solution

$$y(t) = y_0 \exp\left[\int_{t_0}^{t} a(s)ds\right] + \int_{t_0}^{t} \exp\left[\int_{s}^{t} a(u)du\right] b(s)ds,$$

and this solution is the unique solution for which $y(t_0) = y_0$.

Proof. The fact that $y(t)$ is a solution is immediately checked through differentiation. Let us show that the solution is unique. Let $\tilde{y}(t)$ be another solution with $\tilde{y}(t_0) = y_0$, $z(t) = \tilde{y}(t) - y(t)$. It follows that $z(t_0) = 0$ and $z'(t) = a(t)z(t)$; hence $z(t) = \int_{t_0}^{t} a(s)z(s)ds$. Therefore, $|z(t)| \leqslant M \int_{t_0}^{t} |z(s)|\, ds$. If there exists $t_1 > t_0$ such that $\int_{t_0}^{t_1} |z(s)|\, ds = 0$, then $z(s) \equiv 0$ for $t_0 \leqslant t \leqslant t_1$ and we take t_1 instead of t_0. We suppose then that for $t > t_0$ we have $\int_{t_0}^{t} |z(s)|\, ds \neq 0$.

Let $v(t) = \int_{t_0}^{t} |z(s)|\, ds$. We have $v'(t)/v(t) \leqslant M$; hence

$$\int_{\tilde{t}}^{t} \frac{v'(t)}{v(t)}\, dt \leqslant M(t - \tilde{t}),$$

and thus $\ln v(t) - \ln v(\tilde{t}) \leqslant M(t - \tilde{t})$ for $t_0 < \tilde{t} < t$. Thus, finally, $\ln v(t) \leqslant \ln v(\tilde{t}) + M(t - \tilde{t})$. However, for $\tilde{t} \to t_0$ we have $\ln v(\tilde{t}) \to -\infty$, since $v(t_0) = 0$. The inequality is contradictory, hence $z(t) \equiv 0$.

Lemma I.6. *Let φ, ψ, χ be real functions defined in $[a, b]$ and continuous, $\chi(t) > 0$. We suppose that on $[a, b]$ we have the inequality*

$$\varphi(t) \leqslant \psi(t) + \int_a^t \chi(s)\varphi(s)ds.$$

Then

$$\varphi(t) \leqslant \psi(t) + \int_a^t \chi(s)\psi(s) \exp\left[\int_s^t \chi(u)du\right] ds$$

in $[a, b]$.

Proof. Let

$$R(t) = \int_a^t \chi(s)\varphi(s)ds.$$

We have

$$R'(t) = \chi(t)\varphi(t) \leqslant \chi(t)\psi(t) + \chi(t) \int_a^t \chi(s)\varphi(s)ds$$
$$= \chi(t)\psi(t) + \chi(t)R(t).$$

Let us consider the equation

$$z'(t) = \chi(t)z(t) + \chi(t)\psi(t).$$

This equation admits in $[a, b]$ the unique solution

$$z(t) = \int_a^t \exp\left[\int_s^t \chi(u)du\right] \chi(s)\psi(s)ds,$$

which verifies the condition $z(a) = 0$. On the basis of Lemma I.4 it follows that $R(t) \leqslant z(t)$ on $[a, b]$; hence $\varphi(t) \leqslant \psi(t) + R(t) \leqslant \psi(t) + z(t)$, and the lemma is proved.

Consequence 1. *If ψ is differentiable, from $\varphi(t) \leqslant \psi(t) + \int_a^t \chi(s)\varphi(s)ds$ it follows that*

$$\varphi(t) \leqslant \psi(a) \exp\left[\int_a^t \chi(u)du\right] + \int_a^t \exp\left[\int_s^t \chi(u)du\right] \psi'(s)ds.$$

Proof. We have, with the above notations,

$$z(t) = -\int_a^t \psi(s) \frac{d}{ds} \exp\left[\int_s^t \chi(u)du\right] ds$$
$$= -\psi(s) \exp\left[\int_s^t \chi(u)du\right]\Big|_a^t + \int_a^t \exp\left[\int_s^t \chi(u)du\right] \psi'(s)ds$$
$$= -\psi(t) + \psi(a) \exp\left[\int_a^t \chi(u)du\right] + \int_a^t \exp\left[\int_s^t \chi(u)du\right] \psi'(s)ds.$$

Hence

$$\psi(t) + z(t) = \psi(a) \exp\left[\int_a^t \chi(u)du\right] + \int_a^t \exp\left[\int_s^t \chi(u)du\right] \psi'(s)ds.$$

Consequence 2. *If ψ is constant, from*

$$\varphi(t) \leqslant \psi + \int_a^t \chi(s)\varphi(s)ds$$

follows

$$\varphi(t) \leqslant \psi \exp\left[\int_a^t \chi(u)du\right].$$

1.4. The Uniqueness Theorem

Lemma 1.7. *Let f be defined in $D \in R^{n+1}$ and* $|f(t, x_1) - f(t, x_2)| < k(t) | x_1 - x_2 |$.

Let φ_1, φ_2, be, *respectively*, ϵ_1- *and* ϵ_2-*solutions of equation* (1) *on* (a, b), *such that for* $t_0 \in (a, b)$ *we have* $| \varphi_1(t_0)| - \varphi_2(t_0)] \leqslant \delta$. *Then*

$$| \varphi_1(t) - \varphi_2(t)| \leqslant \delta.\exp\left[\left|\int_{t_0}^t k(u)du\right|\right]$$

$$+ (\epsilon_1 + \epsilon_2)\left|\int_{t_0}^t \exp\left[\int_s^t k(u)du\right] ds\right| \qquad \text{in } (a, b).$$

Proof. We suppose $t_0 \leqslant t \leqslant b$; in the interval $[a, t_0]$ the proof is carried out in the same way. We have

$$| \dot\varphi_1(s) - f[s, \varphi_1(s)]| \leqslant \epsilon_1, \qquad | \dot\varphi_2(s) - f[s, \varphi_2(s)]| \leqslant \epsilon_2$$

with the exception of a finite number of points. It follows that

$$\left|\varphi_1(t) - \varphi_1(t_0) - \int_{t_0}^t f[s, \varphi_1(s)]ds\right| \leqslant \epsilon_1(t - t_0),$$

$$\left|\varphi_2(t) - \varphi_2(t_0) - \int_{t_0}^t f[s, \varphi_2(s)]ds\right| \leqslant \epsilon_2(t - t_0),$$

and thus

$$\left|\varphi_1(t) - \varphi_2(t) - [\varphi_1(t_0) - \varphi_2(t_0)] - \int_{t_0}^t [f(s, \varphi_1(s)) - f(s, \varphi_2(s))]ds\right|$$
$$\leqslant (\epsilon_1 + \epsilon_2)(t - t_0).$$

Hence

$$|\varphi_1(t) - \varphi_2(t)| \leqslant |\varphi_1(t_0) - \varphi_2(t_0)| + (\epsilon_1 + \epsilon_2)(t - t_0)$$
$$+ \int_{t_0}^{t} |f(s, \varphi_1(s)) - f(s, \varphi_2(s))| \, ds,$$

or

$$|\varphi_1(t) - \varphi_2(t)| \leqslant |\varphi_1(t_0) - \varphi_2(t_0)| + (\epsilon_1 + \epsilon_2)(t - t_0)$$
$$+ \int_{t_0}^{t} k(s) \, |\varphi_1(s) - \varphi_2(s)| \, ds.$$

We apply Lemma I.6 (Consequence 1), taking $\varphi = |\varphi_1(t) - \varphi_2(t)|$,

$$\psi = (\epsilon_1 + \epsilon_2)(t - t_0) + |\varphi_1(t_0) - \varphi_2(t_0)|, \qquad \chi = k(t).$$

We get

$$|\varphi_1(t) - \varphi_2(t)| \leqslant |\varphi_1(t_0) - \varphi_2(t_0)| \exp\left[\int_{t_0}^{t} k(s)ds\right]$$
$$+ (\epsilon_1 + \epsilon_2) \int_{t_0}^{t} \exp\left[\int_{s}^{t} k(u)du\right] ds,$$

and the lemma is proved.

Theorem I.2. *If*

$$|f(t, x_1) - f(t, x_2)| \leqslant k(t) \, |x_1 - x_2|$$

in $D \subset R^{n+1}$ *and* φ_1, φ_2 *are two solutions of system* (1) *with* $\varphi_1(t_0) = \varphi_2(t_0)$, *then* $\varphi_1(t) = \varphi_2(t)$ *in the interval* (a, b) *in which these solutions are defined.*

Proof. In Lemma I.7 we may take $\delta = 0$, $\epsilon_1 = \epsilon_2 = 0$, and we get $|\varphi_1(t) - \varphi_2(t)| = 0$.

Theorem I.1 shows that the solution of system (1) exists in a neighborhood of the initial point. An important problem is the extension of the solution on as large an interval as possible. Let $\varphi(t)$ be a solution of equation (1) defined in (a, b). Then

$$\varphi(t) = \varphi(t_0) + \int_{t_0}^{t} f[s, \varphi(s)]ds.$$

If $a < t_1 < t_2 < b$, it follows that $|\varphi(t_1) - \varphi(t_2)| \leqslant \int_{t_1}^{t_2} |f(s, \varphi(s))| \, ds \leqslant M(t_2 - t_1)$; hence $\lim_{t \to a, t > a} \varphi(t)$ and $\lim_{t \to b, t < b} \varphi(t)$ exist. If the point

$(b, \varphi(b-0))$ is in D, the function $\tilde{\varphi}$ defined through $\tilde{\varphi}(t) = \varphi(t)$ for $t \in (a, b)$, $\tilde{\varphi}(b) = \varphi(b-0)$ is a solution of the system in (a, b); this solution may be extended for $t > b$, by taking b as the initial point and $\varphi(b-0)$ as the initial value. From this it follows that a solution may be extended as long as it does not leave D.

I.5. Theorems of Continuity and Differentiability with Respect to Initial Conditions

In what follows we shall denote by $x(t; t_0, x_0)$ the solution of system (1) which for $t = t_0$ takes the value x_0.

Theorem I.3. *If* $|f(t, x_1) - f(t, x_2)| < k(t) \mid x_1 - x_2 \mid$ *in* D, *then from* $x_n \to x_0$ *follows* $x(t; t_0, x_n) \to x(t; t_0, x_0)$.

Proof. We have

$$x(t; t_0, x_n) = x_n + \int_{t_0}^{t} f[s, x(s; t_0, x_n)]ds,$$

$$x(t; t_0, x_0) = x_0 + \int_{t_0}^{t} f[s, x(s; t_0, x_0)]ds.$$

It follows that for $t \geqslant t_0$,

$$| x(t; t_0, x_n) - x(t; t_0, x_0)|$$

$$\leqslant | x_n - x_0 | + \int_{t_0}^{t} |f[s, x(s; t_0, x_n)] - f[s, x(s; t_0, x_0)]| \, ds$$

$$\leqslant | x_n - x_0 | + \int_{t_0}^{t} k(s) \, | x(s; t_0, x_n) - x(s; t_0, x_0)| \, ds.$$

Applying Lemma I.6 (Consequence 2), we have

$$| x(t; t_0, x_n) - x(t; t_0, x_0)| \leqslant | x_n - x_0 | \exp \left[\int_{t_0}^{t} k(s)ds \right],$$

and the theorem is proved.

Remark. It follows from the proof that the convergence is uniform with respect to t on any interval $[a, b]$ on which the solutions are defined.

Let us assume now that $f(t, x)$ is differentiable in D, for $t \in I$. That means that for any $x_0 \in D$, $t \in I$, we have the relation

$$f(t, x) - f(t, x_0) = f'_x(t, x_0)(x - x_0) + o(| x - x_0 |).$$

Let us consider now a solution $x(t; t_0, x_0)$ lying in D for $t \in I$.

Theorem I.4. *If f is differentiable in D for $t \in I$, and $x(t; t_0, x_0)$ is in D for $t \in I$, then $x(t; t_0, x_0)$ is differentiable with respect to x_0 and $\partial x(t; t_0, x_0)/\partial x_0$ is a fundamental matrix of solutions of the linear system*

$$\frac{dy}{dt} = \frac{\partial f(t, x(t; t_0, x_0))}{\partial x} y,$$

called the variational system corresponding to the solution $x(t; t_0, x_0)$.

Proof. Let x_1 be such that the solution $x(t; t_0, x_1)$ is in D for all $t \in I$. Let $Y(t, t_0)$ be a fundamental matrix of the variational system, i.e., a matrix whose columns are solutions of the variational system such that $Y(t_0, t_0) = E$, E being the unity matrix. Then $Y(t, t_0)(x_1 - x_0)$ will be a solution of the variational system which for $t = t_0$ coincides with $x_1 - x_0$.

We have the relations

$$x(t; t_0, x_0) = x_0 + \int_{t_0}^{t} f[s, x(s; t_0, x_0)]ds,$$

$$x(t; t_0, x_1) = x_1 + \int_{t_0}^{t} f[s, x(s; t_0, x_1)]ds,$$

$$Y(t, t_0)(x_1 - x_0) = x_1 - x_0 + \int_{t_0}^{t} \frac{\partial f[s, x(s; t_0, x_0)]}{\partial x} Y(s, t_0)(x_1 - x_0)ds.$$

It follows that

$$x(t; t_0, x_1) - x(t; t_0, x_0) - Y(t, t_0)(x_1 - x_0)$$

$$= \int_{t_0}^{t} \Big\{ f[s, x(s; t_0, x_1)] - f[s, x(s; t_0, x_0)] - \frac{\partial f[s, x(s; t_0, x_0)]}{\partial x} Y(s, t_0)(x_1 - x_0) \Big\} ds.$$

Taking into account the hypothesis on the differentiability of the function f, we deduce

$$x(t; t_0, x_1) - x(t; t_0, x_0) - Y(t, t_0)(x_1 - x_0)$$
$$= \int_{t_0}^{t} f'_x[s, x(s; t_0, x_0)][x(s; t_0, x_1) - x(s; t_0, x_0) - Y(s, t_0)(x_1 - x_0)]ds$$
$$+ \int_{t_0}^{t} o(| x(s; t_0, x_1) - x(s; t_0, x_0)|)ds.$$

On the basis of the relation in the proof of Theorem I.3, it follows that

$$| x(s; t_0, x_1) - x(s; t_0, x_0)| \leqslant \exp\left(\int_{t_0}^{s} k(s)\, ds\right) | x_1 - x_0 |;$$

hence

$$o(| x(s; t_0, x_1) - x(s; t_0, x_0)|) = o(| x_1 - x_0 |)$$

for fixed t. Consequently,

$$| x(t; t_0, x_1) - x(t; t_0, x_0) - Y(t, t_0)(x_1 - x_0)|$$
$$\leqslant \int_{t_0}^{t} k(s)\, | x(s; t_0, x_1) - x(s; t_0, x_0) - Y(s; t_0)(x_1 - x_0)|\, ds + o(| x_1 - x_0 |).$$

Thus on the basis of Lemma I.6,

$$| x(t; t_0, x_1) - x(t; t_0, x_0) - Y(t, t_0)(x_1 - x_0)| = o(| x_1 - x_0 |),$$

which proves the theorem.

Analogously, we can prove a theorem concerning the differentiability with respect to t_0 and, generally, with respect to parameters.

NOTES

For the general theory of differential equations see [1] and [2]. In a form analogous to that presented here, this general theory may be found in [3–6]. Questions related to the differential inequalities are discussed in [7].

CHAPTER I

Stability Theory

The general theorem (I.3) on continuous dependence of initial conditions shows that the problem of determining the solution through initial conditions is correct; it has a physical sense.

Indeed, practically, the initial conditions are determined by means of measurements, and every measurement can be only approximate. The continuity with respect to initial conditions expresses precisely the fact that these errors of measurement do not affect the solution too seriously, and Lemma I.7 shows that they also do not affect the approximate solutions too seriously. In other words, if an admissible error ϵ is given for the solution, there exists $\delta > 0$ such that if when establishing the initial conditions the error is smaller than δ, we may be sure that the error in every $\epsilon/2$-solution determined by this initial condition is smaller than ϵ.

It must be stressed that this property is set up on a finite interval (a, b) of variation of t; δ depends upon the size of this interval and decreases when the size of the interval increases. It follows that a solution will have a physical character in reality only if for sufficiently large intervals δ is sufficiently large, of the order of the errors of measurement. This can be achieved by requiring that δ *shall not depend* upon the size of the considered interval. We thus reach the notion of stability in the sense of Lyapunov.

Another way to attain this notion is the following. We consider the solution of a system which describes a certain phenomenon. Let us suppose that perturbations of short duration have occurred during the development of the phenomenon which cannot be exactly known and hence cannot be taken into account in the mathematical description of the phenomenon. After the stopping of the action of these perturbations, the phenomenon will be described by the same system of differential equations as before their occurrence. But what has happened? The phenomenon was modified under the influence of the perturbations; hence the value corresponding to the moment when the perturbations have stopped their action will be different from the one given by the solution initially considered. It follows that after the stopping of the perturbations' action, the phenomenon will be described by a solution other than the initial one. In other words, the effect of some perturbations of short duration consists in the passing from a solution with certain initial conditions to a solution with other initial conditions, the initial moment being considered the moment when the perturbations stop their action. Since these kinds of perturbations are neglected in every mathematical model of natural phenomena, it is necessary, to correctly describe the phenomenon and confer a physical sense upon the mathematical solution, that slight modifications of the initial conditions should not have too serious effects on the solution. This condition is always assured on a given interval (a, b) by the theorem of continuity with respect to initial conditions. The same reasoning as before lets us consider as necessary the independence of δ with respect to the size of the interval and leads us therefore to the notion of stability of the solution.

1.1. Theorems on Stability and Uniform Stability

We shall now be concerned with the precise definition of stability. Let us consider the system

$$\frac{dx}{dt} = f(t, x) \tag{1}$$

and let $\tilde{x}(t)$ be a solution of the system defined for $t \geqslant t_0$.

Definition. *We will say that the solution $\tilde{x}(t)$ is stable if for every $\epsilon > 0$ there exists $\delta(\epsilon; t_0)$ such that if $|\tilde{x}(t_0) - x_0| < \delta$ there follows $|\tilde{x}(t) - x(t; t_0, x_0)| < \epsilon$ for $t \geqslant t_0$.*

There are circumstances in which not all the solutions of a system of differential equations have a physical sense. It is obvious that in such cases we are not interested that all the solutions whose initial conditions are close to those of solution $\tilde{x}(t)$ remain in the neighborhood of this solution; it is sufficient that this property occurs only for the solutions having a physical sense. We thus reach the following specification of the notion of stability.

Definition. *We will say that the solution $\tilde{x}(t)$ is stable with respect to a set M of solutions if for every $\epsilon > 0$ there exists $\delta(\epsilon; t_0)$ such that if $|x_0 - \tilde{x}(t_0)| < \delta$ and the solution $x(t; t_0, x_0)$ belongs to the set M, then $|x(t; t_0, x_0) - \tilde{x}(t)| < \epsilon$ for $t \geqslant t_0$.*

If $\tilde{x}(t)$ is the solution whose stability we are studying (we stress on this occasion that we always deal with the stability of *a certain solution*, which we suppose to be known), by the change of variables $y = x - \tilde{x}(t)$ we can always reduce the problem to the study of stability of the solution $y \equiv 0$. Indeed, we obtain

$$\frac{dy}{dt} = \frac{dx}{dt} - \frac{d\tilde{x}}{dt} = f(t, x) - f(t, \tilde{x}(t)) = f(t, y + \tilde{x}(t)) - f(t, \tilde{x}(t)) = F(t, y),$$

and the new system $dy/dt = F(t, y)$ admits the solution $y \equiv 0$, corresponding to the solution $x = \tilde{x}(t)$. The condition $| \tilde{x}(t_0) - x_0 | < \delta$ is now $| y_0 | < \delta$ and $| x(t; t_0, x_0) - \tilde{x}(t)| < \epsilon$ is now $| y(t; t_0, y_0)| < \epsilon$.

Lyapunov has called the system obtained in this way the system of equations of the perturbed movement; the sense of this denomination resides in the fact that the new unknowns y actually represent the perturbations suffered by the movement $\tilde{x}(t)$. By passing to the system of equations of the perturbed movement, we can say that the stability of the movement is reduced to the study of equilibrium stability.

In all that follows we shall consider only the problem of the stability of the trivial solution $x \equiv 0$.

Theorem 1.1. *Assume that there exists a function $V(t, x)$, defined for $t \geqslant 0$, $| x | \leqslant \delta_0$, continuous and with the following properties:*

(a) $V(t, 0) = 0$.

(b) $V(t, x) \geqslant a(| x |)$, *where $a(r)$ is continuous, monotonically increasing, and $a(0) = 0$.*

(c) $V^*(t) = V(t, x(t))$ *is monotonically decreasing for all solutions $x(t)$ of system* (1) *with $| x(t_0)| < \delta_0$.*

Then the solution $x = 0$ of the system is stable.

Proof. Let ϵ be a given number, $0 < \epsilon < \delta_0$, and $\delta(\epsilon; t_0)$ chosen such that $| x_0 | < \delta$ implies $V(t_0, x_0) < a(\epsilon)$; such a choice is possible, since $V(t_0, 0) \equiv 0$ and $V(t_0, x)$ is continuous.

Let x_0 be a point with $| x_0 | < \delta$; consider the solution $x(t; t_0, x_0)$. The function $V^*(t) = V(t, x(t; t_0, x_0))$ is by hypothesis monotonically decreasing; hence

$$V^*(t) \leqslant V(t_0) = V(t_0, x(t_0; t_0, x_0)) = V(t_0, x_0).$$

It follows that

$$a(| x(t; t_0, x_0)|) \leqslant V(t, x(t; t_0, x_0)) \leqslant V(t_0, x_0) < a(\epsilon).$$

Since $a(r)$ is monotone-decreasing, it follows from here that $| x(t; t_0, x_0)| < \epsilon$ for every $t \geqslant t_0$; hence the solution remains in $| x | \leqslant \delta_0$, where V is defined, and the theorem is proved.

Remarks. 1. If V is differentiable, the function $V^*(t)$ is differentiable and we have

$$\frac{dV^*}{dt} = \frac{\partial V}{\partial t} + \left(\frac{\partial V}{\partial x}, \frac{dx}{dt}\right) = \frac{\partial V}{\partial t} + \left(\frac{\partial V}{\partial x}, f(t, x)\right),$$

since x is the solution of the system of differential equations.

The function

$$W(t, x) = \frac{\partial V(t, x)}{\partial t} + \left(\frac{\partial V(t, x)}{\partial x}, f(t, x)\right)$$

is called the total derivative of the function V with respect to the system. Condition (c) of the theorem is evidently satisfied if V is differentiable and $W(t, x) \leqslant 0$.

2. The stability of the trivial solution obviously implies that the solutions with initial conditions in a neighborhood of $x \equiv 0$ are defined for every $t \geqslant t_0$, since the fact that $|x(t; t_0, x_0)| < \epsilon$ assures the possibility of extension, the solution remaining in the domain in which the conditions of the existence theorem are fulfilled.

3. Let us analyze the theorem if we only want to obtain the stability with respect to a manifold M of solutions. It is sufficient to require that $V(t, x(t)) \geqslant a(|x(t)|)$ and $V(t, x(t))$ be monotone-decreasing only for solutions $x(t)$ belonging to the manifold M of solutions; we may also assume that the function $V(t, x)$ is defined only in points (t, x) on the graphs of the solutions in M and is continuous only in these points. The theorem will be formulated as follows.

Suppose that there exists a function $V(t, x)$, defined and continuous on the intersection of $(t \geqslant 0, |x| \leqslant \delta_0)$ with the union of the graphs of solutions in M, with the properties $V(t, 0) \equiv 0$, $V(t, x(t)) \geqslant a(|x(t)|)$, $V(t, x(t))$ monotone-decreasing for every solution $x(t)$ of M. Then the trivial solution of the system is stable with respect to M.

The notion of stability defined above has the disadvantage of depending on the initial moment t_0; the value δ of the permissible initial deviations depends not only on the deviation permissible for the solution, but also on the initial moment. Or, if we return to the problem of perturbations with an action of short duration, it is obvious that such perturbations may occur in different moments of the development of the phenomenon, and these moments (more exactly the moments when the perturbative action stops) are precisely considered as initial moments. Hence, to confer a greater physical value to the notion of stability introduced, it is desirable that the initial admissible perturbations which have no detrimental effect do not depend upon the initial moment. Thus we reach the notion of *uniform stability*.

Definition. *The trivial solution* $x \equiv 0$ *is said to be uniformly stable if for every* $\epsilon > 0$ *there exists* $\delta(\epsilon) > 0$ *such that if* $|x_0| < \delta$ *it follows that* $|x(t; t_0, x_0)| < \epsilon$ *for* $t \geqslant t_0$, *whichever be* t_0.

The difference with respect to the preceding case considered consists in the independence of $\delta(\epsilon)$ from t_0.

Theorem 1.1′. *Assume that there exists a function* $V(t, x)$ *defined and continuous for* $t \geqslant 0$, $|x| \leqslant \delta_0$, *with the following properties*:

(a) $V(t, 0) \equiv 0$.

(b) $a(|x|) \leqslant V(t, x) \leqslant b(|x|)$, $a(r)$ *and* $b(r)$ *being continuous, monotone-increasing, and* $a(0) = b(0) = 0$.

(c) $V^*(t) = V(t, x(t))$ *is monotone-decreasing for every solution* $x(t)$ *of the system with* $|x(t)| \leqslant \delta_0$.

Then the solution $x \equiv 0$ *is uniformly stable.*

The corresponding statement for uniform stability relative to a manifold M of solutions is obvious.

Proof. Let $0 < \epsilon < \delta_0$ and $\delta = b^{-1}[a(\epsilon)]$; let x_0 with $|x_0| < \delta$. Consider the solution $x(t; t_0, x_0)$. The function $V^*(t) = V[t, x(t; t_0, x_0)]$ is monotone-decreasing; hence

$$V^*(t) \leqslant V^*(t_0) = V[t_0, x(t_0; t_0, x_0)] = V(t_0, x_0) \leqslant b(|x_0|) < b(\delta)$$
$$= b[b^{-1}(a(\epsilon))] = a(\epsilon).$$

It follows that

$$a(|x(t; t_0, x_0)|) \leqslant V^*(t) < a(\epsilon);$$

hence

$$|x(t; t_0, x_0)| < \epsilon \qquad \text{for} \quad t \geqslant t_0.$$

Theorem 1.2. *If the trivial solution of the system is uniformly stable, there exists a function* $V(t, x)$ *with the properties of the preceding theorem.*

Proof. Put $V(t, x) = \sup_{\sigma \geqslant 0} |x(t + \sigma; t, x)|$. The function $V(t, x)$ is defined for $t \geqslant 0$, $|x| < \delta_0 = \sup \delta(\epsilon)$. From

$$|x(t + \sigma; t, x)| < \epsilon(|x|),$$

where $\epsilon(\delta)$ is the inverse function of the function $\delta(\epsilon)$ (which may be chosen continuous and monotone-increasing), it follows that $V(t, x) \leqslant \epsilon(|x|)$. Further on,

$$\sup_{\sigma \geqslant 0} |x(t + \sigma; t, x)| \geqslant |x(t; t, x)| = |x|;$$

hence

$$V(t, x) \geqslant |x|.$$

Finally, let

$$V^*(t) = V[t, x(t; t_0, x_0)] = \sup_{\sigma \geqslant 0} |x(t + \sigma; t, x(t; t_0, x_0))|$$

$$= \sup_{\sigma \geqslant 0} |x(t + \sigma; t_0, x_0)|.$$

Let $t_1 > t_2$, $d = t_1 - t_2$. We have

$$V^*(t_1) = \sup_{\sigma \geqslant 0} |x(t_1 + \sigma; t_0, x_0)| = \sup_{\sigma \geqslant 0} |x(t_2 + d + \sigma; t_0, x_0)|$$

$$= \sup_{\sigma \geqslant d} |x(t_2 + \sigma; t_0, x_0)| \leqslant \sup_{\sigma \geqslant 0} |x(t_2 + \sigma; t_0, x_0)| = V^*(t_2);$$

hence $V^*(t)$ is monotone-decreasing. The theorem is proved.

Let us consider now a system of the form

$$\frac{dx}{dt} = X(t, x, y), \qquad \frac{dy}{dt} = Y(t, x, y), \tag{2}$$

where X and Y are defined for $t \geqslant t_0$, $|x| \leqslant H$, y arbitrary (x, y vectors), $X(t, 0, 0) = 0$, $Y(t, 0, 0) = 0$.

Definition. *The solution $x = 0$, $y = 0$ of the system is said to be stable with respect to components x if for all $\epsilon > 0$ there exists $\delta > 0$ (depending on ϵ and t_0, and in the case of uniform stability only on ϵ) such that, if $|x_0| + |y_0| < \delta$ it follows that $|x(t; t_0, x_0, y_0)| < \epsilon$ for $t \geqslant t_0$.*

Theorem 1.1″. *Suppose that there exists a function $V(t, x, y)$ defined for $t \geqslant t_0$, $|x| \leqslant H$, y arbitrary, with the following properties:*

1. *$V(t, 0, 0) \equiv 0$, $V(t, x, y)$ continuous for $x = 0$, $y = 0$.*

2. *$V(t, x, y) \geqslant a(|x|)$ with $a(r)$ continuous, monotone-increasing, $a(0) = 0$.*

3. *$V[t, x(t), y(t)]$ is monotone-decreasing for every solution $x(t)$, $y(t)$ of the system with $|x(t)| \leqslant H$.*

Then the trivial solution of system (2) *is stable with respect to components* x. *If, in addition,* $V(t, x, y) \leqslant b(|x| + |y|)$, *where* $b(r)$ *is as in Theorem* 1.1′, *then the stability is uniform.*

Proof. Let $\epsilon > 0$, $\delta > 0$ chosen such that $V(t_0, x_0, y_0) < a(\epsilon)$, if $|x_0| + |y_0| < \delta$; if $V(t, x, y) \leqslant b(|x| + |y|)$, we take $\delta = b^{-1}[a(\epsilon)]$. Consider the solution $x(t; t_0, x_0, y_0)$, $y(t; t_0, x_0, y_0)$ and the function $V^*(t) = V[t, x(t; t_0, x_0, y_0), y(t; t_0, x_0, y_0)]$ which is, by hypothesis, monotone-decreasing. It follows that

$$a(|x(t; t_0, x_0, y_0)|) \leqslant V^*(t) \leqslant V^*(t_0) = V(t_0, x_0, y_0) < a(\epsilon);$$

hence

$$|x(t; t_0, x_0, y_0)| < \epsilon \qquad (\text{for} \quad t \geqslant t_0).$$

Theorem 1.2′. *If the solution* $x = 0$, $y = 0$ *of system* (2) *is uniformly stable with respect to the components* x, *there exists a function* $V(t, x, y)$ *with all the properties of the preceding theorem.*

Proof. We take $V(t, x, y) = \sup_{\sigma \geqslant 0} |x(t + \sigma; t, x, y)|$. Obviously,

$$V(t, x, y) \leqslant \epsilon(|x| + |y|) \qquad \text{and} \qquad V(t, x, y) \geqslant |x|.$$

Further,

$$\begin{aligned} V^*(t) &= V[t, x(t; t_0, x_0, y_0), y(t; t_0, x_0, y_0)] \\ &= \sup_{\sigma \geqslant 0} |x(t + \sigma; t, x(t; t_0, x_0, y_0), y(t; t_0, x_0, y_0))| \\ &= \sup_{\sigma \geqslant 0} |x(t + \sigma; t_0, x_0, y_0)|. \end{aligned}$$

Let $t_1 > t_2$, $d = t_1 - t_2$; we have

$$\begin{aligned} V^*(t_1) &= \sup_{\sigma \geqslant 0} |x(t_1 + \sigma; t_0, x_0, y_0)| \\ &= \sup_{\sigma \geqslant 0} |x(t_2 + d + \sigma; t_0, x_0, y_0)| \\ &= \sup_{\sigma \geqslant d} |x(t_2 + \sigma; t_0, x_0, y_0)| \leqslant \sup_{\sigma \geqslant 0} |x(t_2 + \sigma; t_0, x_0, y_0)| = V^*(t_2); \end{aligned}$$

hence $V^*(t)$ is monotone-decreasing.

Let us emphasize some particularities of the systems which are periodic with respect to t. In system (1) let $f(t + \omega, x) = f(t, x)$. Then, if $x(t; t_0, x_0)$ is a solution, $x(t + \omega; t_0, x_0)$ is also a solution. From here, if system (1) satisfies the conditions of the uniqueness theorem, it follows that

$$x(t + \omega; t_0 + \omega, x_0) = x(t; t_0, x_0),$$

since in both members of the equality we have solutions of system (1), and these solutions coincide for $t = t_0$.

Proposition 1. *If $f(t + \omega, x) = f(t, x)$, the stability of the trivial solution of system* (1) *is always uniform.*

Proof. For fixed t_0, let $\delta_0(t_0) = \sup_{\epsilon>0} \delta(\epsilon, t_0)$.

Let $\delta = \inf_{0 \leqslant t_0 \leqslant \omega} \delta_0(t_0)$; $\delta_0 > 0$, since $\delta_0(t_0)$ may be chosen continuous. For $0 < \delta < \delta_0$ define

$$\epsilon(\delta) = \sup_{\sigma \geqslant 0} | x(t_0 + \sigma; t_0, x_0)|.$$

The function $\epsilon(\delta)$ is monotone-increasing; let $\delta(\epsilon)$ be its inverse. For $| x_0 | < \delta(\epsilon)$ it follows that $| x(t; t_0, x_0)| < \epsilon$ for every $0 \leqslant t_0 \leqslant \omega$. For $t_0 > 0$ arbitrary, we have $k\omega \leqslant t_0 < (k + 1)\omega$; hence $0 \leqslant t_0 - k\omega < \omega$ and $| x(t; t_0, x_0)| = | x(t - k\omega, t_0 - k\omega, x_0)| < \epsilon(\delta)$ if $| x_0 | < \delta$; hence $| x(t; t_0, x_0)| < \epsilon$ if $| x_0 | < \delta(\epsilon)$.

Proposition 2. *If $f(t + \omega, x) = f(t, x)$, the function $V(t, x)$ from Theorem* 1.2′ *is periodic of period ω.*

Proof. We have $V(t + \omega, x) = \sup_{\sigma \geqslant 0} | x(t + \omega + \sigma; t + \omega, x)| = \sup_{\sigma \geqslant 0} | x(t + \sigma; t, x)| = V(t, x)$.

A particular case of periodic systems is constituted by systems in which f does not depend on t. It follows that for such systems the stability is always uniform and the function V may be chosen independent of t.

Definition. *A solution $x(t)$ of system* (1) *is said to be unstable if it is not stable.*

Now let us formulate a theorem which allows to recognize the instability of the trivial solution $x = 0$.

Theorem 1.3. *If there exists a function $V(t, x)$ with the properties*

1. $| V(t, x)| \leqslant b(| x |)$, *where $b(r)$ is monotone-increasing and continuous,*

2. *For every $\delta > 0$ and every $t_0 > 0$ there exists x_0 with $| x_0 | < \delta$ such that $V(t_0, x_0) < 0$,*

3.

$$\limsup_{h \to 0+} \frac{V(t + h, x(t + h, t, x)) - V(t, x)}{h} \leqslant -c(| x |),$$

where $c(r)$ is monotone-increasing and continuous, $c(0) = 0$, then the solution $x = 0$ of the system is unstable.

Proof. Let us suppose that the solution is stable. Then for every $\epsilon > 0$ and $t_0 > 0$ there exists $\delta(\epsilon, t_0) > 0$ such that $|x_0| < \delta$ implies that $|x(t; t_0, x_0)| < \epsilon$ for $t \geqslant t_0$. Choose x_0 such that $|x_0| < \delta$ and $V(t_0, x_0) < 0$.

From $|x_0| < \delta$ it follows that $|x(t; t_0, x_0)| < \epsilon$; hence $|V(t, x(t; t_0, x_0)| \leqslant b(|x(t; t_0, x_0)|) < b(\epsilon)$ for every $t \geqslant t_0$. From condition 3 it follows that $V(t, x(t; t_0, x_0))$ is monotone-decreasing; hence for every $t \geqslant t_0$ it follows that $V(t, x(t; t_0, x_0)) \leqslant V(t_0, x_0) < 0$; hence $|V(t, x(t; t_0, x_0))| \geqslant |V(t_0, x_0)|$; hence $b(|x(t; t_0, x_0)|) \geqslant |V(t_0, x_0)|$; hence $|x(t; t_0, x_0)| \geqslant b^{-1}(|V(t_0, x_0)|)$. From condition 3 it follows that

$$\limsup_{h \to 0+} \frac{V(t+h, x(t+h; t_0, x_0)) - V(t, x(t; t_0, x_0))}{h} \leqslant -c(|x(t; t_0, x_0)|);$$

hence

$$V(t, x(t; t_0, x_0)) \leqslant V(t_0, x_0) - \int_{t_0}^{t} c(|x(u; t_0, x_0)|)du.$$

From

$$|x(t; t_0, x_0)| \geqslant b^{-1}(|V(t_0, x_0)|)$$

it follows that

$$c(|x(t; t_0, x_0)|) \geqslant c[b^{-1}(|V(t_0, x_0)|)];$$

hence

$$V(t, x(t; t_0, x_0)) \leqslant V(t_0, x_0) - (t - t_0)c[b^{-1}(|V(t_0, x_0)|)].$$

But this means that

$$\lim_{t \to \infty} V(t, x(t; t_0, x_0)) = -\infty,$$

which contradicts the fact that

$$|V(t, x(t; t_0, x_0))| < b(\epsilon).$$

Remark. Analyzing the proof, it is obvious that the existence of a function V with the properties of the statement implies a very strong instability: for every $\epsilon > 0$, every $t_0 > 0$, and every $\delta > 0$ there exists x_0 with $|x_0| < \delta$ and $T > t_0$ such that $|x(T; t_0, x_0)| \geqslant \epsilon$.

1.2. Asymptotic Stability

Very often it is not sufficient merely that perturbations of short duration do not lead to large changes in the solution. We may also require that the effect of these perturbations be damped down, that they disappear after a sufficiently large interval of variation of t. Thus we come to the notion of asymptotic stability, which we shall define in what follows.

Definition. *The solution $x \equiv 0$ is said to be asymptotically stable if it is stable and, in addition, there exists a $\delta_0(t_0) > 0$ with the property that if $|x_0| < \delta_0$, then*

$$\lim_{t\to\infty} x(t; t_0, x_0) = 0.$$

The solution $x \equiv 0$ is said to be uniformly asymptotically stable if there exists a $\delta_0 > 0$ and functions $\delta(\epsilon)$ and $T(\epsilon)$ with the property that $|x_0| < \delta$ implies $|x(t; t_0, x_0)| < \epsilon$ for $t \geqslant t_0$, and $|x_0| < \delta_0$, $t \geqslant t_0 + T(\epsilon)$ implies $|x(t; t_0, x_0)| < \epsilon$.

Uniform asymptotic stability means uniform stability and $\lim_{t\to\infty} x(t; t_0, x_0) = 0$ uniformly with respect to t_0 and $x_0 (t_0 \geqslant 0, |x_0| < \delta_0)$.

Proposition. *If $|f(t, x_1) - f(t, x_2)| < k(t) |x_1 - x_2|$ in $t \geqslant 0$, $|x| \leqslant H$, and $\int_{t_0}^{t} k(s)ds = O(t - t_0)$, then the existence of the function $T(\epsilon)$ is sufficient for uniform asymptotic stability.*

Indeed, let $\epsilon > 0$ and $T(\epsilon)$ be the corresponding value; we choose $\delta(\epsilon)$ such that $|x_0| < \delta$ implies $|x(t; t_0, x_0)| < \epsilon$ for $t_0 \leqslant t \leqslant t_0 + T$. Such a choice is possible on the grounds of Lemma I.7 upon taking $\varphi_1 = x(t; t_0, x_0)$, $\varphi_2 = 0$, $\epsilon_1 = \epsilon_2 = 0$.

We have

$$|x(t; t_0, x_0)| \leqslant \delta \exp\left[\int_{t_0}^{t_0+T} k(u)du\right]$$

and hence

$$\delta < \epsilon \exp\left[-\int_{t_0}^{t_0+T(\epsilon)} k(u)du\right];$$

taking into account the property imposed to $k(u)$, it follows that δ depends only on ϵ.

Theorem 1.4. *Suppose that there exists a function $V(t, x)$ defined for $t \geqslant t_0$, $|x| \leqslant H$ continuous, and with the following properties:*

(a) $V(t, 0) \equiv 0$.

(b) $V(t, x) \geqslant a(|x|)$, *where $a(0) = 0$ and is continuous and monotone-increasing.*

(c)

$$\limsup_{h\to 0+} \frac{V[t + h, x(t + h; t_0, x_0)] - V[t, x(t; t_0, x_0)]}{h} \leqslant -c[V(t, x(t; t_0, x_0))],$$

where $c(r)$ is continuous and monotone-increasing, $c(0) = 0$.

Then the solution $x \equiv 0$ is asymptotically stable.

Proof. On the basis of Theorem 1.1, the solution is stable. By hypothesis, $V(t, x(t; t_0, x_0)$ is monotone-decreasing; hence the limit

$$V_0 = \lim_{t\to\infty} V[t, x(t; t_0, x_0)]$$

exists. If $V_0 \neq 0$, we have $c(V_0) \neq 0$, and since $c(r)$ is monotone,

$$c[V(t, x(t; t_0, x_0))] > c(V_0).$$

Hence

$$-c[V(t, x(t; t_0, x_0))] < -c(V_0)$$

and

$$\limsup_{h\to 0+} \frac{V[t+h, x(t+h; t_0, x_0)] - V[t, x(t; t_0, x_0)]}{h} \leqslant -c(V_0).$$

Integrating, we have

$$V[t, x(t; t_0, x_0)] - V(t_0, x_0) \leqslant -c(V_0)(t - t_0).$$

Thus $V[t, x(t; t_0, x_0)]$ converges to $-\infty$ as $t \to \infty$, which contradicts the fact that

$$V[t, x(t; t_0, x_0)] \geqslant a(|x(t; t_0, x_0)|).$$

It follows that $V_0 = 0$; from $V[t, x(t; t_0, x_0)] \to 0$, it follows that $a(|x(t; t_0, x_0)|) \to 0$, and thus that $|x(t; t_0, x_0)| \to 0$ when $t \to \infty$. This proves the theorem.

Remarks. 1. Consider the system

$$\frac{dx}{dt} = X(t, x, y), \qquad \frac{dy}{dt} = Y(t, x, y), \qquad X(t, 0, 0) \equiv 0, \qquad Y(t, 0, 0) \equiv 0.$$

Suppose that there exists a function $V(t, x, y)$ continuous and with the properties $V(t, x, y) \geqslant a(|x|)$, $V(t, 0, 0) = 0$,

$$\limsup_{h\to 0+} \frac{V^\alpha(t+h) - V^\alpha(t)}{h} \leqslant -c[V^\alpha(t)],$$

where

$$V^\alpha(t) = V[t, x(t; t_0, x_0, y_0), y(t; t_0, x_0, y_0)].$$

Then the solution $x = 0$, $y = 0$ is asymptotically stable with respect to components x.

Indeed, the proof develops as above. We deduce that

$$\lim_{t\to\infty} V[t, x(t; t_0, x_0, y_0), y(t; t_0, x_0, y_0)] = 0,$$

and therefore that

$$\lim_{t\to\infty} a(|x(t; t_0, x_0, y_0)|) = 0,$$

and thus that

$$\lim_{t\to\infty} x(t; t_0, x_0, y_0) = 0.$$

2. It is easy to see that the definition of asymptotic stability, as well as the whole theorem, may be related to a manifold M of solutions.

Theorem 1.5. *Suppose that there exists a function $V(t, x)$ with the following properties:*

$$a(|x|) \leqslant V(t, x) \leqslant b(|x|),$$

$$\limsup_{h\to 0+} \frac{V[t+h, x(t+h; t_0, x_0)] - V[t, x(t; t_0, x_0)]}{h} \leqslant -c(|x(t; t_0, x_0)|).$$

Then the trivial solution of the system is uniformly asymptotically stable.

Proof. Let $\epsilon > 0$, $\delta(\epsilon) < b^{-1}[a(\epsilon)]$; if $|x| < \delta(\epsilon)$ we have

$$a(|x(t; t_0, x_0)|) \leqslant V[t, x(t; t_0, x_0)] \leqslant V(t_0, x_0)$$
$$\leqslant b(|x_0|) < b(\delta) < a(\epsilon),$$

and thus $|x(t; t_0, x_0)| < \epsilon$ for $t \geqslant t_0$.

Let $|x| < H$ be the range in which the conditions of the statement are satisfied and define $\delta_0 = \delta(H)$, $T(\epsilon) = b(\delta_0)/c[\delta(\epsilon)]$. Let $|x_0| < \delta_0$. Suppose that in $[t_0, t_0 + T]$, we would have $|x(t; t_0, x_0)| \geqslant \delta(\epsilon)$. Then

$$\limsup_{h\to 0+} \frac{V[t+h; x(t+h; t_0, x_0)] - V[t; x(t; t_0, x_0)]}{h} \leqslant -c[\delta(\epsilon)]$$

for $t \in [t_0, t_0 + T]$, and integrating,

$$V[t, x(t; t_0, x_0)] - V[t_0, x_0] \leqslant -c[\delta(\epsilon)](t - t_0),$$

$$V[t, x(t; t_0, x_0)] \leqslant V[t_0, x_0] - c[\delta(\epsilon)](t - t_0) \leqslant b(\delta_0) - c[\delta(\epsilon)](t - t_0).$$

For $t = t_0 + T$ we get

$$V[t, x(t; t_0, x_0)] \leqslant b(\delta_0) - c[\delta(\epsilon)]T = 0,$$

which is a contradiction. It follows that there exists a $t_1 \in [t_0, t_0 + T]$ such that $|x(t_1; t_0, x_0)| < \delta(\epsilon)$, and that $|x(t; t_0, x_0)| < \epsilon$ for $t \geqslant t_1$, and therefore in every case for $t \geqslant t_0 + T(\epsilon)$.

Remarks. 1. If

$$\lim_{r\to\infty} a(r) = \lim_{r\to\infty} b(r),$$

then

$$\lim_{\epsilon\to\infty} \delta(\epsilon) = \infty,$$

and if the properties in the statement hold for all x, then it follows that $\delta_0 = \infty$. In this case we say that we are concerned with global stability, or stability in the large.

2. As above, it is obvious that if we are in the situation of remark 1 of the preceding theorem, and function $V(t, x, y)$ verifies the conditions

$$a(|x|) \leqslant V(t, x, y) \leqslant b(|x| + |y|),$$

$$\limsup_{h\to 0+} \frac{V^\alpha(t+h) - V^\alpha(t)}{h}$$

$$\leqslant -c(|x(t; t_0, x_0, y_0)| + |y(t; t_0, x_0, y_0)|),$$

then uniform stability holds with respect to the components x. Indeed it is shown, as in the proof of the theorem, that there exists a $t_1 \in [t_0, t_0 + T]$ such that

$$|x(t_1; t_0, x_0, y_0)| + |y(t_1; t_0, x_0, y_0)| < \delta(\epsilon);$$

then everything follows from the property of $\delta(\epsilon)$.

3. The evaluation of the numbers $\delta(\epsilon)$, δ_0, $T(\epsilon)$ is very important in practical problems. Let us remark that from the proof of the theorem it follows that if we have available a function $V(t, x)$ and functions $a(r)$, $b(r)$, $c(r)$, then we can take $\delta(\epsilon) = b^{-1}[a(\epsilon)]$, $\delta_0 = \delta(H)$. When V is defined for every x, $\delta_0 = \lim_{\epsilon\to\infty} \delta(\epsilon) = b^{-1}[a(\infty)]$, $T(\epsilon) = b(\delta_0)/c[\delta(\epsilon)]$.

Let us make now some remarks in connection with uniform asymptotic stability.

1. In the definition of uniform asymptotic stability there enter functions $\delta(\epsilon)$ and $T(\epsilon)$. Let us prove that these functions can be chosen continuous and monotone.

Proof. Let ϵ_n be a positive sequence, monotone, converging to zero, $\delta_1(\epsilon) = \sup \delta(\epsilon_{n+1})$ for $\epsilon_{n+1} \leqslant \epsilon < \epsilon_n$; $|x_0| < \delta_1(\epsilon)$ implies $|x(t; t_0, x_0)| < \epsilon_{n+1} \leqslant \epsilon$ for $t \geqslant t_0$. Define $\delta^*(\epsilon)$ linear in $[\epsilon_{n+1}, \epsilon_n]$ and $\delta^*(\epsilon_{n+1}) = \delta_1(\epsilon_{n+2})$, $\delta^*(\epsilon_n) = \delta_1(\epsilon_{n+1})$. Since $\delta_1(\epsilon_{n+1}) \leqslant \delta_1(\epsilon_n)$ [$\delta_1(\epsilon_n)$ having been defined as an upper bound of the set of numbers δ with the property that $|x_0| < \delta$ implies $|x(t; t_0, x_0)| < \epsilon_n$], and in addition $\delta_1(\epsilon_n) \to 0$ when $n \to \infty$, it follows that $\delta_1(\epsilon_{n+1}) = \delta_1(\epsilon_n)$ only on finite parts of the sequence, which we can eliminate, with the result that $\delta_1(\epsilon_n)$, and hence $\delta^*(\epsilon)$ be made strictly monotone-increasing. The function $\delta^*(\epsilon)$ will be continuous, strictly increasing, $\delta^*(0) = 0$. The inequality $|x_0| < \delta^*(\epsilon)$ implies that $|x_0| < \delta^*(\epsilon_n) = \delta_1(\epsilon_{n+1})(\epsilon_{n+1} \leqslant \epsilon \leqslant \epsilon_n)$; hence $|x(t; t_0, x_0)| < \epsilon_{n+1} \leqslant \epsilon$. Thus $\delta^*(\epsilon)$ has all the required properties.

Analogously, let $T_1(\epsilon) = \inf_T T(\epsilon_{n+1})$ for $\epsilon_{n+1} \leqslant \epsilon \leqslant \epsilon_n$; then $|x_0| < \delta_0$ and $t \geqslant t_0 + T_1(\epsilon)$ implies $|x(t; t_0, x_0)| < \epsilon_{n+1} \leqslant \epsilon$. Define $T^*(\epsilon)$ linear in $[\epsilon_{n+1}, \epsilon_n]$ and $T^*(\epsilon_{n+1}) = T_1(\epsilon_{n+2})$, $T^*(\epsilon_n) = T_1(\epsilon_{n+1})$. Since $T_1(\epsilon_{n+1}) \geqslant T_1(\epsilon_n)$ [$T_1(\epsilon_n)$ having been defined as the lower bound of numbers T with the property that $t \geqslant t_0 + T$ implies $|x(t; t_0, x_0)| < \epsilon_n$, and $T_1(\epsilon_{n+1})$ has this property], and $\lim_{n\to\infty} T_1(\epsilon_n) = \infty$, the equality $T_1(\epsilon_{n+1}) = T_1(\epsilon_n)$ may occur only on finite parts of the sequence, which we can eliminate.

The function $T^*(\epsilon)$ is monotone-decreasing, continuous, with $\lim_{\epsilon\to 0} T^*(\epsilon) = \infty$. Further, $t \geqslant t_0 + T^*(\epsilon)$ implies $t \geqslant t_0 + T^*(\epsilon_n) = t_0 + T_1(\epsilon_{n+1})$; hence $|x(t; t_0, x_0)| < \epsilon_{n+1} \leqslant \epsilon$, if $\epsilon_{n+1} \leqslant \epsilon \leqslant \epsilon_n$.

2. Let $\epsilon(\delta)$ be the inverse of the function $\delta(\epsilon)$ and $\eta(T)$ the inverse of the function $T(\eta)$; we have $|x(t; t_0, x_0)| < \epsilon(|x_0|)$ for $t \geqslant t_0$, $|x(t; t_0, x_0)| < \eta(t - t_0)$ for $t \geqslant t_0$, $|x_0| < \delta_0$. It follows that $|x(t; t_0, x_0)|^2 < \epsilon(|x_0|)\eta(t - t_0)$ for $|x_0| < \delta_0$, $t \geqslant t_0$. Consequently, uniform asymptotic stability is equivalent to the existence of two functions $\chi(r)$ and $\psi(T)$, the first monotone-increasing, the second monotone-decreasing, such that

$$|x(t; t_0, x_0)| \leqslant \chi(|x_0|)\psi(t - t_0).$$

3. If $\chi(r)$ is linear and $|f(t, x)| \leqslant L(r)\,|x|$ for $|x| < r$, the stability is exponential; namely, there exist constants $\alpha > 0$ and $\beta > 0$ such that

$$|x(t; t_0, x_0)| \leqslant Be^{-\alpha(t-t_0)}\,|x_0|.$$

Define the Lyapunov function

$$V(t, x) = \int_t^{t+T} |x(\tau; t, x)|^2\, d\tau.$$

We have $| x(t; t_0, x_0)| \leqslant k | x_0 |\psi(0)$. Thus

$$| x(\tau; t, x)| \leqslant k\psi(0) | x | \qquad (\text{for } \tau \geqslant t),$$

and

$$V(t, x) \leqslant \int_t^{t+T} k^2\psi^2(0) | x |^2 \, d\tau = Tk^2\psi^2(0) | x |^2.$$

Furthermore,

$$\frac{d}{d\tau} x(\tau; t, x) = f(\tau, x(\tau; t, x)),$$

$$\left(x(\tau; t, x), \frac{d}{d\tau} x(\tau; t, x)\right) = (x(\tau; t, x), f(\tau, x(\tau; t, x))).$$

Hence

$$\frac{1}{2} \frac{d}{d\tau} | x(\tau; t, x)|^2 = (x(\tau; t, x), f(\tau, x(\tau; t, x))).$$

If $| x | \leqslant r_1$, it follows that

$$| x(\tau; t, x)| \leqslant k\psi(0)r_1$$

and

$$| f(t, x(\tau; t, x))| \leqslant L(r_1) | x(\tau; t, x)|.$$

From this we deduce

$$\left| \frac{1}{2} \frac{d}{d\tau} | x(\tau; t, x)|^2 \right| \leqslant L(r_1) | x(\tau; t, x)|^2,$$

$$\frac{d}{d\tau} \ln | x(\tau; t, x)|^2 \geqslant -2L(r_1), \qquad | x(\tau; t, x)|^2 \geqslant e^{-2L(r_1)(\tau - t)} | x |^2.$$

It follows that

$$V(t, x) \geqslant | x |^2 \int_t^{t+T} e^{-2L(r_1)(\tau-t)} \, d\tau = | x |^2 \int_0^T e^{-2L(r_1)s} \, ds.$$

Finally, $\alpha(T) | x |^2 \leqslant V(t, x) \leqslant \beta(T) | x |^2$. Furthermore,

$$V[t, x(t; t_0, x_0)] = \int_t^{t+T} | x(\tau; t, x(t; t_0, x_0))|^2 \, d\tau = \int_t^{t+T} | x(\tau; t_0, x_0)|^2 \, d\tau,$$

$$\begin{aligned} \frac{d}{dt} V[t, x(t; t_0, x_0)] &= | x(t + T; t_0, x_0)|^2 - | x(t; t_0, x_0)|^2 \\ &= (| x(t + T; t, x(t; t_0, x_0))| - | x(t; t_0, x_0)|)(| x(t + T; t_0, x_0)| + | x(t; t_0, x_0)|) \\ &\leqslant (k\psi(T) | x(t; t_0, x_0)| - | x(t; t_0, x_0)|)(| x(t + T; t_0, x_0)| + | x(t; t_0, x_0)|). \end{aligned}$$

We choose T sufficiently large so that $\psi(T) < 1/2k$, or $k\psi(T) < 1/2$. We obtain finally,

$$\frac{d}{dt} V(t, x(t; t_0, x_0)) \leqslant -\tfrac{1}{2} \mid x(t, t_0, x_0)\mid(\mid x(t + T; t_0, x_0)\mid + \mid x(t; t_0, x_0)\mid)$$
$$\leqslant -\tfrac{1}{2} \mid x(t; t_0, x_0)\mid^2.$$

Exponential stability follows immediately from the existence of a function $V(t, x)$ with the above properties. From

$$V(t, x(t; t_0, x_0)) \leqslant \beta(T) \mid x(t; t_0, x_0)\mid^2$$

follows

$$- \mid x(t; t_0, x_0)\mid^2 \leqslant - \frac{1}{\beta(T)} V[t, x(t; t_0, x_0)],$$

and thus

$$\frac{d}{dt} V(t, x(t; t_0, x_0)) \leqslant - \frac{1}{2\beta(T)} V(t, x(t; t_0, x_0)).$$

From this we obtain

$$\alpha(T) \mid x(t; t_0, x_0)\mid^2 \leqslant V(t, x(t; t_0, x_0)) \leqslant V(t_0, x_0) \exp\left[- \frac{1}{2\beta(T)} (t - t_0)\right]$$
$$\leqslant \beta(T) \mid x_0 \mid^2 \exp\left[- \frac{1}{2\beta(T)} (t - t_0)\right],$$

and finally

$$\mid x(t; t_0, x_0)\mid^2 \leqslant \frac{\beta(T)}{\alpha(T)} \exp\left[- \frac{1}{2\beta(T)} (t - t_0)\right] \mid x_0 \mid^2;$$

i.e.,

$$\mid x(t; t_0, x_0)\mid \leqslant \sqrt{\frac{\beta(T)}{\alpha(T)}} \exp\left[- \frac{1}{4\beta(T)} (t - t_0)\right] \mid x_0 \mid.$$

4. From what has just been proved, it follows that if $f(t, x)$ is homogeneous in x of first degree, then uniform asymptotic stability implies exponential stability.

Indeed, if $f(t, x)$ is homogeneous in x of first degree, it follows that $x(t; t_0, kx_0) = kx(t; t_0, x_0)$. We have solutions of the equation for both members of the equality, and these solutions coincide for $t = t_0$. Indeed,

$$\frac{d}{dt} kx(t; t_0, x_0) = k \frac{d}{dt} x(t; t_0, x_0)$$
$$= kf(t, x(t; t_0, x_0)) = f(t, kx(t; t_0, x_0)).$$

It follows that

$$x(t; t_0, kx_0) = |k| \, |x(t; t_0, x_0)| \leqslant k\chi(|x_0|)\psi(t - t_0),$$

$$|x(t; t_0, x_0)| = \left| x\left(t; t_0, \frac{|x_0|}{\delta_0} \frac{x_0}{|x_0|} \delta_0\right) \right| \leqslant \frac{1}{\delta_0} |x_0| \chi(\delta_0)\psi(t - t_0),$$

and thus

$$|x(t; t_0, x_0)| \leqslant \chi^*(|x_0|)\psi(t - t_0) \qquad \left(\text{with } \chi^*(r) = \frac{1}{\delta_0} \chi(\delta_0)r\right),$$

which demonstrates that $\chi(r)$ may be taken linear.

Particularly, if $f(t, x) = A(t)x$, the condition of homogeneity is fulfilled and we obtain the *theorem of Persidski; uniform asymptotic stability implies, in linear systems, exponential stability*.

5. Let us show that if $f(t, x)$ is periodic in t with period ω, $f(t + \omega, x) \equiv f(t, x)$, then asymptotic stability is always uniform.

Uniform stability has already been emphasized. Let us take $\sigma(\tau) = \sup |x(t_0 + u; t_0, x_0)|$ for $u \geqslant \tau$, $0 \leqslant t_0 \leqslant \omega$, $|x_0| < r$. The function $x(t_0 + u; t_0, x_0)$ is periodic in t_0 and continuous. Hence $\sigma(\tau)$ is, in fact, an upper bound on the whole axis t_0.

Obviously, $\sigma(\tau)$ is monotone-decreasing; the function $T(\epsilon)$ from the definition of uniform asymptotic stability is its inverse function.

We shall now set down an existence theorem for Lyapunov's function in the case of uniform asymptotic stability. There exist at present many different means for constructing a Lyapunov function. Among these we shall choose the one recently given by Massera as being the most simple.

Theorem 1.6. *If the trivial solution of the system is uniformly asymptotically stable, there exists a function $V(t, x)$ with all the properties of Theorem* 1.4.

Proof. Let $G(r)$ be such that $G(0) = 0$, $G'(0) = 0$, $G(r) > 0$, $G''(r) > 0$, and $\alpha > 1$. We denote $g(r) = G''(r)$. Then

$$G(r) = \int_0^r du \int_0^u g(v)dv, \qquad G\left(\frac{r}{\alpha}\right) = \int_0^{r/\alpha} du \int_0^u g(v)dv.$$

Put $u = w/\alpha$; we obtain

$$G\left(\frac{r}{\alpha}\right) = \frac{1}{\alpha}\int_0^r dw \int_0^{w/\alpha} g(v)dv < \frac{1}{\alpha}\int_0^r dw \int_0^w g(v)dv = \frac{1}{\alpha} G(r).$$

Choose

$$V(t, x) = \sup_{\sigma \geqslant 0} G(|\, x(t + \sigma; t, x)|)\, \frac{1 + \alpha\sigma}{1 + \sigma};$$

for $\sigma = 0$ we obtain $G(|\, x\, |)$; hence $V(t, x) \geqslant G(|\, x\, |)$. Let $\epsilon(\delta)$ be the inverse function of $\delta(\epsilon)$. We have

$$|\, x(t + \sigma; t, x)| < \epsilon(|\, x\, |), \quad G(|\, x(t + \sigma; t, x)|) < G(\epsilon(|\, x\, |)), \quad \frac{1 + \alpha\sigma}{1 + \sigma} < \alpha;$$

hence $V(t, x) \leqslant \alpha G[\epsilon(|\, x\, |)]$.

For $\sigma \geqslant T(\epsilon)$ we have $|\, x(t + \sigma; t, x)| < \epsilon$; hence if $\sigma \geqslant T((1/\alpha)\, |\, x\, |)$ it follows that $|\, x(t + \sigma; t, x)| < (1/\alpha)\, |\, x\, |$ and thus that $G(|\, x(t + \sigma; t, x)|) < G((1/\alpha)\, |\, x\, |)$ and $G(|\, x(t + \sigma; t, x)|)\, (1 + \alpha\sigma)/(1 + \sigma) < \alpha G((1/\alpha)\, |\, x\, |) < G(|\, x\, |) \leqslant V(t, x)$.

We see then that

$$V(t, x) = \sup_{0 \leqslant \sigma \leqslant T((1/\alpha)|x|)} G(|\, x(t + \sigma; t, x)|) \left(\frac{1 + \alpha\sigma}{1 + \sigma}\right).$$

Since the function is continuous, there exists a point σ_1 in which the upper bound is reached. We may therefore write

$$V(t, x) = G(|\, x(t + \sigma_1; t, x)|)\, \frac{1 + \alpha\sigma_1}{1 + \sigma_1}.$$

Let $x = x(t; t_0, x_0)$, $x^* = x(t + h; t, x)$. We have

$$V(t + h, x^*) = G(|\, x(t + h + \sigma^*; t + h, x^*)|)\, \frac{1 + \alpha\sigma^*}{1 + \sigma^*}$$

$$= G(|\, x(t + h + \sigma^*; t, x)|)\, \frac{1 + \alpha\sigma^*}{1 + \sigma^*}.$$

Denote $\sigma^* + h = \sigma$. We have

$$V(t + h, x^*) = G(|\, x(t + \sigma; t, x)|)\, \frac{1 + \alpha\sigma^*}{1 + \sigma^*}$$

$$= G(|\, x(t + \sigma; t, x)|)\, \frac{1 + \alpha\sigma}{1 + \sigma}\left[1 - \frac{(\alpha - 1)h}{(1 + \sigma^*)(1 + \alpha\sigma)}\right].$$

Indeed,

$$\frac{1 + \alpha\sigma}{1 + \sigma}\left(1 - \frac{(\alpha - 1)h}{(1 + \sigma^*)(1 + \alpha\sigma)}\right)$$

$$= \frac{1 + \alpha\sigma}{1 + \sigma} - \frac{\alpha h - h}{(1 + \sigma)(1 + \sigma^*)} = \frac{1 + \sigma^* + \alpha\sigma + \alpha\sigma\sigma^* - \alpha h + h}{(1 + \sigma)(1 + \sigma^*)}$$

$$= \frac{1 + \sigma^* + \alpha\sigma^* + \alpha\sigma\sigma^* + h}{(1 + \sigma)(1 + \sigma^*)} = \frac{1 + \sigma + \alpha\sigma^*(1 + \sigma)}{(1 + \sigma)(1 + \sigma^*)} = \frac{1 + \alpha\sigma^*}{1 + \sigma^*}.$$

It follows that

$$V(t+h, x^*) \leqslant V(t, x)\left[1 - \frac{(\alpha-1)h}{(1+\sigma^*)(1+\alpha\sigma)}\right]$$

$$= V(t, x) - \frac{(\alpha-1)hV(t, x)}{(1+\sigma^*)(1+\alpha\sigma)}$$

and that

$$\frac{V(t+h, x^*) - V(t, x)}{h} \leqslant -\frac{(\alpha-1)V(t, x)}{(1+\sigma^*)(1+\alpha\sigma)}.$$

We have $0 \leqslant \sigma^* \leqslant T((1/\alpha) \mid x \mid)$, $0 < \sigma \leqslant T((1/\alpha) \mid x^* \mid) + h$; hence

$$\frac{V(t+h, x^*) - V(t, x)}{h} \leqslant -\frac{(\alpha-1)V(t, x)}{[1 + T((1/\alpha)| x^* |)][1 + \alpha T((1/\alpha)| x^* |) + \alpha h]}$$

From this it follows that

$$\limsup_{h\to 0+} \frac{V[t+h, x(t+h; t_0, x_0)] - V[t, x(t; t_0, x_0)]}{h}$$

$$\leqslant -\frac{(\alpha-1)G(| x(t; t_0, x_0)|)}{[1 + T((1/\alpha)| x(t; t_0, x_0)|)][1 + \alpha T((1/\alpha)| x(t; t_0, x_0)|)]}$$

We have used the facts that

$$x^* = x(t+h; t, x) = x(t+h; t, x(t; t_0, x_0)) = x(t+h; t_0, x_0),$$

$V(t, x) \geqslant G(| x |)$, $\lim_{h\to 0} | x^* | = | x(t; t_0, x_0)|$ and that $T(\epsilon)$ is continuous.

We have thus proved that $V(t, x)$ verifies all the conditions of Theorem 1.4. Let us now study the regularity properties of $V(t, x)$.

We shall suppose that $f(t, x)$ has the following property:

$$| f(t, x_1) - f(t, x_2)| \leqslant L_h(t)| x_1 - x_2 |$$

for every pair x_1 and x_2 with $| x_1 | \leqslant h$, $| x_2 | \leqslant h$. On the basis of Lemma I.7 it follows that for every pair of solutions $x(t; t_0, x_1)$, $x(t; t_0, x_2)$ which stay in the region $| x | \leqslant h$ we have

$$| x(t; t_0, x_1) - x(t; t_0, x_2)| \leqslant | x_1 - x_2 | \exp\left[\int_{t_0}^{t} L_h(s)ds\right].$$

We have previously seen that

$$V(t, x) = G(| x(t+\sigma_1; t, x)|)\frac{1+\alpha\sigma_1}{1+\sigma_1}, \quad \left[\text{where } 0 \leqslant \sigma_1 \leqslant T\left(\frac{1}{\alpha} | x |\right)\right].$$

Now let x_1 and x_2 satisfy the bounds $|x_1| < \delta(h)$, $|x_2| < \delta(h)$ so that the solutions $x(t; t_0, x_1)$ and $x(t; t_0, x_2)$ remain in $|x| \leqslant h$. Define the quantities

$$T_1 = T\left(\frac{1}{\alpha}|x_1|\right), \qquad T_2 = T\left(\frac{1}{\alpha}|x_2|\right).$$

We have

$$\left| G(|x(t+\sigma_1; t, x_1)|)\frac{1+\alpha\sigma_1}{1+\sigma_1} - G(|x(t+\sigma_1; t, x_2)|)\frac{1+\alpha\sigma_1}{1+\sigma_1} \right|$$
$$\leqslant \alpha G'(r_0)\Big| |x(t+\sigma_1; t, x_1)| - |x(t+\sigma_1; t, x_2)| \Big| ,$$

where r_0 is between $|x(t+\sigma_1; t, x_1)|$ and $|x(t+\sigma_1; t, x_2)|$; hence $0 \leqslant r_0 < h$.

Since $G'(r)$ is monotonous, we obtain $G'(r_0) < G'(h)$. It follows that

$$\left|\{G(|x(t+\sigma_1; t, x_1)|) - G(|x(t+\sigma_1; t, x_2)|)\}\frac{1+\alpha\sigma_1}{1+\sigma_1}\right|$$
$$\leqslant \alpha G'(h)\exp\left[\int_t^{t+T_1} L_h(s)ds\right]|x_1 - x_2|.$$

Hence

$$-\alpha G'(h)\exp\left[\int_t^{t+T_1} L_h(s)ds\right]|x_1 - x_2| + G(|x(t+\sigma_1; t, x_1)|)\frac{1+\alpha\sigma_1}{1+\sigma_1}$$
$$\leqslant G(|x(t+\sigma_1; t, x_2)|)\frac{1+\alpha\sigma_1}{1+\sigma_1}.$$

From this follows

$$-\alpha G'(h)\exp\left[\int_t^{t+T_1} L_h(s)ds\right]|x_1 - x_2| + V(t, x_1)$$
$$\leqslant G(|x(t+\sigma_1; t, x_2)|)\frac{1+\alpha\sigma_1}{1+\sigma_1} \leqslant V(t, x_2).$$

Consequently,

$$V(t, x_1) - V(t, x_2) \leqslant \alpha G'(h)\exp\left[\int_t^{t+T_1} L_h(s)ds\right]|x_1 - x_2|.$$

The same computations yield the inequality

$$V(t, x_2) - V(t, x_1) \leqslant \alpha G'(h)\exp\left[\int_t^{t+T_2} L_h(s)ds\right]|x_1 - x_2|.$$

Let $\bar{T} = \max(T_1, T_2)$. It follows then that

$$| V(t, x_2) - V(t, x_1)| \leqslant \alpha G'(h) \exp\left[\int_t^{t+\bar{T}} L_h(s)ds\right] | x_1 - x_2 |$$

or

$$| V(t, x_2) - V(t, x_1)| \leqslant M(h, t, r) | x_1 - x_2 |$$

for $r \leqslant | x_1 | < \delta(h)$, $r \leqslant | x_2 | < \delta(h)$, $t \geqslant 0$, where

$$M(h; t, r) = \alpha G'(h) \exp\left[\int_t^{t+T((1/\alpha)r)} L_h(s)ds\right].$$

If L_h is constant, or if it has the property $| \int_t^{t+u} L_h(s)ds | \leqslant K | u |$, then M does not depend on t. We shall make this assumption in what follows. We shall also suppose that h is fixed.

By choosing $G(r)$ such that

$$G'(r) \leqslant A \exp\left[-KT\left(\frac{1}{\alpha}\delta(r)\right)\right]$$

we obtain the relation $| V(t, x_1) - V(t, x_2)| \leqslant M | x_1 - x_2 |$ for $| x_i | \leqslant h_0$. Indeed, let $| x(t + \sigma_1; t, x_1)| = r_1$, $| x(t + \sigma_1; t, x_2)| = r_2$. If $r_2 \geqslant r_1$, we have $G(r_2) \geqslant G(r_1)$; hence

$$V(t, x_2) \geqslant G(| x(t + \sigma_1; t, x_2)|) \frac{1 + \alpha\sigma_1}{1 + \sigma_1}$$

$$\geqslant G(| x(t + \sigma_1; t, x_1)|) \frac{1 + \alpha\sigma_1}{1 + \sigma_1} = V(t, x_1).$$

If $r_2 \leqslant r_1$, we may write

$$0 \leqslant G(r_1) - G(r_2) = G'(\rho)(r_1 - r_2) \leqslant G'(r_1)(r_1 - r_2)$$

$$\leqslant A \exp\left[-KT\left(\frac{1}{\alpha}\delta(r_1)\right)\right](r_1 - r_2)$$

$$\leqslant A \exp\left[-KT\left(\frac{1}{\alpha}\delta(r_1)\right)\right] | x(t + \sigma_1; t, x_1) - x(t + \sigma_1; t, x_2)|$$

$$\leqslant A \exp\left[-KT\left(\frac{1}{\alpha}\delta(r_1)\right)\right] \exp\left[KT\left(\frac{1}{\alpha}| x_1 |\right)\right] | x_1 - x_2 |.$$

Since $| x(t + \sigma_1; t, x_1)| = r_1$, we have $| x_1 | \geqslant \delta(r_1)$, and thus $T((1/\alpha)| x_1 |) \leqslant T((1/\alpha)\,\delta(r_1))$. Hence, $0 \leqslant G(r_1) - G(r_2) \leqslant A| x_1 - x_2 |$.

It follows from these relations that

$$0 \leqslant V(t, x_1) - G(| x(t + \sigma_1; t, x_2)|) \frac{1 + \alpha\sigma_1}{1 + \sigma_1} \leqslant \alpha A| x_1 - x_2 | \qquad (*)$$

and thus that

$$V(t, x_2) \geqslant G(| x(t + \sigma_1; t, x_2)|) \frac{1 + \alpha\sigma_1}{1 + \sigma_1} \geqslant V(t, x_1) - \alpha A| x_1 - x_2 |.$$

It follows therefore that in all cases we have

$$V(t, x_2) - V(t, x_1) \geqslant -\alpha A| x_1 - x_2 |.$$

By interchanging the roles of x_1 and x_2, now we obtain

$$V(t, x_1) - V(t, x_2) \geqslant -\alpha A| x_1 - x_2 |$$

and thus the desired result

$$V(t, x_1) - V(t, x_2)| \leqslant \alpha A| x_1 - x_2 |,$$

if $| x_i | \neq 0$.

If $x_2 = 0$, the first inequality (*) yields $0 \leqslant V(t, x_1) \leqslant \alpha A| x_1 |$; hence the relation obtained above holds in this case also. If $x_1 = x_2 = 0$, the relation is trivial.

It remains to prove that we can choose G such that it verifies the required condition. To that end we may take

$$G(r) = A \int_0^r \exp \left[-KT \left(\frac{1}{\alpha} \delta(r) \right) \right] dr.$$

We have $G(0) = 0$, $G'(r) = Ae^{-KT((1/\alpha)\delta(r))} > 0$, $G'(0) = 0$, since $\delta(0) = 0$ and $T(0) = \infty$. $G'(r)$ is monotone-increasing, and thus $G''(r)$ exists almost everywhere, and is positive.

Finally, we may state

Theorem 1.6′. *Let the trivial solution of the system is uniformly asymptotically stable,*

$$| f(t, x_1) - f(t, x_2)| \leqslant L_h(t) \,| x_1 - x_2 | \qquad \text{for} \quad | x_1 | \leqslant h, \, | x_2 | \leqslant h,$$

and

$$\left| \int_t^{t+u} L_h(s) ds \right| \leqslant K| u |;$$

then there exists a function $V(t, x)$ with the following properties:

1. $a(|x|) \leqslant V(t, x) \leqslant b(|x|)$.
2.

$$\limsup_{h\to 0+} \frac{V[t+h, x(t+h; t_0, x_0)] - V[t, x(t; t_0, x_0)]}{h} \leqslant -c(|x(t; t_0, x_0)|).$$

3. $|V(t, x_1) - V(t, x_2)| \leqslant M |x_1 - x_2|$,

for $|x_1| \leqslant \delta(\delta_0)$, $|x_2| \leqslant \delta(\delta_0)$.

This theorem will play an important role in what follows. We will deduce, on the bases of the theorem, a series of propositions which emphasize the importance of uniform asymptotic stability.

Let us remark in concluding these considerations that if the trivial solution is globally uniformly asymptotically stable, then $\lim_{\epsilon\to\infty} \delta(\epsilon) = \infty$ hence $\lim_{\delta\to\infty} \epsilon(\delta) = \infty$. Since $a(r) = G(r)$, $b(r) - \alpha G(\epsilon(r))$, it follows that

$$\lim_{r\to\infty} a(r) = \lim_{r\to\infty} b(r) = \infty.$$

Likewise, if f is periodic with respect to t of period ω, then $V(t, x)$ is periodic of period ω and if, in particular, f does not depend on t, then V does not depend on t. These facts are established in the same way as in the case of uniform stability.

We shall give another theorem which represents a weakening of the general theorem 1.5 in the case of systems which are periodic in t and independent of t.

Theorem 1.5′. *Let $f(t, x)$ be periodic in t, with period ω: $f(t+\omega, x) \equiv f(t, x)$. If there exists a function $V(t, x)$ periodic with period ω and with the following properties:*

(a) $a(|x|) \leqslant V(t, x) \leqslant b(|x|)$, $b(h_0) < a(h_1)$, $h_0 < h_1 < h$.

(b)

$$\limsup_{h\to 0+} \frac{V[t+h, x(t+h; t, x)] - V(t, x)}{h} \leqslant 0 \qquad \text{for} \quad |x| \leqslant h.$$

with the equality in (b) *occurring only in the points of a set $\mathfrak{M}$ which does not contain whole semitrajectories, then the solution $x = 0$ is asymptotically stable and the sphere $|x| < h_0$ lies in the domain of attraction.*

Proof. Stability, and the fact that $|x_0| < h_0$ implies $|x(t; t_0, x_0)| < h_1$, follows from

$$a(|x(t; t_0, x_0)|) \leqslant V(t, x(t; t_0, x_0)) \leqslant V(t_0, x_0) \leqslant b(|x_0|) < b(h_0) < a(h_1).$$

Suppose that there exists a trajectory and a positive number η such that $|x(t; t_0, x_0)| > \eta$ for $t > t_0$, $|x_0| \leqslant h$. Consider the function $V^*(t) = V(t, x(t; t_0, x_0))$. This function is monotone-decreasing; hence $V_0 = \lim_{t\to\infty} V^*(t)$ exists and $V^*(t) \geqslant V_0$ for $t \geqslant t_0$.

Consider the sequence $x^{(k)} = x(t_0 + k\omega; t_0, x_0)$; from $|x^{(k)}| < h_1$ it follows that a convergent subsequence can be extracted; let x_0^* be its limit; then $x_0^* \neq 0$. We have

$$\lim_{k\to\infty} V^*(t_0 + k\omega) = V_0, \qquad V^*(t_0 + k\omega) = V(t_0 + k\omega, x^{(k)}) = V(t_0, x^{(k)}),$$

and thus

$$\lim_{k\to\infty} V^*(t_0 + k\omega) = V(t_0, x_0^*).$$

It follows that $V(t_0, x_0^*) = V_0$.

Consider the semitrajectory $x(t; t_0, x_0^*)$; since this trajectory cannot be wholly contained in $\mathfrak{M}$, the function $V(t, x(t; t_0, x_0^*))$ is not constant. Therefore there exists a $t^* > t_0$ such that $V(t^*, x(t^*; t_0, x_0)) < V(t_0, x_0^*) = V_0$.

For every $\gamma > 0$ we have $|x(t^*; t_0, x_0^*) - x(t^*; t_0, x^{(k)})| < \gamma$ if $k > N(\gamma)$; hence

$$\lim_{k\to\infty} V(t^*, x(t^*; t_0, x^{(k)})) = V(t^*; x(t^*; t_0, x_0^*)) < V_0.$$

But

$$\begin{aligned} x(t^*; t_0, x^{(k)}) &= x(t^*; t_0, x(t_0 + k\omega; t_0, x_0)) \\ &= x(t^* + k\omega, t_0 + k\omega, x(t_0 + k\omega; t_0, x_0)) = x(t^* + k\omega; t_0, x_0) \end{aligned}$$

and

$$V(t^*, x) = V(t^* + k\omega, x).$$

Consequently,

$$V(t^*, x(t^*; t_0, x^{(k)})) = V(t^* + k\omega, x(t^* + k\omega; t_0, x_0)) = V^*(t^* + k\omega).$$

It follows that

$$\lim_{k\to\infty} V(t^*; x(t^*; t_0, x^{(k)})) = V_0,$$

which is a contradiction.

The contradiction obtained above proves that for every trajectory with $|x_0| < h_0$ and every $\eta > 0$ there exists a $t_1 > t_0$ such that $|x(t_1; t_0, x_0)| < \eta$. We choose $\eta = \delta(\epsilon)$, and deduce from $|x(t_1; t_0, x_0)| < \delta(\epsilon)$ that $|x(t; t_1, x(t_1; t_0, x_0))| < \epsilon$. From this follows $|x(t; t_0, x_0)| < \epsilon$ for $t > t_1(\epsilon)$, and thus

$$\lim_{t\to\infty} x(t; t_0, x_0) = 0.$$

At the end of this paragraph we shall give some criteria of stability in which weaker conditions are required for Lyapunov functions. These are all based on the lemma concerning differential inequalities given in the Introduction. These criteria are due to C. Corduneanu.

Theorem 1.5″. *Let $\omega(t, y)$ be a continuous function for $t \geqslant 0$, $0 \leqslant y < Y \leqslant \infty$, $\omega(t, 0) = 0$. Consider the equation*

$$\frac{dy}{dt} = \omega(t, y) \tag{1'}$$

and suppose that through every point (t_0, y_0), $t_0 \geqslant 0$, $0 \leqslant y_0 < Y$ there passes a unique solution. Let $V(t, x)$ be a differentiable function, for $t \geqslant 0$, $|x| < M$, $V'(t, x) = \lim_{h\to 0} V(t + h, x + hf(t, x))/h$; suppose that

$$V'(t, x) \leqslant \omega(t, V(t, x)).$$

1. *If the solution $y = 0$ of equation (1′) is stable and $V(t, x) \geqslant a(|x|)$, the solution $x = 0$ of system (1) is likewise stable.*

2. *If the solution $y = 0$ of equation (1′) is uniformly stable and $a(|x|) \leqslant V(t, x) \leqslant b(|x|)$, the solution $x = 0$ of system (1) is likewise uniformly stable.*

3. *If the solution $y = 0$ of equation (1) is asymptotically stable and $V(t, x) \geqslant a(|x|)$, the solution $x = 0$ of system (1) is likewise asymptotically stable.*

4. *If the solution $y = 0$ of equation (1′) is uniformly asymptotically stable and $a(|x|) \leqslant V(t, x) \leqslant b(|x|)$, the solution $x = 0$ of system (1) is likewise uniformly asymptotically stable.*

Proof. 1. Let $\epsilon > 0$, $t_0 \geqslant 0$, $\eta(\epsilon, t_0) > 0$ such that $0 < y_0 < \eta$ implies $y(t; t_0, y_0) < a(\epsilon)$ for $t \geqslant t_0$. It follows from the continuity of function V that there exists a $\delta(\epsilon, t_0) > 0$ such that $|x_0| < \delta$ implies $V(t_0, x_0) < \eta$. We have

$$\frac{d}{dt} V(t, x(t; t_0, x_0)) = V'(t, x(t; t_0, x_0)) \leqslant \omega(t, V(t, x(t; t_0, x_0))).$$

It follows from Lemma I.3 that

$$V(t, x(t; t_0\ x_0)) \leqslant y(t; t_0, V(t_0, x_0)) < a(\epsilon).$$

From this follows $a(|\ x(t; t_0, x_0)|) < a(\epsilon)$; hence $|\ x(t; t_0, x_0)| < \epsilon$ for $t \geqslant t_0$, if $|\ x_0\ | < \delta(\epsilon, t_0)$.

2. From $V(t, x) \leqslant b(|\ x\ |)$ it follows that δ may be chosen independent of t_0. The demonstration then proceeds as above, since η may be also chosen independent of t_0.

3. From

$$V(t, x(t; t_0, x_0)) \leqslant y(t; t_0, V(t_0, x_0))$$

and

$$\lim_{t\to\infty} y(t; t_0, V(t_0, x_0)) = 0$$

it follows that

$$\lim_{t\to\infty} V(t, x(t; t_0, x_0)) = 0.$$

Thus, $\lim_{t\to\infty} a(|\ x(t; t_0, x_0)|) = 0$, from which we deduce that $\lim_{t\to\infty} x(t; t_0, x_0) = 0$.

4. It follows from the hypothesis that there exists an $\eta_0 > 0$ such that for $\epsilon > 0$ there exists a quantity $T(\epsilon) > 0$ with the property that from $y_0 < \eta_0$ follows $y(t; t_0, y_0) < a(\epsilon)$ for $t > t_0 + T(\epsilon)$. We choose δ_0 such that $b(\delta_0) < \eta_0$. If $|\ x_0\ | < \delta_0$, we conclude that

$$V(t_0, x_0) < b(|\ x_0\ |) < b(\delta_0) < \eta_0 .$$

Consequently,

$$y(t; t_0, V(t_0, x_0)) < a(\epsilon) \qquad \text{for} \quad t \geqslant t_0 + T(\epsilon).$$

Since $V[t, x(t; t_0, x_0)] \leqslant y(t; t_0, V(t_0, x_0))$, it follows that

$$a(|\ x(t; t_0, x_0)|) < a(\epsilon) \qquad \text{for} \quad t \geqslant t_0 + T(\epsilon).$$

Thus, finally,

$$|\ x(t; t_0, x_0)| < \epsilon \qquad \text{for} \quad t \geqslant t_0 + T(\epsilon),\ |\ x_0\ | < \delta_0 ,$$

and the theorem is proved.

1.3. Linear Systems

We shall now study the characteristic features of the stability problem in the case of linear systems. In connection with this we shall emphasize a series of essential general properties of the linear systems.

A homogeneous linear system is written in the form

$$\frac{dx}{dt} = A(t)x, \tag{3}$$

where we shall assume that $A(t)$ is a quadratic matrix whose elements are continuous functions of t defined for $t \geqslant 0$. In this case the theorem of existence has a global character; the solutions are defined on the entire semiaxis $t \geqslant 0$.

To see this it is sufficient to prove that on every finite interval the solutions remain bounded; hence they do not leave the domain in which the conditions of the existence theorem are verified.

Let $x(t; t_0, x_0)$ be the solution of system (3) which for $t = t_0$ passes through point x_0. We have, for the values for which the solution is defined,

$$x(t; t_0, x_0) = x_0 + \int_{t_0}^{t} A(s)x(s; t_0, x_0)ds.$$

It follows that

$$|x(t; t_0, x_0)| \leqslant |x_0| + \int_{t_0}^{t} |A(s)|\,|x(s; t_0, x_0)|\,ds.$$

By applying Lemma I.6 (Consequence 2), it follows that

$$|x(t; t_0, x_0)| \leqslant |x_0| \exp\left[\int_{t_0}^{t} |A(s)|\,ds\right],$$

and thus we see that the solution remains bounded on every finite interval.

We remark that we have used here the estimate

$$|A(s)x(s; t_0, x_0)| \leqslant |A(s)|\,|x(s; t_0, x_0)|$$

which follows directly from the definition of the norm of a matrix; namely, $|A| = \sup_{|x| \leqslant 1} |Ax|$.

Let us remark that if the Euclidean norm is used for vectors, then $|A|$ is given by $\sqrt{\Lambda}$, where Λ is the largest eigenvalue of the matrix A^*A. (A^* is the transposed matrix of A when A is real, and the conjugate of A when A is complex.)

Indeed, we have, in conformity with the definition of the Euclidean norm, $|Ax|^2 = (Ax, Ax) = (A^*Ax, x) \leqslant \Lambda(x, x)$; hence $|Ax| \leqslant \sqrt{\Lambda}|x|$. Consequently $|A| \leqslant \sqrt{\Lambda}$. On the other hand, taking into account the extremal properties of the eigenvalues of the symmetrical matrices, it follows that there exists a vector x with $|x| = 1$ such that $(A^*Ax, x) = \Lambda$; hence $|A| = \sqrt{\Lambda}$.

If $x_1(t)$ and $x_2(t)$ are two arbitrary solutions of the system, it is immediately verified that $\alpha_1 x_1(t) + \alpha_2 x_2(t)$ is likewise a solution of the system. (α_1 and α_2 will be supposed to be real numbers. In general, in all of the theory we shall work only with real functions; any other cases will be explicitly indicated.)

From the foregoing it follows that the set of solutions of system (3) *forms a linear space.*

Let $x(t; t_0, x_0)$ be the solution of system (3) which for $t = t_0$ passes through the point x_0. This solution defines for fixed t and t_0 a transformation of R^n in itself which attaches to the point x_0 the point $x(t; t_0, x_0)$; we shall denote this transformation by $C(t; t_0)$.

Proposition. *The transformation $C(t; t_0)$ is linear.*

Proof. We have

$$C(t; t_0)(\alpha_1 x_1 + \alpha_2 x_2) = x(t; t_0, \alpha_1 x_1 + \alpha_2 x_2).$$

On the other hand,

$$\alpha_1 C(t; t_0)x_1 + \alpha_2 C(t; t_0)x_2 = \alpha_1 x(t; t_0, x_1) + \alpha_2 x(t; t_0, x_2)$$

is a linear combination of solutions of system (3) and hence is a solution of the system. Furthermore,

$$x(t; t_0, \alpha_1 x_1 + \alpha_2 x_2) = \alpha_1 x(t; t_0, x_1) + \alpha_2 x(t; t_0, x_2),$$

since both solutions coincide for $t = t_0$. The proposition is thus proved.

We shall write $x(t; t_0, x_0) = C(t; t_0)x_0$. If a basis of the space is fixed, every linear transformation is given by a matrix whose columns are the images, under the given transformation, of the vectors of the basis. The vectors of the basis have the coordinates

$$\begin{pmatrix} 1 \\ 0 \\ \vdots \\ 0 \end{pmatrix}, \begin{pmatrix} 0 \\ 1 \\ \vdots \\ 0 \end{pmatrix}, \dots, \begin{pmatrix} 0 \\ 0 \\ \vdots \\ 1 \end{pmatrix};$$

hence $C(t; t_0)$ will correspond to a matrix whose columns are the solutions of system (3) which at the moment t_0 coincide with the columns of the unity matrix. Denoting the unit matrix by E, and making no distinction between the transformation $C(t; t_0)$ and the corresponding matrix, we shall write $C(t_0; t_0) = E$. We shall say that $C(t; t_0)$ is a fundamental matrix of solutions of system (3). Since the columns of the matrix $C(t; t_0)$ are solutions of system (3), we may write

$$\frac{dC(t; t_0)}{dt} = A(t)C(t; t_0).$$

The relation $x(t; t_0, x_0) = C(t; t_0)x_0$ shows that every solution of system (3) is expressed as a linear combination of the solutions of a fundamental system.

Let us now point out some fundamental properties of the matrix $C(t; t_0)$.

Proposition. *For all t, s, u we have*

$$C(t; s)C(s; u) = C(t; u).$$

Proof. It is sufficient to show that for every vector x_0 we have $C(t; s)C(s; u)x_0 = C(t; u)x_0$. But

$$C(s; u)x_0 = x(s; u, x_0),\ C(t; s)C(s; u)x_0 = x(t; s, C(s; u)x_0)$$
$$= x(t; s, x(s; u, x_0)) = x(t; u, x_0) = C(t; u)x_0,$$

and the relation is proved.

The equality

$$x(t; s, x(s; u, x_0)) = x(t; u, x_0)$$

is a consequence of the fact that both solutions coincide for $t = s$.

From this proposition it follows immediately for $s = t_0$, $u = t$:

$$C(t; t_0)C(t_0; t) = E.$$

This means that the matrix $C(t; t_0)$ is nonsingular, and its inverse is $C(t_0; t)$.

It is useful to consider in some problems the adjoint system of system (3). Namely, we shall call the *adjoint system* of system (3) the system

$$\frac{dy}{dt} = -yA(t),$$

where y is a row vector.

Proposition. *If x is a solution of the given system and y a solution of the adjoint system, then the product yx is constant.*

Proof. We have

$$\frac{d}{dt} yx = \frac{dy}{dt} x + y \frac{dx}{dt} = -yA(t)x + yA(t)x = 0;$$

hence yx is constant. The proposition is proved.

Obviously, the whole theory developed for system (3) is correspondingly transposed for the adjoint system [which can be also written in the form $dy/dt = -A^*(t)y$, y now being a column vector]. Let $\tilde{C}(t; t_0)$ be a fundamental matrix of solutions of the adjoint system; we stress now that the rows of the matrix $\tilde{C}(t; t_0)$ are solutions of the adjoint system. Taking into account the above proposition, it follows that the matrix $\tilde{C}(t; t_0)C(t; t_0)$ is constant, since its elements are products of the rows of the matrix $\tilde{C}(t; t_0)$ with the columns of $C(t; t_0)$, hence products of solutions of the adjoint system and of system (3). But

$$\tilde{C}(t_0; t_0)C(t_0; t_0) = EE = E.$$

It follows that

$$\tilde{C}(t; t_0)C(t; t_0) = E,$$

and thus that

$$\tilde{C}(t; t_0) = [C(t; t_0)]^{-1} = C(t_0; t).$$

We have thus established the following

Proposition. *We have $\tilde{C}(t; t_0) = C(t_0; t)$; hence the rows of matrix $C(t_0; t)$ form a fundamental system of solutions of the adjoint system.*

We shall close these general considerations on linear systems by stating the so-called "formula of variation of constants," which will prove useful in many circumstances.

Let us consider the nonhomogeneous system

$$\frac{dx}{dt} = A(t)x + f(t).$$

Let $C(t; t_0)$ be, as above, the fundamental matrix of solutions of the corresponding homogeneous system. We make the change of variables $x(t) = C(t; t_0)y(t)$. We obtain

$$\frac{dx}{dt} = \frac{dC(t; t_0)}{dt} y(t) + C(t; t_0) \frac{dy}{dt}$$
$$= A(t)x + f(t) = A(t)C(t; t_0)y(t) + f(t).$$

From $dC(t; t_0)/dt = A(t)C(t; t_0)$ it follows that $C(t; t_0)(dy/dt) = f(t)$ and thus that

$$\frac{dy}{dt} = [C(t; t_0)]^{-1}f(t) = C(t_0; t)f(t).$$

From here

$$y(t) = y(t_0) + \int_{t_0}^{t} C(t_0; s)f(s)ds.$$

From the relation which connects $x(t)$ to $y(t)$ it follows that $x(t_0) = y(t_0)$, since $C(t_0; t_0) = E$. Finally we obtain

$$x(t; t_0, x_0) = C(t; t_0)x_0 + C(t; t_0) \int_{t_0}^{t} C(t_0; s)f(s)ds$$

or

$$x(t; t_0, x_0) = C(t; t_0)x_0 + \int_{t_0}^{t} C(t; t_0)C(t_0; s)f(s)ds,$$

which yields the desired result:

$$x(t; t_0, x_0) = C(t; t_0)x_0 + \int_{t_0}^{t} C(t; s)f(s)ds.$$

1.4. Stability for Linear Systems

After this introductory part concerning linear systems we may proceed to the study of stability problems for these systems. We have seen above, as a consequence of a more general proposition, that for linear systems in which the matrix $A(t)$ is bounded, uniform asymptotic stability is always exponential; i.e., there exist constants B and α such that we shall have

$$| x(t; t_0, x_0)| \leqslant Be^{-\alpha(t-t_0)} | x_0 |.$$

Let us present a different proof of this proposition. According to the definition of uniform asymptotic stability, there exists a $\delta_0 > 0$ and $T(\epsilon)$ such that if $| x_0 | \leqslant \delta_0$ and $t \geqslant t_0 + T(\epsilon)$ we will have $| x(t; t_0, x_0)| < \epsilon$. Since $| x(t; t_0, x_0)| = | C(t; t_0)x_0 |$, from $| x_0 | < \delta_0$ and $t \geqslant t_0 + T(\epsilon)$, we deduce that $| C(t; t_0)x_0 | < \epsilon$. In what follows we fix $0 < \epsilon < 1$.

Let u_0 be an arbitrary vector with $| u_0 | \leqslant 1$. Then $| \delta_0 u_0 | < \delta_0$; hence $| C(t; t_0)\delta_0 u_0 | < \epsilon$ for $t \geqslant t_0 + T(\epsilon)$. The relation $| C(t; t_0)\delta_0 u_0 | = \delta_0 | C(t; t_0)u_0 |$ yields $| C(t; t_0)u_0 | < \epsilon/\delta_0$. Since u_0 is arbitrary, with

$|u_0| \leqslant 1$, we will have $|C(t;t_0)| < \epsilon/\delta_0$ for $t > t_0 + T(\epsilon)$; i.e., $|C(t;t_0)| < \epsilon$ for $t \geqslant t_0 + T_1(\epsilon)$, where we set $T_1(\epsilon) = T(\delta_0\epsilon)$.

From the relation $C(t;t_0) = C(t;t_0+T_1)C(t_0+T_1;t_0)$ we obtain $|C(t;t_0)| \leqslant |C(t;t_0+T_1)|\,|C(t_0+T_1;t_0)| < \epsilon^2$ for $t \geqslant t_0 + 2T_1$. By induction it is immediately verified that $|C(t;t_0)| < \epsilon^m$ for $t \geqslant t_0 + mT_1$.

Now let $t \geqslant t_0$, arbitrary. Then there exists an $m \geqslant 1$ such that $t_0 + (m-1)T_1 \leqslant t < t_0 + mT_1$. Furthermore, $mT_1 > t - t_0$, $m > (1/T_1)(t - t_0)$, $\epsilon^m < \epsilon^{(1/T_1)(t-t_0)}$, since $\epsilon < 1$. On the other hand, there exists a $\delta(\epsilon)$ such that $|x(t;t_0,x_0)| < \epsilon$ if $|x_0| \leqslant \delta(\epsilon)$ and $t \geqslant t_0$. From these we will have, as above, $|C(t;t_0)\delta(\epsilon)u_0| < \epsilon$ for $t \geqslant t_0$; hence $|C(t;t_0)| < \epsilon/\delta(\epsilon)$ for $t \geqslant t_0$. Since $t \geqslant t_0 + (m-1)T_1$, we will have $|C(t;t_0)| < [\epsilon/\delta(\epsilon)]\epsilon^{m-1}$. Indeed, if $m \geqslant 2$, this inequality follows from the fact that $\delta(\epsilon) \leqslant \epsilon$, and if $m = 1$ from the fact that $|C(t;t_0)| < \epsilon/\delta(\epsilon)$ for all $t \geqslant t_0$. Finally, we have shown that for every $t \geqslant t_0$, $|C(t;t_0)| < [1/\delta(\epsilon)]\epsilon^m$ and thus that $|C(t;t_0)| < [1/\delta(\epsilon)]\epsilon^{(1/T_1)(t-t_0)}$.

Let us set $1/\delta(\epsilon) = \beta$, $\alpha = -(1/T_1)\ln\epsilon$. Then $\beta > 0$, $\alpha > 0$, $\epsilon = e^{-\alpha T}$, and the previous estimate becomes

$$|C(t;t_0)| < \beta e^{-\alpha(t-t_0)}.$$

Thus we have proved once again that for linear systems, uniform asymptotic stability is always exponential. We remark that in this demonstration *we have not used the hypothesis that matrix $A(t)$ is bounded.*

We shall now prove with the help of this fundamental property of linear systems that if the trivial solution of a linear system is uniform asymptotically stable, then there exists a Lyapunov function which is a quadratic form.

Theorem 1.6″. *If the trivial solution of system* (3) *is uniformly asymptotically stable, then for an arbitrary quadratic form* $(W(t)x, x)$, *with*

$$\lambda(x,x) \leqslant \lambda(t)(x,x) \leqslant (W(t)x,x) \leqslant \Lambda(t)(x,x) \leqslant \Lambda(x,x),$$

where $\lambda > 0$, *there exists a quadratic form* $(V(t)x, x)$ *with the properties that*

$$\mu(x,x) \leqslant (V(t)x,x) \leqslant M(x,x) \qquad (\mu > 0)$$

and

$$\frac{d}{dt}(V(t)x(t), x(t)) = -(W(t)x(t), x(t))$$

for any solution $x(t)$ *of system* (3).

Proof. Define

$$(V(t)x, x) = \int_t^\infty (W(s)C(s; t)x, C(s; t)x)ds,$$

which is to say the matrix $V(t)$ is given by the relation

$$V(t) = \int_t^\infty C^*(s; t)W(s)C(s; t)ds.$$

The convergence of the integral is assured, since $| C(t; t_0)| \leqslant Be^{-\alpha(t-t_0)}$, and $| W | < \Lambda$. From this also follows that

$$| V(t)| \leqslant \int_t^\infty Be^{-\alpha(s-t)}\Lambda Be^{-\alpha(s-t)}\, ds = \Lambda B^2 \int_0^\infty e^{-2\alpha s}\, ds = \frac{\Lambda B^2}{2\alpha}.$$

For every solution $x(t; t_0, x_0)$ of system (3), we have

$$\begin{aligned}(V(t)x(t; t_0, x_0), x(t; t_0, x_0)) &= \int_t^\infty (W(s)C(s; t)x(t; t_0, x_0), C(s; t)x(t; t_0, x_0))ds\\ &= \int_t^\infty (W(s)x(s; t_0, x_0), x(s; t_0, x_0))ds,\end{aligned}$$

and thus

$$\frac{d}{dt}(V(t)x(t; t_0, x_0), x(t; t_0, x_0)) = \quad (W(t)x(t; t_0, x_0), x(t; t_0, x_0)).$$

It remains to prove that $(V(t)x, x) \geqslant \mu(x, x)$ with $\mu > 0$.
We have

$$(V(t)x, x) \geqslant \int_t^\infty \lambda(C(s; t)x, C(s; t)x)ds = \lambda \int_t^\infty | x(s; t, x)|^2\, ds.$$

Since $x(s; t, x) = x + \int_t^s A(u)x(u; t, x)du$, and since $| x(u; t, x)| \leqslant B| x |$ for $u \geqslant t$, we have

$$| x(s; t, x) \quad x | \leqslant B| x | \int_t^s | A(u)|\, du.$$

Assuming that the matrix A has the property that

$$\int_t^s | A(u)|\, du < \omega(s - t),$$

where $\omega(r) \to 0$ *when* $r \to 0$, we will have for $t \leqslant s \leqslant t + \alpha$, $| x(s; t, x) - x | \leqslant \frac{1}{2} | x |$, and thus

$$| x(s; t, x)| \geqslant | x | - | x(s; t, x) - x | \geqslant \tfrac{1}{2} | x |.$$

Since

$$(V(t)x, x) \geqslant \lambda \int_t^\infty |x(s; t, x)|^2 \, ds > \lambda \int_t^{t+\alpha} |x(s; t, x)|^2 \, ds \geqslant \frac{\lambda}{4} \alpha |x|^2$$

we can take $\mu = \lambda\alpha/4$. The theorem is therefore completely proved.

Remark. If the matrix A is constant and the matrix W is chosen independent of t, then the matrix V does not depend on t.

To prove this, note that for the systems which do not depend explicitly on t we have $x(t + t_0; t_0, x_0) = x(t; 0, x_0)$. (We have proved the corresponding property for periodic systems; if the system does not depend on t, then every real t_0 may be considered as period.) For linear systems, this relation is $C(t + t_0; t_0)x_0 = C(t; 0)x_0$; hence $C(t + t_0; t_0) = C(t; 0)$. Therefore,

$$V(t) = \int_t^\infty C^*(s; t)WC(s; t)ds = \int_0^\infty C^*(s + t; t)WC(s + t; t)ds$$
$$= \int_0^\infty C^*(s; 0)WC(s; 0)ds.$$

Hence, V does not depend on t.

1.5. Linear Systems with Constant Coefficients

The proposition proved in the preceding section has, in reality, a purely algebraic character, as already pointed out by Lyapunov. To reproduce Lyapunov's reasoning, we shall recall some fundamental propositions relative to linear systems with constant coefficients, and, in connection with this, the reduction of the matrices to the normal Jordan form, which will prove useful later.

Given a linear transformation T in a linear n-dimensional complex space and a basis $e_1, e_2, \ldots, e_n$ of the space, a matrix A is attached to the transformation, whose columns are vectors Te_k written in the basis $e_1, e_2, \ldots, e_n$. If $y = Tx$, then $y = Ax$, x and y denoting the representation of the vectors with respect to the basis $e_1, e_2, \ldots, e_n$.

Indeed, let $x = \sum_{i=1}^n x_i e_i$, $y = \sum_{i=1}^n y_i e_i$. We have $\sum_{i=1}^n y_i e_i = \sum_{k=1}^n x_k Te_k$. Upon writing $Te_k = \sum_{i=1}^n a_{ik} e_i$, we will have

$$\sum_{i=1}^n y_i e_i = \sum_{k=1}^n x_k \sum_{i=1}^n a_{ik} e_i = \sum_{i=1}^n \left(\sum_{k=1}^n a_{ik} x_k \right) e_i,$$

and thus $y_i = \sum_{k=1}^n a_{ik} x_k$.

Proposition. *If to the transformation T correspond the matrix A in the basis $e_1, e_2, \ldots, e_n$ and the matrix B in the basis $f_1, f_2, \ldots, f_n$, then $B = C^{-1}AC$, where C is the matrix corresponding to the passage from a basis to another.*

Proof. Elements b_{ij} are obtained by writing the images of f_j in the basis $f_1, \ldots, f_n$. We have $Tf_j = \sum_{i=1}^n b_{ij}f_i$. Let $f_j = \sum_{k=1}^n c_{kj}e_k$. It follows that $Tf_j = \sum_{k=1}^n c_{kj}Te_k$. Since $Te_k = \sum_{l=1}^n a_{lk}e_l$, we obtain $Tf_j = \sum_{k=1}^n c_{kj} \sum_{l=1}^n a_{lk}e_l$. On the other hand, $e_l = \sum_{i=1}^n d_{il}f_i$, where D is the inverse of matrix C. Then

$$Tf_j = \sum_{k=1}^n c_{kj} \sum_{l=1}^n a_{lk} \sum_{i=1}^n d_{il}f_i = \sum_{i=1}^n \Big(\sum_{l,k} d_{il}a_{lk}c_{kj} \Big) f_i$$

Finally, $b_{ij} = \sum_{l,k} d_{il}a_{lk}c_{kj}$, and therefore $B = DAC = C^{-1}AC$.

A vector u is an *eigenvector* of the transformation T if u is not zero, and there exists a complex number λ such that $Tu = \lambda u$. If $e_1, e_2, \ldots, e_n$ is a basis of the space and A is the matrix corresponding to the transformation, the condition that u be an eigenvector is written $\sum_{k=1}^n a_{ik}u_k = \lambda u_i$. It is clear that in order that there exists a nonzero vector u which verifies this condition, it is necessary and sufficient that $\det (A - \lambda E) = 0$. The values λ which verify this equation are called the *eigenvalues* of the transformation (or of the matrix). One of the consequences of the preceding proposition is the following: the matrix A and the matrix $C^{-1}AC$ have the same eigenvalues.

Let $\lambda_1, \lambda_2, \ldots, \lambda_s$ be distinct eigenvalues of the transformation T, and $u_1, u_2, \ldots, u_s$ the corresponding eigenvectors. Then the vectors $u_1, u_2, \ldots, u_s$ are linearly independent. Indeed, let us suppose that $c_1u_1 + c_2u_2 + \cdots + c_su_s = 0$. Upon applying transformation T, we obtain $c_1Tu_1 + c_2Tu_2 + \cdots + c_sTu_s = 0$. Since $Tu_k = \lambda_k u_k$, we see that $c_1\lambda_1u_1 + c_2\lambda_2u_2 + \cdots + c_s\lambda_su_s = 0$. From $\sum c_ku_k = 0$, we get $c_su_s = -c_1u_1 - c_2u_2 - \cdots - c_{s-1}u_{s-1}$. It follows that

$$\lambda_1c_1u_1 + \lambda_2c_2u_2 + \cdots + \lambda_{s-1}c_{s-1}u_{s-1} - \lambda_sc_1u_1 - \lambda_sc_2u_2 - \cdots - \lambda_sc_{s-1}u_{s-1} = 0;$$

i.e.,

$$(\lambda_1 - \lambda_s)c_1u_1 + (\lambda_2 - \lambda_s)c_2u_2 + \cdots + (\lambda_{s-1} - \lambda_s)c_{s-1}u_{s-1} = 0.$$

If $u_1, u_2, \ldots, u_{s-1}$ are linearly independent, then

$$(\lambda_k - \lambda_s)c_k = 0 \qquad (k = 1, \ldots, s - 1).$$

By hypothesis, however, $\lambda_k - \lambda_s \neq 0$; hence $c_k = 0$ for $k = 1, \ldots, s - 1$. But then $c_su_s = 0$; hence $c_s = 0$.

The linear independence of the system of s vectors can therefore be established by induction (for $s = 1$ it follows from the fact that $u_1 \neq 0$).

It follows from this that if the transformation T admits n distinct eigenvalues, then it admits n linearly independent eigenvectors. Taking these vectors $u_1, u_2, \dots, u_n$ as a basis of the space, the relations $Tu_k = \lambda_k u_k$ show that in this basis the matrix of the transformation is diagonal, and has λ_k as the diagonal elements.

According to what has been stated above, it follows that if the roots of the equation $\det(A - \lambda E) = 0$ are distinct, there exists a matrix C such that the matrix $C^{-1}AC$ will have a diagonal form, the diagonal elements being the roots of the above equation.

Application. Consider the system $dx/dt = Ax$. Suppose that the equation $\det(A - \lambda E) = 0$, which we shall call the *characteristic equation* of the system, has distinct roots.

According to the above statements there exists a matrix C such that $C^{-1}AC$ shall be diagonal and shall have elements $\lambda_1, \dots, \lambda_n$ on the diagonal. By performing the change of variables $x = Cy$, $y = C^{-1}x$ in the system, we obtain

$$\frac{dy}{dt} = C^{-1}\frac{dx}{dt} = C^{-1}Ax = C^{-1}ACy.$$

Therefore, the system in y has the form $dy_k/dt = \lambda_k y_k$.

A fundamental matrix of solutions of this system has the form

$$Y = \begin{pmatrix} e^{\lambda_1 t} & & & 0 \\ & e^{\lambda_2 t} & & \\ & & \ddots & \\ 0 & & & e^{\lambda_n t} \end{pmatrix}.$$

It follows that the fundamental matrix of solutions of the given system is $X = CY$, where the columns of matrix C are the eigenvectors of matrix A.

It remains therefore to study the case when the transformation T does not admit n linearly independent eigenvectors. We shall prove that it is possible to choose a basis of the space formed by k groups of vectors:

$$e_1, \dots, e_p; \quad f_1, \dots, f_q; \quad \dots; \quad h_1, \dots, h_s$$

in which the transformation shall have the form

$$\begin{aligned} &Te_1 = \lambda_1 e_1, \ Te_2 = e_1 + \lambda_1 e_2, \ \dots, \ Te_p = e_{p-1} + \lambda_1 e_p, \\ &Tf_1 = \lambda_2 f_1, \ Tf_2 = f_1 + \lambda_2 f_2, \ \dots, \ Tf_q = f_{q-1} + \lambda_2 f_q, \\ &\qquad \dots \\ &Th_1 = \lambda_k h_1, \ Th_2 = h_1 + \lambda_k h_2, \dots, \ Th_s = h_{s-1} + \lambda_k h_s. \end{aligned}$$

In this basis the matrix corresponding to the transformation has the form

$$\begin{pmatrix} \begin{matrix} \lambda_1 & 1 & 0 & \cdots & 0 \\ 0 & \lambda_1 & 1 & \cdots & 0 \\ & \cdots & & & \\ 0 & 0 & 0 & \cdots & \lambda_1 \end{matrix} & & \\ & \begin{matrix} \lambda_2 & 1 & 0 & \cdots & 0 \\ 0 & \lambda_2 & 1 & \cdots & 0 \\ & \cdots & & & \\ 0 & 0 & 0 & \cdots & \lambda_2 \end{matrix} & \\ & & \ddots \end{pmatrix}$$

This form is called the *normal Jordan form* of the matrix. The corresponding theorem is stated in the following way: *There exists for every matrix A a matrix C such that the matrix $C^{-1}AC$ has the normal Jordan form.*

In the particular case when there exist n linearly independent eigenvectors, the normal Jordan form is reduced to the diagonal form. It may happen, without the normal form being diagonal, that some Jordan cells are of first order. The diagonal form corresponds to the case where all the cells are of first order.

A Jordan cell is written $A_1 = \lambda_1 E + I$. If the cell is of order p, we have

$$I = \begin{pmatrix} 0 & 1 & 0 & \cdots & 0 & 0 \\ 0 & 0 & 1 & \cdots & 0 & 0 \\ \cdots & \cdots & \cdots & \cdots & \cdots & \cdots \\ 0 & 0 & 0 & \cdots & 0 & 1 \\ 0 & 0 & 0 & \cdots & 0 & 0 \end{pmatrix}, \quad I^2 = \begin{pmatrix} 0 & 0 & 1 & & \cdots & 0 & 0 \\ 0 & 0 & 0 & 1 & \cdots & 0 & 0 \\ \cdots & \cdots & \cdots & \cdots & \cdots & \cdots & \cdots \\ 0 & 0 & 0 & 0 & \cdots & 0 & 0 \\ 0 & 0 & 0 & & \cdots & 0 & 0 \end{pmatrix}, \ldots,$$

$$I^{p-1} = \begin{pmatrix} 0 & 0 & 0 & \cdots & 0 & 1 \\ 0 & 0 & 0 & \cdots & 0 & 0 \\ \cdots & \cdots & \cdots & \cdots & \cdots & \cdots \\ 0 & 0 & 0 & \cdots & 0 & 0 \\ 0 & 0 & 0 & \cdots & 0 & 0 \end{pmatrix}, \quad I^p = I^{p+1} = \cdots = 0.$$

A polynomial $P(t)$ may be written with the help of Taylor's formula in the form

$$P(t) = P(\lambda_1) + (t - \lambda_1)P'(\lambda_1) + \frac{(t - \lambda_1)^2}{2} P''(\lambda_1) + \cdots + \frac{(t - \lambda_1)^n}{n!} P^{(n)}(\lambda_1).$$

Thus

$$P(A_1) = P(\lambda_1)E + (A_1 - \lambda_1 E)P'(\lambda_1) + \frac{(A_1 - \lambda_1 E)^2}{2!} P''(\lambda_1) + \cdots + \frac{(A_1 - \lambda_1 E)^n}{n!} P^{(n)}(\lambda_1).$$

Hence

$$P(A_1) = P(\lambda_1)E + IP'(\lambda_1) + \frac{P''(\lambda_1)}{2!} I^2 + \cdots + \frac{P^{(n)}(\lambda_1)}{n!} I^n,$$

or

$$P(A_1) = P(\lambda_1)E + \frac{P'(\lambda_1)}{1!} I + \frac{P''(\lambda_1)}{2!} I^2 + \cdots + \frac{P^{(p-1)}(\lambda_1)}{(p-1)!} I^{p-1}.$$

Finally,

$$P(A_1) = \begin{pmatrix} P(\lambda_1) & \frac{P'(\lambda_1)}{1!} & \frac{P''(\lambda_1)}{2!} & \cdots & \frac{P^{(p-1)}(\lambda_1)}{(p-1)!} \\ 0 & P(\lambda_1) & \frac{P'(\lambda_1)}{1!} & \cdots & \frac{P^{(p-2)}(\lambda_1)}{(p-1)!} \\ & & \cdots & & \\ 0 & 0 & 0 & \cdots & P(\lambda_1) \end{pmatrix}.$$

The proof of the existence of a basis of the required form will be carried out by induction with respect to n. If T acts in a unidimensional space, the corresponding matrix has a single element and corresponds therefore to the normal form. We shall assume that the theorem holds in n-dimensional spaces and we prove that it also holds for spaces with $(n + 1)$ dimensions. A fundamental role will be played in this proof by induction by the following

Lemma. *Any linear transformation T in a complex n-dimensional space admits at least an $(n - 1)$-dimensional invariant subspace.*

Proof. Recall that a subspace R' of the linear space R is called invariant with respect to the linear transformation T if for every $x \in R'$ we have $Tx \in R'$.

Consider any basis $e_1, \ldots, e_n$; let $A = (a_{ij})$ be the matrix attached to the transformation in this basis. Consider the matrix A' obtained through transposition from A; let u be an eigenvector of this matrix. Hence we have $\sum_{j=1}^{n} a_{ji}u_j = \lambda u_i$. Consider the relation $\sum_{i=1}^{n} x_i u_i = 0$. Since $u \neq 0$, the manifold of solutions of this equation forms a linear $(n - 1)$-dimensional subspace (the space generated by $(n - 1)$ linearly independent solutions). This is the space R' invariant with respect to the transformation T.

Indeed, let $x \in R'$; hence $\sum_{i=1}^{n} x_i u_i = 0$ and $y_j = \sum_{i=1}^{n} a_{ji} x_i$. We have

$$\sum_{j=1}^{n} y_j u_j = \sum_{j=1}^{n} \sum_{i=1}^{n} a_{ji} x_i u_j = \sum_{i=1}^{n} x_i \sum_{j=1}^{n} a_{ji} u_j = \sum_{i=1}^{n} x_i \lambda u_i = \lambda \sum_{i=1}^{n} x_i u_i = 0;$$

hence $y \in R'$.

The proof by induction is performed in the following way. Let T be a transformation in the space R with $(n+1)$ dimensions. According to the lemma, there exists a subspace R' with n dimensions, invariant with respect to T. We may therefore consider the transformation T as operating in the subspace R'; on the strength of the induction hypothesis, there exists in R' a basis $e_1, e_2, \ldots, e_p, f_1, f_2, \ldots, f_q, \ldots, h_1, h_2, \ldots, h_s$ such that

$$\begin{gathered}
Te_1 = \lambda_1 e_1, \ Te_2 = e_1 + \lambda_1 e_2, \ \ldots, \ Te_p = e_{p-1} + \lambda_1 e_p, \\
Tf_1 = \lambda_2 f_1, \ Tf_2 = f_1 + \lambda_2 f_2, \ \ldots, \ Tf_q = f_{q-1} + \lambda_2 f_q, \\
\cdots \\
Th_1 = \lambda_k h_1, \ Th_2 = h_1 + \lambda_k h_2, \ \ldots, \ Th_s = h_{s-1} + \lambda_k h_s.
\end{gathered}$$

We have to prove that we can find in R a basis in which the transformation T will act in the required way. To this end, we shall begin by adding to the basis of R' a vector e, linearly independent of the others, so that we obtain a basis in R. We have

$$\begin{aligned}
Te = {} & \alpha_1 e_1 + \cdots + \alpha_p e_p + \beta_1 f_1 + \beta_2 f_2 + \cdots + \beta_q f_q + \cdots + \delta_1 h_1 \\
& + \cdots + \delta_s h_s + \tau e.
\end{aligned}$$

Now we try to replace e by another vector e', so that the vector Te' will have the simplest possible form. We look for e' of the form

$$e' = e - \chi_1 e_1 - \cdots - \chi_p e_p - \mu_1 f_1 - \cdots - \mu_q f_q - \cdots \cdot \omega_1 h_1 - \cdots - \omega_s h_s$$

Then

$$\begin{aligned}
Te' = {} & Te - \chi_1 Te_1 - \cdots - \chi_p Te_p - \mu_1 Tf_1 - \cdots - \mu_q Tf_q - \cdots \\
& - \omega_1 Th_1 - \cdots - \omega_s Th_s \\
= {} & \alpha_1 e_1 + \cdots + a_p e_p + \beta_1 f_1 + \cdots + \beta_q f_q + \cdots + \delta_1 h_1 + \cdots + \delta_s h_s + \tau e \\
& - \chi_1 \lambda_1 e_1 - \cdots - \chi_p e_{p-1} - \chi_p \lambda_1 e_p - \mu_1 \lambda_2 f_1 - \cdots \\
& - \mu_{q-1} f_{q-1} - \mu_q \lambda_2 f_q - \cdots \\
& - \omega_1 \lambda_k h_1 - \cdots - \omega_s h_{s-1} - \omega_s \lambda_k h_s.
\end{aligned}$$

But

$$e = e' + \chi_1 e_1 + \cdots + \chi_p e_p + \mu_1 f_1 + \cdots + \mu_q f_q + \cdots + \omega_1 h_1 + \cdots + \omega_s h_s;$$

hence

$$\begin{aligned} Te' &= \tau e' + \tau\chi_1 e_1 + \cdots + \tau\chi_p e_p + \tau\mu_1 f_1 + \cdots + \tau\mu_q f_q + \cdots + \tau\omega_1 h_1 + \cdots \\ &\quad + \tau\omega_s h_s + \alpha_1 e_1 + \cdots + \alpha_p e_p + \beta_1 f_1 + \cdots + \beta_q f_q + \cdots + \delta_1 h_1 + \cdots \\ &\quad + \delta_s h_s - (\lambda_1\chi_1 + \chi_2) e_1 - \cdots - \chi_p \lambda_1 e_p - (\lambda_2\mu_1 + \mu_2) f_1 - \cdots \\ &\quad - \lambda_2 \mu_q f_q - \cdots - (\lambda_k\omega_1 + \omega_2) h_1 - \cdots - \lambda_k \omega_s h_s \\ &= \tau e' + [\alpha_1 + \chi_1(\tau - \lambda_1) - \chi_2] e_1 + \cdots + [\alpha_p + \chi_p(\tau - \lambda_1)] e_p \\ &\quad + [\beta_1 + \mu_1(\tau - \lambda_2) - \mu_2] f_1 + \cdots + [\beta_q + \mu_q(\tau - \lambda_2)] f_q + \cdots \\ &\quad + [\delta_1 + \omega_1(\tau - \lambda_k) - \omega_2] h_1 + \cdots + [\delta_s + \omega_s(\tau - \lambda_k)] h_s . \end{aligned}$$

If τ is different from λ_j, the coefficients χ, μ, ..., ω may be determined in turn so that the relation $Te' = \tau e'$ holds, and by adding e' to the basis of R' we obtain a normal basis in R. If τ is different from some of the values λ_j, we may choose coefficients corresponding to these values. For the sake of simplicity, let us suppose that $\tau = \lambda_1$, $\tau = \lambda_2$, $\tau \neq \lambda_j$, $j > 2$. The initial relation is

$$Te' = \tau e' + (\alpha_1 - \chi_2) e_1 + \cdots + \alpha_p e_p + (\beta_1 - \mu_2) f_1 + \cdots + \beta_q f_q .$$

We choose $\chi_2 = \alpha_1$, ..., $\mu_2 = \beta_1$, ... and obtain

$$Te' = \tau e' + \alpha_p e_p + \beta_q f_q .$$

Assume $p > q$.

We now choose the canonical basis in R in the following way: we put

$$e'_{p+1} = e , \qquad e'_p = Te'_{p+1} - \tau e'_{p+1} ,$$
$$e'_{p-1} = Te'_p - \tau e'_p , \ldots, e'_1 = Te'_2 - \tau e'_2 .$$

We take the first group formed by vectors e'_1, ..., e'_{p+1}, the other groups the remaining f_1, ..., f_q, ..., h_1, ..., h_s. To prove that we have a canonical basis, it still remains to verify that $e'_1 \cdots e'_{p+1}$ behaves as a part of a canonical basis.

We have

$$Te'_2 = e'_1 + \tau e'_2 , \ldots, Te'_p = e'_{p-1} + \tau e'_p , \; Te'_{p+1} = e'_p + \tau e'_{p+1};$$

hence it only remains to verify that $Te_1' = \tau e_s'$:

$$e_p' = Te' - \tau e' = \alpha_p e_p + \beta_q f_q, \qquad e_{p-1}' = \alpha_p Te_p + \beta_q Tf_q - \tau\alpha_p e_p - \tau\beta_q f_q$$
$$= \alpha_p(e_{p-1} + \tau e_p) + \beta_q(f_{q-1} + \tau f_q) - \tau\alpha_p e_p - \tau\beta_q f_q$$
$$= \alpha_p e_{p-1} + \beta_q f_{q-1}.$$

Continuing, $e_{p-q}' = \alpha_p e_{p-q}$, ..., $e_1' = \alpha_p e_1$; hence $Te_1' = \alpha_p Te_1 = \tau\alpha_p e_1 = \tau e_1'$. The theorem is thus proved.

Application. Consider again the system $dx/dt = Ax$, assuming A arbitrary. If C is the matrix which leads A to the normal Jordan form, the change of variables $x = Cy$ leads the system to the form $dy/dt = By$, where B has the normal Jordan form. Then

$$\frac{dy_1}{dt} = \lambda_1 y_1 + y_2, \quad \frac{dy_2}{dt} = \lambda_1 y_2 + y_3, \ldots, \frac{dy_p}{dt} = \lambda_1 y_p$$

$$\frac{dy_{p+1}}{dt} = \lambda_2 y_{p+1} + y_{p+2}, \quad \frac{dy_{p+2}}{dt} = \lambda_2 y_{p+2} + y_{p+3}, \ldots, \frac{dy_{p+q}}{dt} = \lambda_2 y_{p+q}$$

$$\cdots$$

$$\frac{dy_{p+q+\cdots+1}}{dt} = \lambda_k y_{p+q+\cdots+1} + y_{p+q+\cdots+2}, \ldots, \frac{dy_{p+q+\cdots+s}}{dt} = \lambda_k y_{p+q+\cdots+s}.$$

In this form the system can be immediately solved and we obtain the structure of the solutions. It is easier, however, to proceed otherwise.

From Cauchy's general existence theorem it follows that the solution $x(t; t_0, x_0)$ will be an analytic function of t; hence we may write

$$x(t; t_0, x_0) = x_0 + \dot{x}(t_0)(t - t_0) + \tfrac{1}{2}\ddot{x}(t_0)(t - t_0)^2 + \cdots$$
$$+ \frac{1}{n!} x^{(n)}(t_0)(t - t_0)^n + \cdots.$$

We immediately obtain from the system

$$\frac{dx}{dt} = Ax, \quad \frac{d^2x}{dt^2} = A\frac{dx}{dt}, \quad \frac{d^3x}{dt^3} = A\frac{d^2x}{dt^2}, \ldots, \frac{d^nx}{dt^n} = A\frac{d^{n-1}x}{dt^{n-1}};$$

hence

$$\dot{x}(t_0) = Ax_0, \; \ddot{x}(t_0) = A\dot{x}(t_0) = A^2x_0, \; \dddot{x}(t_0) = A\ddot{x}(t_0) = A^3x_0, \ldots, x^{(n)}(t_0) = A^nx_0.$$

Then

$$x(t; t_0, x_0)$$
$$= x_0 + \frac{1}{1!}Ax_0(t - t_0) + \frac{1}{2!}A^2x_0(t - t_0)^2 + \cdots + \frac{1}{n!}A^nx_0(t - t_0)^n + \cdots$$
$$= \left[E + \frac{1}{1!}A(t - t_0) + \frac{1}{2!}A^2(t - t_0)^2 + \cdots + \frac{1}{n!}A^n(t - t_0)^n + \cdots\right]x_0.$$

The convergence of the series should be understood here as being the convergence of the n^2 series formed with the elements of the matrices.

Introduce the matrix exponential function

$$e^{A(t-t_0)} = E + \frac{1}{1!} A(t - t_0) + \frac{1}{2!} A^2(t - t_0)^2 + \cdots + \frac{1}{n!} A^n(t - t_0)^n + \cdots.$$

With this notation the solution of the system may be written

$$x(t; t_0, x_0) = e^{A(t-t_0)}x_0 .$$

Let us remark that the power series corresponding to the matrix series may be differentiated term by term, and we have

$$\frac{d}{dt} e^{A(t-t_0)} = Ae^{A(t-t_0)};$$

since $e^{A(t_0-t_0)} = E$, $e^{A(t-t_0)}$ represents a fundamental system of solutions. If $A = C^{-1}BC$, then $A^n = C^{-1}B^nC$, so that $e^{At} = C^{-1}e^{Bt}C$. If

$$A = \begin{pmatrix} A_1 & 0 \\ 0 & A_2 \end{pmatrix},$$

then

$$A^n = \begin{pmatrix} A_1^n & 0 \\ 0 & A_2^n \end{pmatrix};$$

hence

$$e^{At} = \begin{pmatrix} e^{A_1t} & 0 \\ 0 & e^{A_2t} \end{pmatrix}.$$

Thus, if B has the normal Jordan form,

$$e^{Bt} = \begin{pmatrix} e^{J_1t} & & \\ & \ddots & \\ & & e^{J_kt} \end{pmatrix},$$

where $J_1, \ldots, J_k$ are the Jordan cells of the matrix B.

Hence it remains to make precise the structure of a matrix e^{Jt}, where J is a Jordan cell. We have

$$e^{Jt} = E + \frac{t}{1!} J + \frac{t^2}{2!} J^2 + \cdots + \frac{t^n}{n!} J^n + \cdots.$$

But

$$J^k = \begin{pmatrix} \lambda^k & \frac{k\lambda^{k-1}}{1!} & \frac{k(k-1)\lambda^{k-2}}{2!} & \cdots & \frac{k(k-1)\cdots(k-p+2)}{(p-1)!}\lambda^{k-p+1} \\ 0 & \lambda^k & \frac{k}{1!} & \cdots & \frac{k(k-1)\cdots(k-p+3)}{(p-2)!}\lambda^{k-p+2} \\ & & \cdots & & \\ 0 & 0 & 0 & \cdots & \lambda^k \end{pmatrix},$$

$$e^{Jt} = E + \sum_{k=1}^{\infty} \begin{pmatrix} \frac{\lambda^k t^k}{k!} & \frac{\lambda^{k-1}t^k}{(k-1)!} & \frac{\lambda^{k-2}t^k}{2!(k-2)!} & \cdots & \frac{\lambda^{k-p+1}t^k}{(p-1)!\,(k-p+1)!} \\ 0 & \frac{\lambda^k t^k}{k!} & \frac{\lambda^{k-1}t^k}{(k-1)!} & \cdots & \frac{\lambda^{k-p+2}t^k}{(p-2)!\,(k-p+2)!} \\ & & & \cdots & \\ 0 & 0 & 0 & \cdots & \frac{\lambda^k t^k}{k!} \end{pmatrix}$$

$$= \begin{pmatrix} 1 + \sum_{k=1}^{\infty} \frac{\lambda^k t^k}{k!} & t\sum_{k=1}^{\infty} \frac{\lambda^{k-1}t^{k-1}}{(k-1)!} & \frac{t^2}{2!}\sum_{k=2}^{\infty} \frac{\lambda^{k-2}t^{k-2}}{(k-2)!} & \cdots \\ 0 & 1 + \sum_{k=1}^{\infty} \frac{\lambda^k t^k}{k!} & & \cdots \\ & \cdots & & \end{pmatrix}$$

$$= \begin{pmatrix} e^{\lambda t} & \frac{t}{1!}e^{\lambda t} & \frac{t^2}{2!}e^{\lambda t} & \cdots & \frac{t^{p-1}}{(p-1)!}e^{\lambda t} \\ 0 & e^{\lambda t} & \frac{t}{1!}e^{\lambda t} & \cdots & \frac{t^{p-2}}{(p-2)!}e^{\lambda t} \\ & & & \cdots & \\ 0 & 0 & \cdots & & e^{\lambda t} \end{pmatrix}$$

$$= \begin{pmatrix} 1 & \frac{t}{1!} & \frac{t^2}{2!} & \cdots & \frac{t^{p-1}}{(p-1)!} \\ 0 & 1 & \frac{t}{1!} & \cdots & \frac{t^{p-2}}{(p-2)!} \\ & & & \cdots & \\ 0 & 0 & 0 & \cdots & 1 \end{pmatrix} e^{\lambda t}.$$

In this way the structure of the solutions of linear systems with constant coefficients is completely determined. The behavior of the solutions depends upon the structure of the normal form of matrix A.

The numbers λ_k, the eigenvalues of matrix A, play an essential role. Namely, if $\operatorname{Re} \lambda_k < 0$, then all the solutions approach zero when $t \to \infty$; this is what occurs in *damped oscillations*. If λ_k are real, we have the so-called *aperiodic behavior*; if λ_k have imaginary nonzero parts, there appear *oscillatory* terms. If we have $\operatorname{Re} \lambda_k > 0$ at least for one k, there appear oscillations whose amplitude increases when $t \to \infty$. If all λ_k have zero or negative real parts, we have stable (bounded) oscillations provided that, if $\operatorname{Re} \lambda_k = 0$, the respective Jordan cell shall be of dimension 1. If there exists a root with a zero real part for which the Jordan cell has a dimension greater than 1, there appear terms in t^n which make the solution unbounded; these terms are sometimes called *secular terms*. If all the roots have zero real parts and the normal form is diagonal, the solutions are bounded on the whole axis. In this case, the solutions are in general almost-periodic functions.

1.6. The Lyapunov Function for Linear Systems with Constant Coefficients

Let us consider a linear form (α, x) and see what are the conditions that should be verified by vector α in order that $(d/dt)(\alpha, x) = \lambda(\alpha, x)$, x being a solution of system (3) with a constant matrix A. We have

$$\frac{d}{dt}(\alpha, x) = \left(\alpha, \frac{dx}{dt}\right) = (\alpha, Ax) = (A^*\alpha, x) = (\lambda\alpha, x) = \lambda(\alpha, x).$$

If $A^*\alpha = \lambda\alpha$, i.e., if α is an eigenvector of the conjugate matrix of matrix A and λ is an eigenvalue of matrix A, then the relation is certainly verified.

Let us now see in what conditions there exists a quadratic form V of the form $V = (\alpha, x)(\beta, x)$ such that $dV/dt = \lambda V$. We have, where x is a solution of the system,

$$\begin{aligned}\frac{dV}{dt} &= \left(\alpha, \frac{dx}{dt}\right)(\beta, x) + (\alpha, x)\left(\beta, \frac{dx}{dt}\right)\\ &= (\alpha, Ax)(\beta, x) + (\alpha, x)(\beta, Ax).\end{aligned}$$

This equality is verified if $\lambda = \lambda_1 + \lambda_2$, where λ_1 and λ_2 are eigenvalues of A and α and β are eigenvectors for A^*. Let us see now which is the general condition that there exists a quadratic form $V = (Bx, x)$ such that $dV/dt = \lambda V$.

We have

$$\frac{dV}{dt} = \left(B\frac{dx}{dt}, x\right) + \left(Bx, \frac{dx}{dt}\right) = (BAx, x) + (Bx, Ax)$$

$$= (BAx, x) + (A^*Bx, x) = ((BA + A^*B)x, x).$$

The condition $dV/dt = \lambda V$ becomes $((BA + A^*B)x, x) = (\lambda Bx, x)$ and hence $BA + A^*B = \lambda B$, or $BA + A^*B - \lambda B = 0$. This equation may be considered as a linear system in the elements of matrix B; the system admits a nontrivial solution if and only if the determinant $D(\lambda)$ is equal to zero.

We have already seen that if λ is of the form $\lambda_1 + \lambda_2$, where λ_1 and λ_2 are eigenvalues of matrix A, there exist forms V with the required property. But the degree of equation $D(\lambda) = 0$ is equal to the number of the values of the form $\lambda_1 + \lambda_2$ and is equal to $n(n + 1)/2$. From this it follows that the values of the form $\lambda_1 + \lambda_2$ represent all the roots of the equation $D(\lambda) = 0$, if they are distinct. If these numbers are not distinct, we reason in the following way. Let λ^* be a root of the equation $D(\lambda) = 0$ which is not of the form $\lambda_1 + \lambda_2$, and let α be the shortest distance from λ^* to the numbers of the form $\lambda_1 + \lambda_2$; by a sufficiently slight modification of matrix A we can make the numbers $\tilde{\lambda}_1 + \tilde{\lambda}_2$ distinct, and differ from the numbers $\lambda_1 + \lambda_2$ by less than $\alpha/4$, and have $\tilde{\lambda}^*$ differ from λ^* by less than $\alpha/4$.

It follows that $\tilde{\lambda}^*$ coincides with one of the numbers $\tilde{\lambda}_1 + \tilde{\lambda}_2$, hence we have

$$\alpha = |\lambda^* - (\lambda_1 + \lambda_2)| \leqslant |\lambda^* - \tilde{\lambda}^*| + |\tilde{\lambda}^* - (\tilde{\lambda}_1 + \tilde{\lambda}_2)|$$

$$+ |(\tilde{\lambda}_1 + \tilde{\lambda}_2) - (\lambda_1 + \lambda_1)| < \frac{\alpha}{4} + \frac{\alpha}{4} = \frac{\alpha}{2},$$

which is a contradiction. Consequently, in all cases, the roots of equation $D(\lambda) = 0$ are of the form $\lambda_1 + \lambda_2$. It follows that if the roots λ_i of the characteristic equation of matrix A are nonzero and if all the sums $\lambda_i + \lambda_j$ are different from zero, we will have $D(0) \neq 0$. But from this it will follow that for every quadratic form (Cx, x) there exists a quadratic form (Bx, x) such that $(d/dt)(Bx, x) = (Cx, x)$. Indeed, $(d/dt)(Bx, x) = ((BA + A^*B)x, x)$, and we obtain the condition $BA + A^*B = C$. Considered as a linear system in the elements of matrix B, this system has solutions for any C if and only if the determinant of the system is different from zero; but this determinant is just $D(0)$, which in our conditions is different from zero. We see now that the form B will be uniquely determined in this case.

We can see from the general form of the solution of linear systems with constant coefficients that the trivial solution of linear systems with constant coefficients is asymptotically stable if and only if the roots of the characteristic equation of matrix A have negative real parts. In this case the condition formulated above, that $D(0) \neq 0$, is obviously fulfilled; hence the form (Bx, x) exists for any (Cx, x). Let us show that if (Cx, x) is a negative definite quadratic form, then the quadratic form (Bx, x) is positive-definite. Indeed, let $x_0 \neq 0$ such that $(Bx_0, x_0) \leqslant 0$. From

$$\frac{d}{dt}(Bx(t; 0, x_0), x(t; 0, x_0)) = (Cx(t; 0, x_0), x(t; 0, x_0)) < 0$$

it follows that for $t_0 > 0$ we have

$$(Bx(t_0; 0, x_0), x(t_0; 0, x_0)) < 0.$$

According to the theorem of instability, the trivial solution of system (3) will be unstable, which contradicts the hypothesis.

Consequently, we have established, by nonalgebraic means, the following *algebraic fact*: *If the eigenvalues of matrix A have negative real parts, then for any negative definite matrix, there exists a unique positive-definite matrix B such that*

$$BA + A^*B = C.$$

The algebraic proof of this proposition is interesting. Such a proof has been given in 1956 by W. Hahn by using the canonical form of the matrices.

1.7. Stability by the First Approximation

One of the main problems of the stability theory is the following. Assume that we have to investigate the stability of a solution $x_0(t)$ of system (1). According to the procedure already described, we pass to the system of equations of the perturbed movement. Put $y = x - x_0(t)$, obtaining the equation

$$\frac{dy}{dt} = \frac{dx}{dt} - \frac{dx_0}{dt} = f(t, x) - f(t, x_0) = f(t, y + x_0(t)) - f(t, x_0(t))$$
$$= \frac{\partial f}{\partial x}(t, x_0(t))y + o(|y|).$$

We have denoted the matrix $\{\partial f_i/\partial x_j\}$ by $\partial f/\partial x$.

The problem of whether it is legitimate to neglect the terms of the form $o(|y|)$ may quite naturally be raised; practically, this is the procedure in most cases. The justification of this procedure is given by the theory of stability by the first approximation. The fundamental theorem of this theory shows that if the trivial solution of the linear system of first approximation is uniformly asymptotically stable, neglecting the terms of higher degree is admissible in the study of stability.

Theorem 1.7. *Consider the system*

$$\frac{dy}{dt} = A(t)y + Y(t, y), \tag{4}$$

where $A(t)$ is bounded [or, more generally, $\int_s^t |A(u)|\, du = \omega(t-s)$] and $|Y(t, y)| < c|y|$ for $|y| < h$, c being a sufficiently small constant. If the trivial solution of the linear system of first approximation is uniformly asymptotically stable, then the trivial solution of system (4) is uniformly asymptotically stable.

Proof. Let $y(t; t_0, y_0)$ be a solution of system (4). Let $(V(t)x, x)$ be the quadratic form defined for system (3) according to Theorem 1.6″, with $W(t) = E$. We shall prove that, with respect to system (4), this function fulfils all the conditions of Theorem 1.5. We have to prove only that

$$\limsup_{h\to 0+} \frac{(V(t+h)y(t+h; t_0, y_0), y(t+h; t_0, y_0)) - (V(t)y(t; t_0, y_0), y(t; t_0, y_0))}{h}$$
$$\leqslant -c(|y(t; t_0, y_0)|).$$

Let

$$V^*(t) = (V(t)y(t; t_0, y_0), y(t; t_0, y_0)).$$

The function $V^*(t)$ is differentiable and we have

$$\frac{dV^*(t)}{dt} = 2\left(V(t)y(t; t_0, y_0), \frac{dy(t; t_0, y_0)}{dt}\right) + \left(\frac{dV}{dt} y(t; t_0, y_0), y(t; t_0, y_0)\right)$$
$$= 2(V(t)y(t; t_0, y_0), A(t)y(t; t_0, y_0)) + 2(V(t)y(t; t_0, y_0), Y(t, y(t; t_0, y_0)))$$
$$+ \left(\frac{dV}{dt} y(t; t_0, y_0), y(t; t_0, y_0)\right).$$

Consider the solution $x(u; t, y(t; t_0, y_0))$ of system (3) and let $V^{**}(u) = (V(u)x(u; t, y(t; t_0, y_0)), x(u; t, y(t; t_0, y_0)))$. According to what has been stated in Theorem 1.6″ we have $dV^{**}(u)/du = -|\,x(u;\, t,\, y(t;\, t_0\,,\, y_0))|^2$. On the other hand,

$$\frac{dV^{**}(u)}{du} = 2(V(u)x(u;\, t,\, y(t;\, t_0\,,\, y_0)),\, A(u)x(u;\, t,\, y(t;\, t_0\,,\, y_0)))$$
$$+ \left(\frac{dV}{du}\, x(u;\, t,\, y(t;\, t_0\,,\, y_0)),\, x(u;\, t,\, y(t;\, t_0\,,\, y_0))\right).$$

Therefore,

$$2(V(u)x(u;\, t,\, y(t;\, t_0\,,\, y_0)),\, A(u)x(u;\, t,\, y(t;\, t_0\,,\, y_0)))$$
$$+ \left(\frac{dV}{du}\, x(u;\, t,\, y(t;\, t_0\,,\, y_0)),\, x(u;\, t,\, y(t;\, t_0\,,\, y_0))\right) = -|\,x(u;\, t,\, y(t;\, t_0\,,\, y_0))|^2.$$

This equality becomes, for $u = t$,

$$2(V(t)y(t;\, t_0\,,\, y_0),\, A(t)y(t;\, t_0\,,\, y_0)) + \left(\frac{dV}{dt}\, y(t;\, t_0\,,\, y_0),\, y(t;\, t_0\,,\, y_0)\right)$$
$$= -|\,y(t;\, t_0\,,\, y_0)|^2.$$

Using this result, we deduce

$$\frac{dV^*}{dt} = -|\,y(t;\, t_0\,,\, y_0)|^2 + 2(V(t)y(t;\, t_0\,,\, y_0),\, Y(t,\, y(t;\, t_0\,,\, y_0))).$$

We have

$$|\,(V(t)y(t;\, t_0\,,\, y_0),\, Y(t,\, y(t;\, t_0\,,\, y_0)))| \leqslant M|\,y(t;\, t_0\,,\, y_0)|\,|\,Y(t,\, y(t;\, t_0\,,\, y_0))|.$$

Assume that $c < 1/4M$ and $|\,y_0\,| < \sqrt{\mu/M}\,h$. Then, for values $t \geqslant t_0$ close enough to t_0, it will follow that $|\,y(t;\, t_0\,,\, y_0)| < h$; for values t for which $|\,y(t;\, t_0\,,\, y_0\,| < h$, we have

$$|\,(V(t)y(t;\, t_0\,,\, y_0),\, Y(t,\, y(t;\, t_0\,,\, y_0)))| \leqslant Mc|\,y(t;\, t_0\,,\, y_0)|^2 < \tfrac{1}{4}\,|\,y(t;\, t_0\,,\, y_0)|^2,$$

and hence $dV^*/dt < -\tfrac{1}{2}\,|\,y(t;\, t_0\,,\, y_0)|^2$. It follows that $V^*(t)$ is decreasing, and thus that

$$V^*(t) < V^*(t_0) = (V(t_0)y_0\,,\, y_0) < M|\,y_0\,|^2 < \mu h^2.$$

From $V^*(t) > \mu|\,y(t;\, t_0\,,\, y_0)|^2$ follows $|\,y(t;\, t_0\,,\, y_0)|^2 < h^2$.

Let T be such that $|\,y(T;\, t_0,\, y_0)| = h$, $|\,y(t;\, t_0\,,\, y_0)| < h$ for $t_0 \leqslant t < T$. From the above computations we see that $|\,y(T;\, t_0\,,\, y_0)|^2 < h^2$. Hence the existence of T is contradictory. It follows that for all $t \geqslant t_0$, we have

$|y(t; t_0, y_0)| < h$, and thus $dV^*/dt < -\frac{1}{2}|y(t; t_0, y_0)|^2$. The theorem is thus proved.

Theorem 1.7 may be proved by a simpler method, which does not use the method of Lyapunov functions and is based on certain specific consideration of the theory of linear systems. Let $y(t; t_0, y_0)$ be a solution of system (4). We have

$$\frac{dy(t; t_0, y_0)}{dt} = A(t)y(t; t_0, y_0) + Y(t; y(t; t_0, y_0)).$$

Considering $Y(t, y(t; t_0, y_0))$ as a given function of t, we apply the formula of variation of the constants stated in Section 1.3. Thus

$$y(t; t_0, y_0) = C(t; t_0)y_0 + \int_{t_0}^{t} C(t; s)Y(s, y(s; t_0, y_0))ds.$$

Since by hypothesis the trivial solution of system (3) is uniformly asymptotically stable, it will be exponentially stable; hence

$$|C(t; t_0)| \leqslant Be^{-\alpha(t-t_0)}.$$

It follows that

$$|y(t; t_0, y_0)| \leqslant Be^{-\alpha(t-t_0)}|y_0| + \int_{t_0}^{t} Be^{-\alpha(t-s)}|Y(s, y(s; t_0, y_0))| ds.$$

For all values of t with the property that $t_0 \leqslant s \leqslant t$ implies $|y(s; t_0, y_0)| < h$, we deduce that

$$|y(t; t_0 \; y_0)| \leqslant Be^{-\alpha(t-t_0)}|y_0| + Be^{-\alpha t}\int_{t_0}^{t} ce^{\alpha s}|y(s; t_0, y_0)| ds.$$

Let $u(t) = e^{\alpha t}|y(t; t_0, y_0)|$. We have $u(t) \leqslant Bu(t_0) + Bc\int_{t_0}^{t} u(s)\, ds$. According to Lemma I.6 (Consequence 2), $u(t) \leqslant Bu(t_0)e^{Bc(t-t_0)}$. Hence $e^{\alpha t}|y(t; t_0, y_0)| \leqslant Be^{\alpha t_0}e^{Bc(t-t_0)}|y_0|$. From this follows $|y(t; t_0, y_0)| \leqslant Be^{-(\alpha-Bc)(t-t_0)}|y_0|$.

If $c < \alpha/B$, we will have in any case $|y(t; t_0, y_0)| < B|y_0|$. Hence if $|y_0| < h/B$ (we assume $B > 1$), the relation $|y(t; t_0, y_0)| < h$ will hold for all $t \geqslant t_0$. Then, for all $t \geqslant t_0$ we will have $|y(t; t_0, y_0)| \leqslant Be^{-\alpha_1(t-t_0)}|y_0|$ with $\alpha_1 = \alpha - Bc > 0$. Therefore the trivial solution of system (4) is exponentially stable.

We shall remark that *in this proof the fact that*

$$\int_{s}^{t} |A(u)| du \leqslant \omega(t-s)$$

is not used any more; in the preceding proof this fact occurred in setting up the properties of the function $(V(t)x, x)$ from Theorem 1.6″.

We shall now emphasize some generalizations of Theorem 1.7. We have seen in Section 1.2 that if $|f(t, x)| \leqslant L(r)|x|$ for $|x| < r$, and if the trivial solution of system (1) is uniformly asymptotically stable, and if, in addition, $|x(t; t_0, x_0)| \leqslant \psi(t - t_0)|x_0|$, the stability is exponential. The proof was performed by constructing a Lyapunov function of the form

$$V(t, x) = \int_t^{t+T} |x(\tau; t, x)|^2 \, d\tau.$$

Consequently, if f fulfills the above condition and the trivial solution is exponentially stable, there exists a function V with the properties

$$\mu|x|^2 \leqslant V(t, x) \leqslant M|x|^2, \qquad \frac{d}{dt} V(t, x(t; t_0, x_0)) \leqslant -\tfrac{1}{2}|x(t; t_0, x_0)|^2.$$

We shall assume, in addition, that

$$|f(t, x_1) - f(t, x_2)| \leqslant L(r)|x_1 - x_2| \qquad \text{for} \quad |x_1| < r, |x_2| < r,$$

and we shall prove that in this case there exists a constant K such that

$$|V(t, x_1) - V(t, x_2)| \leqslant K(|x_1| + |x_2|)|x_1 - x_2| \quad \text{for } |x_1| < \delta_0, |x_2| < \delta_0.$$

We have

$$x(u; t, x_1) = x_1 + \int_t^u f(s, x(s; t, x_1))ds;$$

if $|x_1| \leqslant \delta(r)$ it follows that $|x(s; t, x_1)| < r$, and thus that

$$|f(s, x(s; t, x_1))| < L(r)|x(s; t, x_1)|.$$

For $|x_1| \leqslant \delta(r)$, we will have

$$|x(u; t, x_1)| \leqslant |x_1| + \int_t^u L(r)|x(s; t, x_1)| \, ds$$

According to Lemma I.6 (Consequence 2),

$$|x(u; t, x_1)| \leqslant |x_1| e^{L(r)(u-t)},$$

and, therefore, $| x(u; t, x_1)| \leqslant | x_1 | e^{TL(r)}$ for $t \leqslant u \leqslant t + T$, $| x_1 | \leqslant \delta(r)$. Further,

$$| x(u; t, x_1) - x(u; t, x_2)| \leqslant \int_t^u L(r) \, | x(s; t, x_1) - x(s; t, x_2)| \, ds + | x_1 - x_2 |$$

if $| x_1 | < \delta(r)$, $| x_2 | < \delta(r)$. Thus

$$| x(u; t, x_1) - x(u; t, x_2)| \leqslant | x_1 - x_2 | e^{TL(r)}, \qquad \text{for} \quad t \leqslant u \leqslant t + T.$$

By using these evaluations, we deduce for $| x_1 | < \delta(r)$, $| x_2 | < \delta(r)$, that

$$\begin{aligned} V(t, x_1) - V(t, x_2)| &= \left| \int_t^{t+T} | x(u; t, x_1)|^2 \, du - \int_t^{t+T} | x(u; t, x_2)|^2 \, du \right| \\ &= \int_t^{t+T} (| x(u; t, x_1)| + | x(u; t, x_2)|) \Big| | x(u; t, x_1)| - | x(u; t, x_2)| \Big| \, du \\ &\leqslant \int_t^{t+T} (| x(u; t, x_1)| + | x(u; t, x_2)|) \, | x(u; t, x_1) - x(u; t, x_2)| \, du \\ &\leqslant \int_t^{t+T} (| x_1 | e^{TL(r)} + | x_2 | e^{TL(r)}) \, | x_1 - x_2 | e^{TL(r)} \, du \\ &= Te^{2L(r)}(| x_1 | + | x_2 |) \, | x_1 - x_2 |. \end{aligned}$$

Upon putting $K = Te^{2TL(r)}$, we will have

$$| V(t, x_1) - V(t, x_2)| < K(| x_1 | + | x_2 |) \, | x_1 - x_2 |.$$

We can now prove

Theorem 1.7′. *If $| f(t, y_1) - f(t, y_2)| < L(r) \, | y_1 - y_2 |$ for $| y_1 | < r$, $| y_2 | < r$ and $| g(t, y)| < L_1(r) \, | y |$ for $| y | < r$, and if $L_1(r)$ is sufficiently small, then from the exponential stability of the trivial solution of system (1) will follow the exponential asymptotic stability of the trivial solution of the system*

$$\frac{dy}{dt} = f(t, y) + g(t, y). \tag{5}$$

Proof. Let $y(v; t, y)$ be a solution of system (5) with $| y | \leqslant r/2$. We have

$$y(v; t, y) = y + \int_t^v f[u, y(u; t, y)]du + \int_t^v g[u, y(u; t, y)]du;$$

hence

$$| y(v; t, y)| \leqslant | y | + \int_t^v L(r) \,| y(u; t, y)| \,du + \int_t^v L_1(r) \,| y(u; t, y)| \,du$$

for all values $t \leqslant v$ such that if $t \leqslant u \leqslant v$ we shall have $| y(u; t, y)| < r$. Then

$$| y(v; t, y)| \leqslant | y | e^{h(L(r)+L_1(r))} \qquad \text{for} \quad t \leqslant v \leqslant t + h.$$

From here it follows that if $| y | \leqslant r/2$ and h is sufficiently small, $| y(u; t, y)| < r$ for all $t \leqslant u \leqslant v$, and the inequality holds for every v with $t \leqslant v \leqslant t + h$.

Let $x(v; t, y)$ be a solution of system (1). We have

$$y(v; t, y) - x(v; t, y)$$
$$= \int_t^v [f(u, y(u; t, y)) - f(u, x(u; t, y))]du + \int_t^v g(u, y(u; t, y))du;$$

hence

$$| y(v; t, y) - x(v; t, y)| \leqslant \int_t^v L_1(r) \,| y(u; t, y)| \,du$$
$$+ \int_t^v L(r) \,| y(u; t, y) - x(u; t, y)| \,du \leqslant hL_1(r)e^{h(L(r)+L_1(r))} \,| y |$$
$$+ \int_t^v L(r) \,| y(u; t, y) - x(u; t, y)| \,du.$$

Thus

$$| y(v; t, y) - x(v; t, y)| \leqslant hL_1(r)e^{h(L_1(r)+L_2(r))}e^{hL(r)} \,| y |$$

for $t \leqslant v \leqslant t + h$.

Taking into account this evaluation, we deduce

$$| V(t + h, y(t + h; t, y)) - V(t + h, x(t + h; t, y))|$$
$$\leqslant K(e^{h(L(r)+L_1(r))} \,| y | + e^{hL(r)} \,| y |)hL_1(r)e^{2hL(r)+hL_1(r)} \,| y |;$$

hence

$$| V(t + h, y(t + h; t, y)) - V(t + h, x(t + h; t, y))| \leqslant 2KL_1(r)e^{4h(L(r)+L_1(r))} \,| y |^2.$$

From here follows

$$\limsup_{h \to 0+} \frac{V[t + h, y(t + h; t\ y)] - V[t + h, x(t + h; t, y)]}{h} \leqslant 2KL_1(r) \,| y |^2.$$

We have

$$\limsup_{h\to 0+} \frac{V[t+h, y(t+h; t_0, y_0)] - V[t, y(t; t, y_0)]}{h}$$

$$= \limsup_{h\to 0+} \frac{V[t+h, y(t+h; t, y(t; t_0, y_0))] - V[t, y(t; t_0, y_0)]}{h}$$

$$\leqslant \limsup_{h\to 0+} \frac{V[t+h, y(t+h;t, y(t;t_0, y_0))] - V[t+h, x(t+h;t,y(t;t_0, y_0))]}{h}$$

$$+ \limsup_{h\to 0+} \frac{V[t+h, x(t+h; t, y(t; t_0, y_0))] - V[t, y(t; t_0, y_0)]}{h}$$

$$\leqslant 2KL_1(r) \mid y(t; t_0, y_0)|^2 - \tfrac{1}{2} \mid y(t; t_0, y_0)|^2$$

if $| y(t; t_0, y_0)| \leqslant r/2$. If $L_1(r)$ is sufficiently small that $L_1(r) < 1/8K$, then

$$\limsup_{h\to 0+} \frac{V[t+h, y(t+h; t_0, y_0)] - V[t, y(t; t_0, y_0)]}{h} < - \tfrac{1}{4} \mid y(t; t_0, y_0)|^2$$

if $| y(t; t_0, y_0)| < r/2$. From this it follows that $V[t, y(t; t_0, y)]$ is decreasing. Hence

$$| y(t; t_0, y_0)|^2 \leqslant V[t, y(t; t_0, y_0)] \leqslant V(t_0, y_0) < M| y_0 |^2.$$

Thus if $| y_0 | < \sqrt{M/\mu}\, r/2$, it follows that for every $t \geqslant t_0$ we shall have $| y(t; t_0, y_0)| < r/2$ and hence that the function $V(t, x)$ constructed for system (1) from the property of exponential stability verifies for system (5) all the conditions from Theorem 1.5. Thus, Theorem 1.7′ is proved.

We shall give for this theorem still another proof, essentially based on a new idea due to Barbasin. We shall suppose that

$$| g(t, y_2) - g(t, y_1)| \leqslant L(r) \mid y_1 - y_2 \mid \qquad \text{for} \quad | y_1 | < r, | y_2 | < r.$$

As above, we shall write

$$y(t; t_0, y_0) - x(t; t_0, y_0)$$

$$= \int_{t_0}^{t} \{f [u, y(u; t_0, y_0)] - f [(u, x(u; t_0, y_0)]\}du + \int_{t_0}^{t} g[u, y(u; t_0, y_0)]du$$

$$= \int_{t_0}^{t} \{f [u, y(u; t_0, y_0)] - f [u, x(u; t_0, y_0)]\}du$$

$$+ \int_{t_0}^{t} \{g[u, y(u; t_0, y_0)] - g[u, x(u; t_0, y_0)]\}du + \int_{t_0}^{t} g[u, x(u; t_0, y_0)]du.$$

Thus

$$| y(t; t_0, y_0) - x(t; t_0, y_0)| \leqslant L_1(r)B \int_{t_0}^{t} e^{-\alpha(u-t_0)} \,| y_0 |\, du$$

$$+ \int_{t_0}^{t} 2L(r) \,| y(u; t_0, y_0) - x(u; t_0, y_0)|\, du;$$

hence

$$| y(t; t_0, y_0) - x(t; t_0, y_0)| \leqslant \frac{L_1(r)B}{\alpha} e^{2L(r)(t-t_0)} \,| y_0 |$$

for all $t \geqslant t_0$, for which

$$| y(u; t_0, y_0)| \leqslant \frac{r}{2}, \; | x(u; t_0, y_0)| \leqslant \frac{r}{2} \quad \text{if} \quad t_0 \leqslant u \leqslant t.$$

Let $\epsilon > 0$, $| y_0 | < \epsilon/2B$, $T = (1/\alpha) \ln 4B$ and $L_1(r)$ such that $(L_1(r)B/\alpha)e^{2TL(r)} < \frac{1}{4}$.

We have

$$| x(u; t_0, y_0)| \leqslant Be^{-\alpha(u-t_0)} \,| y_0 | < B| y_0 | < \frac{\epsilon}{2} < \frac{r}{4} \quad \text{if} \quad \epsilon \leqslant \frac{r}{2}.$$

Further, for those $t_0 \leqslant t \leqslant t_0 + T$ for which

$$| y(u; t_0, y_0)| \leqslant \frac{r}{2} \quad (t_0 \leqslant u \leqslant t),$$

it follows that

$$| y(u; t_0, y_0) - x(u; t_0, y_0)| \leqslant \frac{L_1(r)B}{\alpha} e^{2TL(r)} \,| y_0 | < \frac{1}{4} | y_0 | < \frac{\epsilon}{8B}.$$

Thus

$$| y(u; t_0, y_0)| \leqslant | x(u; t_0, y_0)| + | y(u; t_0, y_0) - x(u; t_0, y_0)|$$

$$\leqslant Be^{-\alpha(u-t_0)} \,| y_0 | + \frac{\epsilon}{8B} < \frac{\epsilon}{2} + \frac{\epsilon}{8B} < \epsilon \leqslant \frac{r}{2}.$$

Hence $| y(u; t_0, y_0)| \leqslant r/2$ for $t_0 \leqslant u \leqslant t_0 + T$ and, in addition, $| y(u; t_0, y_0)| < \epsilon$ for $t_0 \leqslant u \leqslant t_0 + T$. Further,

$$| y(t_0 + T; t_0, y_0)| \leqslant Be^{-\alpha T} \frac{\epsilon}{2B} + \frac{\epsilon}{8B} = \frac{\epsilon}{8B} + \frac{\epsilon}{8B} = \frac{\epsilon}{4B}.$$

We consider now the interval $t_0 + T \leqslant t \leqslant t_0 + 2T$; instead of y_0 we will start with the value $y(t_0 + T;\ t_0, y_0)$, for which we have stated the evaluation $|y(t_0 + T;\ t_0, y_0)| < \epsilon/4B$. The same computations as above (in which the role of ϵ is taken by $\epsilon/2$) lead to $|y(t; t_0, y_0)| < \epsilon/2$ for $t_0 + T \leqslant t \leqslant t_0 + 2T$ and $|y(t_0 + 2T; t_0, y_0)| < \epsilon/8B$. Continuing in the same way, we obtain for $t_0 + nT \leqslant t \leqslant t_0 + (n+1)T$ the evaluation $|y(t; t_0, y_0)| < \epsilon/2^{n+1}$.

It follows in any case that if $|y_0| < \epsilon/2B$ we have $|y(t; t_0, y_0)| < \epsilon$ for every $t \geqslant t_0$. If $|y_0| < r/4B$, then $|y(t;\ t_0, y_0)| < r/2^{n+2}$ for $t_0 + nT \leqslant t \leqslant t_0 + (n+1)T$. Let $t \geqslant t_0$; there exists $m \geqslant 1$ such that $t_0 + (m-1)T \leqslant t < t_0 + mT$; then $mT > t - t_0$, $m > (1/T)(t - t_0)$, $2^m > 2^{(1/T)(t-t_0)}$, $1/2^m < 2^{-(1/T)(t-t_0)}$. From $t \geqslant t_0 + (m-1)T$ we obtain

$$|y(t; t_0, y_0)| < \frac{r}{2}\frac{1}{2^m} < \frac{r}{2}2^{-(1/T)(t-t_0)};$$

taking $\alpha_1 = (1/T)\ln 2$ we have $2 = e^{\alpha_1 T}$; hence $|y(t; t_0, y_0)| < (r/2)e^{-\alpha_1(t-t_0)}$, which proves that the trivial solution of system (5) is exponentially stable.

We shall now prove a theorem of stability by the first approximation, which holds only in the case when the system of first approximation does not explicitly depend on t. Its extension to the general case is still an open problem. The theorem was proved for the first time in 1951 by I. G. Malkin. Other proofs have been given by J. L. Massera and N. N. Krasovski. We shall give here a new demonstration based on some results previously stressed.

Theorem 1.7″. *Consider the system*

$$\frac{dx}{dt} = X(x) + R(t, x), \tag{6}$$

where $X(kx) = k^m X(x)$, $|R(t, x)| \leqslant \gamma |x|^m$, γ being a sufficiently small constant. If the trivial solution of system $dx/dt = X(x)$ is asymptotically stable, then the trivial solution of system (6) is uniformly asymptotically stable.

Proof. Consider the system

$$\frac{dz}{d\tau} = \begin{cases} \dfrac{X(z)}{|z|^{m-1}} & \text{for } |z| \neq 0, \\ 0 & \text{for } |z| = 0. \end{cases} \tag{7}$$

Let $z(\tau; \tau_0, x_0)$ be a solution of system (7),

$$t(\tau) = \int_0^\tau \frac{1}{|z(u; \tau_0, x_0)|^{m-1}} du,$$

$\tau(t)$ being the corresponding inverse function. Let $y(t) = z[\tau(t); \tau_0, x_0]$. We have

$$\frac{dy(t)}{dt} = \frac{d}{d\tau} z[\tau(t); \tau_0, x_0] \frac{d\tau(t)}{dt} = \frac{X(z[\tau(t); \tau_0, x_0])}{|z[\tau(t); \tau_0, x_0]|^{m-1}} \frac{1}{\frac{dt(\tau)}{d\tau}}$$

$$= X(z[\tau(t); \tau_0, x_0]),$$

and thus $dy(t)/dt = X(y(t))$; in addition, $y(t_0) = x_0$, where $t_0 = t(\tau_0)$.

Since we have supposed that the solution of the homogeneous system is asymptotically stable, we may write

$$|y(t)| \leqslant \chi(|x_0|)\psi(t - t_0),$$

implying that

$$|z[\tau(t); \tau_0, x_0]| \leqslant \chi(|x_0|)\psi(t - t_0).$$

Thus

$$|z(\tau; \tau_0, x_0)| \leqslant \chi(|x_0|)\psi(t(\tau) - t(\tau_0))$$

$$= \chi(|x_0|)\psi\left(\int_{\tau_0}^{\tau} \frac{1}{|z(u; \tau_0, x_0)|^{m-1}} du\right).$$

Since $z(u; \tau_0, x_0)$ is bounded, we have

$$\frac{1}{|z(u; \tau_0, x_0)|^{m-1}} \geqslant l > 0;$$

hence

$$|z(\tau; \tau_0, x_0)| \leqslant \chi(|x_0|)\psi(l(\tau - \tau_0)) = \chi(|x_0|)\psi^*(\tau - \tau_0),$$

where $\psi^*(r)$ is monotone-decreasing and $\lim_{r\to\infty} \psi^*(r) = 0$.

From this evaluation it follows that the trivial solution of system (7) is uniformly asymptotically stable. By virtue of a remark from Section 1.2, it is exponentially stable. Now let $x(t; t_0, x_0)$ be a solution of system (6). Put

$$\tau(t) = \int_0^t |x(u; t_0, x_0)|^{m-1} du;$$

let $t(\tau)$ be the inverse of this function and $y(\tau) = x(t(\tau); t_0, x_0)$. We have

$$\begin{aligned}\frac{dy}{d\tau} &= \frac{d}{dt} x(t(\tau); t_0, x_0) \frac{dt(\tau)}{d\tau}\\ &= (X[x(t(\tau); t_0, x_0)] + R[t(\tau), x(t(\tau); t_0, x_0)]) \frac{1}{\dfrac{d\tau(t)}{dt}}\\ &= (X[x(t(\tau); t_0, x_0)] + R[t(\tau), x(t(\tau); t_0, x_0)]) \frac{1}{| x(t(\tau); t_0, x_0)|^{m-1}}\\ &= \frac{X[y(\tau)]}{| y(\tau)|^{m-1}} + \frac{R[t(\tau), y(\tau)]}{| y(\tau)|^{m-1}} .\end{aligned}$$

Thus $y(\tau)$ verifies the system

$$\frac{dy}{d\tau} = \begin{cases} \dfrac{X(y)}{| y |^{m-1}} + \dfrac{R(t(\tau), y)}{| y |^{m-1}} & \text{if } \quad | y | \neq 0, \\ 0 & \text{if } \quad | y | = 0. \end{cases}$$

From $| R(t, y)| \leqslant \gamma | y |^m$ we obtain

$$\left| \frac{R(t(\tau), y)}{| y |^{m-1}} \right| \leqslant \gamma | y |.$$

Since the trivial solution of the first approximation system (7) is exponentially stable, we may apply Theorem 1.7′, and it follows that the trivial solution of the system in y is exponentially stable; hence

$$| y(\tau)| \leqslant Be^{-\alpha(\tau-\tau_0)}| x_0 | \qquad [\tau_0 = \tau(t_0)].$$

Thus

$$| x(t(\tau); t_0, x_0)| \leqslant Be^{-\alpha(\tau-\tau_0)} | x_0 |;$$

i.e.,

$$| x(t; t_0, x_0)| \leqslant Be^{-\alpha(\tau(t)-\tau(t_0))} | x_0 |;$$

hence

$$| x(t; t_0, x_0)| \leqslant B \exp \left[-\alpha \int_{t_0}^{t} | x(u; t_0, x_0)|^{m-1} du\right] | x_0 |.$$

If for $t \to \infty$, $\tau(t) \to \tau_\infty < \infty$, then the solution

$$y(\tau) = x(t(\tau); t_0, x_0)$$

would not be defined beyond τ_∞, since for $\tau \to \tau_\infty$ we have $t \to \infty$. But the solution $y(\tau)$ is defined for any τ; hence $\tau_\infty = \infty$. It follows that the integral is divergent and therefore asymptotic stability occurs. The theorem is proved.

Let us now emphasize the character of asymptotic stability for the homogeneous systems considered above. We assume that $m > 1$. For the system

$$\frac{dz}{d\tau} = \begin{cases} \dfrac{X(z)}{|z|^{m-1}} & (|z| \neq 0), \\ 0 & (z = 0), \end{cases}$$

asymptotic stability is always exponential; i.e.,

$$|z(\tau; \tau_0, x_0)| \leqslant Be^{-\alpha(\tau-\tau_0)} |x_0|$$

and

$$|y(t; t_0, x_0)| \leqslant Be^{-\alpha(\tau(t)-\tau(t_0))} |x_0|.$$

Let us evaluate $|z(\tau; \tau_0, x_0)|$. We have $(d/d\tau)z(\tau; \tau_0, x_0) = Z(z(\tau; \tau_0, x_0))$, where we have set

$$Z(z) = \begin{cases} \dfrac{X(z)}{|z|^{m-1}} & (|z| \neq 0), \\ 0 & (z = 0). \end{cases}$$

Hence

$$\left(z(\tau; \tau_0, x_0), \frac{d}{d\tau} z(\tau; \tau_0, x_0)\right) = (z(\tau; \tau_0, x_0), Z(z(\tau; \tau_0, x_0))).$$

But $Z(z)$ is homogeneous of first degree; hence $|Z(z)| \leqslant L|z|$, where $L = \sup_{|z| \leqslant 1} |Z(z)|$. Therefore,

$$\frac{1}{2}\frac{d}{d\tau} |z(\tau; \tau_0, x_0)|^2 \leqslant L|z(\tau; \tau_0, x_0)|^2;$$

hence

$$\left|\frac{1}{2}\frac{d}{d\tau} \ln |z(\tau; \tau_0, x_0)|^2\right| \leqslant L, \qquad \frac{d}{d\tau} \ln |z(\tau; \tau_0, x_0)|^2 \geqslant -2L,$$

$$\ln |z(\tau; \tau_0, x_0)|^2 \geqslant -2L(\tau - \tau_0) + \ln |x_0|^2$$

$$|z(\tau; \tau_0, x_0)|^2 \geqslant e^{-2L(\tau-\tau_0)} |x_0|^2;$$

hence

$$| z(\tau; \tau_0, x_0)| \geqslant e^{-L(\tau-\tau_0)} | x_0 |, \qquad | z(\tau; \tau_0, x_0)|^{m-1} \geqslant e^{-L(m-1)(\tau-\tau_0)} | x_0 |^{m-1},$$

$$\frac{1}{| z(\tau; \tau_0, x_0)|^{m-1}} \leqslant \frac{1}{| x_0 |^{m-1}} e^{(m-1)L(\tau-\tau_0)}.$$

Thus

$$\frac{dt(\tau)}{d\tau} \leqslant \frac{1}{| x_0 |^{m-1}} e^{(m-1)L(\tau-\tau_0)}$$

and

$$t(\tau) - t_0 \leqslant \frac{1}{| x_0 |^{m-1}} \int_{\tau_0}^{\tau} e^{(m-1)L(\tau-\tau_0)} \, d\tau$$

$$= \frac{1}{| x_0 |^{m-1}} \int_{\tau}^{\tau-\tau_0} e^{(m-1)L\sigma} \, d\sigma = \frac{1}{(m-1)L| x_0 |^{m-1}} (e^{(m-1)L(\tau-\tau_0)} - 1).$$

From this follows

$$1 + (m-1)L| x_0 |^{m-1}(t - t_0) \leqslant e^{(m-1)L(\tau-\tau_0)},$$

$$[1 + (m-1)L| x_0 |^{m-1}(t - t_0)]^{1/L} \leqslant e^{(m-1)(\tau-\tau_0)},$$

$$[1 + (m-1)L| x_0 |^{m-1}(t - t_0)]^{\alpha/L} \leqslant e^{(m-1)\alpha(\tau-\tau_0)},$$

and

$$e^{-(m-1)\alpha(\tau-\tau_0)} \leqslant \frac{1}{[1 + (m-1)L| x_0 |^{m-1}(t - t_0)]^{\alpha/L}}.$$

Thus

$$| y(t; t_0, x_0)|^{m-1} \leqslant B^{m-1} e^{-(m-1)\alpha(\tau-\tau_0)} | x_0 |^{m-1}$$

$$\leqslant \frac{B^{m-1} | x_0 |^{m-1}}{[1 + (m-1)L| x_0 |^{m-1}(t - t_0)]^{\alpha/L}};$$

i.e.,

$$| y(t; t_0, x_0)| \leqslant B[1 + (m-1)L| x_0 |^{m-1}(t - t_0)]^{-\alpha/L(m-1)} | x_0 |$$

$$= B[| x_0 |^{(m-1)} (m-1)L(t - t_0)]^{-\alpha/L(m-1)} | x_0 |^{1-(\alpha/L)}.$$

Krasovski has proved that if the trivial solution of the system $dy/dt = Y(t, y)$ verifies an evaluation of this type, we can obtain a theorem on stability by the first approximation of the same type as Theorem 1.7″. It is, however, an open problem if such an evaluation always occurs for homogeneous systems.

We shall state now some theorems of stability in the first approximation of a less general character, which however, may prove effective in different concrete cases.

Proposition 1. *Consider the system*

$$\frac{dx}{dt} = A(t)x + X(x, t),$$

where $| X(x, t)| \leqslant \beta^2(t) \,| x |$, *for* $| x | \leqslant c$.

If there exists a matrix $G(t)$ *self-adjoint and positive* [i.e., *such that the Hermitian form* (Gx, x) *is positive-definite*], *such that*

$$\int_{t_0}^{\infty} \left[q_M(t) + 2\beta \sqrt{\frac{\Lambda}{\lambda}}\right] dt = -\infty$$

then the trivial solution of the system is asymptotically stable.

Here q_M *is the largest eigenvalue of the matrix* $A + G^{-1}\dot{G} + G^{-1}A^*G$, *and* λ *and* Λ *are, respectively, the smallest and the largest eigenvalue for matrix* G.

Proof. Let

$$\xi(t) = (G(t)x(t; t_0, x_0), x(t; t_0, x_0)).$$

We have

$$\begin{aligned}
\frac{d\xi}{dt} &= \left(\frac{dG}{dt} x(t; t_0, x_0), x(t; t_0, x_0)\right) + \left(G(t) \frac{d}{dt} x(t; t_0, x_0), x(t; t_0, x_0)\right) \\
&\quad + \left(G(t)x(t; t_0, x_0), \frac{d}{dt} x(t; t_0, x_0)\right) = \left(\frac{dG}{dt} x(t; t_0, x_0), x(t; t_0, x_0)\right) \\
&\quad + (G(t)A(t)x(t; t_0, x_0), x(t; t_0, x_0)) + (G(t)X(x(t; t_0, x_0), t), x(t; t_0, x_0)) \\
&\quad + (G(t)x(t; t_0, x_0), A(t)x(t; t_0, x_0)) + (G(t)x(t; t_0, x_0), X(x(t; t_0, x_0), t)) \\
&= \left(\frac{dG(t)}{dt} x(t; t_0, x_0), x(t; t_0, x_0)\right) + (G(t)A(t)x(t; t_0, x_0), x(t; t_0, x_0)) \\
&\quad + (A^*(t)G(t)x(t; t_0, x_0), x(t; t_0, x_0)) + (G(t)X(x(t; t_0, x_0), t), x(t; t_0, x_0)) \\
&\quad + (G(t)x(t; t_0, x_0), X(x(t; t_0, x_0), t) = (Q(t)x(t; t_0, x_0), x(t; t_0, x_0)) \\
&\quad + (G(t)X(x(t; t_0, x_0), t), x(t; t_0, x_0)) + (G(t)x(t; t_0, x_0), X(x(t; t_0, x_0), t)),
\end{aligned}$$

where we have set

$$Q(t) = \frac{dG}{dt} + GA + A^*G.$$

We have

$$G^{-1}(t)Q(t) = G^{-1}\frac{dG}{dt} + A + G^{-1}A^*G;$$

hence q_M is the largest eigenvalue of the matrix $G^{-1}Q$. We have

$$(Qx, x) \leqslant q_M(Gx, x)\ddagger.$$

Likewise, the inequality

$$(Gx, y) + (Gy, x) \leqslant 2\sqrt{(Gx, x)(Gy, y)}$$

is immediately proved.

Thus taking into account these inequalities,

$$\frac{d\xi}{dt} \leqslant q_M\xi + 2\sqrt{\xi(GX, X)}.$$

But

$$(GX, X) \leqslant \Lambda(X, X) \leqslant \Lambda\beta^2(x, x) = \frac{\Lambda}{\lambda}\beta^2\lambda(x, x) \leqslant \frac{\Lambda}{\lambda}\beta^2(Gx, x).$$

Consequently,

$$\frac{d\xi}{dt} \leqslant q_M\xi + 2\xi\beta\sqrt{\frac{\Lambda}{\lambda}};$$

and hence

$$\frac{d\xi}{dt} \leqslant \left(q_M + 2\beta\sqrt{\frac{\Lambda}{\lambda}}\right)\xi.$$

‡ Indeed, let us consider the function (Qx, x) defined on $(Gx, x) = 1$; since $(Gx, x) = 1$ is compact, there exists $\lambda_M = \sup_{(Gx,x)=1}(Qx, x)$. According to the general theory of conditional extremes, the points of maximum verify the relation

$$(\partial/\partial x)\{(Qx, x) - (\lambda Gx, x)\} = 0;$$

hence $(Q - \lambda G)x = 0$, this equation has nonzero solutions only if $\det(Q - \lambda G) = 0$. But

$$\det(Q - \lambda G) = \det G \det(G^{-1}Q - \lambda E);$$

hence λ verifies the equation $\det(G^{-1}Q - \lambda E) = 0$ hence is an eigenvalue of matrix $G^{-1}Q$.
If x_0 is the point of maximum, x_0 is an eigenvector for $G^{-1}Q$; hence

$$(Qx_0, x_0) - \lambda(Gx_0, x_0) = 0;$$

since $(Gx_0, x_0) = 1$, it follows that $(Qx_0, x_0) = \lambda$; hence λ_M is the eigenvalue of $G^{-1}Q$ corresponding to x_0. Since the value (Qx_0, x_0) is maximal, $\lambda_M = q_M$. The written evaluation follows immediately from here.

It follows that

$$\xi(t) \leqslant G(x_0, x_0) \exp \left[\int_{t_0}^{t} \left(q_M + 2\beta \sqrt{\frac{\Lambda}{\lambda}} \right) dt \right].$$

On the other hand,

$$\xi(t) = (G(t)x(t; t_0, x_0), x(t; t_0, x_0)) \geqslant \lambda | x(t; t_0, x_0)|^2.$$

Thus

$$\lambda(t) \mid x(t; t_0, x_0)|^2 \leqslant \Lambda(t_0) \mid x_0 \mid^2 \exp \left[\int_{t_0}^{t} \left(q_M + 2\beta \sqrt{\frac{\Lambda}{\lambda}} \right) dt \right];$$

hence

$$| x(t; t_0, x_0)| \leqslant \sqrt{\frac{\Lambda(t_0)}{\lambda(t)}} \exp \left[\tfrac{1}{2} \int_{t_0}^{t} \left(q_M + 2\beta \sqrt{\frac{\Lambda}{\lambda}} \right) dt \right] | x_0 |.$$

If $\lambda(t) \geqslant \lambda_0 > 0$ and if $\int_{t_0}^{t} (q_M + 2\beta \sqrt{\Lambda/\lambda})\, dt \to -\infty$ when $t \to \infty$, the trivial solution is asymptotically stable. If, in addition,

$$\int_{t_0}^{t} \left(q_M + 2\beta \sqrt{\frac{\Lambda}{\lambda}} \right) dt < -\alpha(t - t_0),$$

the stability is even exponential. The theorem is proved.

Let us consider a particularly important case. Assume that A is constant and that the corresponding normal Jordan form is diagonal. Let C be the matrix which leads A to the normal Jordan form, $G = C^*C$. Then

$$G^{-1}Q = A + G^{-1}A^*G = A + C^{-1}C^{*-1}A^*C^*C$$

and

$$CG^{-1}QC^{-1} = CAC^{-1} + C^{*-1}A^*C^* = CAC^{-1} + (CAC^{-1})^*.$$

Thus the eigenvalues of the matrix $CG^{-1}QC^{-1}$ (which coincide with those of matrix $G^{-1}Q$) are just twice the real parts of the eigenvalues of the matrix A. Assuming that the real parts of the eigenvalues of matrix A are negative, and denoting the largest of them by $-d$, the condition of the theorem becomes

$$\int_{t_0}^{\infty} \left(-d + \beta \sqrt{\frac{\Lambda}{\lambda}} \right) dt = -\infty.$$

The significance of this result is the following. It is known that if matrix A has eigenvalues with negative real parts, the trivial solution of the linear system of first approximation is uniform asymptotically stable; hence we can apply the theorem of stability in the first approximation. The above result allows the evaluation of β such that the stability be maintained; e.g., assuming that β is constant, we obtain the evaluation $\beta < d\sqrt{\lambda/\Lambda}$.

Finally, let us note that the method used leads us not only to a theorem of stability by the first approximation, but also to an evaluation of the solutions. By conveniently choosing matrix G, we may obtain more precise formulas of evaluation of the solution.

Proposition 2. *Consider again the system of the preceding proposition and assume*

$$\int^{\infty} \beta^2(t)dt < \infty.$$

If the trivial solution of the system

$$\frac{dy}{dt} = A(t)y$$

is uniformly stable, then the trivial solution of the given system is uniformly stable. If the trivial solution of the system

$$\frac{dy}{dt} = A(t)y$$

is uniformly asymptotically stable, then the trivial solution of the given system is uniformly asymptotically stable. It is assumed here that

$$\int_{t_0}^{t} | A(u)| \, du \leqslant \omega(t - t_0).$$

Proof. We shall prove this proposition in two ways. The first demonstration is based upon the construction of a Lyapunov function.

From the uniform-stability hypothesis it follows that $| C(t, s)| \leqslant M$; hence $| y(t; t_0, x_0)| \leqslant M | x_0 |$ for all solutions of the linear system of first approximation. Let $V(t, x) = \sup_{\sigma \geqslant 0} | y(t + \sigma; t, x)|$.

We have $V(t, x) \geqslant | x |$, $V(t, x) \leqslant M| x |$. Further,

$$|| y(t + \sigma; t, x_1)| - | y(t + \sigma; t, x_2)|| \leqslant | y(t + \sigma; t, x_1 - x_2)| \leqslant M| x_1 - x_2 |$$

(we have used the *linearity* of the system of first approximation).

Thus

$$| y(t + \sigma; t, x_1)| \leqslant | y(t + \sigma; t, x_2)| + M| x_1 - x_2 |$$

and

$$V(t, x_1) \leqslant V(t, x_2) + M| x_1 - x_2 |.$$

Likewise,

$$V(t, x_2) \leqslant V(t, x_1) + M| x_1 - x_2 |,$$

which implies

$$| V(t, x_1) - V(t, x_2)| \leqslant M| x_1 - x_2 |.$$

The function

$$V^*(t) = V(t, y(t; t_0, x_0))$$

is monotone-decreasing (see Theorem 1.2′).

We have

$$x(v; t, x_0) = x_0 + \int_t^v \{A(u)x(u; t, x_0) + X(x(u; t, x_0), u)\}du$$

For $| x_0 | < c/2$ it follows, if $t \leqslant v \leqslant t + h$ and h is sufficiently small, that

$$| x(v; t, x_0)| \leqslant | x_0 | + \int_t^v \{| A(u)| \, | x(u; t, x_0)| + \beta^2(u) \, | x(u; t, x_0)|\}du;$$

hence

$$| x(v; t, x_0)| \leqslant | x_0 | \exp\left(\int_t^{t+h} \{| A(u)| + \beta^2(u)\}du\right).$$

Further,

$$x(v; t, x_0) - y(v; t, x_0)$$
$$= \int_t^v A(u)[x(u; t, x_0) - y(u; t, x_0)]du + \int_t^v X(x(u; t, x_0), u)du.$$

We will have

$$| x(v; t, x_0) - y(v; t, x_0)| \leqslant | x_0 | \exp\left[\int_t^{t+h} (| A(u)| + \beta^2(u))du\right] \int_t^{t+h} \beta^2(u)du$$
$$+ \int_t^v | A(u)| \, | x(u; t, x_0) - y(u; t, x_0)| \, du$$

and

$$| x(v; t, x_0) - y(v; t, x_0)| \leqslant | x_0 | \int_t^{t+h} \beta^2(u)du \exp \left[\int_t^{t+h} \{2|A(u)| + \beta^2(u)\}du\right]$$

for $t \leqslant v \leqslant t + h$. Taking this evaluation into account, we deduce

$$| V[t + h, x(t + h; t, x)] - V[t + h, y(t + h; t, x)]|$$
$$\leqslant M \int_t^{t+h} \beta^2(u)du \exp \left[\int_t^{t+h} \{2|A(u)| + \beta^2(u)\}du\right];$$

hence

$$\limsup_{h\to 0+} \frac{V[t + h, x(t + h, t, x)] - V[t + h, y(t + h; t, x)]}{h} \leqslant M\beta^2(t)| x |.$$

In this way, with the help of a computation which we have already performed (see, for example, Theorem 1.7′), we obtain

$$\limsup_{h\to 0+} \frac{V[t + h, x(t + h; t, x)] - V(t, x)}{h} \leqslant M\beta^2(t)| x | \leqslant M\beta^2(t)V(t, x).$$

Setting

$$V^{**}(t) = V[t, x(t, t_0, x_0)],$$

we deduce

$$\limsup_{h\to 0+} \frac{V^{**}(t + h) - V^{**}(t)}{h} \leqslant M\beta^2(t)V^{**}(t)$$

and hence

$$V^{**}(t) \leqslant V^{**}(t_0) \exp \left[M \int_{t_0}^t \beta^2(u)du\right].$$

Thus

$$| x(t; t_0, x_0)| \leqslant V[t, x(t; t_0, x_0)] \leqslant V(t_0, x_0) \exp \left[M \int_{t_0}^t \beta^2(u)du\right]$$
$$\leqslant M| x_0 | \exp \left[M \int_{t_0}^t \beta^2(u)du\right],$$

which together with $\int^\infty \beta^2(u)\,du < K$ implies $| x(t; t_0, x_0)| \leqslant M \exp(MK)| x_0 |$, and the first assertion of the proposition is proved.

For the second assertion, proceeding as in Theorem 1.7, we choose the function $(V(t)x, x)$, given by Theorem 1.6″, and setting

$$V^*(t) = (V(t)x(t; t_0, x_0), x(t; t_0, x_0)),$$

we deduce that

$$\frac{dV^*}{dt} = -|x(t; t_0, x_0)|^2 + 2(V(t)x(t; t_0, x_0), X(x(t; t_0, x_0), t))$$
$$\leqslant -|x(t; t_0, x_0)|^2 + 2M\beta^2|x(t; t_0, x_0)|^2 \leqslant -\frac{1 - 2M\beta^2}{M} V^*(t).$$

Hence

$$\frac{d \ln V^*}{dt} \leqslant -\frac{1}{M} + 2M\beta^2;$$

from this we deduce that

$$\ln V^*(t) - \ln V^*(t_0) \leqslant -\frac{1}{M}(t - t_0) + 2M \int_{t_0}^{t} \beta^2(u)du$$

and that

$$V^*(t) \leqslant V^*(t_0) \exp\left[-\frac{1}{M}(t - t_0)\right] \exp\left[2M \int_{t_0}^{t} \beta^2(u)du\right]$$
$$\leqslant M|x_0|^2 \exp\left[2MK - \frac{1}{M}(t - t_0)\right]$$

We finally obtain

$$|x(t; t_0, x_0)| \leqslant \sqrt{\frac{M}{\mu}}\, e^{MK} e^{-(1/2M)(t-t_0)} |x_0|,$$

and the proposition is proved.

The second proof uses the variation-of-constants formula,

$$x(t; t_0, x_0) = C(t; t_0)x_0 + \int_{t_0}^{t} C(t; s)X(x(s; t_0, x_0), s)ds.$$

Thus

$$|x(t; t_0, x_0)| \leqslant M|x_0| + \int_{t_0}^{t} M\beta^2(s)|x(s; t_0, x_0)|\, ds.$$

From here we obtain

$$|x(t; t_0, x_0)| \leqslant M|x_0| \exp\left[M \int_{t_0}^{t} \beta^2(s)ds\right],$$

and the first assertion of the proposition is proved.

Finally, if the trivial solution of the linear system of first approximation is uniformly asymptotically stable, we deduce

$$| C(t; s)| \leqslant Be^{-\alpha(t-s)}.$$

Hence

$$| x(t; t_0, x_0)| \leqslant Be^{-\alpha(t-t_0)} | x_0 | + \int_{t_0}^{t} Be^{-\alpha(t-s)}\beta^2(s)| x(s; t_0, x_0)| \, ds.$$

Setting

$$u(t) = | x(t; t_0, x_0)| e^{\alpha t}$$

we deduce that

$$u(t) \leqslant Bu(t_0) + B \int_{t_0}^{t} \beta^2(s)u(s)ds,$$

whence

$$u(t) \leqslant Bu(t_0) \exp \left(B \int_{t_0}^{t} \beta^2(s)ds\right)$$

and

$$| x(t; t_0, x_0)| \leqslant Be^{-\alpha(t-t_0)} | x_0 | \exp \left[B \int_{t_0}^{t} \beta^2 \, ds\right] < Be^{KB}e^{-\alpha(t-t_0)} | x_0 |.$$

The proposition is proved.

Proposition 3. *Consider the system*

$$\frac{dx}{dt} = X(t, x, y), \qquad \frac{dy}{dt} = A(t)y + Y(t, x, y),$$

where $| X(t, x, y)| \leqslant K| y |^{\beta}$, $\beta > 0$, $| Y(t, x, y)| \leqslant k| y |$ *for* $| x | \leqslant \alpha_0$, $| y | \leqslant \alpha_0$, k *sufficiently small. Suppose that the trivial solution of the linear system*

$$\frac{dz}{dt} = A(t)z$$

is uniformly asymptotically stable. Then the trivial solution of the given system is uniformly stable and, in addition, for every solution for which the initial values are sufficiently small we have

$$y(t) \to 0, \; x(t) \to l \qquad \textit{for} \quad t \to \infty.$$

Proof. For this theorem, too, we shall give two proofs, the first based on the construction of a Lyapunov function, the second on the formula of the variation of constants. Let $V(t)$ be the matrix constructed as in Theorem 1.6″ for the system in z. Setting

$$V^*(t) = (V(t)y(t; t_0, x_0, y_0), y(t; t_0, x_0, y_0)),$$

we obtain, as in Theorem 1.7,

$$\frac{dV^*}{dt} = -|y(t; t_0, x_0, y_0)|^2 + 2(V(t)y(t; t_0, x_0, y_0), Y(t, x(t; t_0, x_0, y_0), y(t; t_0, x_0, y_0)))$$

and

$$\frac{dV^*}{dt} \leqslant -|y(t; t_0, x_0, y_0)|^2 + 2Mk|y(t; t_0, x_0, y_0)|^2.$$

Further, as in Theorem 1.7, we deduce that

$$\frac{dV^*}{dt} \leqslant -\tfrac{1}{2}|y(t; t_0, x_0, y_0)|^2 \leqslant -\frac{1}{2M}V^*(t),$$

whence

$$\mu|y(t; t_0, x_0, y_0)|^2 \leqslant V^*(t) \leqslant M|y_0|^2 \exp\left[-\frac{1}{2M}(t-t_0)\right]$$

and

$$|y(t; t_0, x_0, y_0)| \leqslant \sqrt{\frac{M}{\mu}} \exp\left[-\frac{1}{4M}(t-t_0)\right]|y_0|.$$

From

$$x(t; t_0, x_0, y_0) = x_0 + \int_{t_0}^{t} X[u, x(u; t_0, x_0, y_0), y(u; t_0, x_0, y_0)]du$$

we obtain

$$|x(t; t_0, x_0, y_0)| \leqslant |x_0| + \int_{t_0}^{t} K\left(\sqrt{\frac{M}{\mu}}\right)^{\beta} e^{-(\beta/4M)(u-t_0)}\,du\,|y_0|^{\beta}$$

$$= |x_0| + K\left(\sqrt{\frac{M}{\mu}}\right)^{\beta} \int_{0}^{t-t_0} e^{-(\beta/4M)u}\,du\,|y_0|^{\beta}$$

$$\leqslant |x_0| + \left(\sqrt{\frac{M}{\mu}}\right)^{\beta} \frac{4M}{\beta}|y_0|^{\beta}$$

which shows the uniform stability. In addition, $\int_{t_0}^{t} X[u, x(u; t_0, x_0, y_0), y(u, t_0, x_0, y_0)]\, du$ will be convergent; hence $\lim_{t\to\infty} x(t; t_0, x_0, y_0)$ exists. The proposition is proved.

Now, the second proof. Let $C(t, s)$ be the fundamental matrix of solutions for the system in z; we have

$$| C(t, s)| \leqslant Be^{-\alpha(t-s)}$$

From

$$y(t; t_0, x_0, y_0) = C(t; t_0)y_0 + \int_{t_0}^{t} C(t, s)Y(s; x(s; t_0, x_0, y_0), y(s; t_0, x_0, y_0))ds,$$

we obtain

$$| y(t; t_0, x_0, y_0)| \leqslant Be^{-\alpha(t-t_0)} | y_0 | + Bk \int_{t_0}^{t} e^{-\alpha(t-s)} | y(s; t_0, x_0, y_0)| \, ds.$$

Setting

$$u(t) = e^{\alpha t}| y(t; t_0, x_0, y_0)|,$$

we obtain

$$u(t) \leqslant Bu(t_0) + Bk \int_{t_0}^{t} u(s)ds,$$

whence

$$u(t) \leqslant Bu(t_0)e^{Bk(t-t_0)}.$$

Thus

$$| y(t; t_0, x_0, y_0)| \leqslant Be^{-\alpha(t-t_0)}e^{Bk(t-t_0)} | y_0 |.$$

If we have $k < \alpha/\beta$, then we shall have the exponential evaluation for $| y(t; t_0, x_0, y_0)|$ and the proof continues as above.

With the help of Proposition 3, we shall state a stability criterion of a special type relative to systems of the second order.

Proposition 4. *Consider the second-order system $dy/dt = Y(y, t)$, where Y depends analytically on y and has a development in series with bounded coefficients for $t \geqslant 0$. Let $\varphi(t, h)$ be a family of bounded solutions of the system for $t \geqslant 0$ depending analytically on h and with the property that the functions $\varphi_{h^k}^{(k)}(t, 0)$ are bounded for $t \geqslant 0$. If*

$$| \varphi_h'(t, 0)| \geqslant \gamma > 0$$

and

$$\int_{t_0}^{t} \left\{\mathrm{Tr} \frac{\partial Y}{\partial y} [\varphi(t, 0), t]\right\} dt \leqslant -\nu(t - t_0) + \chi(t),$$

where $\chi(t)$ is a bounded function, then $y = \varphi(t, 0)$ is uniformly stable.

Remark. If Y does not explicitly depend on t and the system admits a bounded solution $y = \varphi(t)$, then it has also the solutions $\varphi(t + h)$; in this case $\varphi'_h(t, 0) = \dot{\varphi}(t)$ and in general

$$\varphi^{(k)}_{h^k}(t, 0) = \frac{d^k}{dt^k}\varphi(t).$$

Hence the condition that these derivatives be bounded is automatically verified. For the case when Y does not depend explicitly on t and the solution $\varphi(t)$ is periodic, the result has been stated by Poincaré.

Proof. Let $\varphi(t, 0) = \varphi(t)$. We make the change of variables $x = y - \varphi(t)$ and we obtain

$$\frac{dx}{dt} = A(t)x + X(t, x),$$

where

$$A(t) = \frac{\partial Y}{\partial y}(\varphi(t), t),$$

and the development in series with respect to x of $X(t, x)$ begins with terms of degree higher or equal to two. Both $A(t)$ and $X(t, x)$ are bounded as functions of t for $t \geqslant 0$. The system in x admits the family of solutions

$$x = \varphi(t, h) - \varphi(t, 0) = h\varphi'_h(t, 0) + \tfrac{1}{2}h^2\varphi''_{h^2}(t, 0) + \cdots.$$

By substituting in the system we find that $\varphi'_h(t, 0)$ is a solution of the linear system $dz/dt = A(t)z$. By virtue of the hypothesis, this solution is bounded.

In what follows we shall denote by ψ_1, ψ_2 the components of the vector $\varphi'_h(t, 0)$. We have, by hypothesis, $\psi_1^2 + \psi_2^2 \geqslant \gamma^2 > 0$. Let

$$\psi = \begin{pmatrix} \psi_1 & -\psi_2 \\ \psi_2 & \psi_1 \end{pmatrix}.$$

It follows that $\det \psi = \psi_1^2 + \psi_2^2$,

$$\psi^{-1} = \frac{1}{\psi_1^2 + \psi_2^2}\begin{pmatrix} \psi_1 & \psi_2 \\ -\psi_2 & \psi_1 \end{pmatrix}, \qquad \dot{\psi} = \begin{pmatrix} \dot{\psi}_1 & -\dot{\psi}_2 \\ \dot{\psi}_2 & \dot{\psi}_1 \end{pmatrix},$$

and it is clear that according to the hypothesis of the theorem, ψ, ψ^{-1}, $\dot{\psi}$ are bounded. We perform the change of variables $x = \psi x^*$. The system becomes

$$\frac{dx^*}{dt} = \left(\psi^{-1}A\psi - \psi^{-1}\frac{d\psi}{dt}\right)x^* + \psi^{-1}X(t, \psi x^*).$$

The linear system

$$\frac{dz}{dt} = A(t)z$$

becomes, by means of the change of variables $z = \psi z^*$,

$$\frac{dz^*}{dt} = \left(\psi^{-1}A\psi - \psi^{-1}\frac{d\psi}{dt}\right)z^*.$$

This system admits the solution $z_1^* = 1$, $z_2^* = 0$, which corresponds to the solution $z_1 = \psi_1$, $z_2 = \psi_2$.

It follows that the first column of the matrix $\psi^{-1}A\psi - \psi^{-1}(d\psi/dt)$ is zero; let $a(t)$, $b(t)$ be the elements of the second column. We have

$$b(t) - \text{Tr}\left[\psi^{-1}A\psi - \psi^{-1}\frac{d\psi}{dt}\right] = \text{Tr}\,\psi^{-1}A\psi - \text{Tr}\,\psi^{-1}\frac{d\psi}{dt}$$

$$= \text{Tr}\,A - \text{Tr}\,\psi^{-1}\frac{d\psi}{dt} = \text{Tr}\,A - \frac{d}{dt}\ln\det\psi = \text{Tr}\,A - \frac{d}{dt}\ln(\psi_1^2 + \psi_2^2).$$

Hence the system in x^* has the form

$$\frac{dx_1^*}{dt} = a(t)x_2^* + X_1(t, x_1^*, x_2^*), \qquad \frac{dx_2^*}{dt} = b(t)x_2^* + X_2^*(t, x_1^*, x_2^*),$$

where X^* has the same properties as X.

From $x^* = \psi^{-1}x$ it follows that this system admits the bounded family of solutions

$$x^* = h\psi^{-1}\varphi_h'(t, 0) + \tfrac{1}{2}h^2\psi^{-1}\varphi_{h^2}''(t, 0) + \cdots.$$

Taking into account that $\varphi_h'(t, 0)$ is the first column of the matrix ψ, we see that $\psi^{-1}\varphi_h'(t, 0)$ has the components 1 and 0. Hence

$$x_1^* = h + h^2\alpha_2(t) + \cdots, \qquad x_2^* = h^2\beta_2(t) + \cdots$$

where, according to the hypotheses, α_k and β_k are bounded functions of t for $t \geqslant 0$. We make a new change of variables

$$x_1^* = u + u^2\alpha_2(t) + \cdots \qquad x_2^* = v + u^2\beta_2(t) + \cdots.$$

In the neighborhood of the point $x_1^* = x_2^* = 0$ we obtain

$$u = x_1^* - x_1^{*2}\alpha_2(t) + \cdots \qquad v = x_2^* - x_1^{*2}\beta_2(t) + \cdots.$$

and the stability properties for the system in (u, v) lead to stability properties for the system in x^*. After the last transformation, the system becomes

$$\frac{du}{dt} = a(t)v + U(t, u, v), \qquad \frac{dv}{dt} = b(t)v + V(t, u, v),$$

where U and V are bounded as functions of t for $t \geqslant 0$ and have developments in series according to the powers of u and v beginning with terms of a degree $\geqslant 2$. This system admits the family of solutions $u = h$, $v = 0$, which requires that $U(t, u, 0) \equiv 0$, $V(t, u, 0) \equiv 0$. From this it follows that for $|u| \leqslant u_0$, $|v| \leqslant v_0$ we have $|U(t, u, v)| < \alpha |v|$, $|V(t, u, v)| \leqslant \beta |v|$, where α and β may be arbitrarily small, if u_0 and v_0 are sufficiently small.

On the other hand, from

$$b(t) = \mathrm{Tr}\,(A) - \frac{d}{dt} \ln (\psi_1^2 + \psi_2^2),$$

we have

$$\int_{t_0}^{t} b(s)ds = \int_{t_0}^{t} (\mathrm{Tr}\, A)ds - \ln \frac{\psi_1^2(t) + \psi_2^2(t)}{\psi_1^2(t) + \psi_2^2(t)} .$$

The general solution of the equation $dw/dt = b(t)w$ is

$$\begin{aligned} w(t) &\doteq w(t_0) \exp \left[\int_{t_0}^{t} b(s)ds\right] \\ &= w(t_0) \exp \left[\int_{t_0}^{t} \mathrm{Tr}\, A\, ds\right] \exp \left[-\ln \frac{\psi_1^2(t) + \psi_2^2(t)}{\psi_1^2(t_0) + \psi_2^2(t_0)}\right] \\ &= w(t_0) \frac{\psi_1^2(t_0) + \psi_2^2(t_0)}{\psi_1(t) + \psi_2(t)} \exp \left[\int_{t_0}^{t} \mathrm{Tr}\, A\, ds\right] . \end{aligned}$$

According to the hypotheses of the statement, $|w(t)| \leqslant |w(t_0)| (|\varphi_h'(t_0, 0)|^2/\gamma^2)\, e^{-\gamma(t-t_0)} e^{\chi(t)}$, which shows that the trivial solution of the equation in w is uniformly asymptotically stable. We can apply Proposition 3. Hence the trivial solution of the system in (u, v) is uniformly asymptotically stable, which entails the uniform stability of the trivial solution for the system in x^*, and hence for the system in x, which establishes the uniform stability of solution $\varphi(t)$. Moreover, for $u(t_0)$, $v(t_0)$ sufficiently small, we have $u(t) \to h$, $v(t) \to 0$; hence $x_1^*(t) - (h + h^2\alpha_2(t) + \cdots) \to 0$, $x_2^*(t) - (h^2\beta_2(t) + \cdots) \to 0$. Thus the solutions $x(t)$ tend to one of the solutions $\varphi(t, h) - \varphi(t)$; hence for every solution $y(t)$ from the neighborhood of $\varphi(t)$, there exists an h such that

$$\lim_{t\to\infty} (y(t) - \varphi(t, h)) = 0.$$

1.8. Total Stability

In what follows we shall state a series of theorems which point out the fact that if a solution is uniformly asymptotically stable it also has certain stability properties with respect to different classes of permanent perturbations. As previously, we shall only be concerned with the case of stability of the trivial solution, since by the preceding we already know that the study of the stability of any solution is reduced to this case.

Definition. *The trivial solution of system* (1) *is said to be stable with respect to permanent perturbations (totally stable) if for every* $\epsilon > 0$ *there exists* $\delta_1(\epsilon)$ *and* $\delta_2(\epsilon)$ *with the properties that for any function* $R(t, x)$ *with* $|R(t, x)| < \delta_2$ *for* $|x| \leqslant \epsilon$, $t \geqslant 0$ *and for any* $|y_0|$ *with* $|y_0| < \delta_1$, *the solution* $y(t; t_0, y_0)$ *of the system*

$$\frac{dy}{dt} = f(t, y) + R(t, y) \tag{8}$$

verifies the inequality $|y(t; t_0, y_0)| < \epsilon$ *for* $t \geqslant t_0$.

Theorem 1.8. *If the trivial solution of system* (1) *is uniformly asymptotically stable, then it is also stable with respect to permanent perturbations.*

It is supposed that f fulfills the condition $|f(t, x_1) - f(t, x_2)| \leqslant L(t)|x_1 - x_2|$ for $|x_1| \leqslant \alpha_0$, $|x_2| \leqslant \alpha_0$ and that $|\int_t^{t+u} L(s)\, ds| < k|u|$.

Proof. According to Theorem 1.6′, it follows from the uniform asymptotic stability of system (1) that there exists a function $V(t, x)$ with the properties

$$a(|x|) \leqslant V(t, x) \leqslant b(|x|),$$

$$\limsup_{h\to 0+} \frac{V[t + h, x(t + h; t_0, x_0)] - V[t, x(t; t_0, x_0)]}{h} \leqslant -c(|x(t; t_0, x_0)|),$$

$$|V(t, x_1) - V(t, x_2)| \leqslant M|x_1 - x_2| \qquad [\text{for } |x_1| \leqslant \delta(\delta_0), |x_2| \leqslant \delta(\delta_0)],$$

where $\delta(\epsilon)$ and δ_0 appear in the definition of uniform asymptotic stability. Let y_0 satisfy $|y_0| < \frac{1}{2}\alpha_0$; consider the solution $y(v; t, y_0)$ of system (8). From

$$y(v; t, y_0) = y_0 + \int_t^v \{f(u, y(u; t, y_0)) + R(u, y(u; t, y_0))\}du$$

we obtain

$$|y(v; t, y_0)| \leqslant |y_0| + \int_t^v L(u)\,|y(u; t, y_0)|\,du + h\eta,$$

where $\eta = \sup_{t\geqslant 0, |y|\leqslant\alpha_0} |R(t, y)|$. The inequality holds for all $t \leqslant v \leqslant t + h$ such that $|y(u, t, y_0)| \leqslant \alpha_0$. Thus

$$|y(v; t, y_0)| \leqslant (|y_0| + h\eta)e^{kh}.$$

Hence for h sufficiently small, we will have, in any case, $|y(u; t, y_0)| \leqslant \alpha_0$, and the inequality holds for every $t \leqslant v \leqslant t + h$ with h sufficiently small.

Further, let $x(v; t, y_0)$ be the solution of system (1). We have

$$y(v; t, y_0) - x(v; t, y_0) = \int_t^v \{f(u, y(u; t, y_0)) - f(u, x(u; t, y_0))\}du + \int_t^v R(u, y(u; t, y_0))du.$$

Let $\epsilon > 0$, $l < \min\{a(\epsilon), a(\frac{1}{2}\alpha_0)\}$, $\delta_1(\epsilon) = b^{-1}(l)$, $\delta_2(\epsilon) = c[b^{-1}(l)]/M$. We choose $|y_0| < \delta_1$ (we shall have, in any case, $|y_0| < \frac{1}{2}\alpha_0$).

If $R(t, x)$ is such that $|R(t, x)| < \delta_2$ for $|x| \leqslant \epsilon$, $t \geqslant t_0$, we shall have $\eta_1 = \sup_{t\leqslant 0, |y|\leqslant\epsilon} |R(t, y)| < \delta_2$. As above, it is clear that if $|y_0| < \delta_1$, then for h sufficiently small we shall have $|y(u; t, y_0)| < \epsilon$ for $t \leqslant u \leqslant t + h$.

Therefore we may write the estimate

$$|y(v; t, y_0) - x(v; t, y_0)| \leqslant h\eta_1 + \int_t^v L(u)\,|y(u; t, y_0) - x(u; t, y_0)|\,du,$$

from which follows

$$|y(v; t, y_0) - x(v; t, y_0)| \leqslant h\eta_1 e^{kh},$$

in any case for h sufficiently small. On the other hand, we have

$$\limsup_{h\to 0+} \frac{V[t+h, y(t+h; t, y)] - V(t, y)}{h} \leqslant \limsup_{h\to 0+} \frac{V[t+h, x(t+h; t, y)] - V(t, y)}{h} + \limsup_{h\to 0+} \frac{V[t+h, y(t+h; t, y)] - V[t+h, x(t+h; t, y)]}{h}.$$

But

$$|V[t+h, y(t+h; t, y)] - V[t+h, x(t+h; t, y)]|$$
$$< M|y(t+h; t, y) - x(t+h; t, y)|$$

if

$$|x(t+h; t, y)| < \delta(\delta_0), \qquad |y(t+h; t, y)| < \delta(\delta_0).$$

If

$$|y| < \min\{\tfrac{1}{2}\delta(\delta_0), \tfrac{1}{2}\alpha_0, \epsilon\}$$

we see, as above, that for h sufficiently small, we have the estimate

$$|y(t+h; t, y) - x(t+h; t, y)| < h\eta_1 e^{kh}.$$

Hence

$$|V[t+h, y(t+h; t, y)] - V[t+h, x(t+h; t, y)]| < Mh\eta_1 e^{kh}.$$

From this we obtain

$$\limsup_{h\to 0+} \frac{V[t+h, y(t+h; t, y)] - V[t+h, x(t+h; t, y)]}{h} \leqslant M\eta_1$$

We deduce then that

$$\limsup_{h\to 0+} \frac{V[t+h, y(t+h; t, y)] - V(t, y)}{h} \leqslant -c(|y|) + M\eta_1$$
$$< -c(|y|) + M\delta_2 = -c(|y|) + c[b^{-1}(l)]$$

if $|y| < \epsilon$ with ϵ sufficiently small.

We may now prove that $|y(t; t_0, y_0)| < \epsilon$ for $t \geqslant t_0$. If the property does not hold, there exists a $t_1 > t_0$ such that $|y(t_1; t_0, y_0)| \geqslant \epsilon$; then there exists $t_0 < t_2 \leqslant t_1$ such that $|y(t_2; t_0, y_0)| = \epsilon$ and $|y(t; t_0, y_0)| < \epsilon$ for $t_0 \leqslant t < t_2$. Let $V^*(t) = V[t, y(t; t_0, y_0)]$. We have

$$V^*(t_2) = V[t_2, y(t_2; t_0, y_0)] \geqslant a(|y(t_2; t_0, y_0)|) = a(\epsilon) > l,$$

$$V^*(t_0) = V(t_0, y_0) \leqslant b(|y_0|) < b(\delta_1) = b[b^{-1}(l)] = l.$$

Thus there exists a t_3 satisfying $t_0 < t_3 < t_2$ such that $V^*(t_3) = l$, $V^*(t) > l$ for $t_3 < t \leqslant t_2$. We have

$$a(|y(t_3; t_0, y_0)|) \leqslant V[t_3, y(t_3; t_0, y_0)] = V^*(t_3) = l \leqslant b(|y(t_3; t_0, y_0)|).$$

Therefore,

$$b^{-1}(l) \leqslant |\, y(t_3; t_0, y_0)| \leqslant a^{-1}(l) < \epsilon.$$

Hence we may write

$$\limsup_{h\to 0+} \frac{V[t_3 + h, y(t_3 + h; t_3, y(t_3; t_0, y_0))] - V[t_3, y(t_3; t_0, y_0)]}{h}$$

$$= \limsup_{h\to 0+} \frac{V^*(t_3 + h) - V^*(t_3)}{h} < -c(|\, y(t_3; t_0, y_0)|) + c[b^{-1}(l)]$$

$$< -c[b^{-1}(l)] + c[b^{-1}(l)] = 0.$$

Therefore, $V^*(t) < V^*(t_3) = l$ for $t > t_3$, which is contradictory. The theorem is thus completely proved.

We shall now give some applications of this theorem.

Applications. 1. Let us suppose that system (1) contains a certain number of parameters; we shall denote by α a point in the parameter space.

System (1) is written

$$\frac{dx}{dt} = f(t, x; \alpha).$$

The manifold of points for which the trivial solution is uniformly asymptotically stable forms in the space of the parameters the domain of stability of the system; let G be this domain. We consider a point α_0 on the boundary of G; *the point is said to be a security point of the boundary of the domain of stability if for every* $\epsilon > 0$ *there exists* $\delta_1(\epsilon) > 0$ *and* $\delta_2(\epsilon) > 0$ *with the property that if* $|\, x_0\,| < \delta_1(\epsilon)$ *and* $\rho(\alpha, \alpha_0) < \delta_2(\epsilon)$, *then* $|\, x(t; t_0, x_0; \alpha)| < \epsilon$ *for* $t \geqslant t_0$. We have denoted here by $\rho(\alpha, \alpha_0)$ the distance between α and α_0 in the space of the parameters.

The significance of this definition is the following. If α_0 is a point of the boundary of the domain of stability, there are some points outside this domain arbitrarily close. At these points the trivial solution, ceases to be stable. The fact that α_0 is a security point of the boundary means that if α is close enough to α_0, even if it is outside the domain of stability, the solution $x(t; t_0, x_0, \alpha)$ continues to remain close to the trivial solution; hence certain stability properties are maintained, which are sufficient for practical requirements. It follows from this that the security points of the boundary of the domain of stability have the property that we can get as close as possible to them without assuming the risk that small errors or perturbations provoke the loss of stability. An immediate consequence of Theorem 1.8 is the following:

If the trivial solution of the system

$$\frac{dx}{dt} = f(t; x, \alpha_0)$$

is uniformly asymptotically stable, the point α_0 *is a security point of the boundary of the domain of stability.*

Indeed, the system

$$\frac{dx}{dt} = f(t, x; \alpha)$$

may be written

$$\frac{dx}{dt} = f(t, x; \alpha_0) + \{f(t, x; \alpha) - f(t, x; \alpha_0)\}.$$

Upon putting

$$R(t, x) = f(t, x; \alpha) - f(t, x; \alpha_0),$$

it follows that if we suppose that f is continuous with respect to α, uniformly with respect to (t, x), then for given $\delta_3(\epsilon) > 0$ there exists a $\delta_2(\epsilon) > 0$ such that $\rho(\alpha_1, \alpha_0) < \delta_2$, $|x| \leqslant \epsilon$ implies $|R(t, x)| < \delta_3(\epsilon)$. Since the trivial solution of the system $dx/dt = f(t, x; \alpha_0)$ is uniformly asymptotically stable, it is stable with respect to permanent perturbations; hence there exists $\delta_1(\epsilon)$ and $\delta_3(\epsilon)$ such that $|x_0| < \delta_1(\epsilon)$, and $|R(t, x)| < \delta_3(\epsilon)$ for $|x| < \epsilon$ implies $|x(t; t_0, x_0)| < \epsilon$ for $t \geqslant t_0$. But $\rho(\alpha, \alpha_0) < \delta_2(\epsilon)$ implies $|R(t, x)| < \delta_3(\epsilon)$. Hence, if $|x_0| < \delta_1(\epsilon)$ and $\rho(\alpha, \alpha_0) < \delta_2(\epsilon)$ it will follow that $|x(t; t, x_0; \alpha)| < \epsilon$ for $t \geqslant t_0$, which shows that α_0 is a security point of the boundary.

Let us remark that those results stated above point out the importance of the study of the stability of the boundary points of the domain of stability. This study is usually much more difficult than for the interior points of the domain of stability.

2. *Consider the system*

$$\frac{dx}{dt} = X(t, x, y), \qquad \frac{dy}{dt} = Y(t, x, y), \tag{9}$$

where x *and* y *are vectors. Suppose that* $X(t, 0, 0) = 0$, $Y(t, 0, 0) = 0$ *and that the trivial solution of system* (9) *is stable with respect to components* x; *this means that there exists a* $\delta_1(\epsilon)$ *such that* $|x_0| + |y_0| < \delta_1$ *implies* $|x(t; t_0, x_0, y_0)| < \epsilon$ *for* $t \geqslant t_0$.

Suppose in addition that the trivial solution of the auxiliary system

$$\frac{dz}{dt} = Y(t, 0, z)$$

is uniformly asymptotically stable. Under this condition, the trivial solution of system (9) *is uniformly stable.*

Proof. The system

$$\frac{dy}{dt} = Y(t, x, y)$$

may be written

$$\frac{dy}{dt} = Y(t, 0, y) + \{Y(t, x, y) - Y(t, 0, y)\}.$$

By hypothesis, the trivial solution of the auxiliary system is uniformly asymptotically stable, and thus, by virtue of Theorem 1.8, is stable with respect to permanent perturbations. It follows that there exist $\delta_2(\epsilon)$ and $\delta_3(\epsilon)$ such that, from $|y_0| < \delta_2$ and $|Y(t, x, y) - Y(t, 0, y)| < \delta_3(\epsilon)$ for $|y| < \epsilon$, follows $|y(t; t_0, x_0, y_0)| < \epsilon$ for $t \geqslant t_0$. Since Y is supposed continuous in x, there exists $\delta_4(\epsilon)$ such that $|x| < \delta_4$ implies $|Y(t, x, y) - Y(t, 0, y)| < \delta_3(\epsilon)$ for $t \geqslant 0$, $|y| < \epsilon$. On the other hand, if $|x_0| + |y_0| < \delta_1[\delta_4(\epsilon)]$, then $|x(t; t_0, x_0, y_0)| < \delta_4(\epsilon)$.

Let $\delta(\epsilon) = \min\{\delta_1(\epsilon), \delta_1[\delta_4(\epsilon)]\}$. Then $|x_0| + |y_0| < \delta(\epsilon)$ implies on the one hand,

$$|x(t; t_0\ x_0, y_0)| < \delta_4(\epsilon) < \epsilon$$

and, on the other,

$$|Y(t, x(t; t_0, x_0\ y_0), y) - Y(t, 0, y)| < \delta_3(\epsilon) \qquad \text{for} \quad |y| < \epsilon;$$

hence

$$|y(t; t_0, x_0, y_0)| < \epsilon \qquad \text{for} \quad t \geqslant t_0 .$$

The proposition is proved.

An example of the application of this proposition has been given by T. Hacker in a study of aircraft stability. In the case when system (9) represents the system of the perturbed motion for a plane, a part of the components may be controlled by the pilot. Considering that these are the components denoted by x and that system (9) also contains in it the pilot's action, the pilot's control will be expressed by the fact that the trivial solution of system (9) is stable with respect to components x. Admitting, of course, that the pilot's action is zero when components x are zero (namely, admitting that the pilot does not act when perturbations do not occur), it follows that the auxiliary system does not depend on the pilot's action but only on the constructive parameters of the plane. By choosing these parameters in such a way that the trivial solution of the auxiliary system be uniformly asymptotically stable, the action of the pilot on the controllable components will be sufficient to assure the stability of the plane's motion.

Let us suppose now that the trivial solution of system (9) *is uniformly asymptotically stable with respect to components x and that the trivial solution of the auxiliary system is also uniformly asymptotically stable. Then the trivial solution of system* (9) *is uniformly asymptotically stable.*

Proof. Since the trivial solution of system (9) is uniformly asymptotically stable with respect to components x, there exist δ_0 and $T(\epsilon)$ such that $|x_0| + |y_0| < \delta_0$ and $t \geqslant t_0 + T(\epsilon)$ implies $|x(t; t_0, x_0, y_0)| < \epsilon$. Let $R(t, y) = Y(t, x(t; t_0, x_0, y_0), y) - Y(t, 0, y)$.

Let $\alpha(\epsilon) < \delta(\epsilon)$, with the property that $|x| < \alpha(\epsilon)$, $|y| < \epsilon(\delta_0)$ implies $|Y(t, x, y) - Y(t, 0, y)| < \gamma(\epsilon)/2M$, where M is the Lipschitz constant of the Lyapunov function constructed for the auxiliary system, and $\gamma(\epsilon) = c[\delta(\epsilon)]$. Let $T_0(\epsilon)$ such that $t \geqslant t_0 + T_0(\epsilon)$ implies $|x(t; t_0, x_0, y_0)| < \alpha(\epsilon)$. Let $b_0 = b(\delta_0)$ and c_1 such that

$$\limsup_{h\to 0+} \frac{V[t+h, y(t+h; t_0, x_0, y_0)] - V[t, y(t; t_0, x_0, y_0)]}{h} \leqslant c_1$$

for $t_0 \leqslant t \leqslant t_0 + T$ and $|x_0| + |y_0| < \delta_0$. The existence of c_1 follows from the fact that, as in the theorem of stability with respect to permanent perturbations, we have

$$\limsup_{h\to 0+} \frac{V[t+h, y(t+h; t_0, x_0, y_0)] - V[t, y(t; t_0, x_0, y_0)]}{h} \leqslant -c(|y(t; t_0, x_0, y_0)|) + M\eta,$$

where $\eta > |R(t, y)|$. But $|x_0| + |y_0| < \delta_0$ implies

$$|y(t; t_0, x_0, y_0)| < \epsilon(\delta_0), \qquad |x(t; t_0, x_0, y_0)| < \epsilon(\delta_0)$$

which shows that η will depend only on δ_0 and not on t_0; hence we may take $c_1 = M\eta$.

Let $T_1(\epsilon) = 2(b_0 + c_1 T_0)/\gamma(\epsilon)$ and $T(\epsilon) = T_0(\epsilon) + T_1(\epsilon)$. In $[t_0 + T_0, t_0 + T]$ there exists a t' such that $|y(t'; t_0, x_0, y_0)| < \delta(\epsilon)$. If t' did not exist, then we would have in the whole interval

$$|y(t; t_0, x_0, y_0)| \geqslant \delta(\epsilon),$$

whence

$$-c(|y(t; t_0, x_0, y_0)|) < -c(\delta(\epsilon)) = -\gamma(\epsilon).$$

It follows that

$$\limsup_{h\to 0+} \frac{V[t+h, y(t+h; t_0, x_0, y_0)] - V[t, y(t; t_0, x_0 \ y_0)]}{h} \leqslant -\gamma(\epsilon) + M\frac{\gamma(\epsilon)}{2M} = -\frac{\gamma(\epsilon)}{2}$$

since for $t \geqslant t_0 + T_0$ we have $|x(t; t_0, x_0, y_0)| < \alpha(\epsilon)$ and $|R(t, y)| < \gamma(\epsilon)/2M$. Upon setting

$$V^*(t) = V[t, y(t; t_0, x_0, y_0)]$$

we will obtain

$$V^*(t_0 + T) - V^*(t_0) = V^*(t_0 + T) - V^*(t_0 + T_0) + V^*(t_0 + T_0) - V^*(t_0) < -\frac{\gamma}{2} T_1 + c_1 T_0,$$

whence

$$V^*(t_0 + T) \leqslant b(\delta_0) - \frac{\gamma}{2} T_1 + c_1 T_0 = 0,$$

which is contradictory. It follows that there exists a $t' \in [t_0 + T_0, t_0 + T]$ such that $|y(t'; t_0, x_0, y_0)| < \delta(\epsilon)$ and $|y(t; t_0, x_0, y_0)| < \epsilon$ for $t \geqslant t_0 + T(\epsilon)$. With this the proof is achieved.

A variant of the notion of stability with respect to permanent perturbations is obtained if instead of requiring that the permanent perturbations be small all along, we only require that they be small in the mean. Taking into consideration larger classes of permanent perturbations, we obtain a stronger property of stability.

Definition. *The trivial solution of system* (1) *is said to be stable under permanent perturbations bounded in the mean if for all* $\epsilon > 0$ *and* $T > 0$

there exist $\delta > 0$ *and* $\eta > 0$ *such that whichever be function* $R(t, y)$ *with* $|R(t, y)| \leqslant \varphi(t)$ *for* $|y| \leqslant \epsilon$ *and* $\int_t^{t+T} \varphi(s)\, ds < \eta$ *and whichever be* y_0 *with* $|y_0| < \delta$ *we will have* $|y(t; t_0, y_0)| < \epsilon$ *for* $t \geqslant t_0$, *where* $y(t; t_0, y_0)$ *is the solution of system* (8).

Theorem 1.8′. *If the trivial solution of system* (1) *is uniformly asymptotically stable, then it is stable under permanent perturbations bounded in the mean. The same conditions as in Theorem* 1.8 *are supposed to be fulfilled.*

Proof. Let $V(t, x)$ be as in the proof of Theorem 1.8. Consider a solution $y(t; t_0, y_0)$ of system (8), $\tau \in [t_0, t]$, and a solution

$$x(t; \tau, y(\tau; t_0, y_0))$$

of system (1). We will have

$$V[\tau + h, y(\tau + h; t_0, y_0)] - V[\tau + h, x(\tau + h; \tau, y(\tau; t_0, y_0))]$$
$$\leqslant M|y(\tau + h; t_0, y_0) - x(\tau + h; \tau, y(\tau; t_0, y_0))|,$$

if $|y(\tau; t_0, y_0)|$ is sufficiently small.

We may write

$$y(\tau + h; t_0, y_0) - x(\tau + h; \tau, y(\tau; t_0, y_0))$$
$$= y(\tau + h; t_0, y_0) - y(\tau; t_0, y_0) - [x(\tau + h; \tau, y(\tau; t_0, y_0)) - y(\tau; t_0, y_0)]$$
$$= \int_\tau^{\tau+h} \dot{y}(t; t_0, y_0)dt - \int_\tau^{\tau+h} f[t, x(t; \tau, y(\tau; t_0, y_0))]dt.$$

Then

$$|V[\tau + h, y(\tau + h; t_0, y_0)] - V[\tau + h, x(\tau + h; \tau, y(\tau; t_0, y_0))]|$$
$$\leqslant M \int_\tau^{\tau+h} |\dot{y}(t; t_0, y_0) - f[t, x(t; \tau, y(\tau; t_0, y_0))]|\, dt.$$

From here we obtain

$$\limsup_{h \to 0+} \frac{V[\tau + h, y(\tau + h; t_0, y_0)] - V[\tau + h, x(\tau + h; \tau, y(\tau; t_0, y_0))]}{h}$$
$$\leqslant M|\dot{y}(\tau; t_0, y_0) - f[\tau, y(\tau; t_0, y_0)]| \leqslant M\varphi(\tau),$$

if $|y(\tau; t_0, y_0)| < \epsilon$. We deduce further that

$$\limsup_{h\to 0+} \frac{V[\tau+h, y(\tau+h; t_0, y_0)] - V[\tau, y(\tau; t_0, y_0)]}{h}$$

$$\leqslant \limsup_{h\to 0+} \frac{V[\tau+h, y(\tau+h; t_0, y_0)] - V[\tau+h, x(\tau+h; \tau, y(\tau; t_0, y_0))]}{h}$$

$$+ \limsup_{h\to 0+} \frac{V[\tau+h, x(\tau+h; \tau, y(\tau; t_0, y_0))] - V[\tau, y(\tau; t_0, y_0)]}{h}$$

$$\leqslant M\,\varphi(\tau) - c(|\,y(\tau; t_0, y_0)\,|)\,.$$

By integrating from t_0 to t we obtain

$$V[t, y(t; t_0, y_0)] - V(t_0, y_0) \leqslant M \int_{t_0}^{t} \varphi(\tau)d\tau - \int_{t_0}^{t} c(|\,y(\tau; t_0, y_0)|)d\tau. \quad (*)$$

Now let $\epsilon > 0$, $T > 0$. We choose $\delta < b^{-1}(\frac{1}{2}a(\epsilon))$ and

$$\eta < \min\left\{\frac{T}{M}\, c[b^{-1}(\tfrac{1}{2}a(\epsilon))], \frac{1}{2M}\, a(\epsilon)\right\}.$$

Let $|\,y_0\,| < \delta$, $\int_{t_0}^{t_0+T} \varphi(s)\, ds < \eta$. We show that $|\,y(t;\, t_0,\, y_0)| < \epsilon$ for $t \geqslant t_0$.

Suppose that it were not so; then there exists $t_1 > t_0$ such that $|\,y(t_1; t_0, y_0)| \geqslant \epsilon$. It follows that there exists $t_0 < t_2 \leqslant t_1$ such that $|\,y(t_2; t_0, y_0)| = \epsilon$ and $|\,y(t; t_0, y_0)| < \epsilon$ for $t_0 \leqslant t < t_2$.

We have

$$a(\epsilon) = a(|\,y(t_2; t_0, y_0)|) \leqslant V[t_2, y(t_2; t_0, y_0)] = V^*(t_2),$$

$$V^*(t_0) = V(t_0, y_0) \leqslant b(|\,y_0\,|) < \tfrac{1}{2}a(\epsilon).$$

Then there exists $t_0 < t_3 < t_2$ such that $V^*(t_3) = \frac{1}{2}a(\epsilon)$ and $V^*(t) > \frac{1}{2}a(\epsilon)$ for $t_3 < t \leqslant t_2$. Therefore, for $t_3 < t \leqslant t_2$, we shall have

$$\tfrac{1}{2}a(\epsilon) < V^*(t) = V[t, y(t; t_0, y_0)] \leqslant b(|\,y(t; t_0, y_0)|),$$

whence

$$|\,y(t; t_0, y_0)| > b^{-1}[\tfrac{1}{2}a(\epsilon)]$$

and

$$c(|\,y(t; t_0, y_0)|) > c[b^{-1}(\tfrac{1}{2}a(\epsilon)].$$

From $t \leqslant t_2$ will follow $|y(t; t_0, y_0)| \leqslant \epsilon$; hence we can apply formula (*) and deduce that

$$V[t_2, y(t_2; t_0, y_0)] \leqslant V[t_3, y(t_3; t_0, y_0)] + M \int_{t_3}^{t_2} \varphi(\tau)d\tau$$

$$- \int_{t_3}^{t_2} c(|y(\tau; t_0, y_0)|)d\tau \leqslant \tfrac{1}{2}a(\epsilon) + M \int_{t_3}^{t_2} \varphi(\tau)d\tau - (t_2 - t_3)c[b^{-1}(\tfrac{1}{2}a(\epsilon))].$$

Let $(m - 1)T \leqslant t_2 - t_3 < mT$; then

$$\int_{t_3}^{t_2} \varphi(\tau)d\tau < \int_{t_3}^{t_3+mT} \varphi(\tau)d\tau < m\eta.$$

Since $m \leqslant (1/T)(t_2 - t_3) + 1$, we have

$$\int_{t_3}^{t_2} \varphi(\tau)d\tau < \frac{\eta}{T}(t_2 - t_3) + \eta < \frac{1}{M} c[b^{-1}(\tfrac{1}{2}a(\epsilon))](t_2 - t_3) + \eta.$$

Thus

$$V[t_2, y(t_2; t_0, y_0)] \leqslant \tfrac{1}{2}a(\epsilon) + M\eta + (t_2 - t_3)\{c[b^{-1}(\tfrac{1}{2}a(\epsilon))] - c[b^{-1}(\tfrac{1}{2}a(\epsilon))]\},$$

whence

$$V[t_2, y(t_2; t_0, y_0)] \leqslant \tfrac{1}{2}a(\epsilon) + M\eta.$$

Since $\eta < (1/2M)a(\epsilon)$, we have finally, $V[t_2, y(t_2; t_0, y_0)] < a(\epsilon)$. It follows that

$$a(|y(t_2; t_0, y_0)|) \leqslant V[t_2, y(t_2; t_0, y_0)] < a(\epsilon);$$

hence $|y(t_2; t_0, y_0)| < \epsilon$, which contradicts the definition of t_2. The theorem is proved.

A slightly different variant of the same type of stability, equally based on the idea of considering perturbations which can be great in certain moments but are small in the mean, has been defined by Ivo Vrkoč. It is called *integral stability*.

Definition. *We will say that the trivial solution of system* (1) *is integrally stable if there exists* $\delta_0 > 0$ *and a function* $B(\delta) > 0$ *defined for* $0 < \delta < \delta_0$ *(which we will suppose monotone and continuous) with* $\lim_{\delta \to 0} B(\delta) = 0$ *such that* $|y_0| < \delta$ *and* $\int_{t_0}^{\infty} \sup_{|y|<B(\delta)} |R(t, y)| \, dt < \delta$ *implies* $|y(t; t_0, y_0)| < B(\delta)$ *for* $t \geqslant t_0$, $y(t; t_0, y_0)$ *being a solution of system* (8).

It is easy to see that this definition is equivalent to the following. *The trivial solution of system* (1) *is integrally stable if for every* $\epsilon > 0$ *there exists* $\delta_1 > 0$ *and* $\delta_2 > 0$ *such that* $|y_0| < \delta_1$ *and*

$$\int_{t_0}^{\infty} \sup_{|y| \leqslant \epsilon} |R(t, y)| \, dt < \delta_2$$

implies $|y(t; t_0, y_0)| < \epsilon$ *for* $t \geqslant t_0$; if we take $\delta = \min(\delta_1, \delta_2)$ and $B(\delta)$ as the inverse of the function $\delta(\epsilon)$, we fall upon the first definition, and the first definition implies the second one with $\delta_1 = \delta_2$.

The trivial solution of system (1) *is said to be asymptotically integrally stable if it is integrally stable and in addition there exist functions* $T(\delta, \epsilon)$ *and* $\gamma(\delta, \epsilon)$ *such that* $|y_0| < \delta$, $\int_{t_0}^{\infty} \sup_{|y| < B(\delta)} |R(t, y)| \, dt < \gamma(\delta, \epsilon)$ *and* $t \geqslant t_0 + T(\delta, \epsilon)$ *imply* $|y(t; t_0, y_0)| < \epsilon$.

In what follows we shall point out a series of conditions equivalent, respectively, to integral stability and asymptotic integral stability.

1. *The trivial solution of system* (1) *is integrally stable if and only if there exists* $\delta_0 > 0$ *and* $B(\delta)$ *defined on* $(0, \delta_0)$, $B(\delta) > 0$, $\lim_{\delta \to 0} B(\delta) = 0$, *such that whichever be the function* $\varphi(t)$ *continuous, with* $\int_{t_0}^{\infty} \varphi(t) \, dt < \delta$, *the solution* $y(t; t_0, y_0)$ *of the system*

$$\frac{dy}{dt} = f(t, y) + \varphi(t) \tag{10}$$

with $|y_0| < \delta$ *verifies the inequality* $|y(t; t_0, y_0)| < B(\delta)$ *for* $t \geqslant t_0$.

Proof. It suffices to prove that if the property from the statement occurs, the trivial solution of the system is integrally stable. Let $R(t, y)$ be such that

$$\int_{t_0}^{\infty} \sup_{|y| \leqslant B(\delta)} |R(t, y)| \, dt < \delta,$$

where $B(\delta)$ is chosen according to the property from the statement. Consider a point y_0 with $|y_0| < \delta$ and the solution $y(t; t_0, y_0)$ of system (8). If we would not have for all $t \geqslant t_0$ the inequality $|y(t; t_0, y_0)| < B(\delta)$, there would exist a first point $t_1 > t_0$ such that $|y(t_1; t_0, y_0)| = B(\delta)$. For $t \in [t_0, t_1]$ take $\varphi(t) = R(t, y(t; t_0, y_0))$; we have

$$\int_{t_0}^{t_1} |\varphi(t)| \, dt = \int_{t_0}^{t_1} |R(t, y(t; t_0, y_0))| \, dt \leqslant \int_{t_0}^{t_1} \sup_{|y| \leqslant B(\delta)} |R(t, y)| \, dt < \delta.$$

We extend $\varphi(t)$ continuously on the whole semiaxis $t \geqslant t_0$ such that $\int_{t_0}^{\infty} \varphi(t)\, dt < \delta$; for this it is sufficient to take $t_2 > t_1$ such that

$$t_2 - t_1 < \frac{2(\delta - \int_{t_0}^{t_1} |\varphi(t)|\, dt)}{|\varphi(t_1)| + 1},$$

to put $\varphi(t_2) = 0$ and to take $\varphi(t)$ linear on $[t_1, t_2]$ and zero for $t \geqslant t_2$.

Now let $z(t; t_0, y_0)$ be the solution of system (10) with $\varphi(t)$ chosen as above. From $|y_0| < \delta$ and $\int_{t_0}^{\infty} |\varphi(t)|\, dt < \delta$ will follow $|z(t; t_0, y_0)| < B(\delta)$ for $t \geqslant t_0$; hence $|z(t_1; t_0, y_0)| < B(\delta)$. But on $[t_0, t_1]$ we have $z(t; t_0, y_0) \equiv y(t; t_0, y_0)$; hence $|y(t_1; t_0, y_0)| < B(\delta)$, which is contradictory.

2. *The trivial solution of system* (1) *is asymptotic integrally stable if and only if it is integrally stable and in addition there exist* $T(\delta, \epsilon) > 0$ *and* $\gamma(\delta, \epsilon) > 0$ *defined on* $(0, \delta_0)$, $\epsilon > 0$ *such that whichever be* $\varphi(t)$ *continuous with* $\int_{t_0}^{\infty} |\varphi(t)|\, dt < \gamma(\delta, \epsilon)$, $|y_0| < \delta$, *and* $t \geqslant t_0 + T(\delta, \epsilon)$, *we will have* $|y(t; t_0, y_0)| < \epsilon$, $y(t; t_0, y_0)$ *being the solution of system* (10).

Proof. It suffices again to show that the statement implies integral asymptotic stability. If it were not so, there would exist $\delta' < \delta_0$ and $\epsilon' > 0$ such that whatever $T > 0$ and $\gamma > 0$ are, there exist y_0 with $|y_0| < \delta'$, $R(t, y)$ with $\int_{t_0}^{\infty} \sup_{|y| \leqslant B(\delta)} |R(t, y)|\, dt < \gamma$ and $t_1 > t_0 + T$, such that $|y(t_1; t_0, y_0)| \geqslant \epsilon'$, where $y(t; t_0, y_0)$ is the solution of system (8). Let $T(\delta', \epsilon')$, $\gamma(\delta', \epsilon')$ defined according to the property from the statement, y_0, $R(t, y)$, and t_1 corresponding on the base of the reductio ad absurdum hypothesis. Let $\varphi(t) = R(t, y(t; t_0, y_0))$ for $t \in [t_0, t_1]$; we have

$$\int_{t_0}^{t_1} |\varphi(t)|\, dt = \int_{t_0}^{t_1} |R(t, y(t; t_0, y_0))|\, dt \leqslant \int_{t_0}^{t_1} \sup_{|y| \leqslant B(\delta)} |R(t, y)|\, dt$$

$$\leqslant \int_{t_0}^{\infty} \sup_{|y| \leqslant B(\delta)} |R(t, y)|\, dt < \gamma(\delta', \epsilon').$$

As in the preceding case, we extend $\varphi(t)$ continuously on the whole axis maintaining this inequality, and take the solution $z(t; t_0, y_0)$ of system (10) with $\varphi(t)$ thus chosen. From $\int_{t_0}^{\infty} |\varphi(t)|\, dt < \gamma(\delta', \epsilon')$, $|y_0| < \delta'$, and $t_1 > t_0 + T(\delta', \epsilon')$ we obtain $|z(t_1; t_0, y_0)| < \epsilon'$. But on $[t_0, t_1]$ we have $z(t; t_0, y_0) \equiv y(t; t_0, y_0)$; hence $|y(t_1; t_0, y_0)| < \epsilon'$, which is a contradiction.

3. *The trivial solution of system* (1) *is integrally stable if and only if for every* $0 < \delta < \delta_0$ *there exist* $B(\delta) > 0$, $\lim_{\delta \to 0} B(\delta) = 0$ (*monotone and*

continuous), such that whichever be $y(t)$ *with continuous derivative on* $[t_0, t_1]$ *with* $|y(t_0)| < \delta$, $\int_{t_0}^{t_1} |\dot{y}(t) - f(t, y(t))|\, dt < \delta$, *it will follow that* $|y(t)| < B(\delta)$ *for* $t \in [t_0, t_1]$.

Proof. Let us suppose that the trivial solution is integrally stable let $B(\delta)$ be defined according to the property of integral stability and let $y(t)$ be as in the statement. Let $\varphi(t)$ be continuous for $t \geqslant t_0$ such that $\varphi(t) = \dot{y}(t) - f(t, y(t))$ on $[t_0, t_1]$, $\int_{t_0}^{\infty} |\varphi(t)|\, dt < \delta$; such a function is defined as above.

We consider system (10) with $\varphi(t)$ so chosen and the solution $z(t; t_0, y(t_0))$. According to the statement in point 1, we will have $|z(t; t_0, y(t_0))| < B(\delta)$ for $t \geqslant t_0$. Since on $[t_0, t_1]$ we have

$$z(t; t_0, y(t_0)) \equiv y(t),$$

it will follow that $|y(t)| < B(\delta)$ on $[t_0, t_1]$.

Now let $B(\delta)$ be as in the statement and $\varphi(t)$ be continuous for $t \geqslant t_0$ with $\int_{t_0}^{\infty} |\varphi(t)|\, dt < \delta$. The solution $y(t; t_0, y_0)$ with $|y_0| < \delta$ of system (10) verifies for every t_1 the condition of the statement; hence for every $t_1 > t_0$ we have $|y(t; t_0, y_0)| < B(\delta)$ on $[t_0, t_1]$. Hence the condition from point 1 is fulfilled and the trivial solution of system (1) is integrally stable.

Property 3 shows that the notion of integral stability defined by Ivo Vrkoč is equivalent to the notion of strong stability defined by Okamura and recently studied by Kyuzo Hayashi.

4. *The trivial solution of system* (1) *is asymptotic integrally stable if and only if it is integrally stable and in addition for every* $0 < \delta < \delta_0$, $\epsilon > 0$ *there exist* $T(\delta, \epsilon) > 0$, $\gamma(\delta, \epsilon) > 0$ *with the property that for every* $y(t)$ *with continuous derivative on* $[t_0, t_1]$, $t_1 > t_0 + T$ *and such that* $|y(t_0)| < \delta$, $\int_{t_2}^{t_1} |\dot{y}(t) - f(t, y(t))|\, dt < \gamma(\delta, \epsilon)$ *it will follow that* $|y(t)| < \epsilon$ *on* $[t_0 + T, t_1]$.

Proof. Suppose the trivial solution of system (1) is asymptotic integrally stable, and let $T(\delta, \epsilon)$, $\gamma(\delta, \epsilon)$ be as in point 2, $y(t)$ as in the statement. We define for $t \geqslant t_0$ the function $\varphi(t)$, putting $\varphi(t) = \dot{y}(t) - f(t, y(t))$ for $t_0 \leqslant t \leqslant t_1$ and requiring that $\int_{t_0}^{\infty} |\varphi(t)|\, dt < \gamma(\delta, \epsilon)$.

Consider the solution $z(t; t_0, y(t_0))$ of system (10). It will follow that $|z(t; t_0, y(t_0))| < \epsilon$ for $t \geqslant t_0 + T$. Since on $[t_0, t_1]$ we have $z(t; t_0, y(t_0)) \equiv y(t)$, we will have $|y(t)| < \epsilon$ on $[t_0 + T, t_1]$.

Conversely, let $T(\delta, \epsilon)$ and $\gamma(\delta, \epsilon)$ be as in the statement and let $\varphi(t)$ be continuous with $\int_{t_0}^{\infty} |\varphi(t)|\, dt < \gamma(\delta, \epsilon)$; then the solution $y(t; t_0, y_0)$ of system (10) with $|y_0| < \delta$ verifies for every $t_1 > t_0$ the condition from the statement; hence $|y(t; t_0, y_0)| < \epsilon$ for $t \geqslant t_0 + T$.

Lemma. *If $V(t, x)$ has the properties*

1. *$V(t, x)$ is continuous,*
2. $|V(t, x_1) - V(t, x_2)| \leqslant M|x_1 - x_2|$ *for* $|x_1| \leqslant \delta_0$,
3. $\limsup_{h\to 0+} \dfrac{V[t+h, x(t+h; t_0, x_0)] - V[t, x(t; t_0, x_0)]}{h} \leqslant \phi[x(t; t_0, x_0)]$,

where $x(t; t_0, x_0)$ is the solution of system (1) and ϕ is continuous, then

$$V(t, y(t)) \leqslant V(t_0, y(t_0)) + M\int_{t_0}^{t} |\dot{y}(t) - f(t, y(t))|\, dt + \int_{t_0}^{t} \phi(y(t))dt$$

for every function with continuous derivative on $[t_0, t]$.

Proof. Let $\tau \in [t_0, t]$; consider the solution $x(t; \tau, y(\tau))$ of system (1). We have

$$\begin{aligned}
&|V[\tau+h, y(\tau+h)] - V[\tau+h, x(\tau+h; \tau, y(\tau))]| \\
&\quad \leqslant M|y(\tau+h) - x(\tau+h; \tau, y(\tau))| \\
&\quad = M\left| y(\tau+h) - y(\tau) - \int_{\tau}^{\tau+h} f[t, x(t; \tau, y(\tau))]dt \right| \\
&\quad = Mh\left| \frac{1}{h}\int_{\tau}^{\tau+h} \dot{y}(t)dt - \frac{1}{h}\int_{\tau}^{\tau+h} f[t, x(t; \tau, y(\tau))]dt \right|;
\end{aligned}$$

hence

$$\limsup_{h\to 0+} \frac{V[\tau+h, y(\tau+h)] - V[\tau+h, x(\tau+h; \tau, y(\tau))]}{h} \leqslant M|\dot{y}(\tau) - f(\tau, y(\tau))|.$$

Thus

$$\begin{aligned}
&\limsup_{h\to 0+} \frac{V[\tau+h, y(\tau+h)] - V[\tau, y(\tau)]}{h} \\
&\quad \leqslant \limsup_{h\to 0+} \frac{V[\tau+h, y(\tau+h)] - V[\tau+h, x(\tau+h; \tau, y(\tau))]}{h} \\
&\qquad + \limsup_{h\to 0+} \frac{V[\tau+h, x(\tau+h; \tau, y(\tau))] - V[\tau, y(\tau)]}{h} \\
&\quad \leqslant M|\dot{y}(\tau) - f[\tau, y(\tau)]| + \phi[y(\tau)].
\end{aligned}$$

Integrating, we obtain the inequality of the statement.

Lemma. *If there exists a continuous function $V(t, x)$ defined for $t \geqslant 0$, $|x| \leqslant \delta_0$ with the properties*

1. $V(t, x) \geqslant a(|x|)$, $V(t, 0) \equiv 0$,
2. $V(t, x_1) - V(t, x_2)| \leqslant M|x_1 - x_2|$,
3. $$\limsup_{h\to 0+} \frac{V[t+h, x(t+h; t_0, x_0)] - V[t, x(t; t_0, x_0)]}{h} \leqslant g(t)V[t, x(t; t_0, x_0)],$$

with $\int_0^\infty g(t)\,dt < \infty$, $g(t) \geqslant 0$, where $x(t; t_0, x_0)$ is a solution of system (1), *then the trivial solution of system* (1) *is integrally stable.*

Proof. We have, as in the preceding lemma,

$$\limsup_{h\to 0+} \frac{V[\tau+h, y(\tau+h)] - V[\tau, y(\tau)]}{h} \leqslant M|\dot{y}(\tau) - f[\tau, y(\tau)]| + g(\tau)V[\tau, y(\tau)].$$

From here we obtain, by integration,

$$V[t, y(t)] \leqslant V[t_0, y(t_0)] \exp\left[\int_{t_0}^t g(t)dt\right] + M \exp\left[\int_{t_0}^t g(t)dt\right] \int_{t_0}^t \exp\left[-\int_{t_0}^\tau g(u)du\right] |\dot{y}(\tau) - f[\tau, y(\tau)]|\, d\tau.$$

If

$$|y(t_0)| < \delta, \qquad \int_{t_0}^\infty g(t)dt = k, \qquad \int_{t_0}^\infty |\dot{y}(\tau) - f[\tau, y(\tau)]|\, d\tau < \delta,$$

then

$$a(|y(t)|) \leqslant V[t, y(t)] < Me^k\delta + Me^k\delta = 2Me^k\delta;$$

hence

$$|y(t)| \leqslant a^{-1}(2Me^k\delta) = B(\delta).$$

The integral stability follows on the basis of property 3.

Lemma. *If there exists $V(t, x)$ defined for $t \geqslant 0$, $|x| \leqslant \delta_0$ with the properties*

(a) $V(t, x) \geqslant a(|x|)$, $V(t, 0) \equiv 0$,

(b) $|V(t, x_1) - V(t, x_2)| < M|x_1 - x_2|$,

(c) $$\limsup_{h\to 0+} \frac{V[t+h, x(t+h; t_0, x_0)] - V[t, x(t; t_0, x_0)]}{h} \leqslant -c(|x(t; t_0, x_0)|),$$

then the trivial solution of system (1) *is asymptotic integrally stable.*

Proof. On the basis of the preceding lemma, the trivial solution of system (1) is integrally stable. For $\epsilon > 0$ we choose $\gamma_1 > 0$ such that if $|y(t_2)| < \gamma_1$ and $\int_{t_2}^{t_3} |\dot{y}(t) - f[t, y(t)]| \, dt < \gamma_1$, we will have $|y(t)| < \epsilon$ for $t_2 \leqslant t \leqslant t_3$; such a γ_1 exists on the basis of property 3, namely, $\gamma_1 = B^{-1}(\epsilon)$. We then take $\gamma = \min(\delta, \gamma_1)$, $l = c(\gamma_1)$, $T(\delta, \epsilon) = M(\delta + \gamma)/l$. Let $y(t)$ be a function with a continuous derivative on $[t_0, t_1]$, $t_1 > t_0 + T(\delta, \epsilon)$, $|y(t_0)| < \delta$, $\int_{t_0}^{t_1} |\dot{y}(t) - f[t, y(t)]| \, dt < \gamma$. If we would have $|y(t)| \geqslant \gamma$ on $[t_0, t_0 + T]$, then

$$V[t_0 + T, y(t_0 + T)] \leqslant V[t_0, y(t_0)] + M \int_{t_0}^{t_0+T} |\dot{y}(t) - f[t, y(t)]| \, dt$$

$$- \int_{t_0}^{t_0+T} c(|y(t)|) dt \leqslant M\delta + M\gamma - Tl = 0,$$

which is a contradiction.

We deduce that there exists $\tau \in [t_0, t_0 + T]$ such that $|y(\tau)| < \gamma \leqslant \gamma_1$. Since

$$\int_{\tau}^{t_1} |\dot{y}(t) - f(t, y(t))| \, dt \leqslant \int_{t_0}^{t_1} |\dot{y}(t) - f(t, y(t))| \, dt < \gamma \leqslant \gamma_1,$$

it follows, according to the choice of γ_1, that $|y(t)| < \epsilon$ for $\tau \leqslant t \leqslant t_1$, hence, in any case, on $[t_0 + T, t_1]$. According to property 4 the asymptotic integral stability follows immediately.

This lemma immediately yields

Theorem 1.8″. *If the trivial solution of system* (1) *is uniformly asymptotically stable it is also asymptotic integrally stable.*

We have seen in this paragraph that uniform asymptotic stability implies stability under permanent perturbations, stability under permanent perturbations bounded in the mean, integral asymptotic stability. In the final part of this section we shall show that it is also conserved in the case of some permanent perturbations which approach zero when $t \to \infty$. For this purpose a lemma will be necessary, interesting in itself, which presents a weakening of the conditions from Theorem 1.5.

Lemma. *Suppose that there exists a function $V(t, x)$ with the properties*

(a) $a(t, |x|) \leqslant V(t, x) \leqslant b(|x|)$,

(b) $\limsup_{h \to 0+} \dfrac{V[t+h, x(t+h; t, x)] - V[t, x]}{h} \leqslant -c(t, |x|)$,

where $b(r)$ is continuous, monotone-increasing, $b(0) = 0$, and $a(t, r)$, $c(t, r)$ are continuous and such that for every pair $0 < \alpha \leqslant \beta < H$ there exists $\theta(\alpha, \beta) \geqslant 0$, $k(\alpha, \beta) > 0$ such that $a(t, r) > k(\alpha, \beta)$, $c(t, r) > k(\alpha, \beta)$ for $\alpha \leqslant r \leqslant \beta$, $t \geqslant \theta(\alpha, \beta)$. Then the trivial solution of system (1) *is uniformly asymptotically stable.*

Proof. Let $\epsilon > 0$, $\theta_1 = \theta(\epsilon, \epsilon)$, $k_1 = k(\epsilon, \epsilon)$. We have $a(t, \epsilon) > k_1$ for $t \geqslant \theta_1$. Let $\eta_1(\epsilon) \leqslant b^{-1}[k(\epsilon, \epsilon)]$. We will have $V(t, x) \geqslant a(t, |x|) > k_1$ if $|x| = \epsilon$, $t \geqslant \theta_1$ and $V(t, x) \leqslant b(|x|) \leqslant k_1$ if $|x| < \eta_1(\epsilon)$.

Let $\theta_2 = \theta[\eta_1(\epsilon), \epsilon]$. Then for $t \geqslant \theta_2$, $\eta_1 \leqslant r \leqslant \epsilon$ we will have $c(t, r) > 0$.

Now let $\theta = \max(\theta_1, \theta_2)$ and $\eta(\epsilon)$, chosen so that $|x_0| < \eta$ and $0 \leqslant t_0 \leqslant \theta$ implies $|x(t; t_0, x_0)| < \eta_1$ for $t_0 \leqslant t \leqslant \theta$. The choice of $\eta(\epsilon)$ is possible on the basis of Lemma I.7, according to which we have

$$|x(t; t_0, x_0)| \leqslant |x_0| \exp\left[\int_{t_0}^{t} L(u)du\right] \leqslant |x_0| e^{K\theta}.$$

The condition $|x_0| < \eta_1(\epsilon)e^{-K\theta(\epsilon)}$ implies $|x(t; t_0, x_0)| < \eta_1$ for $t_0 \leqslant t \leqslant \theta$; hence we may take $\eta(\epsilon) = \eta_1(\epsilon)e^{-K\theta(\epsilon)}$. If $|x_0| < \eta(\epsilon)$ we will have in particular $|x(\theta; t_0, x_0)| < \eta_1$ for $0 \leqslant t_0 < \theta$.

If there exists $t > \theta$ such that $|x(t; t_0, x_0)| \geqslant \epsilon$, there exists $t_1 > \theta$ such that $|x(t_1; t_0, x_0)| = \epsilon$ and $|x(t; t_0, x_0)| < \epsilon$ for $\theta \leqslant t < t_1$. Since $t_1 > \theta \geqslant \theta_1$ and $|x(t_1; t_0, x_0)| = \epsilon$, it follows that

$$V[t_1, x(t_1; t_0, x_0)] > k_1;$$

on the other hand,

$$V[\theta, x(\theta; t_0, x_0)] < k_1.$$

It follows that there will exist $\theta < t_2 < t_1$ such that

$$V[t_2, x(t_2; t_0, x_0)] = k_1$$

and $V[t, x(t; t_0, x_0)] \geqslant k_1$, for $t_2 \leqslant t \leqslant t_1$. Hence $|x(t_2; t_0, x_0)| \geqslant \eta_1$. From $\eta_1 \leqslant |x(t_2; t_0, x_0)| \leqslant \epsilon$ and $t \geqslant \theta > \theta_2$ it follows that

$$c(t_2, |x(t_2; t_0, x_0)|) > 0;$$

hence

$$\limsup_{h\to 0+} \frac{V[t_2+h, x(t_2+h; t_0, x_0)] - V[t_2, x(t_2; t_0, x_0)]}{h} < -c[t_2, |x(t_2; t_0, x_0)|] < 0.$$

From

$$V[t_2, x(t_2, t_0, x_0)] = k_1, V[t, x(t; t_0, x_0)] \geqslant k_1 \quad \text{for} \quad t_2 \leqslant t$$

we deduce

$$\limsup_{h\to 0+} \frac{V[t_2+h, x(t_2+h; t_0, x_0)] - V[t_2, x(t_2; t_0, x_0)]}{h} \geqslant 0.$$

We have obtained a contradiction; hence $|x(t; t_0, x_0)| < \epsilon$ for all $t \geqslant \theta$ if $|x_0| < \eta(\epsilon)$. Since for $t_0 \leqslant t \leqslant \theta$ we have $|x(t; t_0, x_0)| < \eta_1(\epsilon) < \epsilon$, it follows that $|x_0| < \eta(\epsilon)$ implies $|x(t; t_0, x_0)| < \epsilon$ for all $t \geqslant t_0$.

For $t_0 > \theta$ and $|x_0| < \eta < \eta_1$ we will have $V(t_0, x_0) < k_1$. If there exists $t > t_0$ such that $|x(t; t_0, x_0)| \geqslant \epsilon$, then there exists $t_1 > t_0 > \theta$ such that $|x(t_1; t_0, x_0)| = \epsilon$ and $|x(t; t_0, x_0) < \epsilon$ for $t_0 \leqslant t < t_1$.

From $t_1 > \theta$ follows $V[t_1, x(t_1; t_0, x_0)] > k_1$. The proof continues as above and in this case we will also have $|x(t; t_0, x_0)| < \epsilon$ for $t \geqslant t_0$.

Finally, for any t_0, if $|x_0| < \eta(\epsilon)$ we will have $|x(t; t_0, x_0)| < \epsilon$ for $t \geqslant t_0$.

Now let $h > 0$, $\eta(h)$ be as above, $0 < \delta < \eta(h)$, $\eta(\delta)$ as above. We choose $\theta_1 = \theta(\eta, h)$, $k_1 = k(\eta, h)$, $C_1 = b(h)$, $C_2 = \inf c(t, r)$ for $0 \leqslant t \leqslant \theta_1$, $\eta \leqslant r \leqslant h$, $T_1 = (C_1 + \theta_1 | C_2 |)/k_1$, $T(\delta) = \theta_1 + T_1$. We prove that if $|x_0| < \eta(h)$, there exists a $t' \in [t_0, t_0 + T]$ such that $|x(t'; t_0, x_0)| < \eta$. If this were not so, we would have

$$\eta \leqslant |x(t; t_0, x_0)| \leqslant h$$

[since we have chosen x_0 with $|x_0| < \eta(h)$]; hence $c(t, |x(t; t_0, x_0)| \geqslant C_2$ for $t_0 \leqslant t \leqslant \theta_1$ and $c(t, |x(t; t_0, x_0)|) \geqslant k_1$ for $\theta_1 \leqslant t \leqslant t_0 + T$. Let $V^*(t) = V[t, x(t; t_0, x_0)]$. We have

$$\begin{aligned} V^*(t_0+T) - V^*(t_0) &= V^*(t_0+T) - V^*(\theta_1) + V^*(\theta_1) - V^*(t_0) \\ &\leqslant -k_1 T + \theta_1 | C_2 |; \end{aligned}$$

hence

$$\begin{aligned} V^*(t_0+T) &\leqslant V^*(t_0) - k_1 T_1 + \theta_1 | C_2 | \\ &\leqslant b(h) - k_1 T_1 + \theta_1 | C_2 | = C_1 - k_1 T_1 + \theta_1 | C_2 | = 0, \end{aligned}$$

which contradicts the fact that

$$V^*(t_0 + T) \geqslant a(t_0 + T, | x(t_0 + T; t_0, x_0)|) > k_1 > 0.$$

We deduce that there exists a $t' \in [t_0, t_0 + T]$ such that

$$| x(t'; t_0, x_0)| < \eta;$$

hence $| x(t; t', x(t'; t_0, x_0))| < \delta$ for $t \geqslant t'$. Hence, in any case,

$$| x(t; t_0, x_0)| < \delta \qquad \text{if} \quad | x_0 | < \eta(h), t \geqslant t_0 + T(\delta).$$

With this the uniform asymptotic stability of the trivial solution of the system is proved.

Theorem 1.8‴. *If the trivial solution of system* (1) *is uniformly asymptotically stable, if* $R(t, 0) \equiv 0$, $\lim_{t\to\infty} R(t, x) = 0$ *uniformly with respect to x for* $| x | \leqslant \alpha_0$, *and if R is Lipschitzian, then the trivial solution of system* (8) *is uniformly asymptotically stable.*

Proof. Consider the same function $V(t, x)$ as in Theorem 1.8. By hypothesis $| R(t, x)| < \phi(t)$, where $\phi(t) \to 0$ when $t \to \infty$, and is monotone-decreasing. The same computations as in Theorem 1.8 lead to

$$\limsup_{h\to 0+} \frac{V[t + h, y(t + h; t, y)] - V[t, y]}{h} \leqslant -c(| y |) + M\phi(t).$$

Let $c(t, r) = c(r) - M\phi(t)$. Let $0 < \alpha \leqslant \beta < h$, $k(\alpha, \beta) = \frac{1}{2}c(\alpha)$. From $\lim_{t\to\infty} \phi(t) = 0$ it follows that there exists $\theta(\alpha, \beta) \geqslant 0$ such that for $t \geqslant \theta$ we will have $\phi(t) < (1/2M)c(\alpha)$. Thus if $\alpha \leqslant r \leqslant \beta$, $t \geqslant \theta(\alpha, \beta)$, we have

$$c(t, r) > c(\alpha) - \tfrac{1}{2} c(\alpha) = k(\alpha, \beta).$$

The conditions of the lemma are verified and thus Theorem 1.8‴ is proved.

1.9. Linear Systems with Periodic Coefficients

We shall now study some stability problems for linear systems. We shall begin with linear systems which have periodic coefficients.

A basic theorem in the theory of linear systems with periodic coefficients is the following:

Theorem 1.9. *Given the system*

$$\frac{dx}{dt} = A(t)x, \qquad A(t+\omega) = A(t),$$

there exists a matrix $P(t)$, periodic of period ω and nonsingular, such that the change of variables $x = P(t)y$ transforms the system in a linear system with constant coefficients.

Proof. As for any periodic system, together with $x(t)$, $x(t+\omega)$ is also a solution. For linear systems, we have

$$\begin{aligned} x(t+\omega; s, x_0) &= x(t; t_0, x(t_0+\omega; s, x_0)) \\ &= C(t; t_0)x(t_0+\omega; s, x_0) = C(t; t_0)C(t_0+\omega; s)x_0 . \end{aligned}$$

Since

$$x(t+\omega; s, x_0) = C(t+\omega; s)x_0$$

we have

$$C(t+\omega; s) = C(t; t_0)C(t_0+\omega; s).$$

Taking $s = t_0 + \omega$ we obtain

$$C(t+\omega; t_0+\omega) = C(t; t_0).$$

Taking $t_0 = 0$, $s = 0$ we obtain

$$C(t+\omega; 0) = C(t; 0)C(\omega; 0).$$

Setting $C(t; 0) = U(t)$ this relation becomes

$$U(t+\omega) = U(t)U(\omega).$$

The matrix $U(\omega)$ plays an essential role in the theory of linear systems with periodic coefficients; it is called the *monodromy* matrix of the system. The matrix $U(\omega)$ is nonsingular, since for every t and t_0 the matrix $C(t; t_0)$ has an inverse. Thus we deduce that we can find a matrix B such that $U(\omega) = e^{B\omega}$† We define

$$P(t) = U(t)e^{-Bt};$$

† Indeed, for any nonsingular matrix A we may find a matrix B such that $e^B = A$. To prove this let us first suppose that A has the normal Jordan form:

$$A = \begin{pmatrix} J_1 & & \\ & \ddots & \\ & & J_s \end{pmatrix}, \qquad J_k = \lambda_k\left(E_k + \frac{1}{\lambda_k} Z_k\right), \qquad \lambda_k \neq 0$$

$P(t)$ is differentiable and nonsingular together with $U(t)$ and e^{-Bt}. Let us show that $P(t)$ is periodic.

---

because A is nonsingular and

$$Z_k = \begin{pmatrix} 0 & 1 & & 0 \\ & \cdot & \cdot & \\ & & \cdot & 1 \\ 0 & & & 0 \end{pmatrix}, \qquad Z_k^{q_k} = 0.$$

The series

$$\sum_{i=1}^{\infty} (-1)^{k+1} \frac{Z_k^l/\lambda_k^l}{l}$$

has only a finite number of nonzero terms, hence converges. We put, by definition,

$$\ln\left(E_k + \frac{1}{\lambda_k} Z_k\right) = \sum_{l=1}^{\infty} (-1)^{l+1} \frac{(Z_k/\lambda_k)^l}{l}.$$

By formal calculation it is easily shown that

$$\exp\left[\ln\left(E_k + \frac{1}{\lambda_k} Z_k\right)\right] = E_k + \frac{1}{\lambda_k} Z_k\,;$$

for this we note that the same computations are performed as in the identity

$$1 + x = e^{\ln(1+x)} = 1 + \left(x - \frac{x^2}{2} + \cdots\right) + \frac{1}{2!}\left(x - \frac{x^2}{2} + \cdots\right)^2 + \cdots,$$

where this time the series $x - x^2/x + \cdots$ has a finite number of nonzero terms. Now let

$$B_k = (\ln \lambda_k)E_k + \ln\left(E_k + \frac{1}{\lambda_k} Z_k\right).$$

We have

$$e^{B_k} = \lambda_k\left(E_k + \frac{1}{\lambda_k} Z_k\right)$$

and if we take

$$B = \begin{pmatrix} B_1 & & & \\ & \cdot & & \\ & & \cdot & \\ & & & B_s \end{pmatrix}$$

we will have

$$e^B = \begin{pmatrix} e^{B_1} & & & \\ & \cdot & & \\ & & \cdot & \\ & & & e^{B_s} \end{pmatrix} = \begin{pmatrix} J_1 & & & \\ & \cdot & & \\ & & \cdot & \\ & & & J_s \end{pmatrix} = A.$$

We have

$$\begin{aligned} P(t+\omega) &= U(t+\omega)e^{-B(t+\omega)} \\ &= U(t)U(\omega)e^{-B\omega}e^{-Bt} = U(t)e^{-Bt} = P(t).\ddagger \end{aligned}$$

Let us now perform the change of variables $x = P(t)y$. We have $x(t;\ x_0) = U(t)x_0 = P(t)e^{Bt}x_0 = P(t)y(t;\ x_0)$. Thus

$$y(t;\ x_0) = e^{Bt}x_0\,,$$

and hence

$$\frac{dy(t,\ x_0)}{dt} = Be^{Bt}x_0 = By(t;\ x_0).$$

Therefore $y(t;\ x_0)$ is the solution of the linear system with constant coefficients $dy/dt = By$. The theorem is proved.

Let us remark that from this theorem we deduce the structure of the solutions of systems with periodic coefficients. Indeed, we have

$$x(t;\ t_0\,,\ x_0) = P(t)y(t;\ t_0\,,\ x_0) = P(t)e^{B(t-t_0)}x_0\,.$$

From here we deduce that the whole behavior of the solutions of a linear system with periodic coefficients will depend upon the eigenvalues of matrix B. These eigenvalues are of the form $1/\omega \ln \rho_k$, where ρ_k are the

---

If A is now any nonsingular matrix, there exists T such that $T^{-1}AT = \tilde{A}$, where $\tilde{A}$ is Jordanian; on the basis of what is stated above, there exists a matrix $\tilde{B}$ such that $e^{\tilde{B}} = \tilde{A}$. Then

$$\begin{aligned} Te^{\tilde{B}}T^{-1} &= T\left(E + \frac{1}{1!}\tilde{B} + \frac{1}{2!}\tilde{B}^2 + \cdots + \frac{1}{n!}\tilde{B}^n + \cdots\right)T^{-1} \\ &= E + \frac{1}{1!}(T\tilde{B}T^{-1}) + \frac{1}{2!}(T\tilde{B}T^{-1})^2 + \cdots + \frac{1}{n!}(T\tilde{B}T^{-1})^n + \cdots \\ &= e^{T\tilde{B}T^{-1}} = A. \end{aligned}$$

Hence, by taking $B = T\tilde{B}T^{-1}$, we will have $e^B = A$.

‡ We have used the relation

$$e^{-B(t+\omega)} = e^{-B\omega}e^{-Bt}.$$

This relation follows immediately from the multiplication of the corresponding series, as in the scalar case. We note that the relation

$$e^A \cdot e^B = e^{A+B}$$

is, in general, not valid; however, it is valid if matrices A and B are permutable, i.e., if $AB = BA$.

eigenvalues of the monodromy matrix $U(\omega)$.‡ We may thus state the following theorem:

Theorem 1.10. *If the eigenvalues of the monodromy matrix lie in the circle $|z| \leqslant 1$ and the eigenvalues situated on $|z| = 1$ correspond to unidimensional Jordan cells, then the trivial solution of the system is uniformly stable. If the eigenvalues of the monodromy matrix are in $|z| < 1$, the trivial solution of the system is uniformly asymptotically stable.*

Proof. If $|\rho_k| \leqslant 1$, then $\mathrm{Re}(1/\omega)\ln\rho_k \leqslant 0$; if $|\rho_k| = 1$, then $\mathrm{Re}\,(1/\omega)\ln\rho_k = 0$; hence the eigenvalues of matrix B have negative or zero real parts, and those with zero real parts correspond to unidimensional Jordan cells. Taking into account the structure of the solutions of linear systems with constant coefficients, it will follow that $|e^{B(t-t_0)}| \leqslant M$ for $t \geqslant t_0$. But then

$$|C(t;t_0)| \leqslant |P(t)|\,|e^{B(t-t_0)}|$$

will be uniformly bounded, since $P(t)$, being periodic and continuous, is certainly bounded. If $|\rho_k| < 1$, the eigenvalues of matrix B have negative real parts; hence

$$|e^{B(t-t_0)}| < ke^{-\alpha(t-t_0)}$$

from which follows an analogous evaluation for $|C(t;t_0)|$.

Let us remark that if there exists an eigenvalue of the monodromy matrix situated in $|z| > 1$, then the trivial solution of the system is certainly unstable.

We shall give a proof of Theorem 1.10 which does not make use of Theorem 1.9. From the relation

$$U(t+\omega) = U(t)U(\omega)$$

we obtain

$$U(t+k\omega) = U(t)[U(\omega)]^k.$$

‡ In general, if B is constructed as in the preceding note, it is clear that matrix $\tilde{B}_k$ has the eigenvalues equal to $\ln\lambda_k$, since $\ln(E_k + (1/\lambda_k)Z_k)$ has all the terms situated above the main diagonal. Since

$$\tilde{B} = \begin{pmatrix} \tilde{B}_1 & & & \\ & \cdot & & \\ & & \cdot & \\ & & & \tilde{B}_s \end{pmatrix}$$

it follows that the eigenvalues of $\tilde{B}$ are $\ln\lambda_1, \ldots, \ln\lambda_s$. Since $B = T\tilde{B}T^{-1}$, the eigenvalues of B will likewise be $\ln\lambda_1, \ldots, \ln\lambda_s$.

Since for any $t \geqslant 0$ there exists a natural number m such that $(m - 1)\omega \leqslant t < m$, then

$$U(t) = U(t')[U(\omega)]^{m-1},$$

where $0 \leqslant t' < \omega$. Since U is continuous, we will have

$$|U(t)| \leqslant M|(U(\omega))^{m-1}|;$$

hence the boundedness properties of matrix $U(t)$ will depend upon the behavior of the sequence $[U(\omega)]^k$. If for every $k \geqslant 0$ this sequence is bounded, then $U(t)$ is bounded for $y \geqslant 0$, and stability occurs. If

$$|[U(\omega)]^k| < q^k \qquad (\text{with } q < 1)$$

we will have

$$\lim_{k\to\infty} [U(\omega)]^k = 0;$$

hence

$$\lim_{t\to\infty} U(t) = 0,$$

and asymptotic stability occurs. If T is the matrix which transform $U(\omega)$ to the normal Jordan form, we have

$$T^{-1}U(\omega)T = \tilde{U}, \qquad U(\omega) = T\tilde{U}T^{-1}, \qquad [U(\omega)]^k = T\tilde{U}^kT^{-1}.$$

Thus we deduce that the boundedness properties of sequence $[U(\omega)]^k$ are identical with those of sequence $\tilde{U}^k$. But

$$\tilde{U} = \begin{pmatrix} J_1 & & \\ & \ddots & \\ & & J_s \end{pmatrix},$$

and hence

$$\tilde{U}^k = \begin{pmatrix} J_1^k & & \\ & \ddots & \\ & & J_s^k \end{pmatrix}.$$

Thus the boundedness properties of the sequence U^k will depend on those of sequences J_l^k. The J_l^k have the numbers ρ_l^k along the main diagonal and smaller powers of ρ_l above the diagonal. From this follows that in order for $[U(\omega)]^k$ to be bounded it is necessary that sequences $\{\rho_l^k\}$ be bounded, which means that for the eigenvalues ρ_l we have $|\rho_l| \leqslant 1$. If $|\rho_l| = 1$ and the corresponding Jordan cell is not unidimensional, in the matrix J_l^k will appear terms of the form $k\rho_l^{k-1}$, which become arbitrarily large when $k \to \infty$. Hence the matrix J_l^k is not bounded. It follows that it is necessary and sufficient, in order that $[U(\omega)]^k$ form a bounded sequence, that the eigenvalues ρ_l be in $|z| \leqslant 1$ and those for which $|\rho_l| = 1$ correspond to unidimensional Jordan cells. If $|\rho_l| < 1$, then $\lim_{k\to\infty} \rho_l^k = 0$, and it is obvious that $\lim_{k\to\infty} [U(\omega)]^k = 0$. The theorem is thus proved.

The eigenvalues ρ_l of the monodromy matrix are called the *multipliers of the system.* The name is justified by the following property.

Proposition. *In order that there exists a solution of the system for which $x(t + \omega) = \rho x(t)$, it is necessary and sufficient that ρ be an eigenvalue of matrix $U(\omega)$.*

Proof. Any solution $x(t)$ may be written in the form

$$x(t) = U(t)x(0).$$

The condition

$$x(t + \omega) = \rho x(t)$$

is therefore

$$U(t + \omega)x(0) = \rho U(t)x(0).$$

But

$$U(t + \omega) = U(t)U(\omega)$$

and hence

$$U(t)U(\omega)x(0) = \rho U(t)x(0).$$

Since $U(t)$ is nonsingular, the condition becomes

$$U(\omega)x(0) = \rho x(0)$$

and we see that ρ must be an eigenvalue of matrix $U(\omega)$.

With the help of Theorem 1.10 we may obtain effective conditions of stability for linear systems with periodic coefficients. Here is the simplest condition of this kind:

Theorem 1.11. *Let C be a constant matrix whose eigenvalues have negative real parts, $A(t)$ a periodic matrix of period ω. If $\int_0^\omega |A(t) - C| \, dt$ is sufficiently small, the trivial solution of the system*

$$\frac{dx}{dt} = A(t)x$$

is asymptotically stable.

Proof. If $x(t; x_0)$ is the solution of the system which for $t = 0$ coincides with x_0, we may write

$$\frac{d}{dt} x(t; x_0) = Cx(t; x_0) + [A(t) - C]x(t; x_0).$$

According to the variation-of-constants formula, we have

$$x(t; x_0) = e^{Ct}x_0 + \int_0^t e^{C(t-s)}[A(s) - C]x(s; x_0)ds.$$

This relation may also be written

$$U(t)x_0 = e^{Ct}x_0 + \int_0^t e^{C(t-s)}[A(s) - C]U(s)x_0 ds,$$

or we may write

$$U(t) = e^{Ct} + \int_0^t e^{C(t-s)}[A(s) - C]U(s)ds.$$

In conformity with the hypotheses we have

$$| e^{Ct} | \leqslant Ke^{-\alpha t};$$

hence

$$| U(t)| \leqslant Ke^{-\alpha t} + \int_0^t Ke^{-\alpha(t-s)}| A(s) - C | | U(s)| ds.$$

Setting

$$v(t) = e^{\alpha t}| U(t)|,$$

we obtain

$$v(t) \leqslant K + K \int_0^t | A(s) - C | v(s)ds,$$

and thus

$$v(t) \leqslant K \exp \left[K \int_0^t | A(s) - C | ds\right].$$

In particular,

$$v(n_0\omega) \leqslant K \exp \left[K \int_0^{n_0\omega} | A(s) - C | ds\right],$$

whence

$$| U(n_0\omega)| < K \exp \left[-\alpha n_0\omega + K \int_0^{n_0\omega} | A(s) - C | ds\right].$$

If

$$\int_0^{n_0\omega} | A(s) - C | \, ds < \frac{\alpha n_0 \omega}{K} + \frac{1}{K} \ln \frac{q}{K} \qquad (q < 1)$$

we will have

$$| U(n_0\omega)| < q < 1.$$

But $n_0\omega$ is a period of the system, and by applying Theorem 1.10 the uniform asymptotic stability will follow.

We have, however, from the periodicity,

$$\int_0^{n_0\omega} | A(s) - C | \, ds = n_0 \int_0^{\omega} | A(s) - C | \, ds;$$

hence the condition of stability becomes

$$\int_0^{\omega} | A(s) - C | \, ds < \frac{\alpha\omega}{K} + \frac{1}{Kn_0} \ln \frac{q}{K} .$$

As n_0 may be chosen arbitrarily large, it follows that if

$$\int_0^{\omega} | A(s) - C | \, ds < \frac{\alpha\omega}{K}$$

the condition of stability is assured.

We shall now state a theorem which gives rise to certain deeper considerations.

Theorem 1.12. *If $B(t)$ is a periodic matrix such that the monodromy matrix of the system*

$$\frac{dx}{dt} = B(t)x$$

has distinct eigenvalues situated on the unit circle, and the periodic matrix $A(t)$ has the property that the characteristic equation of the monodromy matrix of the system

$$\frac{dx}{dt} = A(t)x$$

is reciprocal and, in addition, $\int_0^{\omega} | A(t) - B(t)| \, dt$ is sufficiently small, then the solutions of the system

$$\frac{dx}{dt} = A(t)x$$

are bounded on the whole axis.

Proof. Let $V(t)$ be the fundamental matrix of solutions of the system

$$\frac{dx}{dt} = B(t)x$$

and $U(t)$ that of the system

$$\frac{dx}{dt} = A(t)x, \qquad V(0) = U(0) = E.$$

We have

$$\frac{dU(t)}{dt} = A(t)U(t) = B(t)U(t) + [A(t) - B(t)]U(t).$$

According to the variation-of-constants formula, it follows that

$$U(t) = V(t) + \int_0^t V(t)V^{-1}(s)[A(s) - B(s)]U(s)ds.$$

The monodromy matrix $V(\omega)$ has by hypothesis distinct eigenvalues situated on the unit circle, and hence has a diagonal normal form, the elements along the diagonal having the modulus 1. Hereby it will follow that the sequences $V^n(\omega)$ and $V^{-n}(\omega)$ $(n = 1, 2, ...)$ are bounded; on the basis of the relation

$$V(t + \omega) = V(t)V(\omega)$$

we see that $V(t)$ and $V^{-1}(t)$ are bounded. Indeed, for t arbitrary, there exists an integer m such that $(m - 1)\omega \leqslant t < m\omega$; hence

$$t = t' + (m - 1)\omega,$$

where $0 \leqslant t' < \omega$; thus

$$V(t) = V(t')V[(m - 1)\omega] = V(t')V^{m-1}(\omega);$$

hence $V(t)$ is bounded on *the whole axis*.

Likewise, since $V^{-1}(t)$ is a matrix of solutions for the adjoint system, which is also a system with periodic coefficients, we will have

$$V^{-1}(t + \omega) = V^{-1}(t)V^{-1}(\omega),$$

and thus for every t

$$V^{-1}(t) = V^{-1}(t')V^{-(m-1)}(\omega),$$

which shows that $V^{-1}(t)$ is also bounded on the whole axis. We have

$$U(t) - V(t) = \int_0^t V(t)V^{-1}(s)[A(s) - B(s)][U(s) - V(s)]ds + \int_0^t V(t)V^{-1}(s)[A(s) - B(s)]V(s)ds.$$

We shall obtain for $0 \leqslant t \leqslant \omega$ the evaluation

$$|U(t) - V(t)| \leqslant M_1 \int_0^\omega |A(s) - B(s)|\, ds + M_2 \int_0^\omega |A(s) - B(s)|\,|U(s) - V(s)|\, ds.$$

From here we deduce

$$|U(\omega) - V(\omega)| \leqslant M_1 \int_0^\omega |A(s) - B(s)|\, ds \exp\left[M_2 \int_0^\omega |A(s) - B(s)|\, ds\right],$$

which proves that if $\int_0^\omega |A(s) - B(s)|\, ds$ is sufficiently small, then matrices $U(\omega)$ and $V(\omega)$ differ from one another, however slightly.

We consider the eigenvalues of the matrix $V(\omega)$; according to the hypothesis, they are distinct and situated on the unit circle. We encircle these eigenvalues with small-enough circles so that in every circle there be a single eigenvalue and the circles do not intersect. If $\int_0^\omega |A(s) - B(s)|\, ds$ is sufficiently small, the matrices $U(\omega)$ and $V(\omega)$ are close enough so that each circle of this kind will contain an eigenvalue and only one of matrix $U(\omega)$. By hypothesis the matrix $U(\omega)$ has its characteristic equation reciprocal; hence together with ρ_k, $1/\rho_k$ is also an eigenvalue. Since $U(\omega)$ is real, then $1/\bar{\rho}_k$ is also an eigenvalue. The values ρ_k and $1/\bar{\rho}_k$ are symmetric with respect to the unit circle, and if ρ_k is situated in a small circle with the center on the unit circle, then $1/\bar{\rho}_k$ is in the same circle. But in the above circles there is a single eigenvalue of matrix $U(\omega)$; hence ρ_k and $1/\bar{\rho}_k$ coincide.

Yet this means that $\rho_k\bar{\rho}_k = 1$; hence $|\rho_k| = 1$ and the eigenvalues of matrix $U(\omega)$ are situated on the unit circle. From the fact that the eigenvalues of matrix $V(\omega)$ are distinct, we deduce that those of matrix $U(\omega)$ are likewise distinct, and the theorem is proved.

We shall now set up some facts which will allow us to confer to the theorem proved a more effective character.

Very often in problems of mechanics we come across canonical systems of the form

$$\frac{dp_i}{dt} = \frac{\partial H}{\partial q_i}, \qquad \frac{dq_i}{dt} = -\frac{\partial H}{\partial p_i}.$$

When H is a quadratic form in the variables p_i, q_i with coefficient functions of t, the system will be linear. Setting $p_i = x_i$, $q_i = x_{n+i}$, $H = \frac{1}{2} \Sigma h_{ij}(t) x_i x_j$, the canonical linear system may be written

$$\frac{dx_i}{dt} = \sum_j h_{n+i,j}(t) x_j , \qquad \frac{dx_{n+i}}{dt} = - \sum_j h_{ij} x_j .$$

Denoting by H the matrix h_{ij} and by I the matrix

$$\begin{pmatrix} 0 & E_n \\ -E_n & 0 \end{pmatrix},$$

where E_n is the unity matrix of the nth order, we will have

$$IH = \begin{pmatrix} 0 \cdots 0 & 1 & 0 \cdots 0 \\ 0 \cdots 0 & 0 & 1 \cdots 0 \\ & \cdots & \\ 0 \cdots 0 & 0 & 0 \cdots 1 \\ -1 \cdots 0 & 0 & 0 \cdots 0 \\ & \cdots & \\ 0 \cdots -1 & 0 & 0 \cdots 0 \end{pmatrix} \begin{pmatrix} h_{11} & \cdots h_{1n} & h_{1,n+1} & h_{1,n+2} \cdots & h_{1,2n} \\ h_{21} & \cdots h_{2n} & h_{2,n+1} & h_{2,n+2} \cdots & h_{2,2n} \\ & & \cdots & & \\ h_{n+1,1} & \cdots h_{n+1,n} & h_{n+1,n+1} & \cdots & h_{n+1,2n} \\ & & \cdots & & \\ h_{2n,1} & \cdots h_{2n,n} & h_{2n,n+1} & \cdots & h_{2n,2n} \end{pmatrix}$$

$$= \begin{pmatrix} h_{n+1,1} & \cdots & h_{n+1,n} & h_{n+1,n+1} & \cdots & h_{n+1,2n} \\ & & & \cdots & & \\ -h_{11} & \cdots & -h_{1n} & -h_{1,n+1} & \cdots & -h_{1,2n} \\ & & & \cdots & & \end{pmatrix},$$

and we see that the system may be written in the form

$$\frac{dx}{dt} = IH(t)x.$$

Proposition. *If $U(t)$ is the fundamental matrix of solutions with $U(0) = E$ we have*

$$U^* I U = I.$$

Proof. We have

$$\frac{d}{dt}(U^* I U) = \frac{dU^*}{dt} IU + U^* I \frac{dU}{dt} .$$

From

$$\frac{dU}{dt} = IHU, \qquad \frac{dU^*}{dt} = U^* H^* I^*,$$

we have

$$\frac{d}{dt}(U^*IU) = U^*H^*I^*IU + U^*IIHU,$$

and from

$$I^* = -I, \qquad H^* = H,$$

we have

$$\frac{d}{dt}(U^*IU) = -U^*HIIU + U^*IIHU.$$

It is verified by direct computation that

$$I^2 = \begin{pmatrix} 0 & E_n \\ -E_n & 0 \end{pmatrix}\begin{pmatrix} 0 & E_n \\ -E_n & 0 \end{pmatrix} = \begin{pmatrix} -E_n & 0 \\ 0 & -E_n \end{pmatrix} = -E_{2n}.$$

Thus

$$\frac{d}{dt}(U^*IU) = U^*HU - U^*HU = 0.$$

Hence U^*IU is a constant matrix. For $t = 0$, this coincides with I; hence for all t we have

$$U^*IU = I.$$

The matrices with the property $A^*IA = 1$ are called *symplectic.* The proposition proved affirms that for a canonical system matrix $U(t)$ is symplectic for every t. If we suppose now that $H(t)$ is periodic of period ω, from the proposition proved it follows that *the monodromy matrix is symplectic.*

Proposition. *The characteristic equation of a symplectic matrix is reciprocal.*

Proof. From $A^*IA = I$ follows $I^{-1}A^*I = A^{-1}$; but A and A^* have the same eigenvalues and A^* and $I^{-1}A^*I$ have the same eigenvalues; hence A and $I^{-1}A^*I$ have the same eigenvalues; hence A and A^{-1} have the same eigenvalues. If ρ_k is an eigenvalue of matrix A, then $1/\rho_k$ is an eigenvalue of matrix A^{-1}. Hence together with the eigenvalue ρ_k, the symplectic matrix A admits also the eigenvalue $1/\rho_k$; thus its characteristic equation is reciprocal.

The two propositions above yield the following proposition, known as the Poincaré-Lyapunov theorem:

Proposition. *The characteristic equation of the monodromy matrix of a canonical system is reciprocal.*

For canonical linear periodic systems, as for all the systems for which the characteristic equation of the monodromy matrix is reciprocal, the asymptotic stability is impossible (since if the multiplicator ρ is in $|z| < 1$, then $1/\rho$ is in $|z| > 1$); for such systems, in the case when the multipliers are on the unit circle and the normal Jordan form is diagonal, all solutions are bounded on the whole axis.

We shall now point out another class of systems for which the characteristic equation of the monodromy matrix is reciprocal.

Proposition. *If*

$$GA(-t) + A(t)G = 0,$$

where

$$G = \begin{pmatrix} E_n & 0 \\ 0 & -E_n \end{pmatrix},$$

the characteristic equation of the monodromy matrix of the system

$$\frac{dx}{dt} = A(t)x$$

is reciprocal.

Proof. For the considered systems, we have the relation

$$U(-t) = GU(t)G^{-1}.$$

Indeed, we have

$$\begin{aligned}\frac{d}{dt}[GU(t) - U(-t)G] &= G\frac{dU(t)}{dt} - \frac{d}{dt}U(-t)G \\ &= GA(t)U(t) + A(-t)U(-t)G \\ &= [GA(t) + A(-t)G]U(t) + A(-t)[U(-t)G - GU(t)];\end{aligned}$$

but $G = G^{-1}$; hence

$$\begin{aligned}GA(t) + A(-t)G &= G^{-1}A(t) + A(-t)G^{-1} \\ &= G^{-1}[A(t)G + GA(-t)]G^{-1} = 0.\end{aligned}$$

Thus

$$\frac{d}{dt}[GU(t) - U(-t)G] = -A(-t)[GU(t) - U(-t)G].$$

From this we see that the matrix $GU(t) - U(-t)G$ verifies a linear differential equation. Since for $t = 0$ this matrix is zero, it is identically zero. But if

$$GU(t) = U(-t)G$$

then

$$U(-t) = GU(t)G^{-1}.$$

For $t = \omega$ we obtain

$$U(-\omega) = GU(\omega)G^{-1}.$$

But

$$U(-\omega) = [U(\omega)]^{-1}.$$

It follows that $[U(\omega)]^{-1}$ coincides with $GU(\omega)G^{-1}$, and thus has the same eigenvalues as $U(\omega)$, which shows that the characteristic equation of matrix $U(\omega)$ is reciprocal.

On the basis of the last two propositions we shall immediately obtain effective examples of systems for which the characteristic equation of the monodromy matrix is reciprocal and for which Theorem 1.12 acquires a very effective character.

Proposition. *Consider the second-order system*

$$\frac{d^2}{dt^2} + [C + P(t)]y = 0,$$

where C and P are matrices of the nth *order. If the matrices C and P are real and symmetric or if C is arbitrary real and $P(-t) = P(t)$, then the characteristic equation of the monodromy matrix is reciprocal.*

Proof. If C and P are real and symmetric, the equivalent system

$$\frac{dy}{dt} = z, \qquad \frac{dz}{dt} = -[C + P(t)]y$$

is canonical. Indeed, the matrix of the system is of the form

$$A = \begin{pmatrix} 0 & E_n \\ -C - P & 0 \end{pmatrix}$$

and we see that it is equal to IH, where

$$H = \begin{pmatrix} C + P & \\ 0 & E_n \end{pmatrix};$$

hence H is symmetric if C and P are.

If C is arbitrary real and $P(-t) = P(t)$, we have

$$A(-t) = \begin{pmatrix} 0 & E_n \\ -C - P(-t) & 0 \end{pmatrix} = A(t), \qquad GA(t) = \begin{pmatrix} 0 & E_n \\ C + P & 0 \end{pmatrix},$$

$$A(t)G = \begin{pmatrix} 0 & -E_n \\ -C - P & 0 \end{pmatrix};$$

hence

$$A(t)G + GA(t) = 0,$$

i.e.,

$$GA(-t) + A(t)G = 0$$

and the proposition is proved.

We may now state

Theorem 1.12′. *Consider the system*

$$\frac{d^2y}{dt^2} + [C + \lambda P(t)]y = 0,$$

where

1. *C is symmetric and positive-definite, and $P(t)$ is symmetric or C is an arbitrary real matrix, with distinct and positive eigenvalues, and $P(-t) = P(t)$; $P(t)$ is periodic in t of period ω.*

2. *If $\omega_1^2, \ldots, \omega_n^2$ are the eigenvalues of C and $\bar{\omega} = 2\pi/\omega$, then $\omega_j \pm \omega_h \neq m\bar{\omega}$.*

Then, for $|\lambda|$ sufficiently small, the solutions of the system are bounded on the whole axis.

Proof. Condition 1 assures that the characteristic equation of the system is reciprocal; for $\lambda = 0$ we obtain the system

$$\frac{dy}{dt} = z, \qquad \frac{dz}{dt} = -Cy$$

Let

$$B = \begin{pmatrix} 0 & E_n \\ -C & 0 \end{pmatrix};$$

the corresponding monodromy matrix is $e^{B\omega}$. The eigenvalues of the matrix $e^{B\omega}$ are of the form $e^{\lambda_k \omega}$, where λ_k are the eigenvalues of matrix B. These eigenvalues are given by the equation

$$\det \begin{pmatrix} -\lambda E_n & E_n \\ -C & -\lambda E_n \end{pmatrix} = 0.$$

But

$$\det\begin{pmatrix} -\lambda E_n & E_n \\ -C & -\lambda E_n \end{pmatrix} = \det\begin{pmatrix} 0 & E_n \\ -C-\lambda^2 E_n & -\lambda E_n \end{pmatrix} = \det(-C-\lambda^2 E_n).$$

It follows that $-\lambda^2$ are the eigenvalues of matrix C; hence $-\lambda^2 = \omega_j^2$. Thereby we deduce that the eigenvalues of matrix B are of the form $\pm i\omega_j$; hence the eigenvalues of matrix $e^{B\omega}$ are of the form $e^{\pm i\omega_j\omega}$. If $\omega_j \pm \omega_h \neq m\bar{\omega}$, then $\omega_i \pm \omega_h \neq 2m\pi/\omega$; hence $i\omega_j\omega \pm i\omega_h\omega \neq 2m\pi i$; hence the eigenvalues $e^{\pm i\omega_j\omega}$ are distinct. We are thus in the conditions of Theorem 1.12, and we deduce that the solutions of the system are bounded on the whole axis for $|\lambda|$ sufficiently small.

1.10. The Perron Condition

Definition. *We will say that the system*

$$\frac{dx}{dt} = A(t)x$$

satisfies the Perron condition if for every continuous function $f(t)$, bounded on the semiaxis $t \geqslant 0$, the solution of the system

$$\frac{dx}{dt} = A(t)x + f(t),$$

with $x(0) = 0$, is bounded on the semiaxis $t \geqslant 0$.

Theorem 1.13. *If $|A(t)| \leqslant A_0$ and the system satisfies the Perron condition, then the trivial solution of the system is uniformly asymptotically stable.*

Before proceeding to the proof of the theorem, we will state a series of preliminary facts.

Lemma 1. *There exists $\delta_0 > 0$ such that for all t, $t_0 \geqslant 0$, and $|s - t_0| \leqslant \delta_0$ we will have*

$$|X(t, s) - X(t, t_0)| \leqslant \tfrac{1}{2}|X(t, t_0)|.$$

Proof. From

$$X(t, s) = X(t, t_0)X(t_0, s)$$

follows

$$|X(t, s) - X(t, t_0)| \leqslant |X(t, t_0)|\,|X(t_0, s) - E|.$$

But

$$X(t_0, s) = Y(s, t_0)$$

and

$$\frac{dY(s, t_0)}{ds} = -Y(s, t_0)A(s);$$

hence

$$Y(s, t_0) = E - \int_{t_0}^{s} Y(\sigma, t_0)A(\sigma)d\sigma = E$$

$$- \int_{t_0}^{s} [Y(\sigma, t_0) - E]A(\sigma)d\sigma + \int_{t_0}^{s} A(\sigma)d\sigma,$$

from which

$$| Y(s, t_0) - E | \leqslant \int_{t_0}^{s} | A(\sigma)| \, d\sigma + \int_{t_0}^{s} | Y(\sigma, t_0) - E | \, | A(\sigma)| \, d\sigma;$$

hence

$$| Y(s, t_0) - E | \leqslant A_0\delta_0 e^{A_0\delta_0} \qquad (A_0 = \sup | A(t)|).$$

If δ_0 is sufficiently small,

$$A_0\delta_0 e^{A_0\delta_0} \leqslant \tfrac{1}{2},$$

and the lemma is proved.

Consequence. *There exists a* $\delta_0 > 0$ *such that*

$$\tfrac{1}{2} | X(t, t_0)| \leqslant | X(t, s)| \leqslant \tfrac{3}{2} | X(t, t_0)| \qquad (\textit{if } | s - t_0 | \leqslant \delta_0).$$

Lemma 2. *If* $\int_0^t | X(t, \alpha)| \, d\alpha < C$ *for* $t \geqslant 0$, *there exists* M *such that* $| X(t, \alpha)| < M$ *for* $0 \leqslant \alpha \leqslant t$.

Proof. If the lemma is not true, there exist α_n and t_n such that $0 \leqslant \alpha_n \leqslant t_n$ and $| X(t_n, \alpha_n)| \geqslant n$. The sequence $\{t_n\}$ is unbounded. Indeed, if $t_n < T_0$, we would have $| X(t_n, \alpha_n)| \leqslant e^{A_0 T_0}$, which contradicts the definition of α_n and t_n. If $\{\alpha_n\}$ is bounded, we have

$$C > \int_0^{t_n} | X(t_n, \alpha)| \, d\alpha > \int_{\alpha_n}^{\alpha_n+\delta_0} | X(t_n, \alpha)| \, d\alpha > \tfrac{1}{2}\delta_0 | X(t_n, \alpha_n)| > \tfrac{1}{2}\delta_0 n,$$

which is a contradiction. If α_n is not bounded, we have

$$C > \int_0^{t_n} |X(t_n, \alpha)|\, d\alpha > \int_{\alpha_n-\delta_0}^{\alpha_n} |X(t_n, \alpha)|\, d\alpha > \tfrac{1}{2}\delta_0 |X(t_n, \alpha_n)|,$$

which is again a contradiction. The lemma is proved.

Lemma 3. *If the system satisfies the Perron condition, then there exists C such that*

$$\int_0^t |X(t, \alpha)|\, dt < C \quad \textit{for every} \quad t \geqslant 0.$$

Proof. The solution with condition $x(0) = 0$ of the nonhomogeneous system is given by the formula

$$x(t) = \int_0^t X(t, \alpha) f(\alpha) d\alpha.$$

From the Perron condition it follows that for every continuous and bounded function f defined on $t \geqslant 0$, the function $\int_0^t X(t, \alpha) f(\alpha)\, d\alpha$ is bounded. For fixed t, consider the operator $U(f)$ on the Banach space of the continuous vector functions f, bounded on the semiaxis $t \geqslant 0$, defined by

$$U(f) = \int_0^t X(t, \alpha) f(\alpha) d\alpha.$$

Let $\{t_k\}$ be the sequence of the rational positive numbers, and

$$U_k(f) = \int_0^{t_k} X(t_k, \alpha) f(\alpha) d\alpha.$$

Since for $\| f \| < c_1$ the function $\int_0^t X(t, \alpha) f(\alpha)\, d\alpha$ is bounded, it will follow that

$$\limsup_{k\to\infty} \| U_k(f) \| < \infty.$$

Since the sphere $\| f \| < c_1$ is in the Banach space considered a set of the second category, we may apply the Banach-Steinhaus lemma and we deduce that there exists an M with $\| U_k(f) \| \leqslant M \| f \|$ for every f in the space; hence

$$\left| \int_0^{t_k} X(t_k, \alpha) f(\alpha) d\alpha \right| \leqslant M \| f \|.$$

For any real t there exists a sequence $\{t_{n_k}\}$ of rational numbers whose limit is t. From

$$\left| \int_0^{t_{n_k}} X(t_{n_k}, \alpha) f(\alpha) d\alpha \right| \leqslant M \| f \|$$

follows

$$\left| \int_0^{t} X(t, \alpha) f(\alpha) d\alpha \right| \leqslant M \| f \|$$

for every f in the space. Let x_{ik} be the elements of matrix $X(t, \alpha)$; for fixed t we consider the vector f^i whose components f_k^i are equal to sign x_{ik}. The vector Xf^i will have the components

$$\sum_k x_{ik} \operatorname{sign} x_{ik} = \sum_k | x_{ik} |.$$

Let $f^{i,n}$ be a sequence of vectors, with the elements continuous functions tending to f^i. On the basis of the Lebesgue theorem we will have

$$\lim_{n\to\infty} \int_0^t X(t, \alpha) f^{i,n}(\alpha) d\alpha = \int_0^t X(t, \alpha) f^i(\alpha) d\alpha,$$

and from

$$\left| \int_0^t X(t, \alpha) f^{i,n}(\alpha) d\alpha \right| \leqslant M \| f^{i,n} \|$$

follows

$$\left| \int_0^t X(t, \alpha) f^i(\alpha) d\alpha \right| \leqslant M_1,$$

hence

$$\int_0^t \sum_k | x_{ik}(t, \alpha)| \, d\alpha \leqslant M_1 .$$

Since this relation is true for every i, we deduce that there exists C such that

$$\int_0^t | X(t, \alpha)| \, d\alpha < C,$$

and the lemma is proved.

Proof of Theorem 1.13. The uniform stability follows from Lemmas 2 and 3. There follows further, from $|X(\alpha, t_0)| < M$ and the Perron condition, that

$$\left| \int_{t_0}^{t} X(t, \alpha)X(\alpha, t_0)d\alpha \right| < C_1;$$

hence

$$(t - t_0)|X(t, t_0)| < C_1, \quad X(t, t_0) < \frac{C_1}{t - t_0},$$

which shows that asymptotic stability occurs.

According to Lemma 3, we have

$$\left| \int_{t_0}^{t} X(t, \alpha)X(\alpha, t_0)d\alpha \right| \leqslant \int_{t_0}^{t} |X(t, \alpha)|\,|X(\alpha, t_0)|\, d\alpha$$

$$\leqslant M \int_{0}^{t} |X(t, \alpha)|\, d\alpha < MC = C_1;$$

hence C_1 is independent of t_0. From here follows that the asymptotic stability is uniform and the theorem is proved.

A generalization of Theorem 1.13 due to M. Reghis is obtained in the following way. Let L_a^p be the space of the vector functions defined on the semiaxis $t \geqslant 0$ measurable and such that $\int_0^\infty |h(s)|^p e^{pas}\, ds < \infty$, L_a^∞ the space of the functions for which ess. u. b. $|h(s)|e^{as} < \infty$. Taking in these spaces the norms

$$\| h \|_{(p,a)} = \left(\int_0^\infty |h(s)|^p e^{pas}\, ds \right)^{1/p} \qquad [p \in (1, \infty)],$$

respectively,

$$\| h \|_{(\infty,a)} = \operatorname*{ess.\,u.\,b.}_{s \geqslant 0} |h(s)|e^{as},$$

L_a^p and L_a^∞ become Banach spaces, since the linear operator $\Omega_a^b : L_a^p \to L_b^p$, defined by $\Omega_a^b h = e^{(a-b)s}h(s)$, is an isometric isomorphism between L_a^p and L_b^p, and L_0^p is a Banach space.

Lemma 4. *If*

$$Vu = \int_0^t X(t, s)u(s)ds$$

is an operator from L_a^p *to* L_b^∞, *then*

$$\| Vu \|_{(\infty,b)} \leqslant M \| u \|_{(p,a)}.$$

Proof. If $\{t_k\}$ is the sequence of the rational positive numbers and

$$V_k u = e^{bt_k} \int_0^{t_k} X(t_k, s)u(s)ds,$$

we have, by hypothesis, for $u \in L_a^p$, $\sup_{k \geqslant 1} \| V_k(u) \| < \infty$; hence according to the Banach-Steinhaus lemma, $\| V_k \| \leqslant M$; hence

$$\| V_k u \| \leqslant M \| u \|_{(p,a)},$$

i.e.,

$$\left\| e^{bt_k} \int_0^{t_k} X(t_k, s)u(s)ds \right\| \leqslant M \| u \|_{(p,a)},$$

from where

$$e^{bt} \left| \int_0^t X(t, s)u(s)ds \right| \leqslant M \| u \|_{(p,a)},$$

and the lemma is proved.

Theorem 1.13′. *If there exists a $p \in [1, \infty)$ such that for every $f \in L_a^p$ the solution with $x(0) = 0$ of the system*

$$\frac{dx}{dt} - A(t)x + f$$

belongs to L_b^p, $a, b > 0$, then there exists an $h > 0$ such that

$$| X(t, t_0)| \leqslant h e^{at_0} e^{-bt},$$

for $t \geqslant t_0 \geqslant 0$.

Proof. Let δ_0 be the constant of Lemma 1. We define the functions

$$u_m(s) = \begin{cases} \delta_0^{-1/p} \dfrac{X(s, m\delta_0)x_0}{e^{as}| X(s, m\delta_0)|} & (s \in [m\delta_0, (m+1)\delta_0], \quad | x_0 | = 1), \\ 0 & (s \notin [m\delta_0, (m+1)\delta_0], \quad s \geqslant 0). \end{cases}$$

We have $u_m \in L_a^p$ and $\| u_m \|_{(p,a)} \leqslant 1$. According to Lemma 4,

$$Me^{-bt} \geqslant \left| \int_0^t X(t, s)u_m(s)ds \right| = \delta_0^{-1/p} \left| \int_{m\delta_0}^{(m+1)\delta_0} X(t, s) \frac{X(s, m\delta_0)x_0}{e^{as}| X(s, m\delta_0)|} ds \right|$$

$$= \delta_0^{-1/p} | X(t, m\delta_0)| \int_{m\delta_0}^{(m+1)\delta_0} \frac{ds}{e^{as}| X(s, m\delta_0)|}$$

$$\geqslant \delta_0^{-1/p} \tfrac{2}{3} | X(t, m\delta_0)| \delta_0 e^{-a\delta_0} e^{-am\delta_0},$$

since $| X(s, m\delta_0)| \leqslant \frac{3}{2}$ for $m\delta_0 \leqslant s \leqslant (m+1)\delta_0$.

It follows that

$$| X(t, m\delta_0 | \leqslant \delta_0^{1/p} \tfrac{3}{2} M \delta_0^{-1} e^{a\delta_0} e^{am\delta_0} e^{-bt}.$$

Let $s \in [0, t]$ and m such that $m\delta_0 \leqslant s < (m + 1)\delta_0$. Then

$$\begin{aligned} | X(t, s)| &\leqslant | X(t, m\delta_0)| \, | X(m\delta_0 , s)| \leqslant \tfrac{3}{2} | X(t, m\delta_0)| \\ &\leqslant (\tfrac{3}{2})^2 M e^{a\delta_0} \delta_0^{-1/q} e^{as} e^{-bt} = h e^{as} e^{-bt}, \end{aligned}$$

and the theorem is proved.

We shall now prove a theorem, also due to M. Reghis, relative to the existence of a Lyapunov function for linear systems with the property from Theorem 1.13′.

Theorem 1.6‴. *If* $| X(t, t_0)| \leqslant h e^{at_0} e^{-bt}$, *then for* $\delta < b$ *there exists a* $V(x, t)$ *continuous, with the following properties*:

1. $V(0, t) \equiv 0, \; t \geqslant 0.$
2. $| V(x_1 , t) - V(x_2 , t)| \leqslant L_D(t) \, | x_1 - x_2 |$, *for* $x_i \in D$.
3. $l e^{\delta t} | x | \leqslant V(x, t) \leqslant k(\delta) e^{(a-b+\delta) t} \, | x |$,

$$\limsup_{h \to 0+} \frac{V[x(t + h; t, x), t + h] - V(x, t)}{h} = -e^{\delta t} | x |.$$

Proof. Define

$$V(x, t) = \int_t^\infty e^{\delta\tau} \| x(\tau; t, x)\| \, d\tau.$$

The uniform convergence of the integral is assured for $0 \leqslant t \leqslant T$, $| x | \leqslant K$, by the hypothesis $\delta < b$.

$$\begin{aligned} | V(x_1 , t) - V(x_2 , t)| &\leqslant \int_t^\infty e^{\delta\tau} \Big| \, | x(\tau; t, x_1)| - | x(\tau; t, x_2)| \, \Big| \, d\tau \\ &\leqslant \int_t^\infty e^{\delta\tau} | x(\tau; t, x_1) - x(\tau; t, x_2)| \, d\tau \\ &\leqslant \int_t^\infty e^{\delta\tau} | X(\tau, t)| \, d\tau \, | x_1 - x_2 | \\ &\leqslant L(t) | x_1 - x_2 | \end{aligned}$$

where

$$\begin{aligned} L(t) &= \int_t^\infty e^{\delta\tau} | X(\tau, t)| \, d\tau \leqslant h \int_t^\infty e^{\delta\tau} e^{-b\tau} e^{at} \, d\tau \\ &= \frac{h}{b - \delta} e^{(a-b+\delta) t}. \end{aligned}$$

Further,

$$V(x, t) \leqslant \int_t^\infty e^{\delta\tau}|X(\tau, t)|\,d\tau|\,x\,| = L(t)|\,x\,| = k(\delta)e^{(a-b+\delta)t}$$

$$\geqslant e^{\delta t}\int_t^\infty |\,x(\tau; t, x)|\,d\tau \geqslant e^{\delta t}\int_t^{t+\alpha} |\,x(\tau; t, x)|\,d\tau \geqslant \tfrac{1}{2}\alpha e^{\delta t}|\,x\,|$$

(with the same arguments as in Theorem 1.6″). We immediately see that

$$V[x(t; t_0, x_0), t] = \int_t^\infty e^{\delta\tau}|\,x(\tau; t, x(t; t_0, x_0))|\,d\tau = \int_t^\infty e^{\delta\tau}|\,x(\tau; t_0, x_0)|\,d\tau;$$

hence

$$\frac{d}{dt}V[x(t; t_0, x_0), t] = e^{-\delta t}|\,x(t; t_0, x_0)|.$$

For $t = t_0$ we obtain the condition from the statement.

We shall close these considerations with a theorem of stability in the first approximation.

Theorem 1.7‴. *If* $|X(t, t_0)| \leqslant he^{at_0}e^{-bt}$, *then for an arbitrary function* $\phi(x, t)$, *with* $|\phi(x, t)| \leqslant f(t)\,|\,x\,|^m$, $|\,x\,| \leqslant D$, $f \in L_0^p$, $\|f\|_{(p,0)} \leqslant K$, *the solution* $x(t; t_0, x_0)$ *of the equation*

$$\frac{dx}{dt} = A(t)x + \phi(x, t),$$

with $|\,x_0\,|$ *sufficiently small, verifies the inequality*

$$|\,x(t; t_0, x_0)| \leqslant H(h, m)e^{at_0}e^{-bt}|\,x_0\,| \qquad t \geqslant t_0 \geqslant 0.$$

The initial value x_0 should verify the following relations:

(a) If $a > b$, $m > a/b$, $p \in [1, \infty]$:

$$|\,x_0\,| \leqslant (2(m-1)h^m e^{m(a-b)t_0}\|f\|_{(p,0)}\|\,e^{(a\ \ mb)s}\,\|_{(q,0)})^{-1/(m-1)}, \qquad \frac{1}{p} + \frac{1}{q} = 1.$$

(b) If $a > b$, $m = a/b$, $p = 1$:

$$|\,x_0\,| \leqslant (2(m-1)h^m e^{m(a-b)t_0}\|f\|_{(1,0)})^{-1/(m-1)}.$$

(c) If $a \leqslant b$, $m > 1$, $p \in [1, \infty]$:

$$|\,x_0\,| \leqslant (2(m-1)h^m\|f\|_{(p,0)}\|\,e^{(a-mb)s}\,\|_{(q,0)})^{-1/(m-1)}, \qquad \frac{1}{p} + \frac{1}{q} = 1.$$

(d) $a \leqslant b$, $m = 1$, $p \in [1, \infty]$, $|\,x_0\,| \leqslant D$.

Proof. We have

$$| x(t; t_0, x_0)| \leqslant | X(t, t_0)| \, | x_0 | + \int_{t_0}^{t} | X(t, \tau) | \, | \phi[x(\tau), \tau] | \, d\tau \qquad t \geqslant t_0 \geqslant 0.$$

By putting $t = t_0 + s$, $\tau = t_0 + \sigma$, $| x(t_0 + s; t_0, x_0)| = \varphi(s)$, $\varphi(0) = | x_0 |$, we will have

$$\varphi(s) \leqslant h e^{at_0} e^{-bt_0} e^{-bs} \varphi(0) + \int_0^s h e^{a(t_0+\sigma)} e^{-b(t_0+s)} f(t_0 + \sigma) \varphi^m(\sigma) d\sigma,$$

i.e.,

$$\varphi(s) \leqslant K e^{-bs} \varphi(0) + K e^{-bs} \int_0^s e^{a\sigma} f(t_0 + \sigma) \varphi^m(\sigma) d\sigma$$

where

$$K = \begin{cases} h e^{(a-b)t_0} & (a > b), \\ h & (a \leqslant b). \end{cases}$$

If $\psi(s)$ is defined by the equation

$$\psi(s) = K e^{-bs} \varphi(0) + K e^{-bs} \int_0^s e^{a\sigma} f(t_0 + \sigma) \psi^m(s) ds \qquad (s \geqslant 0),$$

then $\varphi(s) \leqslant \psi(s)$ and $d\psi/ds + b\psi = Q(s)\psi^m$, $Q(s) = K e^{(a-b)s} f(t_0 + s)$.

In cases (a), (b), and (c) this is an equation of Bernoulli type, and we obtain

$$\psi(s) = \left[[\psi(0)]^{1-m} e^{(m-1)bs} - (m-1) K e^{(m-1)bs} \int_0^s e^{(a-mb)\sigma} f(t_0 + \sigma) d\sigma \right]^{-1/(m-1)} \qquad (s \geqslant 0).$$

But $\psi(0) = K\varphi(0)$ and $\varphi(s) \leqslant \psi(s)$; hence

$$\varphi(s) \leqslant K e^{-bs} \varphi(0) \left\{ 1 - (m-1) K^m [\varphi(0)]^{m-1} \int_0^s e^{(a-mb)\sigma} f(t_0 + \sigma) d\sigma \right\}^{-1(m-1)}$$

In case (a) we have

$$K = h e^{(a-b)t_0}, \qquad \int_0^s f(t_0 + \sigma) e^{(a-mb)\sigma} \, d\sigma \leqslant \| f \|_{(p,0)} \| e^{(a-mb)\sigma} \|_{(q,0)}$$

and it will follow, taking into account the evaluation for $| x_0 |$, that

$$\varphi(s) \leqslant 2^{1/(m-1)} h e^{(a-b)t_0} e^{-bs} \varphi(0);$$

hence

$$| x(t; t_0, x_0)| \leqslant H e^{at_0} e^{-bt} | x_0 | \qquad (H = 2^{1/(m-1)} h).$$

The other cases are similarly treated.

NOTES

General expositions on the Lyapunov stability theory are to be found in [8], [9], and [10]. The notion of uniform stability was introduced by K. P. Persidski in [11]. For stability with respect to a part of the variables the fundamental ideas may be found in [12]. Property (3) relative to asymptotic stability has been given in [13]. The first general theorem about the existence of a Lyapunov function in the case of uniform asymptotic stability, as well as the definition of the uniform asymptotic stability have been given in [14]. Theorem 1.5′ is due to N. N. Krasovski. In its first form, for automous systems, the theorem was stated in a common work by E. A. Barbasin and N. N. Krasovski. This theorem, as well as the other important contributions of N. N. Krasovski to the theory of stability, are available in [15]. The results of C. Corduneanu are published in [16]. The existence theorem of Lyapunov function for linear systems has been given in [17]. The elements of linear algebra and the theorem on the normal Jordan form are reproduced from [18]. The algebraic proof of the existence theorem of Lyapunov function for linear systems with constant coefficients has been given in [19]. The first use of Lemma I.6 (Consequence 2) to establish boundedness and stability is due to R. Bellman. For the ideas and methods of R. Bellman see [20] where further references are given. The other proof of the theorem on stability in the first approximation has been given in [21].

The theorem of stability in the first approximation, in the case when the first approximation is homogeneous of degree m, can be found with the proof of I. G. Malkin in [9], with that of J. L. Massera in [10], and of N. N. Krasovski in [15]. The proof in the text is new and is based upon an idea of D. Wexler. Propositions 1, 3, and 4 at the end of Section 1-7 are given in [22] and [23].

Theorem 1.8 has been given by I. G. Malkin in [14]. The notions of security and unsecurity zones of the boundary of the domain of stability have been introduced in [24]. The result of T. Hacker was published in [25]. Theorems on stability under permanent perturbations bounded in the mean have been given in [26], and the notion of integral stability with the corresponding theorems in [27]. The equivalent notion of strong stability defined by Okamura was studied in [28].

The lemma preceding Theorem 1.8‴ and this last theorem have been set up in the form appearing in the text by D. Wexler. Theorem 1.8‴ has been previously published in a paper of I. G. Malkin. Further results on stability were established by T. Yoshizawa; see, for example, [98] and [99].

The reducibility theorem of linear systems with periodic coefficients has been stated by A. M. Lyapunov in [8]. In the form of the text it has been proved in [29] (see also [3]). The fundamental properties of canonical linear systems with periodic coefficients have been stated in [30] and [31]. The results in the text are reproduced from [32]. The Perron condition has been formulated in [33]. The proof based upon the Banach-Steinhaus theorem was given by R. Bellman in [34]. The results of M. Reghis are to be found in [35]. For further references on stability theory see the book of W. Hahn [96]. See also the book of La Salle and Lefchetz [97].

CHAPTER 2

Absolute Stability of Nonlinear Control Systems

A control system consists of the object of control and the controller. The controller has the task of maintaining a certain motion in the object of the control; hence the control process arises from the fact that the controller is opposing all the deviations from this motion.

The motion of the control system considered as a whole is described by a certain system of ordinary differential equations $dx/dt = X(t, x)$. In fact it may happen that equations with partial derivatives, integro-differential equations, or equations with retarded argument also occur; this depends on the nature of the elements which constitute the system. In what follows we shall only consider systems whose motion is described by ordinary differential equations. Let $x = x_0(t)$ be the motion which we want to maintain. The deviations of the system from this motion may be provoked either by sudden perturbations, which, as we have previously seen, are expressed by modifications of the initial conditions, or by the occurrence of some permanent perturbations. Practically, the maintenance of the desired motion amounts to the fact that the real motion of the system is maintained in the proximity of the desired motion. Thus we see that the problem amounts to ensuring the stability of the motion $x = x_0(t)$ with respect to any deviation from the initial conditions and permanent perturbations.

This kind of stability is attained, as we have already seen, if the solution $x = x_0(t)$ is uniformly asymptotically stable in the large. Consequently, the finding of stability conditions for the control systems amounts to the finding of some conditions of asymptotic stability in the large. The equations of ordinary control systems will have particular forms; stability conditions will have to be effective, on the one hand, and, on the other, sufficiently broad to leave a certain liberty to the designer when taking into account other qualities required for the system.

We shall assume that the object of the control is determined by m generalized coordinates $\eta_1, \ldots, \eta_m$ and the controller by a single coordinate μ. The motion of the object of the control will be described by the equations $d\eta/dt = f_k(\eta_1, \ldots, \eta_m, \mu, t)$ and of the controller by the equations $d^2\mu/dt^2 = F(\eta_1, \ldots, \eta_m, \mu, t)$. As always in stability problems, the equations of the perturbed motion will be formed by reducing the problem to the study of the stability of the trivial solution.

For the usual control systems with which we will be concerned, we shall consider that the equations of the perturbed motion do not explicitly depend on t; in addition, other simplifying hypotheses will be made which lead to the fact that some equations will be linear. All these equations correspond to some effective technical schemes and are justified for large classes of systems. The equations of the perturbed motion are supposed linear with constant coefficients for the object of the control $\dot{\eta}_k = \Sigma b_{kj}\eta_j + \eta_k\mu$. For $\mu = 0$ we obtain the free motion of the object of the control without the controller's intervention.

The equation of the controller is supposed of the form

$$V^2\ddot{\mu} + W\dot{\mu} + S\mu = f^*(\sigma),$$

where $\sigma = \Sigma_{j=1}^{m} p_j\eta_j - r\mu$, and $f^*(\sigma)$ is a nonlinear function for which it will be supposed in general only that $f^*(0) = 0$, $\sigma f^*(\sigma) > 0$ for $\sigma \neq 0$; sometimes more general functions are considered with $f^*(\sigma) = 0$ for $|\sigma| \leqslant \sigma_0$, $\sigma f^*(\sigma) > 0$ for $|\sigma| > \sigma_0$.

We suppose that a, b, p_j, r are constant. As we see it, the nonlinearity is introduced in these equations only by the function $f^*(\sigma)$. This type of system was studied particularly during the last 15 to 16 years, after the publication in 1944 of a work by A. I. Lurie and V. N. Postnikov. Recently the problem of widening the class of systems considered, as well as the introduction of several controllers, has been raised more and more often. This amounts to the introduction of several functions $f_j(\sigma_j)$, taking into consideration the real nonlinearities in the equations of the object of the control, of the controller, or in the expression of the functions σ_j which characterize the interactions between the controller and the object of the control. The few results obtained until now in all these directions are in the incipient stage.

The equations of motion are brought to certain normal forms by simple changes of variables. We put $\xi = p\dot{\mu} + q\mu$, and the equation of the controller is written in the form

$$\frac{V^2}{p}\dot{\xi} - \frac{qV^2}{p^2}\xi + \frac{V^2q^2}{p^2}\mu + \frac{W}{p}\xi - \frac{Wq}{p}\mu + S\mu = f^*(\sigma);$$

the coefficients p and q are chosen such that $V^2(q/p)^2 + W(q/p) + S = 0$. Denoting by ρ_{m+1} and ρ_{m+2} the values of q/p which are obtained as roots of this equation, we obtain for the controller two first-order equations of the form

$$\dot{\mu} = -\rho_{m+1}\mu + \frac{1}{p}\xi, \qquad \dot{\xi} = \rho_{m+1}\xi - a\xi + pf^*(\sigma).$$

Setting $\mu = \eta_{m+1}$, we obtain, after the corresponding changes of notations, a system of the form

$$\dot{\eta}_k = \sum_{\alpha=1}^{n} b_{k\alpha}\eta_\alpha + h_k\xi, \qquad \dot{\xi} = -\rho_{n+1}\xi + f(\sigma), \qquad \sigma = \sum_{\alpha=1}^{n} p_\alpha\eta_\alpha. \tag{1}$$

In the particular case when $S = 0$, equations (1) will have the form

$$\dot{\eta}_k = \sum_{\alpha=1}^{n} b_{k\alpha}\eta_\alpha + h_k\xi, \qquad \dot{\xi} = f(\sigma), \qquad \sigma = \sum_{\alpha=1}^{n} p_\alpha\eta_\alpha;$$

in the case when $V^2 = 0$, after simple transformations, we obtain

$$\dot{\eta}_k = \sum_{\alpha=1}^{m} b_{k\alpha}\eta_\alpha + n_k\mu, \qquad \dot{\mu} = -\rho_{m+1}\mu + f(\sigma), \qquad \sigma = \sum_{\alpha=1}^{m} p_\alpha\eta_\alpha + p_{m+1}\mu;$$

in the case when $S = V^2 = 0$, equations (1) will have the form

$$\dot{\eta}_k = \sum_{\alpha=1}^{m} b_{k\alpha}\eta_\alpha + n_k\mu, \qquad \dot{\mu} = f(\sigma), \qquad \sigma = \sum_{\alpha=1}^{m} p_\alpha\eta_\alpha + p_{m+1}\mu.$$

These equations have been investigated for the first time by A. I. Lurie. In what follows we will show how to investigate the stability for these systems.

2.1. The Canonical Form and the Corresponding Lyapunov Function

For systems of control, the following stability problem is formulated. *It is required to formulate conditions relative to the coefficients which appear in the system such that the trivial solution of system (1) be asymptotically stable in the large, for an arbitrary function f of the considered class $[\sigma f(\sigma) > 0$ for $\sigma \neq 0, f(0) = 0]$.*

If the trivial solution of the system is asymptotically stable in the large for any function f of the considered class, we say that the system is absolutely stable.

The method given by A. I. Lurie in the research of absolute stability is based upon certain canonical forms of the systems and upon the convenient construction of Lyapunov function.

Perform the change of variable $x_s = \sum_{\alpha=1}^{n} c_\alpha^{(s)}\eta_\alpha + \xi$; we have

$$\dot{x}_s = \sum_{\alpha=1}^{n} c_\alpha^{(s)}\dot{\eta}_\alpha + \dot{\xi} = \sum_{\alpha=1}^{n} c_\alpha^{(s)}\left[\sum_{\beta=1}^{n} b_{\alpha\beta}\eta_\beta + h_\alpha\xi\right] - \rho_{n+1}\xi + f(\sigma).$$

If we want these equations to take the form $\dot{x}_s = -\rho_s x_s + f(\sigma)$ we must have $\dot{x}_s = -\rho_s \sum_{\beta=1}^{n} c_\beta^{(s)}\eta_\beta - \rho_s\xi + f(\sigma)$. Hence the coefficients $c_\alpha^{(s)}$ should be chosen such that

$$-\rho_s c_\beta^{(s)} = \sum_{\alpha=1}^{n} b_{\alpha\beta}c_\alpha^{(s)}, \qquad \rho_{n+1} - \rho_s = \sum_{\alpha=1}^{n} h_\alpha c_\alpha^{(s)}.$$

The first equations show that $-\rho_s$ are eigenvalues of the matrix $(b_{\alpha\beta})$. If we suppose that the matrix $(b_{\alpha\beta})$ has a normal diagonal form, we may choose the matrix $(c_\alpha^{(s)})$ nonsingular, having as rows a linear independent system of eigenvectors. The last equations serve for the complete determination of the matrix $c_\alpha^{(s)}$, since the eigenvectors are determined up to a constant factor. In this way, the system may be brought to the form

$$\dot{x}_k = -\rho_k x_k + f(\sigma) \qquad \left(k = 1, 2, ..., n+1, \sigma = \sum_{k=1}^{n+1} \gamma_k x_k\right).$$

We have set $\xi = x_{n+1}$.

To understand better the sense of the transformation and to understand what happens in the case where the matrix $(b_{\alpha\beta})$ does not have a normal diagonal form, we shall review the computations, setting

$$(c_\alpha^{(s)}) = C, \qquad (b_{\alpha\beta}) = B,$$

$$\begin{pmatrix} \eta_1 \\ \vdots \\ \eta_n \end{pmatrix} = \eta, \qquad \begin{pmatrix} x_1 \\ \vdots \\ x_n \end{pmatrix} = x, \qquad \begin{pmatrix} 1 \\ \vdots \\ 1 \end{pmatrix} = u, \qquad \begin{pmatrix} h_1 \\ \vdots \\ h_n \end{pmatrix} = h.$$

System (1) is written

$$\dot{\eta} = B\eta + h\xi, \qquad \dot{\xi} = -\rho_{n+1}\xi + f(\sigma), \qquad \sigma = (p, \eta),$$

where

$$p = \begin{pmatrix} p_1 \\ \vdots \\ p_n \end{pmatrix}.$$

The change of variables has the form $x = C\eta + \xi u$. We have

$$\dot{x} = C\dot{\eta} + \dot{\xi}u = C(B\eta + h\xi) + \dot{\xi}u = CB\eta + (Ch - \rho_{n+1}u)\xi + f(\sigma)u.$$

But

$$\eta = C^{-1}(x - \xi u) = C^{-1}x - \xi C^{-1}u;$$

hence

$$x = CBC^{-1}x - [(CBC^{-1} + \rho_{n+1}E)u - Ch]\xi + f(\sigma)u.$$

The canonical form is obtained by requiring that CBC^{-1} has the normal Jordan form and in addition that

$$(CBC^{-1} + \rho_{n+1}E)u - Ch = 0.$$

Let C_0 be such that $C_0BC_0^{-1}$ has the normal Jordan form, and let T be a matrix of the form

$$\begin{pmatrix} T_1 & & \\ & \ddots & \\ & & T_s \end{pmatrix},$$

where the T_k have the same dimensions as the cells of the normal form of matrix B and are of the form

$$\begin{pmatrix} a_1 & a_2 & \cdots & a_{l_k} \\ 0 & a_1 & \cdots & a_{l_k-1} \\ 0 & 0 & \cdots & a_{l_k-2} \\ & & \cdots & \\ 0 & 0 & \cdots & a_2 \\ 0 & 0 & \cdots & a_1 \end{pmatrix};$$

we will obtain, by denoting $C = TC_0$, the relation

$$CBC^{-1} = TC_0BC_0^{-1}T^{-1} = TJT^{-1} = J,$$

where J is the normal Jordan form of matrix B (since it is verified by direct computation that T_k is permutable with the corresponding Jordan cell J_k). Choosing C of the form TC_0, the last equation may be written

$$(J + \rho_{n+1}E) = TC_0h$$

and represents a system of n equations for the n unknowns which are introduced by matrix T. This system in general admits nonzero solutions, and thus the desired canonical form is reached.

Besides systems of the form

$$\dot{\eta}_k = \sum_{\alpha} b_{k\alpha}\eta_\alpha + h_k\xi, \qquad \dot{\xi} = -\rho_{n+1}\xi + f(\sigma),$$

there occurs, in a series of problems, the necessity of considering systems of the general form

$$\dot{\eta}_k = \sum_{\alpha} b_{k\alpha}\eta_\alpha + h_k f(\sigma), \qquad \sigma = \sum_{\alpha} p_\alpha \eta_\alpha.$$

This general form contains the preceding one as a particular case; this is immediately seen if we denote by ξ any of the coordinates η_α. With the above matrix notations the system is written $\dot{\eta} = B\eta + hf(\sigma)$. Perform the change of variables $x = C\eta$; we obtain $\dot{x} = C\dot{\eta} = CB\eta + Chf(\sigma)$; hence $\dot{x} = CBC^{-1}x + Chf(\sigma)$. Choose C such that CBC^{-1} has the normal Jordan form and in addition that $Ch = u$.

The canonical forms thus obtained are convenient in case the matrix B has eigenvalues with negative real parts, as we shall see when constructing the corresponding Lyapunov function. These are the so-called *proper stable systems*. In the other cases other canonical forms are used, which we shall omit.

We shall consider a system of the form

$$\dot{x}_k = -\rho_k x_k + f(\sigma) \qquad (k = 1, ..., n+1) \qquad \sigma = \sum_{k=1}^{n+1} \gamma_k x_k . \tag{2}$$

Differentiating the last relation of (2) we obtain

$$\dot{\sigma} = \sum_{k=1}^{n+1} \gamma_k \dot{x}_k = \sum_{k=1}^{n+1} \gamma_k(-\rho_k x_k + f(\sigma)) = \sum_{k=1}^{n+1} \beta_k x_k - \gamma f(\sigma).$$

Suppose that $\rho_1, ..., \rho_s$ are real and positive and $\rho_{s+1}, ..., \rho_{n+1}$ will be two-by-two complex-conjugated and with positive real parts. Constants $\gamma_1, ..., \gamma_s, \beta_1, ..., \beta_s$ will be real and $\gamma_{s+1}, ..., \gamma_{n+1}$, $\beta_{s+1}, ..., \beta_{n+1}$ will be two-by-two complex-conjugated. We shall consider solutions of the system such that $x_1, ..., x_s$ are real, and $x_{s+1}, ..., x_{n+1}$ two-by-two complex-conjugated. All these considerations are equivalent to the hypothesis that in the initial system the unknowns and the coefficients were real, and the complex elements are introduced as a result of the change of variables which brought the system to the canonical form. To clarify these questions we shall make some general considerations. *We shall say that a vector has the property P if its first s components are real and the others are, in order, two-by-two complex conjugates. We will say that a nonsingular quadratic matrix has the property P if it has the first s rows real and the others, in order, two-by-two complex conjugates.*

Proposition 1. *If a matrix has the property P, the matrix formed by the real rows and by the real parts and the imaginary parts of the complex rows is nonsingular.*

Proof. Let D be the determinant of the given matrix and Δ the determinant of the matrix formed by the real rows and with the real parts and the imaginary parts of the complex rows. We have

$$D = \begin{vmatrix} a_{11} & \cdots & a_{1n} \\ \vdots & & \vdots \\ a_{s1} & \cdots & a_{sn} \\ b_{s+1,1} + ic_{s+1,1} & \cdots & b_{s+1,n} + ic_{s+1,n} \\ b_{s+1,1} - ic_{s+1,1} & \cdots & b_{s+1,n} - ic_{s+1,n} \\ \vdots & & \vdots \end{vmatrix}$$

$$= \begin{vmatrix} a_{11} & \cdots & a_{sn} \\ \vdots & & \vdots \\ a_{s1} & \cdots & a_{sn} \\ b_{s+1,1} + ic_{s+1,1} & \cdots & b_{s+1,n} + ic_{s+1,n} \\ 2b_{s+1,1} & \cdots & 2b_{s+1,n} \\ \vdots & & \vdots \end{vmatrix}$$

$$= 2^{\frac{1}{2}(n-s)} \begin{vmatrix} a_{11} & \cdots & a_{in} \\ \vdots & & \vdots \\ a_{s1} & \cdots & a_{sn} \\ b_{s+1,1} + ic_{s+1,1} & \cdots & b_{s+1,n} + ic_{s+1,n} \\ b_{s+1,1} & \cdots & b_{s+1,n} \\ \vdots & & \vdots \end{vmatrix}$$

$$= (2i)^{\frac{1}{2}(n-s)} \begin{vmatrix} a_{11} & \cdots & a_{1n} \\ \vdots & & \vdots \\ a_{s1} & \cdots & a_{sn} \\ c_{s+1,1} & \cdots & c_{s+1,n} \\ b_{s+1,1} & \cdots & b_{s+1,n} \\ \vdots & & \vdots \end{vmatrix} = (2i)^{\frac{1}{2}(n-s)} \Delta$$

and we see that $\Delta \neq 0$ together with D.

We will say that a vector function $Y(y)$ has the property P if for each vector y with property P, the vector $Y(y)$ has the property P.

Proposition 2. *Let A be a matrix with property P and x a real vector. Then the vector $y = Ax$ has the property P. Conversely, if A is nonsingular and y has property P, then x is real.*

Proof. The first affirmation is obvious, since the first s elements of y follow from the composition of the real rows of A with the real elements of x, and the last by the composition of the complex-conjugated rows of A with the real elements of x. To prove the second affirmation let

$$A = \begin{pmatrix} R \\ U + iV \\ U - iV \end{pmatrix}, \qquad x = u + iv.$$

We have

$$Ax = \begin{pmatrix} Ru + iRv \\ Uu - Vv + i(Uv + Vu) \\ Uu + Vv + i(Uv - Vu) \end{pmatrix}.$$

The condition that Ax has the property P leads to $Rv = 0$, $Vv = 0$, $Uv = 0$. But if $\det A \neq 0$, it follows, according to Proposition 1, that $\det \begin{pmatrix} R \\ U \\ V \end{pmatrix} \neq 0$; hence $v = 0$; hence x is real.

Proposition 3. *Let $dx/dt = X(x)$ be a real system. By means of the change of variables $y = Ax$, where A is a nonsingular matrix with the property P, we obtain a system $dy/dt = Y(y)$, where $Y(y)$ has property P.*

Proof. We have

$$\frac{dy}{dt} = A\frac{dx}{dt} = AX(x) = AX(A^{-1}y) = Y(y).$$

If y has property P, on the basis of Proposition 2, $A^{-1}y$ is real; hence $X(A^{-1}y)$ is real; hence $AX(A^{-1}y)$ has property P.

Returning to the preceding systems of differential equations, let us remark that the rows of matrix C with which the change of variables was performed in order to bring it to the canonical form, were eigenvectors of matrix B; to the real eigenvalues correspond real eigenvectors, hence real rows; to the complex-conjugated eigenvalues correspond complex-conjugate eigenvectors; hence the rows two by two are complex conjugates. It follows that matrix C of the transformation had the property P; hence the system obtained is as in Proposition 3. If in the initial system we were, naturally, interested only by the real solutions, in the transformed system we shall be interested only in solutions with property P.

Proposition 4. *Consider the system $dy/dt = Y(y)$, where $Y(y)$ has the property P. If y_0 has the property P, then $y(t; y_0)$ has the property P for any t.*

Proof. Starting from y_0, consider the sequence of successive approximations:

$$y_{k+1}(t) = y_0 + \int_0^t Y(y_k(t))\, dt.$$

If $y_k(t)$ has property P, then $Y(y_k(t))$ has property P and it is obvious that $y_{k+1}(t)$ has property P. The solution $y(t; y)$ is given by $\lim_{k\to\infty} y_k(t)$, and we see that it will have the property P.

Taking this fact into account, we may apply the method of Lyapunov functions, requiring that the function V has the corresponding property only for vectors with the property P; then it will have the required properties for all the members of the family M of solutions with property P; hence we shall obtain conclusions of stability with respect to the solutions from this set, the only ones which correspond to the real solutions of the initial system.

We consider the quadratic form $F = \Sigma_{i,j} (a_j a_i/\rho_j + \rho_i) x_j x_i$, where $a_1, ..., a_s$ are real, and the others, two by two, complex conjugates.

We have

$$\frac{1}{\rho_j + \rho_i} = \int_0^\infty e^{-(\rho_j+\rho_i)t}\, dt;$$

hence

$$F = \sum_{i,j} a_j a_i \int_0^\infty e^{-(\rho_i+\rho_j)t}\, dt\, x_i x_j = \int_0^\infty \Big[\sum_k a_k x_k\, e^{-\rho_k t}\Big]^2 dt.$$

If x is a vector with the property P, then for $k = 1, ..., s$, $a_k x_k e^{-\rho_k t}$ is real, and for the other values of k, the $a_k x_k e^{-\rho_k t}$ are two-by-two complex conjugates. Hence their sum is real; it follows that $\Sigma\, a_k x_k e^{-\rho_k t}$ is real for every vector x with property P; hence F is real and positive for every vector x with property P.

On the other hand, $\Sigma_k\, a_k x_k e^{-\rho_k t} = 0$ for every t, if and only if $x_k = 0$ for every k. It follows that F is a positive-definite quadratic form for any vector with property P.

Now let

$$\phi = \frac{1}{2}\sum_{i=1}^{s} A_i x_i^2 + C_1 x_{s+1} x_{s+2} + \cdots + C_{n-s} x_n x_{n+1},$$

where A_i, C_j are real and positive. For any vector x with property P, the form ϕ takes real and positive values; $\phi = 0$ if and only if $x = 0$.

In what follows we shall assume that

$$\lim_{|\sigma|\to\infty} \int_0^\sigma f(\sigma)\, d\sigma = \infty$$

and we shall choose the function

$$V = \phi + F + \int_0^\sigma f(\sigma)\, d\sigma.$$

We see immediately that this function takes real and positive values for every x with the property P and that $V = 0$ if and only if $x = 0$, $\sigma = 0$. Let us calculate the total derivative of V. We have

$$\begin{aligned}\frac{dV}{dt} &= \sum_{k=1}^{s} A_k x_k[-\rho_k x_k + f(\sigma)] + C_1 x_{s+2}[-\rho_{s+1} x_{s+1} + f(\sigma)] \\ &\quad + C_1 x_{s+1}[-\rho_{s+2} x_{s+2} + f(\sigma)] + \cdots \\ &\quad + \sum_{i,k} \frac{a_i a_k}{\rho_i + \rho_k} \{x_k(-\rho_i x_i + f(\sigma)) + x_i(-\rho_k x_k + f(\sigma))\} \\ &\quad + f(\sigma)\left[\sum_{k=1}^{n+1} \beta_k x_k - rf(\sigma)\right].\end{aligned}$$

But

$$\sum_{i,k} a_i a_k\, x_i x_k = \left(\sum a_i x_i\right)^2, \qquad \sum_{i,k} \frac{a_k a_i}{\rho_k + \rho_i}(x_k + x_i) = 2\sum_{i,k} \frac{a_k a_i}{\rho_k + \rho_i} x_k;$$

hence

$$\begin{aligned}\frac{dV}{dt} &= -\sum_{k=1}^{s} \rho_k A_k x_k^2 - C_1(\rho_{s+1} + \rho_{s+2}) x_{s+1} x_{s+2} - \cdots \\ &\quad - C_{n-s}(\rho_n + \rho_{n+1}) x_n x_{n+1} - \left(\sum_{k=1}^{n+1} a_k x_k\right)^2 - [\sqrt{r} f(\sigma)]^2 \\ &\quad - 2\sqrt{r} f(\sigma) \sum_{k=1}^{n+1} a_k x_k\end{aligned}$$

$$+f(\sigma)\sum_{k=1}^{s}\left[A_k+\beta_k+2\sqrt{r}\,a_k+2a_k\sum_{i=1}^{n+1}\frac{a_i}{\rho_k+\rho_i}\right]x_k$$

$$+f(\sigma)\sum_{\alpha=1}^{n+1-s}\left[C_\alpha+\beta_{s+\alpha}+2\sqrt{r}\,a_{s+\alpha}+2a_{s+\alpha}\sum_{i=1}^{n+1}\frac{a_i}{\rho_{s+\alpha}+\rho_i}\right]x_{s+\alpha}.$$

For the sake of uniformity of writing we have introduced the notation

$$C_1=C_2\,,\qquad C_3=C_4\cdots C_{n-s}=C_{n-s+1}\,.$$

dV/dt will be negative-definite if we have

$$A_k+\beta_k+2\sqrt{r}\,a_k+2a_k\sum_{i=1}^{n+1}\frac{a_i}{\rho_k+\rho_i}=0\qquad(k=1,\ldots,s),$$

$$C_\alpha+\beta_{s+\alpha}+2\sqrt{r}\,a_{s+\alpha}+2a_{s+\alpha}\sum_{i=1}^{n+1}\frac{a_i}{\rho_k+\rho_i}=0\qquad(\alpha=1,\ldots,n-s+1).$$

If these conditions are fulfilled,

$$\frac{dV}{dt}=-\sum_{k=1}^{s}A_kx_k^2-C_1(\rho_{s+1}+\rho_{s+2})x_{s+1}x_{s+2}-\cdots$$

$$-C_{n-s}(\rho_n+\rho_{n+1})x_nx_{n+1}-\left[\sum_{k=1}^{n+1}a_kx_k+\sqrt{r}f(\sigma)\right]^2$$

and we see that if x has the property P, then $dV/dt\leqslant 0$.

If we take $A_k=0$, $C_k=0$ and we omit the term $-2\sqrt{r}\,f(\sigma)\sum a_kx_k$, we obtain as a condition of stability the existence of a vector with the property P which will verify the equations

$$\beta_k+2a_k\sum_{i=1}^{n+1}\frac{a_i}{\rho_k+\rho_i}=0\qquad(k=1,2,\ldots,n+1).$$

These conditions are simpler, but more restrictive.

We may easily obtain necessary conditions in order that the above equations admit solutions. By adding the equations together, we obtain

$$\sum_{k=1}^{n+1}\beta_k+2\sum_k\sum_i\frac{a_ka_i}{\rho_k+\rho_i}=0;$$

hence

$$\sum\beta_k+2\int_0^\infty\left(\sum a_k\,e^{-\rho_kt}\right)^2dt=0;$$

hence

$$\sum_{k=1}^{n+1} \beta_k < 0.$$

By multiplying each equation by ρ_k and adding them up we obtain

$$\sum \beta_k\rho_k + 2\sum_{i,k} \frac{\rho_k a_i a_k}{\rho_k + \rho_i} = \sum_k \beta_k\rho_k + \sum_{i,k} \frac{\rho_k a_i a_k}{\rho_k + \rho_i} + \sum_{i,k} \frac{\rho_i a_i a_k}{\rho_k + \rho_i}$$

$$= \sum_k \beta_k\rho_k + \sum_{i,k} a_i a_k = \sum_k \beta_k\rho_k + \left(\sum a_k\right)^2 = 0,$$

and hence

$$\sum_k \rho_k\beta_k < 0.$$

By dividing each equation by ρ_k and adding them up we obtain

$$\sum_k \frac{\beta_k}{\rho_k} + 2\sum_k \frac{a_k}{\rho_k} \sum_i \frac{a_i}{\rho_k + \rho_i}$$

$$= \sum_k \frac{\beta_k}{\rho_k} + 2\sum_{i,k} \frac{a_k}{\rho_k}\frac{a_i}{\rho_i}\frac{\rho_i}{\rho_i + \rho_k}$$

$$= \sum_k \frac{\beta_k}{\rho_k} + \sum_{i,k} \frac{a_k a_i}{\rho_k\rho_i} = \sum_k \frac{\beta_k}{\rho_k} + \left(\sum_k \frac{a_k}{\rho_k}\right)^2 = 0,$$

and thus

$$\sum_k \frac{\beta_k}{\rho_k} < 0.$$

Let us observe that in the preceding computations we have in fact studied the stability of the trivial solution of the system

$$\dot{x}_k = -\rho_k x_k + f(\sigma), \qquad \dot{\sigma} = \sum \beta_k x_k - rf(\sigma).$$

The stability of the trivial solution of this system obviously entails the stability of the trivial solution of the system

$$\dot{x}_k = -\rho_k x_k + f(\sigma), \qquad \sigma = \sum \gamma_k x_k.$$

Indeed, every solution of this system is also a solution for the studied system. If all the solutions of the studied system approach zero, the same will also be valid for the solutions of the second system. It is, however, clear that the request of stability for the first system is more than necessary for the stability of the second one. Starting from this observation, we see that it is meaningful to try to choose the Lyapunov function in such a way that it allows us to decide directly on the stability of the trivial solution for the second system. Let us choose

$$V = \sum_{i,k} \frac{a_k a_i}{\rho_k + \rho_i} x_k x_i.$$

We obtain

$$\begin{aligned}\frac{dV}{dt} &= \sum_{i,k} \frac{a_i a_k}{\rho_k + \rho_i} \{x_k[-\rho_i x_i + f(\sigma)] + x_i[-\rho_k x_k + f(\sigma)]\} \\ &= -\sum_{i,k} a_i a_k x_i x_k + \Big(\sum_{i,k} \frac{a_i a_k x_k}{\rho_k + \rho_i} + \sum_{i,k} \frac{a_i a_k x_i}{\rho_k + \rho_i}\Big) f(\sigma) \\ &= -\Big(\sum_k a_k x_k\Big)^2 + 2f(\sigma) \sum_{i,k} \frac{a_i a_k}{\rho_i + \rho_k} x_k.\end{aligned}$$

Taking into account that $-f(\sigma)[\sigma - \sum \gamma_k x_k] \equiv 0$, we may write

$$\frac{dV}{dt} = -\Big(\sum a_k x_k\Big)^2 - \sigma f(\sigma) + f(\sigma) \sum_k \Big[\gamma_k + 2a_k \sum_i \frac{a_i}{\rho_i + \rho_k}\Big] x_k.$$

We assume that we may choose a_k such that equations

$$\gamma_k + 2a_k \sum_i \frac{a_i}{\rho_i + \rho_k} - 0$$

be verified. Then

$$\frac{dV}{dt} = -\Big(\sum_k a_k x_k\Big)^2 - \sigma f(\sigma)$$

and the trivial solution will be stable.

Let us remark that if we choose $A_k = 0$, $C_k = 0$ in the constructions made above, dV/dt may be zero on the manifold $\sum a_k x_k + \sqrt{r} f(\sigma) = 0$ and in the last case on the manifold $\sum a_k x_k - 0$, $\sigma = 0$.

To obtain the asymptotic stability, it is necessary to require in addition that these manifolds do not contain whole semitrajectories (see Theorem 1.5′).

In some cases, taking into account the particular aspects of the system, simplified criteria may be obtained. Thus, if $\beta_1 < 0$ and $\rho_1 > 0$, we choose the function

$$V = \tfrac{1}{2}\beta_1 x_1^2 + \sum_{k,j=2}^{n+1} \frac{a_i a_j}{\rho_i + \rho_j} x_i x_j + \int_0^\sigma f(\sigma)\, d\sigma.$$

We obtain

$$\frac{dV}{dt} = -\beta_1 x_1[-\rho_1 x_1 + f(\sigma)] + \sum_{i,j=2}^{n+1} \frac{a_i a_j}{\rho_i + \rho_j}\{x_i[-\rho_j x_j + f(\sigma)]$$

$$+ x_j[-\rho_i x_i + f(\sigma)]\} + f(\sigma)\left[\beta_1 x_1 + \sum_{j=2}^{n+1} \beta_j x_j - rf(\sigma)\right]$$

$$= \beta_1 \rho_1 x_1^2 - \left(\sum_{j=2}^{n+1} a_j x_j\right)^2 - (\sqrt{r} f(\sigma))^2 - 2\sqrt{r} f(\sigma) \sum_{k=2}^{n+1} a_k x_k$$

$$+ f(\sigma) \sum_{j=2}^{n+1} \left(\beta_j + 2a_j \sum_{i=2}^{n+1} \frac{a_i}{\rho_i + \rho_j} + 2\sqrt{r}\, a_j\right) x_j$$

and we deduce as stability conditions the condition that equations

$$\beta_j + 2a_j \sum_{i=2}^{n+1} \frac{a_i}{\rho_j + \rho_i} + 2\sqrt{r}\, a_j = 0$$

have solutions. In this way, the number of the equations has been reduced by one.

Let us now suppose that the ρ_k are real and distinct. We choose

$$V = \tfrac{1}{2} \sum_{k=1}^{n+1} x_k^2 + R \int_0^\sigma f(\sigma)\, d\sigma \qquad (R > 0).$$

It follows that

$$\frac{dV}{dt} = -\sum_{k=1}^{n+1} \rho_k x_k^2 - rRf^2(\sigma) + \sum_{k=1}^{n+1} (1 + R\beta_k) x_k f(\sigma).$$

Consider $-dV/dt$ as a quadratic form in variables x_k and $f(\sigma)$. Its discriminant is

$$\Delta = \begin{vmatrix} \rho_1 & 0 & \cdots & 0 & -\dfrac{1 + R\beta_1}{2} \\ 0 & \rho_2 & \cdots & 0 & -\dfrac{1 + R\beta_2}{2} \\ \vdots & \vdots & & \vdots & \vdots \\ 0 & 0 & \cdots & \rho_{n+1} & -\dfrac{1 + R\beta_{n+1}}{2} \\ -\dfrac{1 + R\beta_1}{2} & -\dfrac{1 + R\beta_2}{2} & \cdots & -\dfrac{1 + R\beta_{n+1}}{2} & rR \end{vmatrix}.$$

The quadratic form is positive-definite if all ρ_k are positive and in addition $\Delta > 0$. We have

$$\Delta = rR\prod_{k=1}^{n+1}\rho_k - \tfrac{1}{4}\sum_{k=1}^{n+1}\rho_1 \cdots \rho_{k-1}(1 + R\beta_k)^2 \rho_{k+1} \cdots \rho_{n+1} \,.$$

The condition $\Delta > 0$ is written

$$4rR > \sum_{k=1}^{n+1}\frac{(1 + R\beta_k)^2}{\rho_k} \,.$$

If there exists a positive constant R which verifies this inequality, the trivial solution of the system is absolutely stable.

If $\rho_1, \ldots, \rho_s$ are real and $\rho_{s+1}, \ldots, \rho_{n+1}$ are complex, we choose

$$V = \tfrac{1}{2}\sum_{k=1}^{s} x_k^2 + \sum_{\alpha=1}^{n-s} x_{s+\alpha}x_{s+\alpha+1} + R\int_0^\sigma f(\sigma)\, d\sigma,$$

and we obtain

$$\frac{dV}{dt} = -\sum_{k=1}^{s}\rho_k x_k^2 - \sum_{\alpha=1}^{n-s}(\rho_{s+1} + \rho_{s+\alpha+1})x_{s+\alpha}x_{s+\alpha+1}$$

$$+ \sum_{k=1}^{n+1}(1 + R\beta_k)x_k f(\sigma) - rRf^2(\sigma).$$

If

$$x_{s+\alpha} = u_{s+\alpha} + iv_{s+\alpha}\,, \qquad \beta_{s+\alpha} = p_{s+\alpha} + iq_{s+\alpha}\,, \qquad \rho_{s+\alpha} = \sigma_{s+\alpha} + i\tau_{s+\alpha}\,,$$

then

$$\frac{dV}{dt} = -\sum_{k=1}^{s}\rho_k x_k^2 - \sum \sigma_{s+\alpha}(u_{s+\alpha}^2 + v_{s+\alpha}^2) - rRf^2(\sigma)$$

$$+ \sum_{k=1}^{s}(1 + R\beta_k)x_k f(\sigma) + 2\sum [u_{s+\alpha} + R(p_{s+\alpha}u_{s+\alpha} - q_{s+\alpha}v_{s+\alpha})]f(\sigma).$$

We have again obtained a quadratic form, and the stability conditions is obtained by requiring that Re $\rho_j > 0$ and in addition that a certain determinant be positive.

A general procedure for obtaining some simplified criteria was proposed by I. G. Malkin in 1951. It is assumed that the ρ_k are real and distinct. Let

$$W = -\tfrac{1}{2}\sum_{\alpha,\beta} A_{\alpha\beta}x_\alpha x_\beta$$

be a negative-definite quadratic form and

$$F = \tfrac{1}{2} \sum_{\alpha,\beta} B_{\alpha\beta} x_\alpha x_\beta ,$$

where $B_{\alpha\beta} = A_{\alpha\beta}/(\rho_\alpha + \rho_\beta)$. We have

$$F = \sum_{\alpha,\beta} A_{\alpha\beta} \int_0^\infty e^{-(\rho_\alpha+\rho_\beta)t}\, dt\, x_\alpha x_\beta = \int_0^\infty \Big[\sum_{\alpha,\beta} A_{\alpha\beta} x_\alpha\, e^{-\rho_\alpha t}\, x_\beta\, e^{-\rho_\beta t}\Big]\, dt.$$

Since

$$\sum_{\alpha,\beta} A_{\alpha\beta}\, x_\alpha\, e^{-\rho_\alpha t}\, x_\beta\, e^{-\rho_\beta t} \geqslant 0,$$

it follows that F is positive-definite. We choose

$$V = F + \int_0^\sigma f(\sigma)\, d\sigma.$$

It follows that

$$\frac{dV}{dt} = \tfrac{1}{2} \sum B_{\alpha\beta}\{x_\alpha(-\rho_\beta x_\beta + f(\sigma)) + x_\beta(-\rho_\alpha x_\alpha + f(\sigma))\}$$

$$+ f(\sigma)\Big[\sum \beta_k x_k - rf(\sigma)\Big] = -\tfrac{1}{2} \sum B_{\alpha\beta}(\rho_\alpha + \rho_\beta) x_\alpha x_\beta$$

$$+ f(\sigma)\Big[\tfrac{1}{2} \sum_{\alpha,\beta} (x_\alpha + x_\beta)\, B_{\alpha\beta} + \sum \beta_k x_k\Big] - rf^2(\sigma)$$

$$= W - rf^2(\sigma) + f(\sigma) \sum_\alpha \Big[\beta_\alpha + \tfrac{1}{2} \sum_\beta (B_{\alpha\beta} + B_{\beta\alpha})\Big]\, x_\alpha .$$

Considering dV/dt as a quadratic form in $x_1, \ldots, x_{n+1}$ and $f(\sigma)$, we obtain the discriminant

$$\Delta = \begin{vmatrix} A_{11} & \cdots & A_{1,n+1} & P_1 \\ A_{21} & \cdots & A_{2,n+1} & P_2 \\ \vdots & & \vdots & \vdots \\ A_{n+1,1} & \cdots & A_{n+1,n+1} & P_{n+1} \\ P_1 & \cdots & P_{n+1} & 1 \end{vmatrix}, \qquad P_\alpha = \tfrac{1}{2}\Big\{\beta_\alpha + \tfrac{1}{2} \sum_\beta (B_{\alpha\beta} + B_{\beta\alpha})\Big\}.$$

Since W is by construction negative-definite, the condition of stability is reduced to $\Delta > 0$.

2.2. Intrinsic Study of Control Systems

In the preceding section we have studied the problem of absolute stability for systems of the form

$$\frac{dy}{dt} = Ay + bf(\sigma), \qquad \sigma = c^*y,$$

where we assumed that the matrix A has eigenvalues with negative real parts. Differentiating the relation which defines σ, we obtain the system

$$\frac{dy}{dt} = Ay + bf(\sigma), \qquad \frac{d\sigma}{dt} = c^*Ay + c^*\, bf(\sigma).$$

Systems of this form are also reached by convenient changes of variables, starting from other forms which occur in the theory of automatic control. Thus, consider systems of the form

$$\frac{dy}{dt} = Ay + b\xi, \qquad \frac{d\xi}{dt} = f(\sigma), \qquad \sigma = c^*y - r\xi. \tag{3}$$

If we put $\dot{y} = x$, we obtain

$$\frac{dx}{dt} = Ax + bf(\sigma), \qquad \frac{d\sigma}{dt} = c^*x - rf(\sigma). \tag{4}$$

If the matrix $\begin{pmatrix} A & b \\ c^* & -r \end{pmatrix}$ is nonsingular, the two systems are equivalent from the viewpoint of absolute stability.

A few years ago, S. Lefschetz, investigating systems of this form, formulated the problem in the following way. If A has eigenvalues with negative real parts, according to a Lyapunov theorem, a matrix B, positive-definite, may be chosen such that

$$BA + A^*B = -C,$$

for any given positive-definite matrix C.

Then consider the Lyapunov function

$$V = (Bx, x) + \int_0^\sigma f(\sigma)\, d\sigma.$$

The total derivative has the form

$$\frac{dV}{dt} = (BAx, x) + (Bx, Ax) + (Bbf(\sigma), x) + (Bx, bf(\sigma))$$
$$+ f(\sigma)(c^*x - rf(\sigma)) = -(Cx, x) + 2(Bb, x)f(\sigma) + (c, x)f(\sigma) - rf^2(\sigma).$$

Considering dV/dt as a quadratic form in $x, f(\sigma)$, the condition that $-dV/dt$ be positive-definite is that the principal diagonal minors of the matrix

$$\begin{pmatrix} C & -(Bb + \frac{1}{2}c) \\ -(Bb + \frac{1}{2}c)^* & r \end{pmatrix}$$

be positive.

Since by hypothesis the matrix C was chosen positive-definite, the condition reduces to

$$\begin{vmatrix} C & -(Bb + \frac{1}{2}c) \\ -(Bb + \frac{1}{2}c)^* & r \end{vmatrix} > 0.$$

By hypothesis, $\det C > 0$; hence $\det C^{-1} > 0$; hence $\det \begin{pmatrix} C^{-1} & 0 \\ 0 & 1 \end{pmatrix} > 0.$

Therefore, the condition that $-dV/dt$ be positive may also be written

$$\det \begin{pmatrix} C^{-1} & 0 \\ 0 & 1 \end{pmatrix} \det \begin{pmatrix} C & -(Bb + \frac{1}{2}c) \\ -(Bb + \frac{1}{2}c)^* & r \end{pmatrix} > 0.$$

By computing the product of both determinants, we will have

$$\begin{vmatrix} E & -C^{-1}(Bb + \frac{1}{2}c) \\ -(Bb + \frac{1}{2}c)^* & r \end{vmatrix} > 0;$$

hence

$$r - (Bb + \tfrac{1}{2}c)^* C^{-1}(Bb + \tfrac{1}{2}c) > 0.$$

We thus reach the condition $r > (Bb + \frac{1}{2}c)^* C^{-1}(Bb + \frac{1}{2}c)$. This condition depends upon the choice of matrix C; we shall obtain the best condition by considering the minimum for all the positive-definite matrices C.

The computation of this minimum in the general case has not yet been made. S. Lefschetz has considered the case where matrix A is diagonal and matrix C is taken also in the class of diagonal matrices.

Let

$$A = \operatorname{diag}(-\mu_1, \ldots, -\mu_n), \qquad C = \operatorname{diag}(d_1, \ldots, d_n).$$

We have

$$C^{-1} = \operatorname{diag}\left(\frac{1}{d_1}, \ldots, \frac{1}{d_n}\right);$$

therefore

$$B = \operatorname{diag}\left(\frac{d_1}{2\mu_1}, \ldots, \frac{d_n}{2\mu_n}\right).$$

Bb has the elements $d_k b_k/2\mu_k$, $Bb + \frac{1}{2}c$ has the elements $\frac{1}{2}((d_k b_k/\mu_k) + c_k)$, $C^{-1}(Bb + \frac{1}{2}c)$ has the elements $\frac{1}{2}((b_k/\mu_k) + (c_k/d_k))$, and the stability condition becomes

$$r > \sum_{k=1}^{n} \frac{d_k}{4}\left(\frac{b_k}{\mu_k} + \frac{c_k}{d_k}\right)^2 = \frac{1}{4}\sum_{k=1}^{n}\left(\frac{b_k\sqrt{d_k}}{\mu_k} + \frac{c_k}{\sqrt{d_k}}\right)^2.$$

For indices k for which $b_k c_k < 0$ we may choose d_k such that $(b_k\sqrt{dk}/\mu_k) + (c_k/\sqrt{d_k})$ be zero, and this is the choice yielding the minimum. For indices k for which $b_k c_k > 0$, the term $((b_k\sqrt{d_k}/\mu_k) + (c_k/\sqrt{d_k}))^2$ is minimal if $b_k\sqrt{d_k}/\mu_k = c_k/\sqrt{d_k}$, hence if $b_k d_k = c_k\mu_k$, $d_k = c_k\mu_k/b_k$ and then the minimal value is

$$\left(\frac{b_k}{\mu_k}\sqrt{\frac{c_k\mu_k}{b_k}} + c_k\sqrt{\frac{b_k}{c_k\mu_k}}\right)^2 = \left(\sqrt{\frac{b_k c_k}{\mu_k}} + \sqrt{\frac{b_k c_k}{\mu_k}}\right)^2 = \frac{4b_k c_k}{\mu_k}.$$

Thus will follow the stability condition

$$r > \sum_{k=1}^{n} \frac{\epsilon_k b_k c_k}{\mu_k},$$

where $\epsilon_k = 0$ if $b_k c_k \leqslant 0$ and $\epsilon_k = 1$ if $b_k c_k > 0$.

T. Morozan has improved these results by using a Lyapunov function of modified form introduced by V. M. Popov. Let us first observe that a necessary condition for absolute stability is that $r + c^*A^{-1}b > 0$. Indeed, if absolute stability occurs, then the eigenvalues of the matrix $\begin{pmatrix} A & b \\ c^* & -r \end{pmatrix}$ have negative real parts, since the asymptotic stability must be also assured for $f(\sigma) = \sigma$. But the product of the eigenvalues is $\det\begin{pmatrix} A & b \\ c^* & -r \end{pmatrix}$. We have, however,

$$\det\begin{pmatrix} A^{-1} & 0 \\ 0 & 1 \end{pmatrix}\det\begin{pmatrix} A & b \\ c^* & -r \end{pmatrix} = \det\begin{pmatrix} E & A^{-1}b \\ c^* & -r \end{pmatrix} = -(r + c^*A^{-1}b);$$

hence

$$r + c^*A^{-1}b = -\det A^{-1}\det\begin{pmatrix} A & b \\ c^* & -r \end{pmatrix} = -\frac{1}{\det A}\det\begin{pmatrix} A & b \\ c^* & -r \end{pmatrix}.$$

By hypothesis, matrix A and $\begin{pmatrix} A & b \\ c^* & -r \end{pmatrix}$ have eigenvalues with negative real parts. If a matrix has the order k and its eigenvalues have negative real parts, the product of these eigenvalues is positive when k is even and negative when k is odd (the matrices are assumed real; hence the complex roots occur in pairs and their product is positive). Since the product of the eigenvalues is equal to the determinant of the matrix, it follows that this determinant is positive when k is even and negative when k is odd. Since the orders of matrices A and $\begin{pmatrix} A & b \\ c^* & -r \end{pmatrix}$ differ by one unit, it follows that $\det A$ and $\det \begin{pmatrix} A & b \\ c^* & -r \end{pmatrix}$ have different signs; hence $r + c^*A^{-1}b > 0$.

Now let B be as previously. We choose the Lyapunov function of the form

$$V = (Bx, x) + \int_0^\sigma f(\sigma)\, d\sigma + \frac{p}{2(r + c^*A^{-1}b)} (c^*A^{-1}x - \sigma)^2.$$

Let us observe that without supposing that $\int^\infty f(\sigma) d\sigma$ diverges, the function V fulfills the required conditions in order that the asymptotic stability *in the large* be assured; indeed, if $|x| + |\sigma| \to \infty$, we have $V \to \infty$, since for $|x| < M$, $|\sigma| \to \infty$, the last term approaches infinity. The total derivative of this function is

$$\begin{aligned} \frac{dV}{dt} &= (BAx, x) + (Bbf(\sigma), x) + (Bx, Ax) + (Bx, bf(\sigma)) \\ &\quad + f(\sigma)(c^*x - rf(\sigma)) + \frac{p}{r + c^*A^{-1}b} (c^*A^{-1}Ax + c^*A^{-1}bf(\sigma) \\ &\quad - c^*x + rf(\sigma))(c^*A^{-1}x - \sigma) = -(Cx, x) + 2(Bb, x)f(\sigma) \\ &\quad + (c, x)f(\sigma) - rf^2(\sigma) - p\sigma f(\sigma) + pc^*A^{-1}xf(\sigma) = -(Cx, x) \\ &\quad + f(\sigma)(2Bb + c + p(A^*)^{-1}c, x) - rf^2(\sigma) - p\sigma f(\sigma). \end{aligned}$$

Discarding the last term, which is negative, and considering the others as a quadratic form in $x, f(\sigma)$, the condition that $-dV/dt$ be positive-definite is that the principal diagonal minors of the matrix

$$\begin{pmatrix} C & Bb + \frac{1}{2}(E + p(A^*)^{-1})c \\ (Bb + \frac{1}{2}(E + p(A^*)^{-1})c)^* & -r \end{pmatrix}$$

be positive. The same computations as in the preceding case lead to the condition $r > M(C, p)$, where

$$M(C, p) = (Bb + \tfrac{1}{2}(E + p(A^*)^{-1})c)^*\, C^{-1}(Bb + \tfrac{1}{2}(E + p(A^*)^{-1})c).$$

If

$$\min_{C>0,\, p\geqslant 0} M(C, p) \leqslant -c^*A^{-1}b,$$

a necessary and sufficient condition for absolute stability is $r > -c^*A^{-1}b$, since if $r + c^*A^{-1}b > 0$, we also have $r > M(C, p)$ for a conveniently chosen matrix C.

Let us observe that

$$\min_{C>0,p\geqslant 0} M(C, p) \leqslant \min_{C>0} (Bb + \tfrac{1}{2}c)^*C^{-1}(Bb + \tfrac{1}{2}c);$$

hence the new choice of the Lyapunov function is more convenient.

Let us also observe that if

$$r \geqslant \min_{C>0,p\geqslant 0} M(C, p) > -c^*A^{-1}b,$$

absolute stability is assured. Indeed, the quadratic form is only semi-definite, but it may be zero only for $x = 0$, $\sigma \neq 0$, and then the term $-p\sigma f(\sigma)$ is strictly negative.

Taking into account the above-mentioned facts, the problem arises of calculating the value $\min_{C>0,p\geqslant 0} M(C, p)$. This computation has not been carried out in the general case. However, complete results may be obtained by supposing that A is diagonal and choosing C in the class of diagonal matrices, as above. Let us take $A = \operatorname{diag}(-\mu_i)$, $\mu_i > 0$, $C = (\gamma_{ij})$; we obtain $B = (\gamma_{ij}/(\mu_i + \mu_k))$. We may write

$$M(C, P) = (C^{-1}u, u)\,, \qquad u = Bb + \tfrac{1}{2}(E + p(A^*)^{-1})c\,,$$

$$u_i = \sum_{j=1}^{n} \frac{\gamma_{ij}b_j}{\mu_i + \mu_j} + \tfrac{1}{2}\left(1 - \frac{p}{\mu_i}\right)c_i.$$

Since $C > 0$, the quadratic form $(C^{-1}u, u)$ is positive-definite; hence

$$\min_{C>0,p\geqslant 0} M(C, p) \geqslant 0,$$

the zero value being obtained only if $u = 0$. Let us observe that

$$c^*A^{-1}b = -\sum_{i=1}^{n} \frac{b_i c_i}{\mu_i}.$$

When C is a diagonal matrix, $C = (\operatorname{diag} d_i)$:

$$u_i = \frac{d_i b_i}{2\mu_i} + \frac{1}{2}\left(1 - \frac{p}{\mu_i}\right)c_i\,, \qquad C^{-1}u = \left(\frac{b_i}{2\mu_i} + \frac{1}{2d_i}\left(1 - \frac{p}{\mu_i}\right)c_i\right),$$

$$M(C, p) = \frac{1}{4}\sum_{i=1}^{n} d_i \left(\frac{b_i}{\mu_i} + \frac{(1 - (p/\mu_i))c_i}{d_i}\right)^2$$

$$= \frac{1}{4}\sum_{i=1}^{n}\left(\frac{b_i\sqrt{d_i}}{\mu_i} + \frac{(1 - (p/\mu_i)c_i}{\sqrt{d_i}}\right)^2.$$

By the same arguments as above, we deduce

$$\min_{C>0} M(C,p) = N(p) = \sum_{i=1}^{n} \frac{\epsilon_i b_i c_i(\mu_i - p)}{\mu_i^2} = \sum_{i=1}^{n} \frac{\epsilon_i b_i c_i}{\mu_i} - p \sum_{i=1}^{n} \frac{\epsilon_i b_i c_i}{\mu_i^2},$$

where

$$\epsilon_i = \begin{cases} 0 & \text{if } b_i c_i(\mu_i - p) \leqslant 0, \\ 1 & \text{if } b_i c_i(\mu \ \ - p) > 0. \end{cases}$$

If

$$\max_{1 \leqslant i \leqslant n} b_i c_i < 0$$

or

$$\max_{i \in I} \mu_i < \min_{j \in J} \mu_j ,$$

where $I = \{i, 1 \leqslant i \leqslant n, b_i c_i > 0\}$, $J = \{j, 1 \leqslant j \leqslant n, b_j c_j \leqslant 0\}$, then

$$\min_{C>0, p \geqslant 0} M(C,p) = 0;$$

indeed, in the first case we can take

$$p < \min \mu_i ,$$

and in the second

$$\max_{i \in I} \mu_i < p < \min_{j \in J} \mu_j .$$

It is obvious that in these cases the minimum is effectively attained on diagonal matrices.

Likewise, if $\min_{1 \leqslant i \leqslant n} b_i c_i > 0$, by taking $p = 0$ we will have

$$N(0) = \sum \frac{b_i c_i}{\mu_i} > 0,$$

and the necessary and sufficient condition of absolute stability is $r > N(0)$.

We may study the problem of absolute stability by looking for Lyapunov functions of the form

$$V = (Hx, x) + \int_0^\sigma f(\sigma)\, d\sigma,$$

where H is any symmetric matrix. An investigation of this kind has been made by V. A. Iakubovitch. The total derivative of function V is

$$\dot{V} = (H\dot{x}, x) + (Hx, \dot{x}) + f(\sigma)\dot{\sigma} = (H(Ax + bf(\sigma)), x)$$
$$+ (Hx, Ax + bf(\sigma)) + f(\sigma)(c^*x - rf(\sigma)) = ((HA + A^*H)x, x)$$
$$+ 2(Hb, x)f(\sigma) + (c^*x)f(\sigma) - rf^2(\sigma) = -(Gx, x) - 2(g^*x)f(\sigma) - rf^2(\sigma),$$

where we have set

$$-G = HA + A^*H, \qquad -g = Hb + \tfrac{1}{2}c.$$

Further,

$$\dot{V} = -\left\{\left(\left(G - \frac{1}{r}gg^*\right)x, x\right) + r\left(f(\sigma) + \frac{1}{r}g^*x\right)^2\right\},$$

since

$$\frac{1}{r}(gg^*x, x) - \frac{1}{r}(g^*x)^2 = 0.$$

Indeed, gg^* is the matrix with elements g_ig_j; hence (gg^*x, x) is

$$\sum_{i,j} g_ig_jx_ix_j = \left(\sum g_ix_i\right)^2 = (g^*x)^2.$$

It follows that a sufficient condition in order that $\dot{V}$ be negative is that the form

$$\left(\left(G - \frac{1}{r}gg^*\right)x, x\right)$$

be positive-definite.

This condition is also necessary. Let us suppose that there exists $x_0 \neq 0$ such that

$$\left(\left(G - \frac{1}{r}gg^*\right)x_0, x_0\right) \leqslant 0;$$

let $g^*x_0 \neq 0$. We choose λ from the equation

$$\sqrt{r}f(\sigma_0) + \frac{\lambda}{\sqrt{r}}g^*x_0 = 0,$$

with fixed σ_0. Then, for $x = \lambda x_0$, $\sigma = \sigma_0$ we will have $r(f(\sigma) + (1/r)g^*x) = 0$; hence $\dot{V} \geqslant 0$. If $g^*x_0 = 0$, we take $x = x_0 \neq 0$, $\sigma = 0$, and again it will follow that $\dot{V} \geqslant 0$. Consequently, if the form is not positive-definite, we cannot have $\dot{V}$ negative-definite.

Theorem 2.1. *If there exists a symmetric matrix $H > 0$ such that*

$$rG - gg^* > 0^\dagger$$

(where $-G = HA + A^*H$, $-g = Hb + \frac{1}{2}c$), and if A is Hurwitzian ‡ *and $r + (A^{-1}b, c) > 0$, then the trivial solution of system* (4) *is absolutely stable.*

Proof. From the computations performed up to now, it follows that there exists a function

$$V = (Hx, x) + \int_0^\sigma f(\sigma)\, d\sigma$$

whose total derivative is negative. Consequently, the asymptotic stability of the trivial solution is immediate. If $\int^\infty f(\sigma) d\sigma$ diverges, the function V fulfills the conditions required for asymptotic stability in the large. Using the condition $r + (A^{-1}b, c) > 0$, we may nevertheless prove that asymptotic stability in the large occurs without the hypothesis that the integral diverges. For this purpose we will take

$$V_1 = V + \frac{p}{2(r + c^*A^{-1}b)} (c^*A^{-1}x - \sigma)^2.$$

The function V_1 fulfills the condition required for stability in the large:

$$\frac{dV_1}{dt} = \frac{dV}{dt} + \frac{p}{r + c^*A^{-1}b} (c^*A^{-1}x - \sigma)(c^*A^{-1}Ax + c^*A^{-1}bf(\sigma)$$

$$-c^*x + rf(\sigma)) = \frac{dV}{dt} + pf(\sigma)(c^*A^{-1}x - \sigma) = \frac{dV}{dt} + pf(\sigma)c^*A^{-1}x - p\sigma f(\sigma).$$

From the hypotheses of the theorem it follows that dV/dt is a negative-definite quadratic form in x and $f(\sigma)$; for p sufficiently small, the quadratic form $(dV/dt) + pf(\sigma)c^*A^{-1}x$ is negative-definite; hence dV_1/dt is negative-definite and the theorem is proved. The theorem has been proved by indirect means by B. A. Iakubovitch.§ The idea of considering the function V_1 instead of the function V belongs to V. M. Popov.

† If G_1 and G_2 are symmetric matrices, $G_1 > G_2$ means that the quadratic form $((G_1 - G_2)x, x)$ is positive-definite.

‡ We call Hurwitzian a matrix whose eigenvalues have negative real parts.

§ The study of the problem was resumed by J. P. La Salle, who proved that if $r > g^*G^{-1}g$, then the condition $r + c^*A^{-1}b > 0$ is fulfilled.

The practical problem which arises now is to give to the condition in the statement a simple form, one that is easy to check. To this end we observe that this condition may be written

$$-r(A^*H + HA) - (Hb + \tfrac{1}{2}c)(b^*H + \tfrac{1}{2}c^*) = \frac{r}{2} C > 0$$

or

$$Hbb^*H + B^*H + HB + \tfrac{1}{4}cc^* + \frac{r}{2} C = 0,$$

where we have put $B = rA + \frac{1}{2}bc^*$. This condition may be considered as an equation with respect to H for each fixed $C > 0$. The condition of stability may hence be obtained either by arbitrarily choosing $H > 0$ and putting the condition that $C > 0$ or conversely, by arbitrarily choosing $C > 0$ and requiring that the equation admit a solution $H > 0$. We shall follow the second variant and try to attain the simplest conditions possible.

Lemma 1. *If the eigenvalues of matrix K have negative real parts, the solution X of equation $K^*X + XK = -C$ is unique and is given by the formula*

$$X = \int_0^\infty e^{K^*t} C e^{Kt}\, dt.$$

If $C > 0$, then $X > 0$. If $C \geqslant 0$, then $X \geqslant 0$. If $C > 0$ and $X > 0$, then K is Hurwitzian.

Proof. The equation $K^*X + XK = -C$ expresses the fact that the total derivative of the function (Xx, x), by virtue of the system $dx/dt = Kx$, is equal to $-(Cx, x)$. From the theorem of Lyapunov, it follows that if the matrix K is Hurwitzian, then for any C the preceding equation has a unique solution. The fact that the matrix X is given by the formula from the statement follows from Theorem 1.6″.

Indeed, if

$$V = \int_t^\infty (Ce^{K(s-t)}x, e^{K(s-t)}x)\, ds$$

we have

$$V = \int_0^\infty (Ce^{Ks}x, e^{Ks}x)\, ds = \int_0^\infty (e^{K^*s}Ce^{Ks}x, x)\, ds = (Xx, x),$$

with $X = \int_0^\infty e^{K^*s}Ce^{Ks}\, ds$ and $dV/dt = -(Cx, x)$. The solution of the equation being unique, it is given by the formula in the statement.

The fact that $C \geqslant 0$ implies $X \geqslant 0$ and $C > 0$ implies $X > 0$ is seen at once from the formula. If $C > 0$ and $X > 0$, the trivial solution of the system $dx/dt = Kx$ is asymptotically stable and matrix K is Hurwitzian.

Lemma 2. *Let*

$$Hbb^*H + B^*H + HB + \tfrac{1}{4}cc^* + \frac{r}{2}C = 0, \qquad B = rA + \tfrac{1}{2}bc^*,$$

where $C > 0$ and H is symmetric. We suppose that there exists $0 \leqslant \nu \leqslant 1$ such that $K_\nu = rA + \nu bc^*$ is Hurwitzian. Then $H > 0$ and K_ν is Hurwitzian for every $\nu \in (0, 1)$.

Proof. Let

$$C_\mu = \frac{r}{2}C + (\mu Hb + \tfrac{1}{2}c)(\mu Hb + \tfrac{1}{2}c)^*;$$

obviously $C_\mu > 0$.

From the statement,

$$\begin{aligned}\frac{r}{2}C &= -Hbb^*H - (rA^* + \tfrac{1}{2}cb^*)H - H(rA + \tfrac{1}{2}bc^*) - \tfrac{1}{4}cc^* \\ &= -Hbb^*H - r(A^*H + HA) - \tfrac{1}{2}(cb^*H + Hbc^*) - \tfrac{1}{4}cc^*.\end{aligned}$$

If follows that

$$\begin{aligned}C_\mu &= -Hbb^*H - (rA^* + \tfrac{1}{2}cb^*)H - H(rA + \tfrac{1}{2}bc^*) - \tfrac{1}{4}cc^* \\ &\quad + \mu^2 Hbb^*H + \tfrac{1}{2}\mu c(Hb)^* + \tfrac{1}{2}\mu Hbc^* + \tfrac{1}{4}cc^* = (\mu^2 - 1)Hbb^*H \\ &\quad - [rA^* + \tfrac{1}{2}(1 - \mu)cb^*]H - H[rA + \tfrac{1}{2}(1 - \mu)bc^*] \\ &= -(1 - \mu^2)Hbb^*H - K_\nu^*H - HK_\nu\,,\end{aligned}$$

where we have put

$$\nu = \tfrac{1}{2}(1 - \mu).$$

The relation obtained may also be written

$$K_\nu^*H + HK_\nu = -C_\mu - (1 - \mu^2)Hbb^*H.$$

Now let ν be as in the statement. We choose $\mu = 1 - 2\nu$; if $0 \leqslant \nu \leqslant 1$, it follows that $|\mu| \leqslant 1$; hence $C_\mu + (1 - \mu^2)Hbb^*H > 0$. From Lemma 1 it follows that this equation has a solution H, unique, and

$H > 0$. For every $\nu \in [0, 1]$ we have $C_\mu + (1 - \mu^2)Hbb^*H > 0$ and $H > 0$; hence K_ν is Hurwitzian.

From this lemma we deduce in particular that if the equation in H which expresses the stability condition admits a symmetric solution, then this solution is also positive-definite.

Indeed, A being Hurwitzian, K_0 is Hurwitzian; hence $H > 0$.

The system of equations which determines the elements of the matrix H is a system of $n(n + 1)/2$ equations of second degree. We shall reduce the problem to the condition that a system of n equations of second degree has real solutions.

Define the operator $Y = L(X)$ by the formula

$$A^*Y + YA = -X,$$

which is possible, since from Lemma 1, for any X the formula defines one Y and only one, which is positive together with X. According to Lemma 1, we have explicitly

$$L(X) = \int_0^\infty e^{A^*t}Xe^{At}\,dt.$$

Set

$$-g = Hb + \tfrac{1}{2}c.$$

The equation which expresses the stability condition is written

$$r(A^*H + HA) = -\frac{r}{2}C - gg^*,$$

and taking into account the definition of $L(X)$, we will have

$$rH = L(gg^*) + \tfrac{1}{2}\,rL(C).$$

From here, multiplying by b and adding $\frac{1}{2}rc$, we deduce

$$-rg = L(gg^*)b + \tfrac{1}{2}r(c + L(C)b).$$

Setting $a = L(C)b$, we reach the equation

$$L(gg^*)b + rg + \tfrac{1}{2}r(c + a) = 0.$$

Let us suppose that for given $C > 0$, this equation has a real solution g. Then, the matrix H determined by the relation

$$rH = L(gg^*) + \tfrac{1}{2}rL(C)$$

is symmetric, positive-definite, and verifies the relation

$$r(A^*H + HA) = -\frac{r}{2}C - gg^*;$$

hence the stability condition is fulfilled.

Thus will follow

Theorem 2.1′. *If A is Hurwitzian, $\Gamma^2 = r + (A^{-1}b, c) > 0$, and if there exists $C > 0$ such that upon putting $a = L(C)b$ the equation*

$$L(gg^*)b + rg + \tfrac{1}{2}r(c + a) = 0$$

admits a real solution g, then the trivial solution of the system is absolutely stable.

Setting $U = L(gg^*)$, $T = L(C)$, we obtain the equations

$$A^*T + TA = -C, \qquad a = Tb, \qquad A^*U + UA = -gg^*,$$
$$Ub + ru + \tfrac{1}{2}r(c + a) = 0.$$

Let us see what the equations become in the case where A admits a normal diagonal form and the eigenvalues of A are real. We will denote $g = (g_i)$, $U = (\eta_{ij})$. There exists a basis in which A is diagonal and the components of b are equal to 1 (Lurie canonical form). In this basis the preceding equations become

$$-(\rho_j + \rho_i)\eta_{ij} = -g_i g_j\,, \qquad \sum_j \eta_{ij} + rg_i + \tfrac{1}{2}r(c_i + a_i) = 0;$$

hence

$$g_i \sum_j \frac{g_j}{\rho_i + \rho_j} + rg_i + \tfrac{1}{2}(c_i + a_i) = 0,$$

and we see that they are of the same form as those obtained in the preceding section.

Consequence. *In the case where b is an eigenvector of matrix A or c is an eigenvector of matrix A^*, the condition $\Gamma^2 > 0$ is necessary and sufficient for absolute stability.*

Proof. Let $Ab = -\alpha b$, $\alpha > 0$. From $A^*U + UA = -gg^*$ we obtain, multiplying by b, $(A^* - \alpha I)Ub = -(g, b)g$; hence $Ub = -(g, b)(A^* - \alpha I)^{-1}g$ [det $(A^* - \alpha I) \neq 0$, since $\alpha > 0$ and A is Hurwitzian]. From the same relation, multiplying at the left by b^*A^{*-1} and at the right by $A^{-1}b$, we obtain

$$b^*UA^{-1}b + b^*A^{*-1}Ub = -a^*A^{*-1}gg^*A^{-1}b,$$

i.e.,

$$(A^{-1}b, Ub) + (Ub, A^{-1}b) = -(A^{-1}b, g)^2;$$

hence

$$2(Ub, A^{-1}b) = -(A^{-1}b, g)^2.$$

Set $\zeta = (1/\sqrt{r})(g, A^{-1}b)$. From the equation

$$Ub + ru + \tfrac{1}{2}r(c + a) = 0$$

we deduce

$$Ub = -rg - \tfrac{1}{2}r(c + a).$$

It follows that

$$-2(rg + \tfrac{1}{2}r(c + a), A^{-1}b) = -r\zeta^2;$$

hence

$$r\zeta^2 - 2r\sqrt{r}\zeta - r(c + a, A^{-1}b) = 0;$$

hence

$$\zeta^2 - 2\sqrt{r}\zeta - (c + A, A^{-1}b) = 0, \qquad \zeta = \sqrt{r} \pm \sqrt{r + (c + a, A^{-1}b)}.$$

Setting $\tilde{\Gamma}^2 = r + (c + a, A^{-1}b)$, it follows that $\zeta = \sqrt{r} + \tilde{\Gamma}$. From $Ab = -\alpha b$, we obtain

$$b = -\alpha A^{-1}b, \qquad A^{-1}b = -\frac{1}{\alpha}b;$$

hence

$$\zeta = -\frac{1}{\alpha\sqrt{r}}(g, b);$$

hence

$$(g, b) = -\alpha\sqrt{r}(\sqrt{r} \pm \tilde{\Gamma}).$$

From $Ub = -(g, b)(A^* - \alpha I)^{-1}g$ follows

$$-rg - \tfrac{1}{2}r(c + a) = \alpha\sqrt{r}(\sqrt{r} + \tilde{\Gamma})(A^* - \alpha I)^{-1}g;$$

hence

$$-\tfrac{1}{2}r(A^* - \alpha I)(c + a) = r\left(A^* \pm \frac{\alpha}{\sqrt{r}}\tilde{\Gamma}I\right)g.$$

It follows finally that

$$g = -\tfrac{1}{2}\left(A \pm \frac{\alpha\Gamma}{\sqrt{r}} I\right)^{-1}(A^* - \alpha I)(c + a).$$

We see that the equation in g has a real solution if and only if $\tilde{\Gamma}$ is real; hence $\tilde{\Gamma}^2 > 0$. But $\tilde{\Gamma}^2 = \Gamma^2 + (a, A^{-1}b)$.

We have

$$A^*T + TA = -C, \qquad a = Tb, \qquad (a, A^{-1}b) = (A^{*-1}Tb, b),$$

$$T + A^{*-1}TA = -A^{*-1}C, \qquad A^{*-1}T + TA^{-1} = -A^{*-1}CA^{-1};$$

hence

$$(A^{*-1}Tb, b) = -\tfrac{1}{2}(A^{*-1}CA^{-1}b, b) = -\tfrac{1}{2}(CA^{-1}b, A^{-1}b) < 0.$$

If $\Gamma^2 > 0$, then for a sufficiently small, we have $\tilde{\Gamma}^2 > 0$; hence there exists a real solution g; hence, according to Theorem 2.1′, absolute stability occurs.

Let us consider now the case where c is an eigenvector of the matrix A^*. Let (x, σ) be a solution, $\xi = (c, x)$. We have

$$\frac{d\xi}{dt} = \left(c, \frac{dx}{dt}\right) = (c, Ax) + (c, b)f(\sigma) = (A^*c, x) + (c, b)f(\sigma)$$

$$= -\beta(c, x) + (c, b)f(\sigma);$$

hence

$$\frac{d\xi}{dt} = -\beta\xi + (c, b)f(\sigma), \qquad \frac{d\sigma}{dt} = \xi - \sigma f(\sigma).$$

We have obtained a system with $n = 1$, $A = -\beta$, and $c = 1$, and b is replaced by (c, b). The relation $A^*T + TA = -C$ becomes in this case $-2\beta T = -C$; hence $T > 0$, and from $a = T(c, b)$ it follows that a has the same sign as (c, b). The relation $A^*U + UA = -gg^*$ becomes

$$-2\beta U = -g^2, \qquad g^2 = 2\beta U, \qquad U = \frac{1}{2\beta}g^2,$$

and the fundamental equation becomes

$$\frac{(c, b)}{2\beta}g^2 + ru + \tfrac{1}{2}r(1 + a) = 0,$$

i.e.,

$$(c, b)g^2 + 2r\beta g + r\beta(1 + a) = 0.$$

The equation has a real root if and only if $r^2\beta^2 - r\beta(c, b)(1 + a) > 0$; i.e., $r\beta - (cb)(1 + a) > 0$. This condition is fulfilled if and only if $r - (1/\beta)(c, b) > 0$, which coincides with $\Gamma^2 > 0$, since $(c, A^{-1}b) = (A^{*-1}c, b) = -(1/\beta)(b, c)$.

It follows that if $\Gamma^2 > 0$, $\sigma(t) \to 0$ for every solution; hence $f(\sigma(t)) \to 0$ for every solution, and from the formula

$$x(t) = e^{At}x(0) + \int_0^t e^{A(t-s)}\, bf[\sigma(s)]\, ds$$

it follows immediately that $x(t) \to 0$ when $t \to \infty$; hence absolute stability occurs.

2.3. The Method of V. M. Popov

An essentially new method, based upon use of the Fourier transform, has been given in the study of absolute stability of the control systems by V. M. Popov. The method of Popov leads to results which are at the same time stronger and more effective than those considered in the preceding paragraphs.

Consider the system

$$\frac{dx}{dt} = Ax + bf(\sigma), \qquad \frac{d\xi}{dt} = f(\sigma), \qquad \sigma = c^*x - \gamma\xi \qquad \gamma > 0 \tag{5}$$

Suppose, as previously, that A is Hurwitzian. Set

$$\nu(t) = -c^* e^{At}b, \qquad N(i\omega) = \int_0^\infty e^{-i\omega t}\, \nu(t)\, dt, \qquad G(i\omega) = N(i\omega) + \frac{\gamma}{i\omega}.$$

Theorem 2.2. *If there exists $q > 0$ such that for all $\omega \geqslant 0$ we have $\operatorname{Re}(1 + i\omega q)G(i\omega) \geqslant 0$, then the trivial solution of system (5) is absolutely stable.*

Proof. Let $x(t)$, $\xi(t)$ be a solution of system (5).
Set

$$f_T(t) = \begin{cases} f[\sigma(t)] & \text{for} \quad 0 \leqslant t \leqslant T, \\ 0 & \text{for} \quad t > T. \end{cases}$$

Define the function

$$\lambda_T(t) = -\int_0^t \nu(t-\tau)f_T(\tau)\, d\tau - q\int_0^t \frac{d\nu(t-\tau)}{dt} f_T(\tau)\, d\tau - q[\nu(0) + \gamma]f_T(t).$$

To see the significance of this function, we will perform some computations. We have

$$\frac{dx(t)}{dt} = Ax(t) + bf[\sigma(t)].$$

According to the variation-of-constants formula,

$$x(t) = e^{At}\,x(0) + \int_0^t e^{A(t-\tau)}\,bf[\sigma(\tau)]\,d\tau;$$

hence

$$\sigma(t) = c^*\,e^{At}\,x(0) + \int_0^t c^*\,e^{A(t-\tau)}\,bf[\sigma(\tau)]\,d\tau - \gamma\xi(t).$$

Note that $c^*e^{A(t-\tau)}b = -\nu(t-\tau)$; we let $c^*e^{At} = \mu^*(t)$. Thus,

$$\sigma(t) = \mu^*(t)x(0) - \int_0^t \nu(t-\tau)f[\sigma(\tau)]\,d\tau - \gamma\xi(t).$$

From here follows

$$\frac{d\sigma(t)}{dt} = \frac{d\mu^*(t)}{dt}x(0) - \nu(0)f[\sigma(t)] - \int_0^t \frac{d\nu(t-\tau)}{dt}f[\sigma(\tau)]\,d\tau - \gamma\frac{d\xi(t)}{dt}.$$

Since

$$\frac{d\xi(t)}{dt} = f[\sigma(t)],$$

we have

$$\frac{d\sigma(t)}{dt} = \frac{d\mu^*(t)}{dt}x(0) - \int_0^t \frac{d\nu(t-\tau)}{dt}f[\sigma(\tau)]\,d\tau - (\nu(0)+\gamma)f[\sigma(t)].$$

For $0 \leqslant t \leqslant T$ we may write

$$\frac{d\sigma(t)}{dt} = \frac{d\mu^*(t)}{dt}x(0) - \int_0^t \frac{d\nu(t-\tau)}{dt}f_T(\tau)\,d\tau - [\nu(0)+\gamma]f_T(t).$$

If follows that

$$\lambda_T(t) = -\int_0^t \nu(t-\tau)f_T(\tau)\,d\tau + q\frac{d\sigma(t)}{dt} - q\frac{d\mu^*(t)}{dt}x(0) \quad \text{for} \quad 0 \leqslant t \leqslant T,$$

i.e.,

$$\lambda_T(t) = \sigma(t) + q\frac{d\sigma(t)}{dt} + \gamma\xi(t) - \left[\mu^*(t) + q\frac{d\mu^*(t)}{dt}\right]x(0) \quad \text{for} \quad 0 \leqslant t \leqslant T.$$

For $t > T$, taking into account the definition of the function $f_T(t)$, follows the relation

$$\lambda_T(t) = -\int_0^T \nu(t-\tau)f_T(\tau)\,d\tau - q\int_0^T \frac{d\nu(t-\tau)}{dt}f_T(\tau)\,d\tau.$$

Since the matrix A is Hurwitzian, we have

$$| e^{At} | \leqslant K_1 e^{-K_0 t} \qquad (\text{for} \quad t \geqslant 0);$$

hence $| \nu(t) | \leqslant K_2 e^{-K_0 t}$. Thus $| \lambda_T(t) | \leqslant K_3 e^{-K_0 t}$ for $t \geqslant T$; hence $\lambda_T(t)$ admits a Fourier transform. Let

$$L_T(i\omega) = \int_0^\infty e^{-i\omega t} \lambda_T(t)\, dt, \qquad F_T(i\omega) = \int_0^T e^{-i\omega t} f_T(t)\, dt.$$

We have

$$\int_0^\infty e^{-i\omega t} \frac{d\nu(t)}{dt}\, dt = e^{-i\omega t} \nu(t) \Big|_0^\infty + i\omega \int_0^\infty e^{-i\omega t} \nu(t)\, dt = i\omega N(i\omega) - \nu(0).$$

Is is known from the theory of the Fourier transform that if

$$h(t) = \int_0^t f(t-\tau) g(\tau)\, d\tau,$$

then the Fourier transform of h is the product of the Fourier transforms of the functions f and g‡. It follows that

$$L_T(i\omega) = -N(i\omega)F_T(i\omega) - q[i\omega N(i\omega) - \nu(0)]F_T(i\omega)$$
$$-q[\nu(0) + \gamma]F_T(i\omega) = -F_T(i\omega)[(1 + i\omega q)N(i\omega) + q\gamma].$$

Consider the function

$$\rho(T) = \int_0^\infty \lambda_T(t) f_T(t)\, dt.$$

Taking into account the way in which λ_T and f_T have been defined, we shall have

$$\rho(T) = \int_0^T \lambda_T(t) f[\sigma(t)]\, dt = \int_0^T \sigma(t) f[\sigma(t)]\, dt + q \int_0^T f[\sigma(t)] \frac{d\sigma(t)}{dt}\, dt$$
$$+ \gamma \int_0^T \xi(t) f[\sigma(t)]\, dt - \int_0^T f_T(t) \left[\mu^*(t) + q \frac{d\mu^*}{dt}\right] x(0)\, dt$$
$$= \int_0^T \sigma(t) f[\sigma(t)]\, dt + q \int_{\sigma(0)}^{\sigma(T)} f(\sigma)\, d\sigma + \tfrac{1}{2}\gamma[\xi^2(T) - \xi^2(0)]$$
$$- \int_0^T f_T(t) \left[\mu^*(t) + q \frac{d\mu^*(t)}{dt}\right] x(0)\, dt.$$

‡ This is true for the Laplace transform as stated and if we suppose that $f \equiv 0$, $g \equiv 0$ for $t < 0$ for the Fourier transform too.

We have used the fact that $f[\sigma(t)] = d\xi(t)/dt$; hence $\xi(t)f[\sigma(t)] = \frac{1}{2}(d/dt)\xi^2(t)$. In the theory of the Fourier transform the following fundamental formula is proved:

$$\int_0^\infty f_1 f_2\, dt = \frac{1}{2\pi}\int_{-\infty}^\infty \operatorname{Re} F_1(i\omega)F_2(-i\omega)\, d\omega,$$

valid for f_1 and f_2 in $L_1 \cap L_2$.

The functions $\lambda_T(t)$ and $f_T(t)$ fulfill these conditions. Hence we may write

$$\begin{aligned}\rho(T) &= \frac{1}{2\pi}\int_{-\infty}^\infty \operatorname{Re} L_T(i\omega)F_T(-i\omega)\, d\omega\\ &= -\frac{1}{2\pi}\int_{-\infty}^\infty \operatorname{Re}\,[(1+i\omega q)N(i\omega)+q\gamma]\, F_T(i\omega)F_T(-i\omega)\, d\omega\\ &= -\frac{1}{2\pi}\int_{-\infty}^\infty \operatorname{Re}\,[(1+i\omega q)N(i\omega)+q\gamma]\, | F_T(i\omega)|^2\, d\omega.\end{aligned}$$

We have

$$q\gamma = (1+i\omega q)\frac{\gamma}{i\omega} - \frac{\gamma}{i\omega};$$

hence

$$\begin{aligned}(1+i\omega q)N(i\omega)+q\gamma &= (1+i\omega q)N(i\omega) + (1+i\omega q)\frac{\gamma}{i\omega} - \frac{\gamma}{i\omega}\\ &= (1+i\omega q)\left(N(i\omega)+\frac{\gamma}{i\omega}\right) - \frac{\gamma}{i\omega} = (1+i\omega q)G(i\omega) - \frac{\gamma}{i\omega}.\end{aligned}$$

Since $| F_T(i\omega)|^2$ is real,

$$\begin{aligned}&\operatorname{Re}\,[(1+i\omega q)N(i\omega)+q\gamma]\, | F_T(i\omega)|^2\\ &\quad= | F_T(i\omega)|^2 \operatorname{Re}\,[(1+i\omega q)N(i\omega)+q\gamma]\\ &\quad= | F_T(i\omega)|^2 \operatorname{Re}\left[(1+i\omega q)G(i\omega)-\frac{\gamma}{i\omega}\right]\\ &\quad= | F_T(i\omega)|^2 \operatorname{Re}(1+i\omega q)G(i\omega) \geqslant 0\end{aligned}$$

according to the hypothesis of the statement. It follows that

$$\rho(T) \leqslant 0.$$

We state the following inequality:

$$\left| \int_0^T f_T(t)\left[\mu^*(t) + q\frac{d\mu^*(t)}{dt}\right] dt\right| \leqslant K_4 \sup_{0\leqslant t\leqslant T} | \xi(t)|.$$

We have

$$\int_0^T \left[\mu^*(t) + q\frac{d\mu^*(t)}{dt}\right] f_T(t) = \int_0^T \left[\mu^*(t) + q\frac{d\mu^*(t)}{dt}\right]\frac{d\xi(t)}{dt}\,dt$$

$$= \left[\mu^*(t) + q\frac{d\mu^*(t)}{dt}\right]\xi(t)\Big|_0^T - \int_0^T \xi(t)\left[\frac{d\mu^*(t)}{dt} + q\frac{d^2\mu^*(t)}{dt^2}\right]dt.$$

Since

$$\mu^*(t) = c^*e^{At}, \qquad \frac{d\mu^*(t)}{dt} = c^*Ae^{At}, \qquad \frac{d^2\mu^*}{dt^2} = c^*A^2e^{At},$$

we have

$$|\mu^*(t)| \leqslant |c|K_1e^{-K_0t}, \qquad \left|\frac{d\mu^*}{dt}\right| \leqslant |c||A|K_1e^{-K_0t},$$

$$\left|\frac{d^2\mu^*(t)}{dt^2}\right| \leqslant |c||A|^2K_1e^{-K_0t}.$$

Thus

$$\left|\int_0^T \left[\mu^*(t) + q\frac{d\mu^*(t)}{dt}\right] f_T(t)\,dt\right| \leqslant |c|K_1e^{-K_0T}|\xi(T)|$$

$$+ q|c||A|K_1e^{-K_0T}|\xi(T)| + q|c||A|K_1|\xi(0)| + qK_1|\xi(0)|$$

$$+ \sup_{0\leqslant t\leqslant T}|\xi(t)|\int_0^T |c||A|K_1(1 + q|A|)\,e^{-K_0t}\,dt$$

$$\leqslant |c|K_1(1 + q|A|)(|\xi(T)| + |\xi(0)|)$$

$$+ \frac{|c||A|K_1(1 + q|A|)}{K_0}\sup_{0\leqslant t\leqslant T}|\xi(t)| \leqslant K_4\sup_{0\leqslant t\leqslant T}|\xi(t)|,$$

and the inequality is proved.

Setting

$$\phi(\sigma) = \int_0^\sigma f(\sigma)\,d\sigma,$$

from the fact that $\rho(T) \leqslant 0$ we deduce

$$\int_0^T \sigma(t)f[\sigma(t)]\,dt + q\phi[\sigma(T)] + \tfrac{1}{2}\gamma\xi^2(T) \leqslant q\phi[\sigma(0)]$$

$$+ \tfrac{1}{2}\gamma\xi^2(0) + K_4\sup_{0\leqslant t\leqslant T}|\xi(t)||x(0)|.$$

Since $\sigma f(\sigma) > 0$ and $\phi(\sigma) > 0$, it follows that

$$\tfrac{1}{2}\gamma\xi^2(T) \leqslant K_4\sup_{0\leqslant t\leqslant T}|\xi(t)||x(0)| + q\phi[\sigma(0)] + \tfrac{1}{2}\gamma\xi^2(0).$$

Since the inequality has been stated for every T, we may write for $T_1 \leqslant T$,

$$\tfrac{1}{2}\gamma\xi^2(T_1) \leqslant K_4 \mid x(0) \mid \sup_{0\leqslant t\leqslant T} \mid \xi(t) \mid + q\phi[\sigma(0)] + \tfrac{1}{2}\gamma\xi^2(0)$$
$$\leqslant K_4 \mid x(0) \mid \sup_{0\leqslant t\leqslant T} \mid \xi(t) \mid + q\phi[\sigma(0)] + \tfrac{1}{2}\gamma\xi^2(0).$$

Hence

$$\tfrac{1}{2}\gamma \sup_{0\leqslant t\leqslant T} \xi^2(t) \leqslant K_4 \mid x(0) \mid \sup_{0\leqslant t\leqslant T} \mid \xi(t) \mid + q\phi[\sigma(0)] + \tfrac{1}{2}\gamma\xi^2(0).$$

From

$$\left(\sup_{0\leqslant t\leqslant T} \mid \xi(t) \mid\right)^2 \leqslant \sup_{0\leqslant t\leqslant T} \xi^2(t)$$

follows

$$\tfrac{1}{2}\gamma\left(\sup_{0\leqslant t\leqslant T} \mid \xi(t) \mid\right)^2 - K_4 \mid x(0) \mid \sup_{0\leqslant t\leqslant T} \mid \xi(t) \mid - q\phi[\sigma(0)] - \tfrac{1}{2}\gamma\xi^2(0) \leqslant 0.$$

From here it follows that

$$\sup_{0\leqslant t\leqslant T} \mid \xi(t) \mid \leqslant \frac{K_4 \mid x(0) \mid + \sqrt{K_4^2 \mid x(0) \mid^2 + 2\gamma[q\phi[\sigma(0)] + \frac{1}{2}\gamma\xi^2(0)]}}{\gamma}$$

and hence that

$$\mid \xi(t) \mid \leqslant \phi_1(\mid x(0) \mid, \mid \xi(0) \mid),$$

which implies the stability with respect to component ξ.

We now state the inequality

$$\mid x(t) \mid \leqslant K_1 \mid x(0) \mid + K_5 \sup_{0\leqslant \tau\leqslant t} \mid \xi(\tau) \mid .$$

We have

$$x(t) = e^{At}\, x(0) + \int_0^t e^{A(t-\tau)}\, bf[\sigma(\tau)]\, d\tau = e^{At}\, x(0) + \int_0^t e^{A(t-\tau)}\, b\, \frac{d\xi(\tau)}{d\tau}\, d\tau$$
$$= e^{At}\, x(0) + e^{A(t-\tau)}\, b\xi(\tau)\Big|_0^t + \int_0^t Ae^{A(t-\tau)}\, b\xi(\tau)\, d\tau$$
$$= e^{At}\, x(0) + b\xi(t) - e^{At}\, b\xi(0) + \int_0^t A\, e^{A(t-\tau)}\, b\xi(\tau)\, d\tau.$$

Then

$$\mid x(t) \mid \leqslant K_1 \mid x(0) \mid + \mid b \mid \sup_{0\leqslant \tau\leqslant t} \mid \xi(\tau) \mid + K_1 \mid b \mid \sup_{0\leqslant \tau\leqslant t} \mid \xi(\tau) \mid$$
$$+ \frac{K_1}{K_0} \mid A \mid \mid b \mid \sup_{0\leqslant \tau\leqslant t} \mid \xi(\tau) \mid,$$

and finally

$$| x(t) | \leqslant K_1 | x(0) | + K_5 \sup_{0 \leqslant \tau \leqslant t} | \xi(\tau) |.$$

Taking into account the evaluation of $| \xi(t) |$, we will have

$$| x(t) | \leqslant \phi_2(| x(0) |, | \xi(0) |);$$

hence the trivial solution of the system is stable.

It remains to prove that

$$\lim_{t\to\infty} x(t) = \lim_{t\to\infty} \xi(t) = 0.$$

From the fundamental inequality obtained starting from $\rho(T) \leqslant 0$, we deduce that

$$\int_0^T \sigma(t)f[\sigma(t)]\, dt \leqslant K_4 | x(0) | \sup_{0\leqslant t\leqslant T} | \xi(t) | + q\phi[\sigma(0)] + \tfrac{1}{2}\gamma\xi^2(0);$$

hence

$$\int_0^T \sigma(t)f[\sigma(t)]\, dt \leqslant \phi_3(| x(0) |, | \xi(0) |).$$

On the other hand,

$$\frac{d\sigma(t)}{dt} = c^* \frac{dx(t)}{dt} - \gamma \frac{d\xi(t)}{dt} = c^*(Ax(t) + bf[\sigma(t)]) - \gamma f[\sigma(t)],$$

$$\sigma(t) = c^*x(t) - \gamma\xi(t).$$

Hence we have, successively,

$$| \sigma(t) | \leqslant \phi_4(| x(0) |, | \xi(0) |), \qquad | f[\sigma(t)] | \leqslant \phi_5(| x(0) |, | \xi(0) |),$$

and

$$\left| \frac{d\sigma(t)}{dt} \right| \leqslant \phi_6(| x(0) |, | \xi(0) |).$$

We must then have $\lim_{t\to\infty} \sigma(t) = 0$. Indeed, if it were not so, there would exist a $\delta > 0$ and a sequence $t_k \to \infty$ such that $| \sigma(t_k) | > \delta$ A subsequence may be chosen such that $t_n - t_{n-1} > \delta/\phi_6$.

Let $T > 0$ be given, and $N(T)$ be such that $n \leqslant N(T)$ implies $t_n \leqslant T - \delta/2\phi_6$. We have

$$\int^T \sigma(t)f[\sigma(t)]\, dt \geqslant \sum_{n=1}^{N(T)} \int_{t_n-(\delta/2\phi_6)}^{t_n+(\delta/2\phi_6)} \sigma(t)f[\sigma(t)]\, dt.$$

But

$$|\sigma(t) - \sigma(t_n)| = |\sigma(\theta_n)| \, |t - t_n| \leqslant \phi_6 \, |t - t_n| \leqslant \phi_6 \frac{\delta}{2\phi_6} = \frac{\delta}{2};$$

hence $|\sigma(t)| \geqslant |\sigma(t_n)| - \delta/2 > \delta/2$. Let $m = \inf_{\delta/2 \leqslant \sigma \leqslant \phi_6} f(\sigma)$. Then

$$\int_{t_n-(\delta/2\phi_6)}^{t_n+(\delta/2\phi_6)} \sigma(t) f[\sigma(t)] \, dt \geqslant \frac{\delta}{2} m \frac{\delta}{\phi_6};$$

hence

$$\phi_3 \geqslant \int_0^T \sigma(t) f[\sigma(t)] \, dt \geqslant N(T) \frac{\delta}{2} \frac{\delta}{\phi_6} m.$$

But $\lim_{T\to\infty} N(T) = \infty$, which is a contradiction. Consequently, $\lim_{t\to\infty} \sigma(t) = 0$. From this follows $\lim_{t\to\infty} f[\sigma(t)] = 0$.

We have, however,

$$|x(t)| \leqslant K_1 e^{-K_0 t} |x(0)| + \int_0^t K_1 e^{-K_0(t-\tau)} |b| \, |f(\sigma(\tau))| \, d\tau$$

and

$$\lim_{t\to\infty} \int_0^t e^{-K_0(t-\tau)} |b| \, |f(\sigma(\tau))| \, d\tau$$

$$= \lim_{t\to\infty} \frac{\int_0^t e^{K_0\tau} |b| \, |f(\sigma(\tau))| \, d\tau}{e^{K_0 t}} = \lim_{t\to\infty} \frac{e^{K_0 t} |b| \, |f(\sigma(t))|}{K_0 e^{K_0 t}}$$

$$= \frac{|b|}{K_0} \lim_{t\to\infty} |f(\sigma(t))| = 0.$$

Hence

$$\lim_{t\to\infty} |x(t)| = 0.$$

From

$$\xi(t) = \frac{1}{\gamma} c^* x(t) - \frac{1}{\gamma} \sigma(t)$$

follows

$$\lim_{t\to\infty} \xi(t) = 0,$$

and the theorem is proved.

With the view of showing how strong this result of V.M. Popov is, we will show that if there exists a Lyapunov function of the form considered in the preceding paragraph, then the condition of the theorem of V. M. Popov is verified.

Theorem 2.3. *If there exists a function V of the form*

$$V = (Hx, x) - 2\beta \int_0^\sigma f(\sigma)\, d\sigma \qquad (H < 0, \beta > 0)$$

such that for every function f of the considered class the total derivative dV/dt by virtue of system (5) *is positive-definite, then there exists a* $q > 0$ *such that*

$$\mathrm{Re}(1 + i\omega q)G(i\omega) \geqslant 0.$$

Proof. We choose $f(\sigma) = h\sigma$, $h > 0$. According to the hypothesis, the total derivative of the function $V = (Hx, x) - h\beta\sigma^2$, by virtue of system (5), should be positive-definite. This derivative is equal to

$$(H(Ax + bh\sigma), x) + (Hx, Ax + bh\sigma) - 2\beta h\sigma(c^*Ax + c^*bh\sigma - \gamma h\sigma).$$

Given a quadratic form (Wx, x), with a real positive-definite matrix, if we put $x = u + iv$, we will have

$$(W\bar{x}, x) = (W(u - iv), u + iv) = (Wu - iWv, u + iv) = (Wu, u),$$
$$i(Wu, v) - i(Wv, u) + (Wv, v) = (Wu, u) + (Wv, v) \geqslant 0,$$

with the equality occurring only for $u = 0$, $v = 0$, hence only for $x = 0$. [We stress that the scalar product (u, v) means here $\Sigma\, u_i v_i$.]

Since dV/dt is a positive-definite quadratic form, for x and σ complex we will have

$$(HA\bar{x} + Hbh\bar{\sigma}, x) + (H\bar{x}, Ax + bh\sigma) - \beta h\bar{\sigma}(c^*Ax + c^*bh\sigma - \gamma h\sigma)$$
$$-\beta h\sigma(c^*A\bar{x} + c^*bh\bar{\sigma} - \gamma h\bar{\sigma}) > 0.$$

Let

$$M(i\omega) = \int_0^\infty e^{-i\omega t}\, e^{At}\, b\, dt.$$

We have

$$i\omega M(i\omega) = \int_0^\infty i\omega\, e^{-i\omega t}\, e^{At}\, b\, dt = -\int_0^\infty e^{At}\, b\, \frac{d}{dt}\, e^{-i\omega t}\, dt$$
$$= -e^{At}\, be^{-i\omega t}\Big|_0^\infty + \int_0^\infty Ae^{At}be^{-i\omega t}\, dt = b + AM(i\omega).$$

Put $x = M(i\omega)$, $\sigma = 1/h$; we obtain

$$(HA\bar{M}(i\omega) + Hb, M(i\omega)) + (H\bar{M}(i\omega), AM(i\omega) + b) \\ -\beta(c^*AM(i\omega) + c^*b - \gamma) - \beta(c^*A\bar{M}(i\omega) + c^*b - \gamma) > 0.$$

Since

$$A\bar{M}(i\omega) + b = -i\omega\bar{M}(i\omega),$$

it follows that

$$-i\omega(H\bar{M}(i\omega), M(i\omega)) + i\omega(H\bar{M}(i\omega), M(i\omega)) - \beta(c^*i\omega M(i\omega) - \gamma) \\ + \beta(c^*i\omega\bar{M}(i\omega) - \gamma) > 0.$$

Hence

$$\operatorname{Re}\{-\beta(c^*i\omega M(i\omega) - \gamma)\} > 0.$$

Let us remember that

$$N(i\omega) = \int_0^\infty e^{-i\omega t}\,\nu(t)\,dt = -\int_0^\infty e^{-i\omega t}\,c^*\,e^{At}b\,dt \\ = -c^*\int_0^\infty e^{-i\omega t}e^{At}b\,dt = -c^*M(i\omega).$$

It follows that

$$\operatorname{Re}\beta(i\omega N(i\omega) + \gamma) > 0.$$

Since we have set

$$G(i\omega) = N(i\omega) + \frac{\gamma}{i\omega},$$

we reach the conclusion that

$$\operatorname{Re} i\omega G(i\omega) > 0.$$

We have

$$\operatorname{Re}(1 + i\omega q)G(i\omega) = \operatorname{Re} G(i\omega) + q\operatorname{Re} i\omega G(i\omega).$$

To prove that there exists a $q > 0$ such that

$$\operatorname{Re}(1 + i\omega q)G(i\omega) > 0,$$

it remains to prove that $\operatorname{Re} G(i\omega)$ is bounded.

Since dV/dt is positive for $x = 0$, $\sigma = 1/h$, we deduce that

$$-\beta(c^*b - \gamma) > 0.$$

On the other hand, we have the relation

$$i\omega G(i\omega) = i\omega N(i\omega) + \gamma = \int_0^\infty e^{-i\omega t} \frac{d\nu(t)}{dt}\, dt + \gamma + \nu(0).$$

Since

$$\nu(t) = -c^* e^{At} b, \qquad \frac{d\nu}{dt} = -c^* A e^{At} b,$$

we see that $d\nu/dt$ approaches zero exponentially. It follows that

$$\lim_{|\omega|\to\infty} \int_0^\infty e^{-i\omega t} \frac{d\nu(t)}{dt}\, dt = 0;$$

indeed, integrating by parts we have

$$\int_0^\infty e^{-i\omega t} \frac{d\nu(t)}{dt}\, dt = -\frac{1}{i\omega} e^{-i\omega t} \frac{d\nu(t)}{dt}\Big|_0^\infty + \frac{1}{i\omega} \int_0^\infty e^{-i\omega t} \frac{d^2\nu}{dt^2}\, dt$$

$$= -\frac{c^* A b}{i\omega} + \frac{1}{i\omega} \int_0^\infty e^{-i\omega t} \frac{d^2\nu}{dt^2}\, dt;$$

the integral is bounded and the assertion is proved.
It follows that

$$\lim_{|\omega|\to\infty} i\omega G(i\omega) = \gamma + \nu(0) = \gamma - c^* b > 0$$

and hence that

$$\text{Re}\, i\omega G(i\omega) \geqslant N_1 > 0.$$

It also follows from this that $\lim_{|\omega|\to\infty} G(i\omega) = 0$; hence $G(i\omega)$ is bounded. The theorem is thus proved.

Theorem 2.3 shows that the result of V. M. Popov is stronger than any that could be obtained with the help of Lyapunov functions (on the condition that the number q is conveniently chosen). Let us now show that its application to concrete cases amounts to simple algebraic operations.

The elements of the matrix e^{At} are of the form $t^k e^{-\lambda t}$; hence $\nu(t)$ will be a linear combination of this type of element. We have, however,

$$\int_0^\infty e^{-i\omega t} t^k e^{-\lambda t}\, dt = \int_0^\infty t^k e^{-(\lambda + i\omega)t}\, dt = -\frac{1}{\lambda + i\omega} e^{-(\lambda+i\omega)t} t^k \Big|_0^\infty + \frac{k}{\lambda + i\omega} \int_0^\infty t^{k-1} e^{-(\lambda+i\omega)t}\, dt.$$

By hypothesis, Re $\lambda > 0$. Hence

$$\int_0^\infty e^{-i\omega t}\, t^k\, e^{-\lambda t}\, dt = \frac{k}{\lambda + i\omega} \int_0^t t^{k-1}\, e^{-(\lambda+i\omega)t}\, dt.$$

Continuing,

$$\int_0^\infty e^{-i\omega t}\, t^k\, e^{-\lambda t}\, dt = \frac{k!}{(\lambda + i\omega)^k}\,.$$

It follows from here that $N(i\omega)$ is a rational function of $i\omega$, hence that $G(i\omega)$ is a rational function of $i\omega$ and that

$$(1 + i\omega q)G(i\omega) = \frac{P(i\omega)}{Q(i\omega)} = \frac{P(i\omega)\overline{Q(i\omega)}}{|\, Q(i\omega)\,|^2}\,.$$

The condition

$$\operatorname{Re}\,(1 + i\omega q)G(i\omega) \geqslant 0$$

becomes

$$\operatorname{Re}\, P(i\omega)\bar{Q}(i\omega) \geqslant 0$$

i.e.,

$$\operatorname{Re}\, P(i\omega)Q(-i\omega) \geqslant 0.$$

The real part of the product $P(i\omega)Q(-i\omega)$ is a polynomial in ω^2; hence all we have to do is to seek the conditions that a polynomial $R(x)$ be positive for $x \geqslant 0$; we have set $x = \omega^2$.

Let us observe that the systems considered are obtained from systems of the form

$$\frac{dy}{dt} = Ay + b\xi, \qquad \frac{d\xi}{dt} = f(\sigma), \qquad \sigma = c^*y - r\xi,$$

upon putting $\dot{y} = x$. Indeed, we obtain

$$\frac{dx}{dt} = Ax + bf(\sigma), \qquad \frac{d\xi}{dt} = f(\sigma), \qquad \sigma = c^*A^{-1}x - [c^*A^{-1}b + r]\xi,$$

since $x = Ay + b\xi$; hence $y = A^{-1}x - A^{-1}b\xi$. This finally yields system (5) with $\gamma = r + c^*A^{-1}b$.

The considerations made previously show that $\gamma > 0$ is a necessary condition for absolute stability. Let us take $A = \operatorname{diag}\,(-\mu_i)$ and see what becomes of the condition of Theorem 2.2.

We have

$$G = -[c^*A^{-1}(i\omega E - A)^{-1}b] + \frac{r + c^*A^{-1}b}{i\omega},$$

$$c^*A^{-1}(i\omega E - A)^{-1}b = -\sum_{i=1}^{n} \frac{b_i c_i}{\mu_i(\mu_i + \omega)}, \qquad c^*A^{-1}b = -\sum_{i=1}^{n} \frac{b_i c_i}{\mu_i},$$

$$\operatorname{Re}\{(1 + qi\omega)G\} = \sum_{i=1}^{n} \frac{b_i c_i}{\mu_i}\left(q + \frac{\mu_i(1 - q\mu_i)}{\mu_i^2 + \omega^2}\right) + qr - q\sum_{i=1}^{n} \frac{b_i c_i}{\mu_i}$$

$$= q\left[r - \sum_{i=1}^{n} \frac{b_i c_i(\mu_i - (1/q))}{\mu_i^2 + \omega^2}\right].$$

Setting

$$L(A, b, c) = \max\begin{cases} \displaystyle\sum_{i=1}^{n} \frac{b_i c_i}{\mu_i}, \\ \displaystyle\min_{q>0} \max_{\omega} \sum_{i=1}^{n} \frac{b_i c_i(\mu_i - (1/q))}{\mu_i^2 + \omega^2}, \end{cases}$$

the condition of absolute stability is written $r > L(A, b, c)$.

If

$$\min_{q>0} \max_{\omega} \sum_{i=1}^{n} \frac{b_i c_i(\mu_i - (1/q))}{\mu_i^2 + \omega^2} > \sum_{i=1}^{n} \frac{b_i c_i}{\mu_i},$$

the condition of absolute stability is written $r \geqslant L(A, b, c)$. From

$$\lim_{|\omega|\to\infty} \sum_{i=1}^{n} \frac{b_i c_i(\mu_i - (1/q))}{\mu_i^2 + \omega^2} = 0$$

follows $L(A, b, c) \geqslant 0$.

Taking into account that

$$\max_{\omega} \frac{b_i c_i(\mu_i - (1/q))}{\mu_i^2 + \omega^2} = \frac{\epsilon_i b_i c_i(\mu_i - (1/q))}{\mu_i^2},$$

where

$$\epsilon_i = \begin{cases} 0 & \text{if} \quad b_i c_i\left(\mu_i - \dfrac{1}{q}\right) \leqslant 0, \\ 1 & \text{if} \quad b_i c_i\left(\mu_i - \dfrac{1}{q}\right) > 0, \end{cases}$$

we obtain the results of the preceding section.

For matrices A of the second order, T. Morozan has pointed out cases where

$$L(A, b, c) < \min_{q>0} \sum_{i=1}^{n} \frac{\epsilon_i b_i c_i(\mu_i - (1/q))}{\mu_i^2} .$$

In order to point out in what direction the investigation may be continued, let us observe that the systems studied, of form (5), are particular cases of systems of the form

$$\frac{dz}{dt} = Az + af(\sigma) \qquad (\sigma = p^*z),$$

corresponding to the situation in which A admits a zero eigenvalue. Indeed, A may be then brought to the real canonical form $A = \begin{pmatrix} A_1 & 0 \\ 0 & 0 \end{pmatrix}$ and the system may be written

$$\frac{dx}{dt} = A_1 x + a_1 f(\sigma), \qquad \frac{d\xi}{dt} = a_2 f(\sigma).$$

If $a_2 \neq 0$, a new linear change of variables leads to form (5).

We may also obtain stability conditions in the *case where the matrix* A *is Hurwitzian*; this case is simpler than the one previously treated. *We shall consider absolute stability in the class of functions* f *with the property that* $h_1\sigma^2 \leqslant \sigma f(\sigma) \leqslant h_2\sigma^2$, $h_2 < k$, *where* h_1 *and* h_2 *depend on the function* f, *but* k *is the same for the whole class.*

Let $z(t)$ be any solution of the system and $u(t)$ the solution of the homogeneous system

$$\frac{du}{dt} = Au \qquad u(0) = z(0).$$

Let

$$\sigma(t) = p^*z(t)$$

and

$$f_T(t) = \begin{cases} f[\sigma(t)] & \text{for} \quad 0 \leqslant t \leqslant T, \\ 0 & \text{for} \quad T < t. \end{cases}$$

Denote by $w(t)$ the solution of nonhomogeneous linear system

$$\frac{dw}{dt} = Aw + af_T(t) \qquad (w(0) = 0). \tag{$*$}$$

The function $w(t)$ is continuous and has a derivative with a discontinuity of the first kind for $t = T$.

We have $w(t) = z(t) - u(t)$ for $0 \leqslant t \leqslant T$, since the difference $z(t) - u(t)$ satisfies the same system as $w(t)$ and the same initial conditions.

Let

$$\chi(T) = \int_0^T \left[p^* w(t) - \frac{1}{k} f_T(t) + qc^* \frac{dw}{dt}\right] f_T(t)\,dt$$

$$= \int_0^\infty \left[p^* w(t) - \frac{1}{k} f_T(t) + qc^* \frac{dw(t)}{dt}\right] f_T(t)\,dt$$

$$= \frac{1}{2\pi} \int_{-\infty}^{\infty} \operatorname{Re} \left\{p^* \tilde{w} - \frac{1}{k} \tilde{f}_T + i\omega q c^* \tilde{w}\right\} \tilde{f}_T^* \,d\omega$$

We have denoted here by $\tilde{w}$ and $\tilde{f}_T$, the Fourier transforms of the functions w and f_T, respectively.

Since for $t > T$ the function $w(t)$ verifies the homogeneous system, it follows that w and dw/dt decrease exponentially; hence the formula from the theory of Fourier transform may be applied. From the system of equations (*) for w will follow, by applying the Fourier transform,

$$i\omega\tilde{w} = A\tilde{w} + a\tilde{f}_T, \qquad \tilde{w} = -(A - i\omega E)^{-1} a\tilde{f}_T.$$

Set

$$M = (A - i\omega E)^{-1} a, \qquad \mathscr{G} = p^* M.$$

We have

$$\tilde{w} = -M\tilde{f}_T$$

and hence

$$\chi(T) = \frac{1}{2\pi} \int_{-\infty}^{\infty} \operatorname{Re} \left\{-p^* M\tilde{f}_T - \frac{1}{k}\tilde{f}_T - i\omega q p^* M\tilde{f}_T\right\} \tilde{f}_T^* \,d\omega$$

$$= -\frac{1}{2\pi} \int_{-\infty}^{\infty} \operatorname{Re} \left\{\frac{1}{k} + (1 + i\omega q)\mathscr{G}\right\} |\tilde{f}_T|^2 \,d\omega.$$

Assuming $(1/k) + \operatorname{Re}(1 + i\omega q)\mathscr{G} \geqslant 0$, we deduce that $\chi(T) \leqslant 0$.

On the other hand,

$$\chi(T) = \int_0^T \left[p^* z(t) - \frac{1}{k} f(\sigma(t)] + qp^* \frac{dz(t)}{dt} - p^* u(t) - qp^* \frac{du(t)}{dt}\right] f[\sigma(t)]\,dt.$$

It follows that

$$\int_0^T \left[\sigma(t) - \frac{1}{k} f[\sigma(t)] + q\frac{d\sigma(t)}{dt}\right] f[\sigma(t)]\, dt \leqslant \int_0^T \left[p^* u(t) + qp^* \frac{du(t)}{dt}\right] f[\sigma(t)]\, dt.$$

From

$$h_1\sigma^2 \leqslant \sigma f(\sigma) \leqslant h_2\sigma^2 \qquad (h_2 < k)$$

follows

$$\sigma\left(\sigma - \frac{1}{k} f(\sigma)\right) \geqslant \sigma^2 - \frac{h_2}{k}\sigma^2 = \frac{k-h_2}{k}\sigma^2,$$

from which

$$\sigma^2 f(\sigma)\left(\sigma - \frac{1}{k} f(\sigma)\right) \geqslant \left(\frac{k-h_2}{k}\right)\sigma^3 f(\sigma) = \left(\frac{k-h_2}{k}\right)\sigma^2(\sigma f(\sigma))$$

$$\geqslant \frac{k-h_2}{k}\sigma^2 h_1 \sigma^2.$$

Hence

$$f(\sigma)\left(\sigma - \frac{1}{k} f(\sigma)\right) \geqslant \frac{k-h_2}{k} h_1\sigma^2 = h_3\sigma^2.$$

It follows that

$$h_3\int_0^T \sigma^2(t)\, dt + q\int_{\sigma(0)}^{\sigma(T)} f(\sigma)\, d\sigma \leqslant \int_0^T \left\{p^* u(t) + qp^* \frac{du(t)}{dt}\right\} f[\sigma(t)]\, dt.$$

Setting

$$F(\sigma) = \int_0^\sigma f(\sigma)\, d\sigma,$$

we obtain

$$h_3\int_0^T \sigma^2(t)\, dt + qF[\sigma(t)] \leqslant qF[\sigma(0)] + \int_0^T \left[p^* u(t) + qp^* \frac{du(t)}{dt}\right] f[\sigma(t)]\, dt.$$

Let $\sigma(T) > 0$; for $0 < \sigma < \sigma(T)$ we have

$$\sigma f(\sigma) > \sigma^2 h_1;$$

hence

$$f(\sigma) > h_1\sigma, \qquad \int_0^{\sigma(T)} f(\sigma)\, d\sigma > \frac{h_1}{2}\sigma^2(T).$$

If $\sigma(T) < 0$, for $\sigma(T) < \sigma < 0$ we have

$$\sigma f(\sigma) > h_1\sigma^2;$$

hence

$$f(\sigma) < h_1\sigma, \qquad \int_{\sigma(T)}^{0} f(\sigma)\, d\sigma < h_1 \int_{\sigma(T)}^{0} \sigma\, d\sigma = -\frac{h_1}{2}\sigma^2(T)$$

and

$$\int_0^{\sigma(T)} f(\sigma)\, d\sigma > \frac{h_1}{2}\sigma^2(T).$$

It follows in all cases that $F[\sigma(T)] > (h_1/2)\,\sigma^2(T)$. We may consequently write the inequality

$$q\frac{h_1}{2}\sigma^2(T) + h_3\int_0^T \sigma^2(t)\, dt \leqslant qF[\sigma(0)] + \int_0^T \left\{p^*u(t) + qp^*\frac{du(t)}{dt}\right\} f[\sigma(t)]\, dt.$$

We have

$$|\, u(t)\,| \leqslant \beta\, e^{-\alpha t}\,|\, x(0)\,|, \qquad \left|\frac{du(t)}{dt}\right| \leqslant \gamma\, e^{-\alpha t}\,|\, x(0)\,|.$$

From $\sigma f(\sigma) \leqslant h_2\sigma^2$ follows $|\, f(\sigma)| \leqslant h_2\,|\,\sigma\,|$, and thus

$$\left|\int_0^T \left[p^*u(t) + qp^*\frac{du(t)}{dt}\right] f[\sigma(t)]\, dt\right| \leqslant L_1 \sup_{0\leqslant t\leqslant T}|\,\sigma(t)\,|\,|\, x(0)\,| \int_0^T e^{-\alpha t}\, dt.$$

Taking this into account, we have finally,

$$q\frac{h_1}{2}\sigma^2(T) + h_3\int_0^T \sigma^2(t)\, dt \leqslant qF[\sigma(0)] + L_2\,|\, x(0)\,| \sup_{0\leqslant t\leqslant T}|\,\sigma(t)\,|.$$

From the inequality

$$q\frac{h_1}{2}\sigma^2(T) \leqslant qF[\sigma(0)] + L_2\,|\, x(0)\,| \sup_{0\leqslant t\leqslant T}|\,\sigma(t)\,|$$

we deduce, as in the case previously treated,

$$|\,\sigma(t)\,| \leqslant \alpha_1(|\, x(0)\,|).$$

Taking into account the variation-of-constants formula, we also deduce that

$$|\, x(t)\,| \leqslant \alpha_2(|\, x(0)\,|).$$

From this follows $|\, d\sigma/dt\,| \leqslant \alpha_3(|\, x(0)|)$ and, by the same arguments as in the preceding case, from $\int_0^T \sigma^2(t)dt \leqslant C$ follows $\lim_{t\to\infty}\sigma(t) = 0$ and $\lim_{t\to\infty} x(t) = 0$.

We have thus proved

Theorem 2.4. *If matrix A is Hurwitzian and if there exists a $q > 0$ such that $(1/k) + \operatorname{Re}(1 + i\omega q)p^*(A - i\omega E)^{-1}a \geqslant 0$, then for any function f with the property that there exists h_1 and $h_2 < k$ such that $h_1\sigma^2 \leqslant \sigma f(\sigma) \leqslant h_2\sigma^2$, the trivial solution of the system is asymptotically stable in the large.*

We have been concerned until now with the case where the matrix A is Hurwitzian and the case when it admits a zero eigenvalue. Therefore it is natural now to consider the case where A has two zero eigenvalues. If simple elementary divisors correspond to these values, a linear transformation of variables brings matrix A to the form $\begin{pmatrix} A_1 & 0 \\ 0 & 0 \end{pmatrix}$ and the system becomes

$$\frac{dx}{dt} = A_1 x + a_1 f(\sigma), \qquad \frac{d\xi}{dt} = a_2 f(\sigma), \qquad \frac{d\eta}{dt} = a_3 f(\sigma).$$

If one of the numbers a_2 and a_3 is zero, e.g., if $a_3 = 0$, the last equation becomes

$$\frac{d\eta}{dt} = 0,$$

and it is clear that asymptotic stability can only occur with $\eta = 0$.

But in this case the system takes the form previously studied, which corresponds to a zero root. If $a_2 = a_3 = 0$ we cannot have asymptotic stability except by setting $\xi = 0$, $\eta = 0$, and we again reach the above-considered case. If $a_2 a_3 \neq 0$, taking $\zeta = (1/a_2)\xi - (1/a_3)\eta$, we deduce that $d\zeta/dt = 0$, and again we cannot have asymptotic stability except by setting $\zeta = 0$; thus we again reach the case of a zero root. In conclusion, the case of two zero roots with simple elementary divisors does not bring in anything new.

On the other hand, the case of two zero roots, with elementary divisors of the second order, is particularly interesting, and it has been fully investigated by V. M. Popov. We shall now present this case. *It is evidently supposed that nonzero roots have negative real parts.* Let

$$G(s) = -p^*(sE - A)^{-1}a.$$

Let us remark that the function G is invariant with respect to linear transformations of the system. Indeed, let $y = Dz$. We have

$$\frac{dy}{dt} = D\frac{dz}{dt} = DAD^{-1}y + Daf(\sigma) \qquad (\sigma = p^*D^{-1}y);$$

hence

$$\frac{dy}{dt} = DAD^{-1}y + Daf(\sigma).$$

The new function

$$G_1(s) = -p^*D^{-1}(sE - DAD^{-1})Da = -p^*(sE - A)a$$

is thus equal to $G(s)$.
To perform the effective computation of function G it is useful to observe that this function is the solution of the system $s\tilde{z} = A\tilde{z} - a$, $G(s) = p^*\tilde{z}$.

Theorem 2.5. *If*

$$\operatorname{Re} i\omega G(i\omega) \geqslant 0$$

for all $\omega \geqslant 0$ *and*

$$\lim_{\omega\to 0} \operatorname{Re} \omega^2 G(i\omega) < 0,$$

the trivial solution of the system is stable in the large for an arbitrary function f *with* $\sigma f(\sigma) > 0$ *for* $\sigma \neq 0$,

$$\lim_{\sigma\to\pm\infty} \int_0^\sigma f(\sigma)\, d\sigma = \infty.$$

If in addition we have

$$\lim_{\omega\to\infty} \operatorname{Re} i\omega G(i\omega) > 0,$$

then the trivial solution is stable in the large if $\sigma f(\sigma) > 0$ *for* $\sigma \neq 0$ *and*

$$\limsup_{\sigma\to\pm\infty} \left(|f(\sigma)| + \int_0^\sigma f(\sigma)\, d\sigma \right) = \infty.$$

If

$$\operatorname{Re} i\omega G(i\omega) > 0 \qquad \text{and} \qquad \lim_{\omega\to 0} \operatorname{Re} \omega^2 G(i\omega) < 0$$

and if the trivial solution is stable in the large, then it is asymptotically stable in the large.

Consequently, if

$$\operatorname{Re} i\omega G(i\omega) > 0, \qquad \lim_{\omega\to\infty} \operatorname{Re} i\omega G(i\omega) > 0, \qquad \lim_{\omega\to 0} \operatorname{Re} \omega^2 G(i\omega) < 0,$$

the trivial solution is absolutely stable for all functions f with $\sigma f(\sigma) > 0$ for $\sigma \neq 0$,

$$\limsup_{\sigma\to\pm\infty} \left(|f(\sigma)| + \int_0^\sigma f(\sigma)\, d\sigma\right) = \infty.$$

If

$$\operatorname{Re} i\omega G(i\omega) > 0 \quad \text{and} \quad \lim_{\omega\to 0} \operatorname{Re} \omega^2 G(i\omega) < 0,$$

then absolute stability only occurs in the class of functions with

$$\lim_{\sigma\to\pm\infty} \int_0^\sigma f(\sigma)\, d\sigma = \infty.$$

To prove the theorem, let us observe that since the conditions are only imposed on the function G and since this is invariant, we may assume the system brought to a convenient canonical form.

Choosing D such that

$$DAD^{-1} = \begin{pmatrix} B & & 0 \\ 0 & 0 & 1 \\ 0 & 0 & 0 \end{pmatrix},$$

the system becomes

$$\frac{dx}{dt} = Bx + bf(\sigma), \qquad \frac{dy_{n-1}}{dt} = y_n + b_{n-1}f(\sigma), \qquad \frac{dy_n}{dt} = b_n f(\sigma),$$

$$\sigma = q^*x + \tilde{p}_{n-1}y_{n-1} + \tilde{p}_n y_n.$$

Computing $G(s)$ as indicated above, we find

$$G(s) = -q^*(sE - B)^{-1}b - \frac{\tilde{p}_n b_n + \tilde{p}_{n-1}b_{n-1}}{s} - \frac{\tilde{p}_{n-1}b_n}{s^2}.$$

It follows that

$$\lim_{\omega\to 0} \operatorname{Re} \omega^2 G(i\omega) = \tilde{p}_{n-1}b_n;$$

hence we have $p_{n-1}b_n < 0$.

In particular, $b_n \neq 0$. We may therefore apply a new transformation:

$$x = x, \qquad \eta = \frac{1}{b_n^2}(b_n y_{n-1} - b_{n-1}y_n), \qquad \xi = \frac{1}{b_n} y_n,$$

and the system becomes

$$\frac{dx}{dt} = Bx + bf(\sigma), \qquad \frac{d\eta}{dt} = \xi, \qquad \frac{d\xi}{dt} = f(\sigma), \qquad \sigma = q^*x - \alpha\xi - \beta\eta.$$

Since $G(s)$ is invariant, it is sufficient to prove the theorem for systems of this form. For these systems, we have

$$G(s) = -q^*(sE - B)^{-1}b + \frac{\alpha}{s} + \frac{\beta}{s^2}.$$

The condition

$$\lim_{\omega \to 0} \operatorname{Re} \omega^2 G(i\omega) < 0$$

may now be written $\beta > 0$.

Further,

$$\begin{aligned} \operatorname{Re}(i\omega G(i\omega)) &= -\operatorname{Re} i\omega q^*(i\omega E - B)^{-1}b + \alpha \\ &= -\operatorname{Re} q^*(i\omega E - B + B)(i\omega E - B)^{-1}b + \alpha \\ &= -\operatorname{Re} q^*B(i\omega E - B)^{-1}b + \alpha - q^*b. \end{aligned}$$

Taking into account the fact that

$$\begin{aligned} q^*B(i\omega E - B)^{-1}b &= q^*B(-i\omega E - B)(-i\omega E - B)^{-1}(i\omega E - B)^{-1}b \\ &= q^*B(-i\omega E - B)(\omega^2 E + B^2)^{-1}b, \end{aligned}$$

we may write

$$\operatorname{Re}(i\omega G(i\omega)) = q^*B^2(\omega^2 E + B^2)^{-1}b + \alpha - q^*b.$$

The condition

$$\lim_{\omega \to \infty} \operatorname{Re}(i\omega G(i\omega)) > 0$$

is thus written

$$\alpha - q^*b > 0.$$

We shall now state a series of lemmas which successively reduce the problem to a simpler form.

Lemma 1. *Let*

$$\rho = |x| + |\xi| + |\eta|, \qquad \rho_0 = |x_0| + |\xi_0| + |\eta_0|.$$

If for every solution of the system we have $|\xi(t)| \leqslant \psi_1(\rho_0)$, *then we also have for every solution the inequality*

$$|x(t)| \leqslant \psi_2(\rho_0).$$

Proof. From the variation-of-constants formula,

$$x(t) = e^{Bt} x_0 + \int_0^t e^{B(t-\tau)} bf[\sigma(\tau)]\, d\tau$$

$$= e^{Bt} x_0 + \int_0^t e^{B(t-\tau)} b \frac{d\xi(\tau)}{d\tau}\, d\tau$$

$$= e^{Bt}x_0 + b\xi(t) - e^{Bt}b\xi(0) + \int_0^t Be^{B(t-\tau)} b\xi(\tau)\, d\tau.$$

Since B is Hurwitzian, we have

$$| e^{Bt} | \leqslant K_1 e^{-K_0 t}, \qquad t \geqslant 0;$$

hence

$$| x(t) | \leqslant K_1 e^{-K_0 t}\rho_0 + | b | \psi_1(\rho_0) + K_1 | B | | b | \psi_1(\rho_0) \int_0^t e^{-K_0(t-\tau)}\, d\tau < \psi_2(\rho_0).$$

Lemma 2. *If* $\beta > 0$ *and* $\lim_{\sigma\to\pm\infty} \int_0^\sigma f(\sigma) d\sigma = \infty$ *and for every solution we have*

$$| \xi(t) | \leqslant \psi_1(\rho_0), \qquad \int_0^{\sigma(t)} f(\sigma)\, d\sigma \leqslant \psi_3(\rho_0),$$

then for every solution we have

$$\rho(t) \leqslant \psi_9(\rho_0).$$

Proof. The functions

$$\psi_4(r) = \int_0^r f(\sigma) d\sigma, \qquad \psi_5(r) = \int_0^{-r} f(\sigma) d\sigma$$

are monotone-increasing and continuous; let

$$\psi_6(r) = \min\{\psi_4(r), \psi_5(r)\}.$$

From the hypothesis of the lemma it follows that

$$\psi_6(| \sigma(t) |) \leqslant \psi_3(\rho_0);$$

hence

$$| \sigma(t) | \leqslant \psi_6^{-1}(\psi_3(\rho_0)) = \psi_7(\rho_0).$$

From $\sigma = q^*x - \alpha\xi - \beta\eta$ and $\beta > 0$ follows

$$| \eta(t) | = \frac{1}{\beta} | q^*x(t) - \alpha\xi(t) - \sigma(t) | \leqslant \frac{1}{\beta} | q | \psi_2(\rho_0)$$

$$+ \frac{| \alpha |}{\beta} \psi_1(\rho_0) + \frac{1}{\beta} \psi_7(\rho_0) = \psi_8(\rho_0).$$

From $|\xi(t)| \leqslant \psi_1(\rho_0)$, $|x(t)| \leqslant \psi_2(\rho_0)$, $|\eta(t)| \leqslant \psi_8(\rho_0)$ follows $\rho(t) \leqslant \psi_9(\rho_0)$, and the lemma is proved.

Lemma 3. *If* $\beta > 0$, $\alpha - q^*b > 0$, $\limsup_{\sigma\to\pm\infty} (|f(\sigma)| + \int_0^\sigma f(\sigma)d\sigma) = \infty$, *and if for every solution we have* $|\xi(t)| \leqslant \psi_1(\rho_0)$, $\int_0^{\sigma(t)} f(\sigma)d\sigma \leqslant \psi_3(\rho_0)$, *then for every solution we have* $\rho(t) \leqslant \psi_9(\rho_0)$.

Proof. For all t for which

$$|\sigma(t)| \leqslant (|q| + |\alpha| + |\beta|)\rho_0$$

there also occurs the inequality

$$|f(\sigma(t))| \leqslant \sup_{|\mu| \leqslant (|q|+|\alpha|+|\beta|)\rho_0} |f(\mu)|.$$

We show that for all t for which

$$|\sigma(t)| > (|q| + |\alpha| + |\beta|)\rho_0$$

we have the inequality

$$|f(\sigma(t))| \leqslant \psi_{10}(\rho_0),$$

where

$$\psi_{10}(\rho_0) = \frac{|q||B|\psi_2(\rho_0) + |\beta|\psi_1(\rho_0)}{\alpha - q^*b}.$$

We have

$$|\sigma(0)| = |q^*x_0 - \alpha\xi_0 - \beta\eta_0| \leqslant (|q| + |\alpha| + |\beta|)\rho_0;$$

if there exists a $t_1 > 0$ such that

$$|\sigma(t_1)| > (|q| + |\alpha| + |\beta|)\rho_0,$$

then there exists a t_2 with $0 < t_2 \leqslant t_1$ such that

$$\sigma(t_2) = \sigma(t_1), \qquad \frac{d\sigma^2(t_2)}{dt} \geqslant 0.$$

The point t_2 is the lower bound of the set of points in $[0, t_1]$ for which $\sigma(t_2) = \sigma(t_1)$; if at t_2 we have $d\sigma^2(t)/dt < 0$, then there exists a point t_3 in $(0, t_2)$ with $\sigma^2(t_3) < \sigma^2(t_2)$, and since $\sigma^2(0) < \sigma^2(t_2)$, there exists a t_4 in $(0, t_3)$ with $\sigma(t_4) = \sigma(t_2)$. This contradicts the fact that t_2 is the lower bound. The existence of t_4 follows from the fact that $\sigma(t)$ is continuous and hence posesses the Darboux property. We have

$$\frac{1}{2}\frac{d\sigma^2(t_2)}{dt} = \sigma(t_2)\frac{d\sigma(t_2)}{dt} = \sigma(t_2)\left[q^*\frac{dx(t_2)}{dt} - \alpha\frac{d\xi(t_2)}{dt} - \beta\frac{d\eta(t_2)}{dt}\right]$$

$$= \sigma(t_2)[q^*Bx(t_2) + q^*bf[\sigma(t_2)] - \alpha f[\sigma(t_2)] - \beta\xi(t_2)];$$

hence

$$\frac{1}{2}\frac{d\sigma^2(t_2)}{dt} \leqslant -(\alpha - q^*b)\sigma(t_2)f[\sigma(t_2)] + (|\, q\,|\,|\, B\,|\,\psi_2(\rho_0) + |\,\beta\,|\,\psi_1(\rho_0))|\,\sigma(t_2)\,|.$$

But

$$\sigma(t_2)f[\sigma(t_2)] > 0;$$

hence

$$\sigma(t_2)f[\sigma(t_2)] = |\,\sigma(t_2)\,|\,|\,f[\sigma(t_2)]\,|;$$

hence

$$\frac{1}{2}\frac{d\sigma^2(t_2)}{dt} \leqslant |\,\sigma(t_2)\,|\{-(\alpha - q^*b)\,|\,f[\sigma(t_2)]\,| + |\,q\,|\,|\,B\,|\,\psi_2(\rho_0) + |\,\beta\,|\,\psi_1(\rho_0)\}$$

$$= |\,\sigma(t_1)\,|\,[-(\alpha - q^*b)\,|\,f[\sigma(t_1)]\,| + |\,q\,|\,|\,B\,|\,\psi_2(\rho_0) + |\,\beta\,|\,\psi_1(\rho_0)].$$

From

$$\frac{d\sigma^2(t_2)}{dt} \geqslant 0$$

follows

$$-(\alpha - q^*b)\,|\,f[\sigma(t_1)]\,| + |\,q\,|\,|\,B\,|\,\psi_2(\rho_0) + |\,\beta\,|\,\psi_1(\rho_0) > 0;$$

hence

$$|\,f[\sigma(t_1)]\,| < \frac{|\,q\,|\,|\,B\,|\,\psi_2(\rho_0) + |\,\beta\,|\,\psi_1(\rho_0)}{\alpha - q^*b} = \psi_{10}(\rho_0).$$

We have thus proved the statement made above. From this follows

$$\sup_{\mu\in[0,\sigma(t)]} |\,f(\mu)\,| \leqslant \max\left(\sup_{|\mu|\leqslant(|q|+|\alpha|+|\beta|)\rho_0} |\,f(\mu)\,|, \psi_{10}(\rho_0)\right),$$

where we have denoted by $[0, \sigma(t)]$ the segment with the extremities 0 and $\sigma(t)$ even if $\sigma(t) < 0$. Indeed, if $|\,\sigma(t)\,| \leqslant (|\,q\,| + |\,\alpha\,| + |\,\beta\,|)\rho_0$, we have $|\,\mu\,| \leqslant (|\,q\,| + |\,\alpha\,| + |\,\beta\,|)\rho_0$ and $\sup_{\mu\in[0,\sigma(t)]} |f(\mu)| \leqslant \sup_{|\mu|\leqslant(|q|+|\alpha|+|\beta|)\rho_0} |f(\mu)|$. If $|\sigma(t)| > (|\,q\,| + |\,\alpha\,| + |\,\beta\,|)\rho_0$, since

$|\sigma(0)| \leqslant (|q| + |\alpha| + |\beta|)\rho_0$, for every μ with $|\mu| > (|q| + |\alpha| + |\beta|)\rho_0$ and $\mu \in [0, \sigma(t)]$ there exists $t_1 \in [0, t]$ with $\mu = \sigma(t_1)$; hence $|f(\mu)| \leqslant \psi_{10}(\rho_0)$.

From the stated inequality it follows that

$$\int_0^{\sigma(t)} f(\sigma)d\sigma + \sup_{\mu\in[0,\sigma(t)]} |\varphi(\mu)| \leqslant \psi_{11}(\rho_0).$$

Let

$$\psi_{12}(r) = \int_0^r f(\sigma)\, d\sigma + \sup_{\mu\in[0,r]} |f(\mu)|,$$

$$\psi_{13}(r) = \int_0^{-r} f(\sigma)\, d\sigma + \sup_{-r\leqslant\mu\leqslant 0} |f(\mu)|.$$

We have

$$\int_0^{\sigma} f(\sigma)\, d\sigma + \sup_{\mu\in[0,\sigma]} |f(\mu)| \geqslant \min\{\psi_{12}(|\sigma|), \psi_{13}(|\sigma|)\} = \psi_{14}(|\sigma|);$$

hence

$$\psi_{14}(|\sigma(t)|) \leqslant \psi_{11}(\rho_0),$$

whence

$$|\sigma(t)| \leqslant \psi_{15}(\rho_0).$$

The proof continues as in Lemma 2.

Taking into account the lemmas which have been proved, the first part of the theorem is reduced to obtaining the evaluations $|\xi(t)| \leqslant \psi_1(\rho_0)$ and $\int_0^{\sigma(t)} f(\sigma)d\sigma \leqslant \psi_3(\rho_0)$. To obtain these evaluations we use the Fourier transform. Let

$$f_T(t) = \begin{cases} f[\sigma(t)] & (0 \leqslant t \leqslant T), \\ 0 & (t > T), \end{cases}$$

$$\lambda_T(t) = \int_0^t q^*Be^{B(t-\tau)}bf_T(\tau)d\tau + (q^*b - \alpha)f_T(t).$$

As above,

$$\tilde{f}_T = \int_0^{\infty} e^{-i\omega t} f_T(t)\, dt = \int_0^T e^{-i\omega t} f[\sigma(t)]\, dt.$$

Since B is Hurwitzian, the Fourier transform of the function $q^*Be^{Bt}b$ exists and this transform is equal to $q^*B(i\omega E - B)^{-1}b$.

On the basis of the theorem of the convolution of the Fourier transform we have

$$\tilde{\lambda}_T = q^*B(i\omega E - B)^{-1}b\tilde{f}_T + (q^*b - \alpha)\tilde{f}_T.$$

Let

$$\mu(T) = \int_0^T \lambda_T(t)f_T(t)\,dt = \frac{1}{2\pi}\int_{-\infty}^{\infty} \operatorname{Re} \tilde{\lambda}_T\tilde{f}_T^*\,d\omega$$

$$= \frac{1}{2\pi}\int_{-\infty}^{\infty} \operatorname{Re}\{q^*B(i\omega E - B)^{-1}b + q^*b - \alpha\}\,|\,\tilde{f}_T\,|^2\,d\omega$$

$$= -\frac{1}{2\pi}\int_{-\infty}^{\infty} \operatorname{Re}(i\omega G(i\omega))\,|\,\tilde{f}_T\,|^2\,d\omega.$$

The condition $\operatorname{Re}(i\omega G(i\omega)) \geqslant 0$ leads to $\mu(T) \leqslant 0$. We have

$$\frac{d\sigma(t)}{dt} = q^*Be^{Bt}x_0 + (q^*b - \alpha)f[\sigma(t)] - \beta\xi(t)$$
$$+ \int_0^t q^*Be^{B(t-\tau)}bf[\sigma(\tau)]\,d\tau = q^*Be^{Bt}x_0 - \beta\xi(t) + \lambda_T(t)$$

for $0 \leqslant t \leqslant T$. It follows that

$$\mu(T) = \int_0^T \Big(\frac{d\sigma(t)}{dt} - q^*Be^{Bt}x_0 + \beta\xi(t)\Big)f[\sigma(t)]\,dt \leqslant 0.$$

We have

$$\int_0^T \frac{d\sigma(t)}{dt}f[\sigma(t)]\,dt = \int_0^{\sigma(T)} f(\sigma)\,d\sigma - \int_0^{\sigma(0)} f(\sigma)\,d\sigma,$$

$$\int_0^T \beta\xi(t)f[\sigma(t)]\,dt = \beta\int_0^T \xi(t)\frac{d\xi(t)}{dt}\,dt = \tfrac{1}{2}\beta[\xi^2(T) - \xi^2(0)],$$

$$-\int_0^T q^*\,Be^{Bt}x_0f[\sigma(t)]\,dt = -\int_0^T q^*Be^{Bt}\,x_0\frac{d\xi(t)}{dt}\,dt$$
$$= -q^*Be^{BT}x_0\xi(T) + q^*Bx_0\xi(0)$$
$$+ \int_0^T q^*B^2e^{Bt}x_0\xi(t)\,dt$$
$$\geqslant -2\,|\,q\,|\,|\,B\,|\,|\,K_1\,|\,|\,x_0\,|\sup_{0\leqslant t\leqslant T}|\,\xi(t)\,|$$
$$-K_1\,|\,q\,|\,|\,B\,|^2\,|\,x_0\,|\sup_{0\leqslant t\leqslant T}|\,\xi(t)\,|\int_0^T e^{-K_0t}\,dt$$
$$\geqslant -K_2\rho_0\sup_{0\leqslant t\leqslant T}|\,\xi(t)\,|.$$

Thus we will have

$$\int_0^{\sigma(T)} f(\sigma)\,d\sigma + \tfrac{1}{2}\beta\xi^2(T) - K_2\rho_0 \sup_{0\leqslant t\leqslant T} |\,\xi(t)\,| - \int_0^{\sigma(0)} f(\sigma)\,d\sigma - \tfrac{1}{2}\beta\rho_0^2 \leqslant \mu(T) \leqslant 0.$$

Let

$$\psi_{16}(r) = \max\,(\psi_4(r), \psi_5(r)).$$

We have

$$\int_0^{\sigma(0)} f(\sigma)\,d\sigma \leqslant \psi_{16}(|\,\sigma(0)\,|) \leqslant \psi_{16}(|\,q\,| + |\,\alpha\,| + |\,\beta\,|)\rho_0 = \psi_{17}(\rho_0).$$

Then

$$\int_0^{\sigma(T)} f(\sigma)\,d\sigma + \tfrac{1}{2}\beta\xi^2(T) - K_2\rho_0 \sup_{0\leqslant t\leqslant T} |\,\xi(t)\,| - \psi_{18}(\rho_0) \leqslant \mu(T) \leqslant 0.$$

Since $\int_0^{\sigma(T)} f(\sigma)d \geqslant 0$ and $\frac{1}{2}\beta > 0$, we have the inequality

$$\xi^2(T) - 2K_3\rho_0 \sup_{0\leqslant t\leqslant T} |\,\xi(t)\,| \leqslant \frac{2}{\beta}\psi_{18}(\rho_0) = \psi_{19}(\rho_0).$$

From here, proceeding as before, we obtain $|\,\xi(t)\,| \leqslant \psi_1(\rho_0)$ for all $t \geqslant 0$.

Taking into account the evaluation obtained for $\xi(t)$, we immediately deduce from the fundamental inequality

$$\int_0^{\sigma(t)} f(\sigma)\,d\sigma \leqslant K_2\rho_0\psi_{20}(\rho_0) + \psi_{18}(\rho_0) = \psi_3(\rho_0).$$

With this, the first part of the theorem is proved.

The proof of the last assertion relative to asymptotic stability requires certain preparation.

Lemma 4. *L $\gamma(t)$ be defined for $t > 0$ with derivatives up to order l_1 and such that $|\,d^l\gamma(t)/dt^l\,| < K$ for $t > 0$, $l = 1, 2, ..., l_1$. Suppose that $d^{l_1}\gamma(t)/dt^{l_1}$ is uniformly continuous on the semiaxis $t > 0$. If there exists an l_0, $1 \leqslant l_0 \leqslant l_1$ such that $\lim_{t\to\infty} (d^{l_0}\gamma(t)/dt^{l_0}) = 0$, then $\lim_{t\to\infty} (d^l\gamma(t)/dt^l) = 0$ for $l = 2, 3, ..., l_1$.*

Proof. Suppose that the assertion of the lemma does not hold for the derivative of order j, $2 \leqslant j \leqslant l_1$. Then there exists $\Delta > 0$ and a sequence t_k such that $\lim_{k\to\infty} t_k = \infty$, and $|\,d^j\gamma/dt^j\,| \geqslant \Delta$ in the points t_k.

It follows from the hypotheses of the theorem that all the derivatives are uniformly continuous on the semiaxis $t > 0$. Therefore a sequence t^k may be found such that $| d^j\gamma(t)/dt^j | \geqslant \Delta/2$ for $t \in [t_k, t^k]$. We deduce that

$$2K \geqslant \left| \frac{d^{j-1}\gamma(t^k)}{dt^{j-1}} - \frac{d^{j-1}\gamma(t_k)}{dt^{j-1}} \right| = \left| \int_{t_k}^{t^k} \frac{d^j\gamma(t)}{dt^j}\, dt \right| \geqslant \frac{\Delta}{2} \, | t^k - t_k |,$$

since if $| d^j\gamma(t)/dt^j | \geqslant \Delta/2$ on $[t_k, t^k]$, then $d^j\gamma/dt^j$ conserves the sign on this segment (every derivative has the Darboux property).

Thus $| t^k - t_k | \leqslant 4K/\Delta$. From this we deduce that we may choose t^k so that $| d^j\gamma(t^k)/dt^j | = \Delta/2$; indeed, we cannot have on $[t_k - (4K/\Delta), t_k + (4K/\Delta)]$ the strict inequality $| d^j\gamma(t)/dt^j | > \Delta/2$, since it would follow that $2K > (\Delta/2)(4K/\Delta)$, which is a contradiction. Consequently, there exists on this interval points at which $| d^j\gamma(t)/dt^j | \leqslant \Delta/2$. Hence we can choose t^k with the properties $| t^k - t_k | \leqslant 4K/\Delta$, $| d^j\gamma(t^k)/dt^j | = \Delta/2$, $| d^j\gamma(t)/dt^j | \geqslant \Delta/2$ for $t \in [t_k, t^k]$. (We take t^k equal to the upper bound of the set of points for which $| d^j\gamma(t)/dt^j | \geqslant \Delta/2$). From uniform continuity it follows that there exists a $\delta > 0$ such that $| t - t_k | < \delta$ implies $| (d^j\gamma(t)/dt^j) - (d^j\gamma(t_k)/dt^j) | < \Delta/2$; from here it follows that $t^k - t_k \geqslant \delta$; hence

$$\left| \frac{d^{j-1}\gamma(t^k)}{dt^{j-1}} - \frac{d^{j-1}\gamma(t_k)}{dt^{j-1}} \right| \geqslant \frac{\Delta}{2}\, \delta,$$

which shows that $d^{j-1}\gamma/dt^{j-1}$ cannot have the limit zero for $t \to \infty$. On the other hand,

$$\frac{\Delta}{2} \leqslant \left| \frac{d^j\gamma(t^k)}{dt^j} - \frac{d^j\gamma(t_k)}{dt^j} \right| = \left| \int_{t_k}^{t^k} \frac{d^{j+1}\gamma(t)}{dt^{j+1}}\, dt \right|$$

$$\leqslant | t^k - t_k | \sup_{t \in [t_k, t^k]} \left| \frac{d^{j+1}\gamma(t)}{dt^{j+1}} \right| \leqslant \frac{4K}{\Delta} \sup \left| \frac{d^{j+1}\gamma}{dt^{j+1}} \right| ;$$

hence

$$\sup_{t \in [t_k, t^k]} \left| \frac{d^{j+1}\gamma}{dt^{j+1}} \right| \geqslant \frac{\Delta^2}{8K}.$$

Thus if the assertion of the lemma does not hold for the derivative of order j, neither does it hold for the derivative of order $j + 1$, nor for that of order $j - 1$, which leads to a contradiction with respect to the hypothessis of the statement.

Lemma 5. *If for all the solutions* $\rho(t) \leqslant \psi_9(\rho_0)$ *and* $\lim_{t \to \infty} \xi(t) = 0$, *then the trivial solution is asymptotically stable in the large.*

Proof. We have

$$x(t) = e^{Bt} x_0 + \int_0^t e^{B(t-\tau)} bf[\sigma(\tau)]\, d\tau = e^{Bt} x_0 + \int_0^t e^{B(t-\tau)} b \frac{d\xi(\tau)}{d\tau}$$

$$= e^{Bt}(x_0 - b\xi_0) + b\xi(t) + \int_0^t B\, e^{B(t-\tau)} b\xi(\tau)\, d\tau.$$

Since $\lim_{t\to\infty} e^{Bt} = 0$, it immediately follows from this that $\lim_{t\to\infty} \xi(t) = 0$ implies $\lim_{t\to\infty} x(t) = 0$. On the other hand,

$$\frac{d\sigma}{dt} = q^*Bx(t) + (q^*b - \alpha)f[\sigma(t)] - \beta\xi(t).$$

The hypothesis $\rho(t) \leqslant \psi_9(\rho_0)$ yields

$$| x(t) | \leqslant \psi_9(\rho_0), \qquad | \xi(t) | \leqslant \psi_9(\rho_0), \qquad | \eta(t) | \leqslant \psi_9(\rho_0).$$

Hence

$$| \sigma(t) | \leqslant (| q | + | \sigma | + | \beta |)\psi_9(\rho_0), \qquad | f[\sigma(t)] | \leqslant \psi_{20}(\rho_0)$$

and

$$\left| \frac{d\sigma}{dt} \right| \leqslant \psi_{21}(\rho_0)$$

Thus $\sigma(t)$ is uniformly continuous on the semiaxis $t > 0$; hence $f[\sigma(t)]$ is uniformly continuous. Now apply Lemma 4 with

$$\frac{d\gamma}{dt} = \xi(t), \qquad \frac{d^2\gamma}{dt^2} = f[\sigma(t)].$$

We have $\lim_{t\to\infty} (d\gamma/dt) = 0$, and from Lemma 4 we deduce that $\lim_{t\to\infty} (d^2\gamma/dt^2) = 0$; hence $\lim_{t\to\infty} f[\sigma(t)] = 0$. Since $| \sigma(t) | \leqslant (| q | + | \alpha | + | \beta |)\psi_9(\rho_0)$, we deduce that $\lim_{t\to\infty} \sigma(t) = 0$. From $\sigma(t) = q^*x(t) - \alpha\xi(t) - \beta\eta(t)$ and $\beta > 0$ now follows that $\lim_{t\to\infty} \eta(t) = 0$, and finally it is proved that $\lim_{t\to\infty} \rho(t) = 0$.

In this way the complete proof of the theorem has been reduced to proving the fact that in the conditions from the statement we have $\lim_{t\to\infty} \xi(t) = 0$. For this purpose, another lemma is necessary.

Lemma 6. *If* Re $i\omega G(i\omega) > 0$ *for all* $\omega > 0$, *there exists*

$$H(s) = \gamma_0 \frac{s^{m_0}}{s^k + a_1 s^{k-1} + \cdots + a_{k-1}s + a_k}, \qquad 0 \leqslant m_0 \leqslant k,\ a_k \neq 0,\ \gamma_0 \neq 0$$

with the following properties:

1. *The roots of the equation* $s^k + a_1 s^{k-1} + \cdots + a_{k-1}s + a_k = 0$ *have negative real parts.*

2. Re $i\omega G(i\omega) - | H(i\omega)|^2 \geqslant 0$ *for all real* ω.

Proof. We have, after the computation made above,

$$\operatorname{Re}(i\omega G(i\omega)) = q^*B^2(\omega^2 E + B^2)^{-1}b + \alpha - q^*b$$
$$= \frac{\sum_{j=m_0}^{j=m_1} b_j\omega^{2j}}{\sum_{j=0}^{j=m_2} c_j\omega^{2j}}, \qquad 0 \leqslant m_0 \leqslant m_1 \leqslant m_2,$$
$$b_{m_0} \neq 0,\ b_{m_1} \neq 0,\ c_0 \neq 0,\ c_{m_2} \neq 0.$$

Let $k = m_2 + m_0 - m_1$. Consider an arbitrary polynomial of the form $s^k + a_1 s^{k-1} + \cdots + a_{k-1}s + a_k$, whose roots have negative real parts. The function

$$J(\omega^2) = \frac{1}{\operatorname{Re}(i\omega G(i\omega))}\left|\frac{(i\omega)^{m_0}}{(i\omega)^k + a_1(i\omega)^{k-1} + \cdots + a_{k-1}(i\omega) + a_k}\right|$$

is continuous and

$$\lim_{\omega\to 0} J(\omega^2) = \frac{c_0}{b_{m_0} a_k^2}, \qquad \lim_{\omega\to\infty} J(\omega^2) = \frac{c_{m_2}}{b_{m_1}}.$$

Hence there exists a $\gamma_0 \neq 0$ such that $J(\omega^2) < 1/\gamma_0^2$ for all $\omega^2 > 0$; hence $1 - \gamma_0^2 J(\omega^2) > 0$. Multiplying by $\operatorname{Re}(i\omega G(i\omega))$ we obtain

$$\operatorname{Re}(i\omega G(i\omega)) - \gamma_0^2\left|\frac{(i\omega)^{m_0}}{(i\omega)^k + a_1(i\omega)^{k-1} + \cdots + a_{k-1}(i\omega) + a_k}\right|^2 > 0.$$

We observe that since the polynomial $s^k + a_1 s^{k-1} + \cdots + a_{k-1}s + a_k$ is Hurwitzian, the numbers a_j are all positive.

Let us also remark that if $m_0 = 0$, $m_1 = m_2$, then $k = 0$ and the polynomial is reduced to a constant; the statement of the lemma amounts to the fact that in this case $\operatorname{Re}(i\omega G(i\omega))$ is greater than a positive constant. Indeed, the case $m_0 = 0$, $m_1 = m_2$ may occur if and only if

$$\alpha = \lim_{\omega\to 0} \operatorname{Re}(i\omega G(i\omega)) > 0, \qquad \alpha - q^*b = \lim_{\omega\to\infty} \operatorname{Re}(i\omega G(i\omega)) > 0.$$

These inequalities, together with $\operatorname{Re}(i\omega G(i\omega)) > 0$ for all $\omega > 0$, imply the existence of a positive constant which is the lower bound of $\operatorname{Re}(i\omega G(i\omega))$. In this case, the fact that $\lim_{t\to\infty} \rho(t) = 0$ follows immediately. We have

$$\mu(T) = -\frac{1}{2\pi}\int_{-\infty}^{\infty} \operatorname{Re}(i\omega G(i\omega))\,|\tilde{f}_T|^2\, d\omega \leqslant -\frac{\gamma}{2\pi}\int_{-\infty}^{\infty} |\tilde{f}_T|^2\, d\omega$$
$$= -\gamma\int_0^{\infty} f_T^2\, dt = -\gamma\int_0^T f^2[\sigma(t)]\, dt.$$

Hence, taking into account the expression for $\mu(T)$,

$$\int_0^{\sigma(t)} f(\sigma)\,d\sigma - \int_0^{\sigma(0)} f(\sigma)\,d\sigma + \tfrac{1}{2}\beta\xi^2(T) - K_2\rho_0 \sup_{0\leqslant t\leqslant T} |\,\xi(t)\,|$$

$$- \tfrac{1}{2}\beta\xi_0^2 \leqslant -\gamma \int_0^T f^2[\,\sigma(t)]dt.$$

But, by hypothesis, $\rho(t) \leqslant \psi_9(\rho_0)$; therefore

$$\gamma \int_0^T f^2[\sigma(t)]\,dt \leqslant \psi_{21}(\rho_0);$$

hence

$$\lim_{T\to\infty} \int_0^T f^2[\sigma(t)]\,dt = L < \infty.$$

Setting

$$\frac{d\gamma}{dt} = \int_0^t f^2[\sigma(\tau)]\,d\tau - L$$

it follows that

$$\lim_{t\to\infty} \frac{d\gamma}{dt} = 0.$$

On the base of Lemma 4, we deduce

$$\lim_{t\to\infty} \frac{d^2\gamma}{dt^2} = \lim_{t\to\infty} f^2[\sigma(t)] = 0,$$

hence

$$\lim_{t\to\infty} f[\sigma(t)] = 0.$$

But

$$f[\sigma(t)] = \frac{d\xi(t)}{dt}\,;$$

hence

$$\lim_{t\to\infty} \frac{d\xi(t)}{dt} = 0.$$

From

$$x(t) = e^{Bt}x_0 + \int_0^t e^{B(t-\tau)}\,bf[\sigma(\tau)]\,d\tau$$

we also obtain $\lim_{t\to\infty} x(t) = 0$. From

$$\lim_{t\to\infty} f[\sigma(t)] = 0 \qquad \text{and} \qquad |\,\sigma(t)\,| \leqslant \psi_9(\rho_0)$$

follows

$$\lim_{t\to\infty} \sigma(t) = 0.$$

Since

$$\sigma(t) = q^*x(t) - \alpha\xi(t) - \beta\eta(t),$$

it follows that

$$\lim_{t\to\infty} [\alpha\xi(t) + \beta\eta(t)] = 0.$$

Hence

$$\lim_{t\to\infty} \left[\beta\eta(t) + \alpha \frac{d\eta(t)}{dt}\right] = 0.$$

Let us write

$$\alpha \frac{d\eta(t)}{dt} + \beta\eta(t) = \zeta(t).$$

Since by hypothesis we have $\alpha > 0$, $\beta > 0$, we deduce that

$$\eta(t) = e^{-(\beta/\alpha)t}\eta_0 + \int_0^t e^{-(\beta/\alpha)(t-\tau)}\,\zeta(\tau)\,d\tau.$$

Taking into account the fact that $\lim_{t\to\infty} \zeta(t) = 0$, it follows immediately that $\lim_{t\to\infty} \eta(t) = 0$ (e.g., by applying the rule of l'Hôpital). But if $\lim_{t\to\infty} \eta(t) = 0$, then $\lim_{t\to\infty} \xi(t) = 0$, and the proof is finished.

Lemmas 5 and 6 are necessary in the case when $\alpha = 0$ or $\alpha - q^*b = 0$, and hence $k \geqslant 1$. First let $k = 1$. Then the polynomial in Lemma 6 is reduced to $s + a_1$. Let y_1 be defined by the system

$$\frac{dy_1}{dt} = -a_1y_1 + \eta(t), \qquad y_1(0) = -\frac{1}{a_1^2}\,\xi_0 + \frac{1}{a_1}\,\eta_0\,,$$

$$y_2(t) = \frac{dy_1}{dt} = -a_1y_1 + \eta(t),$$

$$y_3(t) = \frac{dy_2}{dt} = -a_1\,\frac{dy_1}{dt} + \xi(t) = -a_1y_2(t) + \xi(t),$$

$$y_4(t) = \frac{dy_3}{dt} = -a_1\,\frac{dy_2}{dt} + f[\sigma(t)] = -a_1y_3(t) + f[\sigma(t)].$$

Let u_1 be defined by

$$\frac{du_1}{dt} = -a_1u_1 + f_T(t), \qquad u_1(0) = 0, \qquad u_2 = -a_1u_1 + f_T(t).$$

We remark that from the choice of $y_1(0)$ follows

$$y_2(0) = -a_1 y_1(0) + \eta_0 = \frac{1}{a_1}\xi_0 - \eta_0 + \eta_0 = \frac{1}{a_1}\xi_0,$$

$$y_3(0) = -a_1 y_2(0) + \xi_0 = -\xi_0 + \xi_0 = 0,$$

and since on $[0, T]$, y_3 and u_1 verify the same differential equation, it follows that $u_1(t) = y_3(t)$, $u_2(t) = y_4(t)$ on $[0, T]$.

Since $f_T(t) \equiv 0$ for $t > T$, for $t > T$ we will have

$$|u_1(t)| \leqslant K' e^{-a_1 t}, \qquad |u_2(t)| \leqslant K' e^{-a_1 t}.$$

We apply the Fourier transform and we obtain

$$i\omega\tilde{u}_1 = -a_1\tilde{u}_1 + \tilde{f}_T; \qquad \tilde{u}_1 = \frac{1}{i\omega + a_1}\tilde{f}_T,$$

$$\tilde{u}_2 = -a_1\tilde{u}_1 + \tilde{f}_T = -\frac{a_1}{i\omega + a_1}\tilde{f}_T + \tilde{f}_T = \frac{i\omega}{i\omega + a_1}\tilde{f}_T.$$

If $m_0 = 0$ we have $\gamma_0\tilde{u}_1 = H(i\omega)\tilde{f}_T$, and if $m_0 = 1$ we have $\gamma_0\tilde{u}_2 = H(i\omega)\tilde{f}_T$; consequently, $\gamma_0\tilde{u}_{m_0+1} = H(i\omega)\tilde{f}_T$. Let

$$\tilde{\mu}(T) = \gamma_0^2 \int_0^\infty u_{m_0+1}^2\, dt = \frac{1}{2\pi}\int_{-\infty}^\infty \gamma_0^2 |\tilde{u}_{m_0+1}|^2\, d\omega$$

$$= \frac{1}{2\pi}\int_{-\infty}^\infty |H(i\omega)|^2 |\tilde{f}_T|^2\, d\omega.$$

We have

$$\mu(T) + \tilde{\mu}(T) = -\frac{1}{2\pi}\int_{-\infty}^\infty [\mathrm{Re}(i\omega G(i\omega)) - |H(i\omega)|^2]\, |\tilde{f}_T|^2\, d\omega \leqslant 0.$$

But

$$\mu(T) \geqslant -\psi_{22}(\rho_0);$$

hence

$$\tilde{\mu}(T) \leqslant \psi_{22}(\rho_0),$$

i.e.,

$$\gamma_0^2 \int_0^\infty u_{m_0+1}^2\, dt < \psi_{22}(\rho_0).$$

Hence

$$\gamma_0^2 \int_0^\infty y_{m_0+3}^2\, dt < \psi_{22}(\rho_0).$$

Let

$$L = \int_0^\infty y_{m_0+3}^2\,dt, \qquad \frac{d\gamma}{dt} = \int_0^t y_{m_0+3}^2\,dt - L;$$

from $\lim_{t\to\infty} (d\gamma/dt) = 0$ we deduce, by applying Lemma 4, that

$$\lim_{t\to\infty} \frac{d^2\gamma}{dt^2} = 0;$$

hence

$$\lim_{t\to\infty} y_{m_0+3}^2 = 0,$$

i.e.

$$\lim_{t\to\infty} y_{m_0+3} = 0.$$

Again apply Lemma 4 with $d^l\gamma/dt^l = y_l$,

$$l = 1, 2, 3, 4, \qquad l_0 = m_0 + 3.$$

Thus

$$\lim_{t\to\infty} y_2(t) = \lim_{t\to\infty} y_3(t) = \lim_{t\to\infty} y_4(t) = 0.$$

But from

$$\lim_{t\to\infty} y_3(t) = \lim_{t\to\infty} y_2(t) = 0$$

we obtain

$$\lim_{t\to\infty} \xi(t) = 0,$$

and the proof is completed.

The case $k \geqslant 2$ will be treated in the same way. Let y_j be defined by the system

$$\frac{dy_j}{dt} = y_{j+1} \qquad (j = 1, 2, \ldots, k-1),$$

$$\frac{dy_k}{dt} = -\sum_{j=1}^{k} a_j y_{k-j+1} + \eta(t),$$

$$y_1(0) = -\frac{a_{k-1}}{a_k^2}\,\xi_0 + \frac{1}{a_k}\,\eta_0, \qquad y_2(0) = \frac{1}{a_k}\,\xi_0, \quad y_j(0) = 0 \quad (j = 3, \ldots, k).$$

We introduce the functions

$$y_{k+1}(t) = \frac{dy_k(t)}{dt} = -\sum_{j=1}^{k} a_j y_{k-j+1} + \eta(t),$$

$$y_{k+2}(t) = \frac{dy_{k+1}(t)}{dt} = -\sum_{j=1}^{k} a_j \frac{dy_{k-j+1}}{dt} + \xi(t)$$

$$= -\sum_{j=1}^{k} a_j y_{k-j+2} + \xi(t),$$

$$y_{k+3}(t) = \frac{dy_{k+2}(t)}{dt} = -\sum_{j=1}^{k} a_j y_{k-j+3}(t) + f[\sigma(t)].$$

From $\rho(t) \leqslant \psi_9(\rho_0)$ it follows that η, ξ, $f[\sigma(t)]$ are bounded and uniformly continuous. From here follows $|y_j(t)| \leqslant \psi_{23}(\rho_0)$ for $j = 1, ..., k + 3$; for the first k, this follows by using the variation-of-constants formula, and for the last this follows directly. Now let $u_j(t)$ be defined by

$$\frac{du_j}{dt} = u_{j+1} \qquad (j = 1, ..., k - 1),$$

$$\frac{du_k}{dt} = -\sum_{j=1}^{k} a_j u_{k-j+1} + f_T(t) \qquad (u_j(0) = 0),$$

$$u_{k+1} = -\sum_{j=1}^{k} a_j u_{k-j+1} + f_T(t).$$

We have $u_j(t) = y_{j+2}(t)$, $j = 1, ..., k + 1$ for $0 \leqslant t \leqslant T$. Indeed, $y_{j+2}(0) = 0$ for $j = 1, ..., k + 1$ and for $0 \leqslant t \leqslant T$ the functions $y_{j+2}(t)$ verify the same system as $u_j(t)$.

For $t > T$ we have $|u_j(t)| < k'e^{-k''t}$, since $f_T \equiv 0$ for $t > T$ and the corresponding homogeneous system is Hurwitzian. Applying the Fourier transform to the system in u_j, we obtain $\gamma_0 \tilde{u}_{m_0+1} = H(i\omega)\tilde{f}_T$, from which we deduce, as in the preceding case,

$$\gamma_0^2 \int_0^\infty u_{m_0+1}^2 \, dt = \gamma_0^2 \int_0^\infty y_{m_0+3}^2 \, dt < \psi_{22}(\rho_0)$$

and then

$$\lim_{t\to\infty} y_{m_0+3}(t) = 0.$$

Applying Lemma 4 with

$$\frac{d^l y}{dt^l} = y_l \qquad (l = 1, 2, ..., k + 3),$$

we deduce

$$\lim_{t\to\infty} y_j(t) = 0 \qquad (j = 2, 3, \ldots, k + 3),$$

$$\lim_{t\to\infty} \xi(t) = \lim_{t\to\infty} \Big[y_{k+1}(t) + \sum_{j=1}^{k} a_k y_{k-j+2}(t)\Big] = 0,$$

and the theorem is proved.

Example. We consider the system formed by the scalar equations

$$\frac{dx}{dt} = -ax + y - f(x),$$

$$\frac{dy}{dt} = z - cf(x)$$

$$\frac{dz}{dt} = -bf(x).$$

The matrix of the linear part of the system is

$$\begin{pmatrix} -a & 1 & 0 \\ 0 & 0 & 1 \\ 0 & 0 & 0 \end{pmatrix}$$

and we see that it has two zero roots with an elementary divisor of the second order and the root $-a$, which is negative if $a > 0$.

Compute $G(s)$ as mentioned before, from the relations

$$s\tilde{x} = -a\tilde{x} + \tilde{y} + 1, \qquad s\tilde{y} = \tilde{z} + c, \qquad s\tilde{z} = b.$$

We obtain

$$\tilde{z} = \frac{b}{s}, \qquad \tilde{y} = \frac{\tilde{z}}{s} + \frac{c}{s} = \frac{b}{s^2} + \frac{c}{s}, \qquad (a + s)\tilde{x} = \tilde{y} + 1;$$

hence

$$\tilde{x} = \frac{\tilde{y}}{a+s} + \frac{1}{a+s},$$

from which follows

$$G(s) = \frac{1}{a+s}\left(1 + \frac{c}{s} + \frac{b}{s^2}\right).$$

We have

$$\lim_{\omega\to 0} \omega^2 G(i\omega) = -\frac{b}{a} < 0 \qquad \text{if} \qquad b > 0.$$

Hence

$$\operatorname{Re}(i\omega G(i\omega)) = \operatorname{Re}\frac{i\omega}{a+i\omega}\left(1+\frac{c}{i\omega}-\frac{b}{\omega^2}\right)$$

$$= \operatorname{Re}\left[\frac{i\omega(a-i\omega)+c(a-i\omega)}{a^2+\omega^2}-\frac{i\omega b(a-i\omega)}{\omega^2(a^2+\omega^2)}\right]$$

$$= \operatorname{Re}\left[\frac{i\omega a+\omega^2+ac-i\omega c}{a^2+\omega^2}-\frac{i\omega ab+b\omega^2}{\omega^2(a^2+\omega^2)}\right]=\frac{ac-b+\omega^2}{a^2+\omega^2}$$

We see that $\lim_{\omega\to\infty}\operatorname{Re}(i\omega G(i\omega)) = 1$. The condition $\operatorname{Re}(i\omega G(i\omega)) > 0$ for $\omega > 0$ is reduced to $ac - b \geqslant 0$. Consequently, if $a > 0, b > 0$, $ac - b \geqslant 0$, the trivial solution is absolutely stable for all functions f with $\sigma f(\sigma) > 0$ for $\sigma \neq 0$, $\limsup_{\sigma\to\pm\infty}(|f(\sigma)| + \int_0^\sigma f(\sigma)d\sigma) = \infty$.

In this case, too, the method of V. M. Popov yields results which are at least as strong as those based upon the construction of a Lyapunov function of the usual type. Namely, *if there exists a Lyapunov function, negative-definite, of the type "quadratic form plus integral" with positive-definite total derivative by virtue of the system, the condition* $\operatorname{Re}(i\omega G(i\omega))\geqslant 0$ *is fulfilled.*

Proof. Write the equivalent system

$$\frac{dx}{dt} = Bx + bf(\sigma),$$

$$\frac{d\xi}{dt} = f(\sigma),$$

$$\frac{d\sigma}{dt} = q^*Bx - \beta\xi + (q^*b - \alpha)f(\sigma),$$

and the Lyapunov function

$$V(x, \xi, \sigma) = x^*Nx + 2\xi c_1^*x + 2\sigma c_2^*x + \gamma_{11}\xi^2 + 2\gamma_{12}\xi\sigma + \gamma_{22}\sigma^2 - 2\int_0^\sigma f(\sigma)\,d\sigma \leqslant 0.$$

For $f(\sigma) = h\sigma$, $h > 0$, $V(x, \xi, \sigma)$ becomes

$$V_h(x, \xi, \sigma) = x^*Nx + 2\xi c_1^*x + 2\sigma c_2^*x + \gamma_{11}\xi^2 + 2\gamma_{12}\xi\sigma + (\gamma_{22} - h)\sigma^2.$$

Using the system, the total derivative will be

$$\frac{dV_h}{dt} = W_h(x, \xi, \sigma) \geqslant 0.$$

We have $W_h(x, \xi, \sigma) \geqslant 0$ also for $h = 0$, since, if it were strictly negative, it would remain negative for h sufficiently small. It follows that

$$\tfrac{1}{2}x^*(NB + B^*N)x + \xi c_1^* Bx + \sigma c_2^* Bx + (c_2^* x + \gamma_{12}\xi + \gamma_{22}\sigma)(q^*Bx - \beta\xi) \geqslant 0,$$

$$x^*Nx + 2\xi c_1^* x + 2\sigma c_2^* x + \gamma_{11}\xi^2 + 2\gamma_{12}\xi\sigma + \gamma_{22}\sigma^2 \leqslant 0.$$

In particular, for $x = 0$, $\xi = \epsilon^2\beta$, $\sigma = \gamma_{22}$ we deduce from the first inequality

$$-\epsilon^2\beta^2(\gamma_{12}\epsilon^2\beta + \gamma_{22}^2) \geqslant 0$$

for all ϵ, hence that $\gamma_{22} = 0$. The second inequality yields for $x = 0$, $\xi = \epsilon^2$, $\sigma = \gamma_{12}$,

$$\epsilon^4\gamma_{11} + 2\gamma_{12}^2\epsilon^2 + \gamma_{22}\gamma_{12}^2 \leqslant 0;$$

hence $\gamma_{12} = 0$.

The same inequality yields for $x = \epsilon^2 c_2$, $\xi = 0$, $\sigma = 1$,

$$\epsilon^4 c_2^* N c_2 + 2\epsilon^2 c_2^* c_2 + \gamma_{22} \leqslant 0;$$

hence $c_2 = 0$.

Again putting $x = B^*c_1\epsilon^2$, $\xi = -1$, $\sigma = 0$ in the first inequality we deduce $B^*c_1 = 0$; hence $c_1 = 0$. It follows that V_h has the form $x^*Nx + \gamma_{11}\xi^2 - h\sigma^2$, and the derivative, by virtue of the linear system, is

$$\tfrac{1}{2}x^*N(Bx + bh\sigma) + \tfrac{1}{2}(Bx + bh\sigma)^*Nx + (h\sigma(\gamma_{11} + \beta)\xi - q^*Bx - (q^*b - \alpha)h\sigma) \geqslant 0.$$

Putting

$$x = \omega B^{-1}U(\omega), \qquad \xi = 0, \qquad \sigma = 0,$$

we deduce that

$$\tfrac{1}{2}\omega^2(B^{-1}U(\omega))^*NU(\omega) + \tfrac{1}{2}\omega^2 U^*(\omega)NB^{-1}U(\omega) \geqslant 0.$$

Taking $U(\omega) = -B(\omega^2 E + B^2)^{-1}b$ and putting $x = U(\omega)$, $\xi = 0$, $\sigma = 1/h$, we deduce that

$$\tfrac{1}{2}U^*(\omega)N(BU(\omega) + b) + \tfrac{1}{2}(BU(\omega) + b)^*NU(\omega) - q^*BU(\omega) + \alpha - q^*b \geqslant 0.$$

But

$$BU(\omega) + b = -B^2(\omega^2 E + B^2)^{-1}b + (\omega^2 E + B^2)(\omega^2 E + B^2)^{-1}b$$
$$= \omega^2(\omega^2 E + B^2)^{-1}b = -\omega^2 B^{-1}U(\omega).$$

Finally, we obtain $-q^*BU(\omega) + \alpha - q^*b \geqslant 0$, which coincides with $\mathrm{Re}(i\omega G(i\omega)) \geqslant 0$.

Let us observe that the derivative of the function V_h for $x = 0$, $\sigma = 0$, $\xi \neq 0$ is zero; hence there do not exist Lyapunov functions of the type considered with positive-definite derivative.

Let us use the method of the Lyapunov function in this problem, too. If $\beta \neq 0$, the system is equivalent from the viewpoint of absolute stability to

$$\frac{dx}{dt} = Bx + bf(\sigma),$$

$$\frac{d\xi}{dt} = f(\sigma),$$

$$\frac{d\sigma}{dt} = q^*Bx + (q^*b - \alpha)f(\sigma) - \beta\xi.$$

A necessary condition for the absolute stability of this system is $\beta > 0$. Indeed, from the absolute stability it follows that the eigenvalues of the matrix

$$H = \begin{pmatrix} B & b & 0 \\ q^*B & q^*b - \alpha & -\beta \\ 0 & 1 & 0 \end{pmatrix},$$

[H is the matrix of the linear system which is obtained for $f(\sigma) = \sigma$] have negative real parts; hence

$$(-1)^{n+2} \det H = (-1)^n \det H > 0.$$

But

$$\det H = -\det \begin{pmatrix} B & 0 \\ q^*B & -\beta \end{pmatrix} = \beta \det B$$

and

$$(-1)^n \det H = (-1)^n \beta \det B.$$

Taking into account the fact that B is Hurwitzian, it follows that $(-1)^n$ *det* $B > 0$, hence that $\beta > 0$.

In what follows we shall suppose therefore that $\beta > 0$ and in addition that

$$\lim_{|\sigma|\to\infty} \int_0^\sigma f(\sigma)\, d\sigma = \infty.$$

For any matrix $\Gamma > 0$ there exists a $C > 0$ such that

$$CB + B^*C = -\Gamma.$$

(see Section 1.6 and Lemma 1, Section 2.2). Consider the function

$$V(x, \xi, \sigma) = (Cx, x) + \beta\xi^2 + 2\int_0^\sigma f(\sigma)\, d\sigma.$$

The total derivative of this function, by virtue of the system, is

$$\frac{dV}{dt} = -\{(\Gamma x, x) - 2((Cb + B^*q), x)f(\sigma) + 2(\alpha - q^*b)f^2(\sigma)\}.$$

It follows that $-dV/dt$ is a quadratic form in x, σ with the matrix

$$\begin{pmatrix} \Gamma & -(Cb + B^*q) \\ -(Cb + B^*q)^* & 2(\alpha - q^*b) \end{pmatrix}.$$

Consequently, it is necessary and sufficient in order that this quadratic form be positive-definite that

$$\det \begin{pmatrix} \Gamma & -(Cb + B^*q) \\ -(Cb + B^*q)^* & 2(\alpha - q^*b) \end{pmatrix} > 0.$$

This leads to the condition

$$\alpha - q^*b > \tfrac{1}{2}(Cb + B^*q)\Gamma^{-1}(Cb + B^*q).$$

Since dV/dt may be zero only for $x = 0$, $\sigma = 0$, and this set does not contain whole semitrajectories, we deduce that a sufficient condition for the absolute stability of the system is that

$$\alpha - q^*b > \min_{\Gamma>0} \tfrac{1}{2}(Cb + B^*q)^*\Gamma^{-1}(Cb + B^*q).$$

Now let

$$B = \operatorname{diag}(-\mu_i), \qquad \Gamma = \operatorname{diag}(\gamma_i).$$

Then

$$C = \operatorname{diag}\left(\frac{\gamma_i}{2\mu_i}\right), \qquad (Cb + B^*q)^*\Gamma^{-1}(Cb + B^*q)$$

$$= \sum_{i=1}^{n} \frac{1}{4\mu_i^2}\left(\frac{\gamma_i b_i - 2\mu_i^2 q_i}{\sqrt{\gamma_i}}\right)^2,$$

where b_i, q_i are the coordinates of vectors b, q. We deduce

$$\min_{\Gamma>0} (Cb + B^*q)^*\Gamma^{-1}(Cb + B^*q) = 2\sum_{i=1}^{n} \epsilon_i' q_i b_i ,$$

$$\epsilon_i' = \begin{cases} 0 & \text{if } b_i q_i > 0, \\ 1 & \text{if } b_i q_i < 0. \end{cases}$$

We thus obtain the following condition of absolute stability:

$$\alpha > \sum_{i=1}^{n} \epsilon_i q_i b_i , \qquad \epsilon_i = \begin{cases} 0 & (q_i b_i < 0), \\ 1 & (q_i b_i > 0). \end{cases}$$

Let us now observe that, when B is diagonal, we have

$$G(i\omega) = -\sum_{k=1}^{n} \frac{b_k q_k}{i\omega + \mu_k} + \frac{\alpha}{i\omega} - \frac{\beta}{\omega^2}$$

and the inequality $\mathrm{Re}\, i\omega G(i\omega) > 0$ becomes

$$\alpha > \sum_{i=1}^{n} \frac{b_i q_i \omega^2}{\mu_i^2 + \omega^2} .$$

The theorem of V. M. Popov leads then to the following condition of stability:

$$\alpha > \max_{\omega>0} \sum_{i=1}^{n} \frac{b_i q_i \omega^2}{\mu_i^2 + \omega^2} .$$

Since $\mathrm{Re}\, i\omega G(i\omega) = \alpha$ for $\omega = 0$, the inequality

$$\mathrm{Re}\, i\omega G(i\omega) > 0 \qquad \text{for every } \omega > 0$$

implies that $\alpha \geqslant 0$ even if matrix B is not diagonal. From

$$\max_{\omega\geqslant 0} \frac{b_i q_i}{\mu_i^2 + \omega^2} = \epsilon_i'' b_i q_i , \qquad \epsilon_i'' = \begin{cases} 1 & (b_i q_i > 0), \\ 0 & (b_i q_i \leqslant 0), \end{cases}$$

we deduce that $\alpha > \sum_{i=1}^{n} \epsilon_i'' b_i q_i$ is a sufficient condition of absolute stability and we again find the result obtained above with the help of Lyapunov function.

In the case where $b_i q_i > 0$ for $i = 1, ..., n$, we have

$$\min_{\substack{\Gamma>0 \\ \Gamma \text{ diag}}} (Cb + B^*q)^*\Gamma^{-1}(Cb + B^*q) = 0$$

and it is obvious that this minimum cannot be improved by considering nondiagonal matrices, since Γ^{-1} is positive-definite; hence

$$(Cb + B^*q)^*\Gamma^{-1}(Cb + B^*q) \geqslant 0.$$

In case $b_i q_i < 0$ for $i = 1, \ldots, n$, we have

$$\min_{\substack{\Gamma>0 \\ \Gamma \text{ diag}}} (Cb + B^*q)^*\Gamma^{-1}(Cb + B^*q) = -2q^*b$$

and again, the minimum cannot be improved by considering nondiagonal matrices. Indeed, if there existed a $\Gamma > 0$ such that

$$(Cb + B^*q)^*\Gamma^{-1}(Cb + B^*q) < -2q^*b$$

we would deduce that for

$$\alpha - q^*b > \tfrac{1}{2}(Cb + B^*q)^*\Gamma^{-1}(Cb + B^*q)$$

there exists a Lyapunov function, and since

$$q^*b + \tfrac{1}{2}(Cb + B^*q)^*\Gamma^{-1}(Cb + B^*q) < 0$$

we could have a Lyapunov function for $\alpha < 0$, which contradict the conclusion drawn on the basis of the theorem of Popov. Since this conclusion did not use the fact that B is diagonal, we deduce that for every Hurwitzian B and every $\Gamma > 0$ there occurs the inequality

$$(Cb + B^*q)^*\Gamma^{-1}(Cb + B^*q) \geqslant -2q^*b.$$

Taking $q = \frac{1}{2} B^{*-1}c$, we obtain

$$(Cb + \tfrac{1}{2}c)^*\Gamma^{-1}(Cb + \tfrac{1}{2}c) \geqslant -c^*B^{*-1}b.$$

This last inequality has been obtained in a different way by J. P. LaSalle.

In what follows we shall emphasize the general ideas contained in the method of V. M. Popov in order to reach a generalization of Theorem 2.2. Let us consider a system of the form

$$\frac{dx}{dt} = Ax + f(y), \qquad f(0) = 0,$$

where y is a vector. We may either suppose that $y = \alpha(x)$ or that the system contains another equation, $dy/dx = g(x, y)$.

Let us suppose that we have succeeded in proving that for every initial condition (x_0, y_0) we have $|y(t)| < \gamma(x_0, y_0)$, where $\gamma \to 0$ when $|x_0| + |y_0| \to 0$. Suppose that matrix A is Hurwitzian. Then there follows an evaluation of the same type for $x(t)$. Indeed, we have

$$x(t) = e^{A(t-t_0)}x(t_0) + \int_{t_0}^{t} e^{A(t-s)} f[y(s)]\, ds$$

Let

$$\lambda(x_0, y_0) = \sup_{|y| \leqslant \gamma(x_0, y_0)} |f(y)|.$$

Since $f(0) = 0$,

$$\lambda(x_0, y_0) \to 0 \qquad \text{when} \quad |x_0| + |y_0| \to 0.$$

We have

$$\begin{aligned}|x(t)| &\leqslant K_1 e^{-k_0(t-t_0)} |x_0| + \int_{t_0}^{t} K_1 e^{-k_0(t-s)} \lambda(x_0, y_0)\, ds \\ &\leqslant K_1 |x_0| + \frac{K_1}{k_0} \lambda(x_0, y_0).\end{aligned}$$

If, in addition,

$$\lim_{t\to\infty} y(t) = 0,$$

we will have

$$\lim_{t\to\infty} x(t) = 0,$$

since

$$|x(t)| \leqslant K_1 e^{-k_0(t-t_0)} |x_0| + \int_{t_0}^{t} K_1 e^{-k_0(t-s)} |f[y(s)]|\, ds$$

and

$$\begin{aligned}\lim_{t\to\infty} \int_{t_0}^{t} e^{-k_0(t-s)} |f[y(s)]|\, ds &= \lim_{t\to\infty} \frac{\int_{t_0}^{t} e^{k_0 s} |f[y(s)]|\, ds}{e^{k_0 t}} \\ &= \lim_{t\to\infty} \frac{e^{k_0 t} |f[y(t)]|}{k_0 e^{k_0 t}} = \frac{1}{k_0} \lim_{t\to\infty} |f[y(t)]| = 0.\end{aligned}$$

We deduce from this that in order to obtain asymptotic stability in the large it is sufficient to emphasize the corresponding properties of $y(t)$. These properties are obtained by showing that there exist three continuous functions $a(r)$, $b(r)$, $c(r, s)$ zero in origin, the first two monotone-increasing, such that

$$a(|y|) + \int_{t_0}^{t} b(|y|)\, dt < c(|x_0|, |y_0|).$$

Indeed, if such an inequality occurs, it follows in particular that

$$a(|y|) < c(|x_0|, |y_0|)$$

and hence that

$$|y(t)| < a^{-1}(c(|x_0|, |y_0|)).$$

It also follows from this inequality that

$$\int_0^\infty b(|y|)\,dt < c(|x_0|, |y_0|).$$

On the other hand, we have seen that

$$|x(t)| < \beta(|x_0|, |y_0|).$$

Hence

$$\left|\frac{dx}{dt}\right| < \gamma(|x_0|, |y_0|)$$

and, in any case,‡

$$\left|\frac{dy}{dt}\right| < \delta(|x_0|, |y_0|).$$

Then the convergence of the integral yields

$$\lim_{t\to\infty} y(t) = 0$$

Let us remark that if there exists a Lyapunov function, an integral inequality of the considered type can always be obtained. Indeed, from

$$a(|y|) \leqslant V(t, y) \leqslant b(|x|, |y|), \qquad \frac{dV}{dt} < -c(|y|)$$

we obtain, by integration,

$$V(t, y) - V(0, y_0) < -\int_0^t c(|y|)\,dt;$$

hence

$$a(|y|) < b(|x_0|, |y_0|) - \int_0^t c(|y|)\,dt$$

i.e.,

$$a(|y|) + \int_0^t c(|y|)\,dt < b(|x_0|, |y_0|).$$

‡ We need only the fact that $y(t)$ is uniformly continuous for $t \geqslant 0$, and this occurs even if dy/dt does not exist.

The method used by V. M. Popov to obtain an integral inequality of the desired form is the following. A quadratic functional $\chi(T)$ is considered in y for which we seek, on the one hand, lower bounds of the form $a(|y|) + \int_0^t b(|y|)dt + \delta(|x_0|, |y_0|)$, and, on the other hand, an upper bound of the form $c(|x_0|, |y_0|)$. The Fourier transform is used to obtain the upper bound. The art of success in the application of the method consists in the convenient choice of the functional $\chi(T)$.

Consider general systems of the form

$$\frac{dx}{dt} = Ax + By, \qquad \frac{dy}{dt} = f(z) \qquad (z = C_1x + D_1y).$$

We perform the change of variables $x' = Ax + By, y' = y, z' = z$. We obtain

$$\frac{dx'}{dt} = A\frac{dx}{dt} + B\frac{dy}{dt} = Ax' + Bf(z), \qquad \frac{dy'}{dt} = f(z)$$

$$z = C_1(A^{-1}x' - A'By') + D_1y'.$$

Suppressing the indices, we write the system in the form

$$\frac{dx}{dt} = Ax + Bf(z), \qquad \frac{dy}{dt} = f(z) \qquad (z = Cx + Dy). \tag{6}$$

Assume that matrix A is Hurwitzian and that D is nonsingular. We look for conditions which assure asymptotic stability in the large, for any function $f(z)$ of the form $\{f_i(z_i)\}$ verifying the conditions

$$\delta_i z_i^2 \leqslant f_i(z_i)z_i \leqslant (h_i - \delta_i')z_i^2,$$

where δ_i, δ_i', h_i are given positive numbers.

Theorem 2.6. *Suppose that there exist matrices P, Q diagonal, with the following properties:*

1. *The elements of matrix P are positive or zero.*

2. *If an element on the diagonal of P is zero, the corresponding element of Q is strictly positive.*

3. *PD is a symmetric matrix, $PD \leqslant 0$.*

4. *Let F_h be the diagonal matrix with elements h_i,*

$$G(i\omega) = P[F_h^{-1} - C(i\omega E - A)^{-1}B] - Q[CA(i\omega E - A)^{-1}B + D + CB]$$

$$H(i\omega) = \tfrac{1}{2}[G(i\omega) + G^*(i\omega)],$$

$$S = \lim_{\omega\to\infty} H(i\omega) = PF_h^{-1} - \tfrac{1}{2}[Q(CB + D) + (B^*C^* + D^*)Q^*].$$

Assume $H(i\omega) > 0$, $S > 0$.

Then the trival solution of system (6) *is asymptotically stable in the large, for any function f of the considered class.*

Let us show first that it follows from the hypotheses that the matrix D is necessarily Hurwitzian. Let

$$P = \begin{pmatrix} P_1 & 0 \\ 0 & 0 \end{pmatrix}, \qquad D = \begin{pmatrix} D_1 & D_2 \\ D_3 & D_4 \end{pmatrix}, \qquad PD = \begin{pmatrix} P_1D_1 & P_1D_2 \\ 0 & 0 \end{pmatrix};$$

PD is symmetric; hence $P_1D_2 = 0$. Since P_1 is nonsingular, it follows that $D_2 = 0$. From this we deduce that the eigenvalues of D are those of D_1 and D_4. From $PD \leqslant 0$ follows $P_1D_1 \leqslant 0$; if there exists a $u_0 \neq 0$ such that $P_1D_1u_0 = 0$, then $D_1u_0 = 0$; hence D_1 is singular, hence D is singular, which we have excluded. Then $P_1D_1 < 0$. The function $V = \frac{1}{2}(P_1D_1(D_1^{-1}u), D_1^{-1}u)$ is therefore negative-definite, and its derivative, by virtue of the system $du/dt = D_1u$, is

$$(P_1D_1(D_1^{-1}u), D_1^{-1}D_1u) = (P_1u, u);$$

hence this derivative is positive-definite; it follows that D_1 is Hurwitzian.

Now consider the matrix

$$H(0) = \begin{pmatrix} H_1 & H_2 \\ H_3 & H_4 \end{pmatrix};$$

since $H(0) > 0$, we see that $H_4 > 0$. We have

$$H(0) = \tfrac{1}{2}(G(0) + G^*(0)),$$

$$G(0) = P[F_h^{-1} + CA^{-1}B] + Q[CB - D - CB] = P[F_h^{-1} + CA^{-1}B] - QD.$$

If

$$G(0) = \begin{pmatrix} G_1 & G_2 \\ G_3 & G_4 \end{pmatrix},$$

taking into account the form of P, it will follow that

$$G_4 = -Q_4D_4,$$

where we have set

$$Q = \begin{pmatrix} Q_1 & 0 \\ 0 & Q_4 \end{pmatrix}.$$

Then

$$H_4 = -\tfrac{1}{2}(Q_4 D_4 + D_4^* Q_4).$$

According to the hypothesis, $Q_4 > 0$; hence $V = -\frac{1}{2}(Q_4 v, v)$ is negative-definite; its total derivative, by virtue of the system $dV/dt = D_4 v$, is $\frac{1}{2}(H_4 v, v)$, hence positive-definite; hence D_4 is Hurwitzian.

Since the matrices A and D are Hurwitzian, there exist symmetric negative-definite matrices M_1 and M_2 such that

$$M_1 A + A^* M_1 = E, \qquad M_2 D + D^* M_2 = E'.$$

The function $V = (M_1 x, x) + (M_2 y, y)$ is negative-definite and its total derivative by virtue of the system

$$\frac{dx}{dt} = Ax + BF(Cx + Dy), \qquad \frac{dy}{dt} = F(Cx + Dy)$$

is

$$\begin{aligned}\frac{dV}{dt} &= (M_1(Ax + BFCx + BFDy), x) + (M_1 x, Ax + BFCx + BFDy) \\ &\quad + (M_2 F(Cx + Dy), y) + (M_2 y, F(Cx + Dy)) \\ &= ((M_1 A + A^* M_1)x, x) + ((M_2 FD + D^* F^* M_2)y, y) \\ &\quad + (M_1 FB(Cx + Dy), x) + (M_1 x, BF(Cx + Dy)) \\ &\quad + (M_2 FCx, y) + (M_2 y, FCx).\end{aligned}$$

Taking $F = \epsilon_0 E'$, we will have

$$\frac{dV}{dt} = (x, x) + \epsilon_0(y, y) + \epsilon_0 T(x, y),$$

where we have set

$$T(x, y) = 2(M_1 B(Cx + Dy), x) + 2(M_2 Cx, y).$$

We have

$$| T(x, y) | \leqslant a(x, x) + b \, | x | \, | y | ;$$

hence

$$\frac{dV}{dt} \geqslant |x|^2 + \epsilon_0 |y|^2 - \epsilon_0(a|x|^2 + b|x||y|)$$

$$= (1 - \epsilon_0 a)\left(|x| - \frac{\epsilon_0 b}{2(1 - \epsilon_0 a)}|y|\right)^2 + \epsilon_0 |y|^2 \left(1 - \frac{\epsilon_0 b^2}{4(1 - \epsilon_0 a)}\right).$$

We see that for ϵ_0 sufficiently small, dV/dt is positive-definite; hence the trivial solution of the system

$$\frac{dx}{dt} = Ax + \epsilon_0 B(Cx + Dy), \qquad \frac{dy}{dt} = \epsilon_0(Cx + Dy)$$

is asymptotically stable; upon putting $z = Cx + Dy$, we have

$$\frac{dz}{dt} = C\frac{dx}{dt} + D\frac{dy}{dt} = C(Ax + \epsilon_0 Bz) + D\epsilon_0 z = CAx + \epsilon_0(CB + D)z.$$

Hence the trivial solution of the system

$$\frac{dx}{dt} = Ax + \epsilon_0 Bz, \qquad \frac{dz}{dt} = CAx + \epsilon_0(CB + D)z$$

is asymptotically stable; therefore the matrix

$$\begin{pmatrix} A & \epsilon_0 B \\ CA & \epsilon_0(CB + D) \end{pmatrix}$$

is Hurwitzian for ϵ_0 sufficiently small.

Consider the matrix

$$\begin{pmatrix} A & BF \\ CA & (CB + D)F \end{pmatrix}.$$

We shall prove that this matrix is Hurwitzian for all diagonal matrices $F > 0$ with the diagonal elements smaller or equal to h_i.

If the assertion were not valid, there would exist a matrix $0 < F_0 \leqslant F_h$ such that the matrix

$$\begin{pmatrix} A & BF_0 \\ CA & (CB + D)F_0 \end{pmatrix}$$

has a purely imaginary root $i\omega_0$, since for $F = \epsilon_0 E'$ the matrix is Hurwitzian.

We have

$$\det\begin{pmatrix} E & 0 \\ -CA(A-\lambda E)^{-1} & E' \end{pmatrix}\begin{pmatrix} A-\lambda E & BF \\ CA & (CB+D)F-\lambda E' \end{pmatrix}$$

$$= \det\begin{pmatrix} A-\lambda E & BF \\ 0 & [-CA(A-\lambda E)B^{-1}+CB+D]F-\lambda E' \end{pmatrix}$$

$$= \det\begin{pmatrix} A-\lambda E & BF \\ CA & (CB+D)F-\lambda E' \end{pmatrix}.$$

For $F = F_0$, $\lambda = i\omega_0$, we will have

$$\det\begin{pmatrix} A-i\omega_0 E & BF_0 \\ 0 & [-CA(A-i\omega_0 E)^{-1}B+CB+D]F_0-i\omega_0 E' \end{pmatrix} = 0.$$

Since

$$\det(A-i\omega_0 E) \neq 0$$

it follows that

$$\det([-CA(A-i\omega_0 E)^{-1}B+CB+D]F_0-i\omega_0 E') = 0.$$

For $\omega_0 = 0$ we obtain $\det DF_0 = 0$, which is impossible.

Let $\omega_0 \neq 0$. We have

$$A(A-i\omega_0 E)^{-1}B = B + i\omega_0(A-i\omega_0 E)^{-1}B,$$

since from

$$(A-i\omega_0 E)(A-i\omega_0 E)^{-1} = E$$

we obtain

$$A(A-i\omega_0 E)^{-1} - i\omega_0(A-i\omega_0 E)^{-1} = E.$$

Hence

$$A(A-i\omega_0 E)^{-1} = E + i\omega_0(A-i\omega_0 E)^{-1}.$$

It follows that

$$CA(A-i\omega_0 E)^{-1}B = CB + i\omega_0 C(A-i\omega_0 E)^{-1}B;$$

hence

$$-CA(A-i\omega_0 E)^{-1}B + CB = -i\omega_0 C(A-i\omega_0 E)^{-1}B$$

and

$$\det([-i\omega_0 C(A-i\omega_0 E)^{-1}B + D]F_0 - i\omega_0 E') = 0;$$

i.e.,

$$\det(-i\omega_0 C(A - i\omega_0 E)^{-1}B + D - i\omega_0 F_0^{-1}) = 0.$$

Thus

$$\det\left[C(A - i\omega_0 E)^{-1}B + F_0^{-1} - \frac{1}{i\omega_0} D\right] = 0.$$

Therefore there exists a vector $z_0 \neq 0$ such that

$$\left[C(A - i\omega_0 E)^{-1}B + F_0^{-1} - \frac{1}{i\omega_0} D\right] z_0 = 0;$$

hence

$$[i\omega_0 C(A - i\omega_0 E)^{-1}B + i\omega_0 F_0^{-1} - D]z_0 = 0;$$

i.e.,

$$[CA(A - i\omega_0 E)^{-1}B - CB - D + i\omega_0 F_0^{-1}]\, z_0 = 0.$$

It follows that

$$\Big\{ P\left[C(A - i\omega_0 E)^{-1}B + F_0^{-1} - \frac{1}{i\omega_0} D\right]$$
$$-Q[-CA(A - i\omega_0 E)^{-1}B + CB + D] + i\omega_0 Q F_0^{-1}\Big\}\, z_0 = 0.$$

Since by hypothesis $H(i\omega_0) > 0$, we have $(H(i\omega_0)z_0 , z_0) > 0$. We have

$$G(i\omega_0)z_0 = PF_h^{-1}z_0 - PC(i\omega_0 E - A)^{-1}Bz_0$$
$$-Q[CA(i\omega_0 E - A)^{-1}B + CB + D]z_0$$
$$= PF_h^{-1}z_0 - PF_0^{-1}z_0 + \frac{1}{i\omega} PDz_0 - i\omega_0 QF_0^{-1}z_0 ,$$

$$G^*(i\omega_0)z_0 = PF_h^{-1}z_0 - PF_0^{-1}z_0 - \frac{1}{i\omega_0} PDz_0 + i\omega_0 QF_0^{-1}z_0;$$

hence

$$(P(F_h^{-1} - F_0^{-1})z_0 , z_0) > 0.$$

But

$$0 < F_0 < F_h , F_0^{-1} > F_h^{-1};$$

hence

$$F_h^{-1} - F_0^{-1} < 0$$

and

$$(P(F_h^{-1} - F_0^{-1})z_0 , z_0) < 0.$$

We have obtained a contradiction; therefore the matrix is Hurwitzian for every $0 < F < F_h$.

We will take in particular $F = F_q$, where the elements of F_q are $\frac{1}{2}\delta_i$ for those i for which $q_i > 0$ and $h_i - \frac{1}{2}\delta'$ for those i for which $q_i \leqslant 0$. Consider the auxiliary system

$$\frac{dx}{dt} = Ax + BF_q z, \qquad \frac{dy}{dt} = F_q z \qquad (z = Cx + Dy)$$

or, equivalently,

$$\frac{dx}{dt} = Ax + BF_q z, \qquad \frac{dz}{dt} = CAx + (CB + D)F_q z.$$

According to the foregoing, the trivial solution of this system is asymptotically stable.

Now let $x(t)$, $y(t)$, $z(t)$ be a solution of system (6). We consider a solution $\bar{\bar{x}}(t)$, $\bar{\bar{y}}(t)$ $\bar{\bar{z}}(t)$ of the auxiliary system defined for $t \geqslant T$ through conditions $\bar{\bar{x}}(T) = x(T)$, $\bar{\bar{y}}(T) = y(T)$, $\bar{\bar{z}}(T) = z(T)$. We define the functions

$$\bar{x}(t) = \begin{cases} x(t) & \text{for } 0 \leqslant t \leqslant T, \\ \bar{\bar{x}}(t) & \text{for } T \leqslant t, \end{cases}$$

$$\bar{y}(t) = \begin{cases} y(t) & \text{for } 0 \leqslant t \leqslant T, \\ \bar{\bar{y}}(t) & \text{for } T \leqslant t, \end{cases}$$

$$\bar{z}(t) = \begin{cases} z(t) & \text{for } 0 \leqslant t \leqslant T, \\ \bar{\bar{z}}(t) & \text{for } T \leqslant t. \end{cases}$$

The functions $\bar{x}(t)$, $\bar{y}(t)$, $\bar{z}(t)$ verify (with the exception of point $t = T$) the system

$$\frac{d\bar{x}}{dt} = A\bar{x} + Bf_T(t), \qquad \frac{d\bar{y}}{dt} = f_T(t), \qquad \bar{z} = C\bar{x} + D\bar{y}$$

where

$$f_T(t) = \begin{cases} f(z(t)) & \text{for } 0 \leqslant t < T, \\ F_q\bar{\bar{z}}(t) & \text{for } T \leqslant t. \end{cases}$$

Since the matrix of the auxiliary system is Hurwitzian, functions $\bar{x}$, $\bar{y}$, $\bar{z}$ decrease exponentially for $t \to \infty$; hence they admit Fourier transforms.

Let

$$\chi(T) = \int_0^\infty (f_T(t), P(\bar{\bar{z}} - D\bar{y} - F_h^{-1}f_T(t)))\, dt + \epsilon_0 \int_0^\infty (f_T(t), f_T(t))\, dt$$

$$+ \int_0^\infty (f_T(t), Q\dot{\bar{\bar{z}}}(t))\, dt = \int_0^\infty (f(z), P(z - F_h^{-1}f(z)))\, dt$$

$$+ \int_T^\infty (F_q\bar{\bar{z}}, P(\bar{\bar{z}} - F_h^{-1}F_q\bar{\bar{z}})\, dt - \int_0^\infty (f\,(t), PD\bar{y})\, dt + \epsilon_0 \int_0^\infty (f_T(t), f_T(t))\, dt$$

$$+ \int_0^T (f(z), Q\dot{z})\, dt + \int_T^\infty (F_q\bar{\bar{z}}, Q\dot{\bar{\bar{z}}})\, dt.$$

From $F_q < F_h$ we obtain

$$F_h^{-1}F_q < E;$$

hence

$$(F_q\bar{\bar{z}}, P(\bar{\bar{z}} - F_h^{-1}F_q\bar{\bar{z}})) > 0.$$

From

$$\frac{d}{dt}(PD\bar{y}, \bar{y}) = 2\left(PD\bar{y}, \frac{d\bar{y}}{dt}\right) = 2(PD\bar{y}, f_T)$$

we obtain

$$-\int_0^\infty (f_T, PD\bar{y})\, dt = -\frac{1}{2}\int_0^\infty \frac{d}{dt}(PD\bar{y}, \bar{y})\, dt = -(PD\bar{y}, \bar{y})\Big|_0^\infty = (PDy_0, y_0)$$

since $\lim_{t\to\infty} \bar{y}(t) = 0$. Further,

$$\int_T^\infty (F_q\bar{\bar{z}}, Q\dot{\bar{\bar{z}}})\, dt = \frac{1}{2}\int_T^\infty \frac{d}{dt}(F_q\bar{\bar{z}}, Q\bar{\bar{z}})\, dt = \frac{1}{2}(F_q\bar{\bar{z}}, Q\bar{\bar{z}})\Big|_T^\infty$$

$$= -\tfrac{1}{2}(F_q z(T), Qz(T))$$

and

$$\int_0^T (F_q z, Q\dot{z})\, dt = \tfrac{1}{2}(F_q z(T), Qz(T)) - \tfrac{1}{2}(F_q z_0, Qz_0);$$

hence

$$\int_T^\infty (F_q\bar{\bar{z}}, Q\dot{\bar{\bar{z}}})\, dt = -\int_0^T (F_q z, Q\dot{z})\, dt - \tfrac{1}{2}(F_q z_0, Qz_0),$$

and

$$\int_0^\infty (f_T(t), Q\dot{\tilde{z}})\, dt = \int_0^T (f(z) - F_q z, Q\dot{z})\, dt - \tfrac{1}{2}(F_q z_0, Qz_0)$$
$$= \int_{z_0}^{z(T)} (f(z) - F_q z, Q\, dz) - \tfrac{1}{2}(F_q z_0, Qz_0)$$
$$= \phi(z(T)) - \phi(z_0) - \tfrac{1}{2}(F_q z_0, Qz_0),$$

where we have set

$$\phi(z) = \int_0^z (f(z) - F_q z, Q\, dz) = \sum_i q_i \int_0^{z_i} (f_i(u) - f_q^i u)\, du.$$

Let us recall that if $q_i > 0$, $f_q^i = \frac{1}{2}\delta_i$, and since $u(f_i(u) - \frac{1}{2}\delta_i u) > 0$ it follows that for these i we have

$$q_i \int_0^{z_i} (f_i(u) - f_q^i u)\, du > 0;$$

if $q_i \leqslant 0$, then

$$f_q^i = h_i - \tfrac{1}{2}\delta_i'$$

and hence

$$u(f_i(u) - f_q^i u) < 0,$$
$$\int_0^{z_i} (f_i(u) - f_q^i u)\, du < 0,$$

and again

$$q_i \int_0^{z_i} (f_i(u) - f_q^i u)\, du \geqslant 0.$$

It follows in any case that $\phi(z) \geqslant 0$.

Taking into account the above computations, we deduce that

$$\chi(T) > \int_0^T (f(z), P(z - F_h^{-1} f(z)))\, dt + \tfrac{1}{2}(PDy_0, y_0)$$
$$+ \epsilon_0 \int_0^\infty (f_T(t), f_T(t))\, dt + \phi(z(T)) - \phi(z_0) - \tfrac{1}{2}(F_q z_0, Qz_0).$$

Transforming $\chi(T)$ by the application of Parseval's theorem from the theory of the Fourier transform, we deduce that

$$\chi(T) = \frac{1}{2\pi} \int_{-\infty}^\infty (\tilde{f}_T, P(\tilde{z} - D\tilde{y} - F_h^{-1}\tilde{f}_T))\, d\omega + \frac{\epsilon_0}{2\pi} \int_{-\infty}^\infty (\tilde{f}_T, \tilde{f}_T)\, d\omega$$
$$+ \frac{1}{2\pi} \int_{-\infty}^\infty (\tilde{f}_T, Q\tilde{\dot{z}})\, d\omega,$$

where $\tilde{f}_T$ is the Fourier transform of f_T, $\tilde{z}$ the transform of z, $\tilde{y}$ of y, $\tilde{\dot{z}}$ of $\dot{z}$. From

$$\frac{d\bar{x}}{dt} = A\bar{x} + Bf_T$$

we deduce

$$i\omega\tilde{x} - x_0 = A\tilde{x} + B\tilde{f}_T,$$

where $\tilde{x}$ is the Fourier transform of $\bar{x}$. Thus

$$(i\omega E - A)\tilde{x} = x_0 + B\tilde{f}_T, \; \tilde{x} = (i\omega E - A)^{-1}x_0 + (i\omega E - A)^{-1}B\tilde{f}_T.$$

From $d\bar{y}/dt = f_T$ we obtain

$$i\omega\tilde{y} - y_0 = \tilde{f}_T;$$

hence

$$\tilde{y} = \frac{1}{i\omega}y_0 + \frac{1}{i\omega}\tilde{f}_T.$$

From $\bar{z} = C\bar{x} + D\bar{y}$ we obtain

$$\tilde{z} = C\tilde{x} + D\tilde{y};$$

hence

$$\tilde{z} = C(i\omega E - A)^{-1}x_0 + C(i\omega E - A)^{-1}B\tilde{f}_T + \frac{1}{i\omega}Dy_0 + \frac{1}{i\omega}D\tilde{f}_T.$$

From this we deduce that

$$\tilde{\dot{z}} = i\omega\tilde{z} - z_0 = i\omega C(i\omega E - A)^{-1}x_0 + i\omega C(i\omega E - A)^{-1}B\tilde{f}_T + Dy_0 + D\tilde{f}_T - z_0.$$

If follows that

$$\chi = \frac{1}{2\pi}\int_{-\infty}^{+\infty}(\tilde{f}_T, P(C(i\omega E - A)^{-1}x_0 + C(i\omega E - A)^{-1}B\tilde{f}_T - F_h^{-1}\tilde{f}_T))\,d\omega$$

$$+ \frac{\epsilon_0}{2\pi}\int_{-\infty}^{\infty}(\tilde{f}_T, \tilde{f}_T)\,d\omega + \frac{1}{2\pi}\int_{-\infty}^{+\infty}(\tilde{f}_T, Q[i\omega C(i\omega E - A)^{-1}x_0$$

$$+ i\omega C(i\omega E - A)^{-1}B\tilde{f}_T + Dy_0 + D\tilde{f}_T - z_0])\,d\omega$$

$$= -\frac{1}{2\pi}\int_{-\infty}^{\infty}(\tilde{f}_T, [-PC(i\omega E - A)^{-1}B + PF_h^{-1}$$

$$+ Q(i\omega C(A - i\omega E)^{-1}B - D]\tilde{f}_T)\,d\omega$$

$$+ \frac{\epsilon_0}{2\pi}\int_{-\infty}^{\infty}(\tilde{f}_T, \tilde{f}_T)\,d\omega + \frac{1}{2\pi}\int_{-\infty}^{\infty}(\tilde{f}_T, Lx_0 + My_0 + Nz_0)\,d\omega$$

$$= -\frac{1}{2\pi}\int_{-\infty}^{\infty} (\tilde{f}_T, G\tilde{f}_T)\, d\omega + \frac{\epsilon_0}{2\pi}\int_{-\infty}^{+\infty} (\tilde{f}_T, \tilde{f}_T)\, d\omega$$

$$+ \frac{1}{2\pi}\int_{-\infty}^{+\infty} (\tilde{f}_T, Lx_0 + My_0 + Nz_0)\, d\omega.$$

Since $\chi(T)$ is real, we will have

$$\chi(T) = -\frac{1}{2\pi}\int_{-\infty}^{\infty} (\tilde{f}_T, (H - \epsilon_0 E')\tilde{f}_T)\, d\omega$$

$$+ \frac{1}{2\pi}\int_{-\infty}^{\infty} (\tilde{f}_T, Lx_0 + My_0 + Nz_0)\, d\omega$$

$$+ \frac{1}{2\pi}\int_{-\infty}^{\infty} (Lx_0 + My_0 + Nz_0, \tilde{f}_T)\, d\omega.$$

Since $H(i\omega) > 0$ and $\lim_{|\omega|\to\infty} H(i\omega) > 0$, it follows that $H(i\omega) > \alpha^2 E'$. By choosing ϵ_0 sufficiently small, we will have $H(i\omega) - \epsilon_0 E' > 0$; hence we may write

$$H(i\omega) - \epsilon_0 E' = K(i\omega)^2.$$

It follows that

$$\chi(T) = \frac{-1}{2\pi}\int_{-\infty}^{\infty} (K\tilde{f}_T - K^{-1}(Lx_0 + My_0 + Nz_0), K\tilde{f}_T - K^{-1}(Lx_0$$

$$+ My_0 + Nz_0))\, d\omega + \frac{1}{2\pi}\int_{-\infty}^{\infty} (K^{-1}(Lx_0 + My_0 + Nz_0), K^{-1}(Lx_0$$

$$+ My_0 + Nz_0))\, d\omega.$$

The convergence of the last integral follows from the fact that the terms under the integral behave at infinity as $1/\omega^2$. Hence we deduce

$$\chi(T) < \frac{1}{2\pi}\int_{-\infty}^{\infty} (K^{-1}(Lx_0 + My_0 + Nz_0), K^{-1}(Lx_0 + My_0 + Nz_0))\, d\omega.$$

Taking into account the estimates previously obtained, we have

$$\int_0^T (f(z), P(z - F_h^{-1}f(z)))\, dt + \tfrac{1}{2}(PDy_0, y_0) + \epsilon_0 \int_0^T (f(z), f(z))\, dt$$

$$+ \phi(z(T)) - \phi(z_0) - \tfrac{1}{2}(F_q z_0, Qz_0) < \gamma(|x_0|, |y_0|, |z_0|);$$

i.e.,

$$\phi(z(T)) + \int_0^T (f(z), P(z - F_h^{-1}f(z)) + \epsilon_0(fz))\, dt < c(|x_0| + |z_0|).$$

We have $\phi(z) > 0$ and $(f(z), P(z - F_h^{-1}f(z))) > 0$.

Indeed, from $\delta_i z_i^2 < z_i f_i(z_i) < h_i^2 z_i^2$ it follows that for $z_i > 0$ we have $\delta_i z_i < f_i < h_i z_i$ and $z_i - (1/h_i) f_i > 0$; hence $p_i(z_i - (1/h_i) f_i) > 0$. Since $f_i > 0$, it follows that $p_i f_i(z_i - (1/h_i) f_i) > 0$; for $z_i < 0$ we have $h_i z_i < f_i < \delta_i z_i$, hence $z_i - (1/h_i) f_i < 0$, hence $p_i(z_i - (1/h_i) f_i) \leqslant 0$; hence, since in this case $f_i < 0$, it follows again that $p_i f_i(z_i - (1/h_i) f_i) > 0$. Now let

$$a(r) = \inf_{|z| \geqslant r} \phi(z), \; b(r) = \inf_{|z| \geqslant r} [(f(z), P(z - F_h^{-1} f(z))) + \epsilon_0(f(z), f(z))].$$

We have

$$\phi(z) \geqslant a(|z|), \; (f(z), P(z - F_h^{-1} f(z)) + \epsilon_0 f(z)) \geqslant b(|z|);$$

hence the inequality obtained may be written

$$a(|z(T)|) + \int_0^T b(|z(t)|)\, dt < c(|x_0| + |z_0|).$$

We have already seen above that such an inequality implies asymptotic stability in the large. With this the theorem is completely proved.

Let us observe that this general theorem may be applied in the study of the stability of control systems with several controllers.

2.4. The Practical Stability of Systems with Elements of Relay Type

In the final part of this chapter we shall expose a result which is also due to V. M. Popov, relative to control systems containing elements of the relay type. This result is interesting from a theoretical viewpoint because it is an example of the modification of the notion of stability; the so-called "practical" stability or ϵ_0-stability which is introduced on this occasion may prove useful in other problems, too.

Definition. *The trivial solution of the system is called ϵ_0-stable if for every $\epsilon > \epsilon_0$ there exists $\delta(\epsilon) > 0$ such that $|y(t_0)| < \delta(\epsilon)$ implies $|y(t)| < \epsilon$ for $t \geqslant t_0$; the ϵ_0 stability is asymptotic if in addition there exists $T(\eta, \epsilon)$ such that $\epsilon_0 < |y(t_0)| < \eta$ and $t \geqslant t_0 + T(\eta, \epsilon)$ implies $|y(t)| < \epsilon$ (again $\epsilon > \epsilon_0$, $\eta > \epsilon_0$).*

We see that this definition differs from the usual definition of uniform stability by the fact that the functions $\delta(\epsilon)$ and $T(\eta, \epsilon)$ are no longer defined for every $\epsilon > 0$ but only for $\epsilon > \epsilon_0$. The justification of this definition consists in the fact that in practice the sufficiently small values may be considered zero; hence it is not necessary to be able to assure that $|y(t)|$ be arbitrarily small but only smaller than some convenient values. Yet it is easy to see that for linear systems this definition does not mean a real weakening of the notion of stability in the sense of Lyapunov.

Proposition. *If there exists a function $V(y)$ with the properties $a(|y|) \leqslant V(y) \leqslant b(|y|)$, $dV/dt < -c(|y|)$ for $\epsilon_1 \leqslant |y| \leqslant \eta_0$, then the trivial solution of the system is ϵ_2-asymptotically stable, $\epsilon_2 = a^{-1}[b(\epsilon_1)]$.*

Proof. Let $\delta(\epsilon) = b^{-1}[a(\epsilon)]$; the function $a(r)$ is defined for $r \geqslant \epsilon_1$; hence $\delta(\epsilon)$ is defined for $\epsilon > \epsilon_1$.

If $\epsilon > \epsilon_2$ it follows that $a(\epsilon) > a(\epsilon_2) = b(\epsilon_1)$ and $\delta(\epsilon) = b^{-1}[a(\epsilon)] > \epsilon_1$. Let $|y(t_0)| < \delta(\epsilon)$; if $|y(t)|$ remains smaller than ϵ_1, then, obviously, $|y(t)| < \epsilon$ for $t \geqslant t_0$. We may hence assume that there exists a t_1 such that $\epsilon_1 \leqslant |y(t_1)| < \delta(\epsilon)$, and, if $t_1 > t_0$ for $t_0 \leqslant t < t_1$, we have $|y(t)| < \epsilon_1$. For $t \geqslant t_1$ it follows that

$$a(|y(t)|) < V(y(t)) \leqslant V(y(t_1)) < b(|y(t_1)|) \leqslant b(\delta(\epsilon)) = a(\epsilon);$$

hence $|y(t)| < \epsilon$.

Now let $T(\eta, \epsilon) = b(\eta)/c[\delta(\epsilon)]$, $\eta > \epsilon_1$ and let $\epsilon_1 < |y(t_0)| < \eta$. We show that in the interval $[t_0, t_0 + T]$ there exists a t' such that $|y(t')| < \delta(\epsilon)$. Indeed, if we would have $|y(t)| \geqslant \delta(\epsilon) > \epsilon_1$, it would follow that

$$\frac{dV}{dt} < -c(|y|) < -c[\delta(\epsilon)];$$

hence

$$V[y(t)] - V[y(t_0)] < -c[\delta(\epsilon)](t - t_0),$$

$$V[y(t_0 + T_0)] - V[y(t_0)] < -c[\delta(\epsilon)]T = -b(\eta),$$

and

$$V[y(t_0 + T_0)] < V[y(t_0)] - b(\eta) < b(|y(t_0)|) - b(\eta) < 0,$$

since $|y(t_0)| < \eta$. But

$$V[y(t_0 + T_0)] > a(|y(t_0 + T_0)|) \geqslant a[\delta(\epsilon)]$$

and we have reached a contradiction. It follows that

$$|y(t')| < \delta(\epsilon);$$

hence

$$|y(t)| < \epsilon \qquad \text{for} \qquad t \geqslant t',$$

thus in any case for $t \geqslant t_0 + T_0$. The proposition is proved.

Let us consider a control system which contains a single nonlinear element, described by the system of differential equations

$$\frac{dx}{dt} = Bx + kf(\sigma) + l\sigma, \qquad \frac{d\sigma}{dt} = (b, x) - pf(\sigma) + r\sigma \tag{7}$$

where $f(\sigma)$ verifies the following conditions:

$$\begin{aligned} f(\sigma) &\geqslant \rho & &\text{for} & \sigma &> \delta, \\ -\alpha\rho \leqslant f(\sigma) &\leqslant \rho & &\text{for} & |\sigma| &\leqslant \delta, \\ f(\sigma) &\leqslant -\rho & &\text{for} & \sigma &< \delta. \end{aligned}$$

We will say that a function f which verifies these conditions belongs to the class $C_{\rho,\delta,\alpha}$.

We will assume in what follows that $p > 0$. Taking $f(\sigma) = h\sigma$ we obtain the system

$$\frac{dx}{dt} = Bx + kh\sigma + l\sigma, \qquad \frac{d\sigma}{dt} = (b, x) - ph\sigma + r\sigma.$$

The matrix of this system will be

$$\begin{pmatrix} B & hk + l \\ b & -ph + r \end{pmatrix}$$

and will have the characteristic equation

$$\det \begin{pmatrix} B - \lambda E & hk + l \\ b & -ph + r - \lambda \end{pmatrix} = 0,$$

i.e.,

$$\det \begin{pmatrix} B - \lambda E & l \\ b & r - \lambda \end{pmatrix} + h \det \begin{pmatrix} B - \lambda E & k \\ b & -p \end{pmatrix} = 0,$$

which may be written in the form

$$Q(\lambda) + hP(\lambda) = 0.$$

Theorem 2.7. *If the equation* $P(\lambda) = 0$ *has all roots with negative real parts, then for given* ϵ_0, η_0, α *we can find* ρ_0, δ_0 *such that if* $f \in C_{\rho_0, \delta_0, \alpha}$ *then the property of* ϵ_0*-stability holds for system* (7).

Proof. We perform in the system the change of variables $\eta = px + k\sigma$, which has an inverse since $p \neq 0$. We consider the vector $\zeta = \binom{\eta}{\sigma}$. We have

$$\begin{aligned}\frac{d\eta}{dt} &= p\frac{dx}{dt} + k\frac{d\sigma}{dt} = pBx + pkf(\sigma) + pl\sigma + k(b, x) - kpf(\sigma) + kr\sigma \\ &= B(\eta - k\sigma) + pl\sigma + kr\sigma + kb^*\left(\frac{1}{p}\eta - \frac{1}{p}k\sigma\right) \\ &= \left(B + \frac{1}{p}kb^*\right)\eta + \left(pl + rk - Bk - \frac{1}{p}kb^*k\right)\sigma \\ &= A\eta + m\sigma\end{aligned}$$

where

$$A = B + \frac{1}{p}kb^*,$$

$$\begin{aligned}\frac{d\sigma}{dt} &= (b, x) - pf(\sigma) + r\sigma = \frac{1}{p}(b, \eta - k\sigma) - pf(\sigma) + r\sigma \\ &= (a, \eta) - pf(\sigma) + r'\sigma.\end{aligned}$$

Finally,

$$\frac{d\eta}{dt} = A\eta + m\sigma, \qquad \frac{d\sigma}{dt} = a\eta - pf(\sigma) + r'\sigma.$$

The characteristic equation of the matrix A is

$$\det\left(B - \lambda E + \frac{1}{p}kb^*\right) = 0.$$

Let us observe that

$$\begin{aligned}P(\lambda) &= \det\begin{pmatrix} B - \lambda E & k \\ b & -p\end{pmatrix} = p\det\begin{pmatrix} B - \lambda E + \frac{1}{p}kb^* & \frac{1}{p}k \\ 0 & -1\end{pmatrix} \\ &= (-1)^n p \det\left(B - \lambda E + \frac{1}{p}kb^*\right).\end{aligned}$$

It follows that $P(\lambda) = 0$ is precisely the characteristic equation of matrix A; hence the condition of the statement assures that A is Hurwitzian.

There exists therefore a matrix $P > 0$ such that $PA + A^*P = N$, with $N < 0$. Choose $V = (P\eta, \eta) + \frac{1}{2}\sigma^2$; then $V > 0$. Further,

$$\begin{aligned}\frac{dV}{dt} &= \left(P\frac{d\eta}{dt}, \eta\right) + \left(P\eta, \frac{d\eta}{dt}\right) + \sigma\frac{d\sigma}{dt} = (P(A\eta + m\sigma), \eta) \\ &\quad + (P\eta, A\eta + m\sigma) + \sigma(a^*\eta - pf(\sigma) + r'\sigma) = ((PA + A^*P)\eta, \eta) \\ &\quad + 2(Pm, \eta)\sigma + (a^*\eta)\sigma - p\sigma f(\sigma) + r'\sigma^2 \\ &= (N\eta, \eta) + \sigma[(\gamma, \zeta) - pf(\sigma)].\end{aligned}$$

We have put

$$(\gamma, \zeta) = 2(Pm, \eta) + (a, \eta) + r'\sigma;$$

hence

$$\gamma = \begin{pmatrix} Pm + a \\ r' \end{pmatrix}.$$

From $N < 0$ we obtain

$$(N\eta, \eta) \leqslant -c \mid \eta \mid^2.$$

Since V is a positive-definite quadratic form, there exist constants a_0 and b_0, positive, such that

$$a_0 \mid \zeta \mid^2 \leqslant V(\eta, \sigma) \leqslant b_0 \mid \zeta \mid^2.$$

Let $M_0 = a_0\epsilon^2$, $N_0 = \eta_0^2$. Consider the domain $\sqrt{M_0/b_0} \leqslant \mid \zeta \mid \leqslant \eta_0$ If in this domain, $\mid \sigma \mid \leqslant \frac{1}{2}\sqrt{M_0/b_0}$, then $\mid \eta \mid \geqslant \frac{1}{2}\sqrt{M_0/b_0}$; hence there exists $\mu > 0$ such that $(N\eta, \eta) \leqslant -\mu$.

Now let ν be such that $|(\gamma, \zeta)| \leqslant \nu$ for ζ such that $\sqrt{M_0/b_0} \leqslant \mid \zeta \mid \leqslant \eta_0$. Choose $\rho_0 = (\nu/p)(1 + \Delta)$, with arbitrary $\Delta > 0$,

$$\delta_0 = \min\left[\frac{\mu(1 - \Delta)}{2\nu[1 + \alpha(1 + \Delta)]}, \frac{1}{2}\sqrt{\frac{M_0}{b_0}}\right]$$

We see that ρ_0 and δ_0 depend on M_0, η_0, α, hence on ϵ_0, η_0, α. Since $p > 0$, it follows that $\rho_0 > 0$. Let $\mid \sigma \mid > \delta_0$. We will have

$$\frac{dV}{dt} = (N\eta, \eta) - p\sigma f(\sigma) + \sigma(\gamma, \zeta) < (N\eta, \eta) - p \mid \sigma \mid \mid f(\sigma) \mid + \nu \mid \sigma \mid.$$

But for $\mid \sigma \mid > \delta_0$ we have $\mid f(\sigma)\mid \geqslant \rho_0$, since $f \in C_{\rho_0, \delta_0, \alpha}$. Thus

$$p \mid f(\sigma) \mid \geqslant \gamma(1 + \Delta), \qquad p \mid f(\sigma) \mid - \nu > \nu\Delta.$$

Hence

$$\frac{dV}{dt} < (N\eta, \eta) - \gamma\Delta \mid \sigma \mid$$

if

$$\sqrt{\frac{M_0}{b_0}} \leqslant \mid \zeta \mid \leqslant \eta_0 , \qquad \mid \sigma \mid > \delta_0.$$

Now let $\mid \sigma \mid \leqslant \delta_0$. It follows that

$$\frac{dV}{dt} < (N\eta, \eta) + \delta_0(\nu + p\alpha\rho_0)$$

since $f \in C_{\rho_0, \delta_0, \alpha}$. But

$$\nu + p\alpha\rho_0 = \nu + \alpha\nu + \alpha\nu\Delta = \nu(1 + \alpha(1 + \Delta))$$

and since

$$\delta_0 \leqslant \frac{\mu(1 - \Delta)}{2\nu(1 + \alpha(1 + \Delta))}$$

we obtain

$$\delta_0(\nu + p\alpha\rho_0) = \delta_0\nu(1 + \alpha(1 + \Delta)) \leqslant \frac{\mu(1 - \Delta)}{2};$$

hence

$$\frac{dV}{dt} < (N\eta, \eta) + \frac{\mu}{2} - \frac{\Delta}{2}.$$

Since $\delta_0 \leqslant \frac{1}{2}\sqrt{M_0/b_0}$, $\mid \sigma \mid \leqslant \delta_0$ implies $\mid \sigma \mid \leqslant \frac{1}{2}\sqrt{M_0/b_0}$; hence $(N\eta, \eta) \leqslant -\mu$ and $dV/dt < -(\mu/2) - (\Delta/2)$.

Finally, $dV/dt < -c(\mid \zeta \mid)$ in the domain $\sqrt{M_0/b_0} \leqslant \mid \zeta \mid \leqslant \eta_0$. Let us now apply the proposition proved above in which

$$\epsilon_1 = \sqrt{\frac{M_0}{b}} \qquad b(r) = b_0 r^2, \qquad a(r) = a_0 r^2, \qquad a^{-1}(r) = \sqrt{\frac{r}{a_0}}.$$

Then

$$b(\epsilon_1) = b_0 \frac{M_0}{b_0} = M_0 , \qquad \epsilon_2 = a^{-1}b(\epsilon_1) = \sqrt{\frac{M_0}{a_0}} = \epsilon_0.$$

According to the preceding proposition we obtain asymptotic ϵ_0-stability, and the theorem is proved.

Remarks. 1. The property of ϵ_0-stability does not imply that the system admits the trivial solution. Therefore it is not necessary to suppose that $f(0) = 0$.

2. The case of the ideal relays is obtained if $\delta_0 = 0$, and it is clear that we have $\delta_0 = 0$ if we take $\epsilon_0 = 0$. Hence in this case we have asymptotic stability in the usual sense.

NOTES

The problem of absolute stability for nonlinear control systems was studied for the first time by means of the method of Lyapunov functions in [36]; see also monographs [37] and [38]. The intrinsic study, without the reduction to the canonical form, has been carried out by V. A. Yakubovič in [39] and [40] and by S. Lefschetz in [41]. The results in the text, which develop those of S. Lefschetz, belong to T. Morozan. The method of V. M. Popov is presented in [42], [43], and [44]. The study of the case of two zero roots by the method of the Lyapunov function has been performed by T. Morozan. The result of V. M. Popov relative to the practical stability for systems with elements of relay type has been published in [45].

The equivalence of the V. M. Popov method with that of Lyapunov function has been proved by V. A. Yakubovič in [46]. Another proof was given by R. E. Kalman [100]. Further results were obtained by V. A. Yakubovič ([101] and [102]). For all these problems see also [103] and [97].

CHAPTER 3

Theory of Oscillations

From a mathematical viewpoint the theory of oscillations contains the problem of the existence and stability of the periodic solutions of systems of differential equations. The periodic solutions of linear systems are usually called *linear oscillations*. The periodic solutions of linear systems with constant coefficients or of some nonlinear systems which do not explicitly depend on t are sometimes called *free oscillations*; when a periodic function of t, appears in the second member of the system, the corresponding oscillations are called *forced oscillations*. The problem of the existence of almost-periodic solutions has been investigated more and more extensively in the last few years.

In this chapter we shall present some fundamental facts relative to the existence of periodic and almost-periodic solutions of systems of ordinary differential equations.

3.1. Linear Oscillations

Let us consider the system

$$\frac{dx}{dt} = A(t)x + f(t), \tag{1}$$

where $A(t)$ and $f(t)$ are periodic of period ω.

Theorem 3.1. *A necessary and sufficient condition in order that for any periodic function $f(t)$ of period ω system (1) admits periodic solutions of period ω is that the corresponding homogeneous system does not admit a periodic solution of period ω other than the trivial one.*

Proof. A solution of the system is periodic of period ω if and only if $x(\omega) = x(0)$. If the solution is periodic, this condition is obviously verified; if this condition is verified, the solutions $x(t + \omega)$ and $x(t)$ coincide for $t = 0$. Hence, according to the uniqueness theorem, they coincide for any t and thus $x(t)$ is periodic of period ω. As we have seen in Chapter 1, the general solution of system (1) may be written

$$x(t; x_0) = U(t)x_0 + \int_0^t C(t, s)f(s)ds.$$

We recall that $U(t) = C(t, 0)$ and that $C(t, s)$ is the matrix whose columns are the solutions of the homogeneous system, so that $C(s, s) = E$. We have

$$x(\omega; x_0) = U(\omega)x_0 + \int_0^\omega C(\omega, s)f(s)ds.$$

The periodicity condition of the solution is written

$$x(\omega; x_0) = x_0 .$$

Hence

$$x_0 = U(\omega)x_0 + \int_0^\omega C(\omega, s)f(s)ds;$$

i.e.,

$$[E - U(\omega)]x_0 = \int_0^\omega C(\omega, s)f(s)ds.$$

The condition that this system allows the determination of x_0, whichever be the function f, may be written

$$\det[E - U(\omega)] \neq 0.$$

This means, however, that the equation

$$U(\omega)x_0 = x_0$$

has no solution other than $x_0 = 0$. But $U(t)x_0$ is the general solution of the homogeneous system and the condition

$$U(\omega)x_0 = x_0$$

represents precisely the periodicity condition for the solutions of the homogeneous system. The condition

$$\det[E - U(\omega)] \neq 0$$

is therefore equivalent to the demand that the homogeneous system does not have other periodic solutions of period ω than the trivial one. The theorem is proved.

Proposition. *Under the conditions of Theorem 3.1, the unique periodic solution of system* (1) *can be put in the form*

$$x(t) = \int_0^\omega G(t, s)f(s)ds,$$

where

$$G(t, s) = \begin{cases} U(t)[E - U(\omega)]^{-1}U^{-1}(s) & \text{for } 0 \leqslant s \leqslant t \leqslant \omega, \\ U(t + \omega)[E - U(\omega)]^{-1}U^{-1}(s) & \text{for } 0 \leqslant t < s \leqslant \omega. \end{cases}$$

Proof. If x_0 is the initial value of the periodic solution of system (1), we have

$$x_0 = [E - U(\omega)]^{-1} \int_0^\omega C(\omega, s)f(s)ds.$$

The periodic solution can therefore be written

$$x(t) = U(t)[E - U(\omega)]^{-1} \int_0^\omega C(\omega, s)f(s)ds + \int_0^t C(t, s)f(s)ds.$$

But

$$C(t, s) = C(t, 0)C(0, s) = U(t)U^{-1}(s).$$

It follows that

$$x(t) = U(t)[E - U(\omega)]^{-1}U(\omega) \int_0^\omega U^{-1}(s)f(s)ds + U(t) \int_0^t U^{-1}(s)f(s)ds.$$

We may write

$$x(t) = \int_0^\omega G(t, s)f(s)ds,$$

where

$$G(t, s) = U(t)[E - U(\omega)]^{-1}U(\omega)U^{-1}(s) + U(t)U^{-1}(s) \quad \text{for } 0 \leqslant s \leqslant t \leqslant \omega,$$

$$G(t, s) = U(t)[E - U(\omega)]^{-1}U(\omega)U^{-1}(s) \quad \text{for } 0 \leqslant t < s \leqslant \omega.$$

These formulas for $G(t, s)$ may be reduced to the form in the statement by observing that

$$\begin{aligned} &U(t)[E - U(\omega)]^{-1}U(\omega)U^{-1}(s) + U(t)U^{-1}(s) \\ &\quad = U(t)\{[E - U(\omega)]^{-1}U(\omega) + E\}U^{-1}(s) = U(t)[E - U(\omega)]^{-1}U^{-1}(s), \end{aligned}$$

since from

$$[E - U(\omega)]^{-1}[E - U(\omega)] = E$$

we obtain

$$[E - U(\omega)]^{-1} - [E - U(\omega)]^{-1}U(\omega) = E.$$

From the relation

$$[E - U(\omega)]^{-1}[E - U(\omega)] = [E - U(\omega)][E - U(\omega)]^{-1}$$

follows

$$[E - U(\omega)]^{-1}U(\omega) = U(\omega)[E - U(\omega)]^{-1};$$

hence

$$\begin{aligned} U(t)[E - U(\omega)]^{-1}U(\omega)U^{-1}(s) &= U(t)U(\omega)[E - U(\omega)]^{-1}U^{-1}(s) \\ &= U(t+\omega)[E - U(\omega)]^{-1}U^{-1}(s). \end{aligned}$$

The proposition is thus proved.

Let us observe that from this proposition follows for the periodic solution the evaluation $|x(t)| \leqslant M \sup |f|$, where M depends only on the homogeneous system.

Theorem 3.2. *If the homogeneous system*

$$\frac{dx}{dt} = A(t)x \tag{2}$$

admits periodic solutions of period ω, *then the adjoint system*

$$\frac{dy}{dt} = -yA(t) \tag{3}$$

admits the same number of linearly independent periodic solutions as system (2). *A necessary and sufficient condition in order that system* (1) *admits periodic solutions is that* f *be orthogonal to the periodic solutions of system* (3), *namely,*

$$\int_0^\omega y_k(t)f(t)dt = 0 \qquad (k = 1, 2, \ldots, l),$$

$y_1, \ldots, y_l$ *being the linearly independent periodic solutions of system* (3).

Proof. If system (2) admits periodic solutions, there exists an x_0 such that

$$U(\omega)x_0 = x_0 .$$

We have seen in Chapter 1 that the rows of $U^{-1}(t)$ are linearly independent solutions of the adjoint system; the general solution of the adjoint system (3) may be written

$$y(t; y_0) = y_0 U^{-1}(t).$$

The condition that this solution be periodic of period ω is likewise written under the form

$$y(\omega; y_0) = y_0 \, .$$

Hence

$$y_0 U^{-1}(\omega) = y_0 \, ;$$

i.e.,

$$y_0 = y_0 U(\omega).$$

Passing to the transposed system we obtain the system

$$U^*(\omega) y_0^* = y_0^* \, .$$

But the matrices $U(\omega) - E$ and $U^*(\omega) - E$ have the same rank. Therefore the systems

$$U(\omega)x_0 = x_0 \qquad \text{and} \qquad U^*(\omega)y_0^* = y_0^*$$

have the same number of linearly independent solutions.

This means, however, that systems (2) and (3) have the same number of linearly independent periodic solutions of period ω. A necessary and sufficient condition in order that system (1) admits periodic solutions of period ω is that the system of linear equations

$$[E - U(\omega)]x_0 = \int_0^\omega C(\omega, s) f(s) ds$$

admits solutions. Let us suppose that the system admits a periodic solution. Let $y(t)$ be a periodic solution of system (3); let us multiply the above equality by $y(0)$. We have

$$y(0)[E - U(\omega)]x_0 = y(0) \int_0^\omega U(\omega)U^{-1}(s) f(s) ds.$$

But we have seen above that if $y(t)$ is the periodic solution of system (3), then

$$y(0) = y(0) U(\omega);$$

hence

$$y(0)[E - U(\omega)] = 0.$$

It also follows that

$$y(0)[E - U(\omega)]x_0 = 0.$$

Hence

$$y(0) \int_0^\omega U(\omega)U^{-1}(s)f(s)ds = 0;$$

i.e.,

$$\int_0^\omega y(0)U(\omega)U^{-1}(s)f(s)ds = 0.$$

But

$$y(0)U(\omega) = y(0) \quad \text{and} \quad y(0)U^{-1}(s) = y(s);$$

hence the condition becomes

$$\int_0^\omega y(s)f(s)ds = 0$$

and we have proved that the condition of the statement is necessary.

Let us suppose now that this condition is fulfilled. It follows that

$$y_0U(\omega) \int_0^\omega U^{-1}(s)f(s)ds = 0$$

for all solutions y_0 of the system

$$y_0 = y_0U(\omega).$$

Thus the system

$$y_0[E - U(\omega)] = 0, \qquad y_0U(\omega) \int_0^\omega U^{-1}(s)f(s)ds = 0$$

has the same number of linearly independent solutions as the system

$$y_0[E - U(\omega)] = 0.$$

Hence the matrix $E - U(\omega)$ and the extended matrix to which was added the column $\int_0^\omega U(\omega)U^{-1}(s)f(s)ds$ have the same rank. But according to the Kronecker-Capelli theorem, this is sufficient in order that the system

$$[E - U(\omega)]x_0 = \int_0^\omega U(\omega)U^{-1}(s)f(s)ds$$

have solutions, and the theorem is proved.

In case the condition of orthogonality from Theorem 3.2. is not verified, system (1) does not admit periodic solutions and then there occurs the *resonance phenomenon*: All the solutions of system (1) are unbounded.

Theorem 3.3. *If system* (1) *does not have periodic solutions, then all the solutions of the system are unbounded.*

Proof. If system (1) does not admit periodic solutions, there exists a periodic solution of period ω of system (3) such that

$$\int_0^\omega y(t)f(t)dt \neq 0.$$

Denoting by y_0 the initial value of this solution, we have

$$y_0[E - U(\omega)] = 0 \qquad \text{and} \qquad y_0 \int_0^\omega U^{-1}(t)f(t)dt \neq 0.$$

Let $x(t)$ be any solution of system (1). We have

$$x(t) = U(t)x(0) + \int_0^t C(t, s)f(s)ds = U(t)\Big[x(0) + \int_0^t U^{-1}(s)f(s)ds\Big];$$

hence

$$x(\omega) = U(\omega)\Big[x(0) + \int_0^\omega U^{-1}(s)f(s)ds\Big],$$

from which we deduce

$$y_0x(\omega) = y_0U(\omega)x(0) + y_0U(\omega)\int_0^\omega U^{-1}(s)f(s)ds$$

$$= y_0x(0) + y_0\int_0^\omega U^{-1}(s)f(s)ds.$$

Further, we may write

$$x(t + \omega) = U(t)x(\omega) + \int_0^t C(t, s)f(s)ds,$$

since in both members we have solutions of the equation which coincide for $t = 0$. We will have

$$x(2\omega) = U(\omega)\Big[x(\omega) + \int_0^\omega U^{-1}(s)f(s)ds\Big],$$

from which follows

$$y_0x(2\omega) = y_0x(\omega) + y_0\int_0^\omega U^{-1}(s)f(s)ds = y_0x(0) + 2y_0\int_0^\omega U^{-1}(s)f(s)ds.$$

We show by induction that

$$y_0x(n\omega) = y_0x(0) + ny_0\int_0^\omega U^{-1}(s)f(s)ds.$$

We have

$$x(t + n\omega) = U(t)x(n\omega) + \int_0^t C(t, s)f(s)ds,$$

since in both members there are solutions of the system and these coincide for $t = 0$. It follows that

$$x[(n + 1)\omega] = U(\omega)\left[x(n\omega) + \int_0^\omega U^{-1}(s)f(s)ds\right];$$

hence

$$\begin{aligned} y_0x[(n+1)\omega] &= y_0x(n\omega) + y_0\int_0^\omega U^{-1}(s)f(s)ds \\ &= y_0x(n\omega) + (n+1)y_0\int_0^\omega U^{-1}(s)f(s)ds. \end{aligned}$$

From the way in which y_0 was chosen, it follows that

$$y_0\int_0^\omega U^{-1}(s)f(s)ds \neq 0.$$

From the formula

$$y_0x(n\omega) = y_0x(0) + ny_0\int_0^\omega U^{-1}(s)f(s)ds$$

we deduce that the solution $x(t)$ cannot be bounded, since the numeric sequence $y_0x(n\omega)$ would then be bounded. The theorem is proved.

3.2. Almost-Periodic Solutions of Linear Systems

The theorems proved until now had a strong algebraic character. We shall now state a theorem weaker than Theorem 3.1, by using a Lyapunov function; the interest of this theorem lays in the fact that it can be extended in the case of almost-periodic systems.

Let us now begin by the following simple remark: *If a periodic system*

$$\dot{x} = f(t, x), \qquad f(t + \omega, x) = f(t, x)$$

admits a bounded solution $x_0(t)$ *such that*

$$\lim_{t\to\infty} [x_0(t + \omega) - x_0(t)] = 0,$$

then it admits a periodic solution.

Indeed, the sequence $x_n = x_0(n\omega)$ is bounded; hence from it a sequence x_{n_k} can be extracted which converges to a point x^*. It follows from the hypothesis that for any n

$$\lim_{n\to\infty} [x_0((n + 1)\omega) - x_0(n\omega)] = 0;$$

thus

$$\lim_{k\to\infty} x_{n_k+1} = x^*.$$

From

$$\lim_{k\to\infty} x_{n_k} = x^*$$

we obtain

$$\lim_{k\to\infty} x(t; x_{n_k}) = x(t; x^*)$$

and from

$$\lim_{k\to\infty} x_{n_k+1} = x^*$$

we obtain

$$\lim x(t; x_{n_k+1}) = x(t; x^*).$$

However,

$$\begin{aligned} x(t; x_{n_k+1}) &= x(t; x_0[(n_k + 1)\omega]) = x_0(t + (n_k + 1)\omega) \\ &= x_0(t + \omega + n_k\omega) = x(t + \omega; x_0(n_k\omega)) = x(t + \omega; x_{n_k}). \end{aligned}$$

We have

$$\lim_{k\to\infty} x(t; x_{n_k+1}) = \lim_{k\to\infty} x(t + \omega; x_{n_k}) = x(t + \omega; x^*);$$

hence

$$x(t; x^*) = x(t + \omega; x^*)$$

and the solution which takes the value x^* for $t = 0$ is periodic.

Let us now consider system (1) and assume that the trivial solution of system (2) is asymptotically stable. Let $x_0(t)$ be any solution of system (1); since $x_0(t+\omega)$ is likewise a solution of system (1), it follows that $x_0(t+\omega) - x_0(t)$ is a solution of system (2); hence

$$\lim_{k\to\infty} [x_0(t+\omega) - x_0(t)] = 0.$$

Consequently, in order to deduce that system (1) admits a periodic solution, it is sufficient to show that the trivial solution of system (2) is asymptotically stable and that system (1) admits a bounded solution. We will, however, show that, even in more general conditions, if the trivial solution of system (2) is uniformly asymptotically stable, then system (1) admits a bounded solution.

Lemma. *Consider system* (1), *where* $A(t)$ *and* $f(t)$ *are assumed to be bounded for* $t \geqslant 0$. *If the trivial solution of system* (2) *is uniformly asymptotically stable, then all the solutions of the system are bounded for* $t \geqslant 0$.

Proof. According to Theorem 1.6″ there exists a quadratic form $(V(t)x, x)$ with the following properties:

$$\mu| x |^2 \leqslant (V(t)x, x) \leqslant M| x |^2, \qquad \left(\frac{dV}{dt}x, x\right) + 2(Vx, A(t)x) = -| x |^2.$$

By means of the same computations as in the proof of Theorem 1.7, we deduce

$$\frac{dV^*}{dt} = -| x(t; t_0, x_0) |^2 + 2(V(t)x(t; t_0, x_0), f(t)),$$

where $x(t; t_0, x_0)$ is the general solution of system (1) and

$$V^*(t) = (V(t)x(t; t_0, x_0), x(t; t_0, x_0)).$$

If

$$L = \sup_{t\geqslant 0} | f(t) |$$

we deduce

$$\frac{dV^*}{dt} \leqslant -| x(t; t_0, x_0) |^2 + 2ML| x(t; t_0, x_0) |.$$

Let us consider now any solution with $| x_0 | < 2LM$. It follows that

$$V^*(t_0) = (V(t_0)x_0, x_0) < M| x_0 |^2 < 4L^2M^3.$$

We prove that for every $t \geqslant 0$ we have

$$V^*(t) < 4L^2M^3.$$

If the assertion were not true, there would exist a $t_1 > t_0$ such that

$$V^*(t_1) = 4L^2M^3 \qquad \text{and} \qquad V^*(t) < 4L^2M^3$$

for $t_0 \leqslant t < t_1$. But then

$$\left.\frac{dV^*}{dt}\right|_{t=t_1} \geqslant 0.$$

On the other hand,

$$4L^2M^3 = V^*(t_1) < M\ x(t_1 ; t_0 , x_0) |^2;$$

hence

$$| x(t_1 ; t_0 , x_0) |^2 > 4L^2M^2, \qquad | x(t_1 ; t_0 , x_0) | > 2LM.$$

We have

$$\left.\frac{dV^*}{dt}\right|_{t=t_1} \leqslant | x(t_1 ; t_0 , x_0) |(2LM - | x(t_1 ; t_0 , x_0) |) < 0,$$

which contradicts the inequality found above. The existence of t_1 is contradictory; hence

$$V^*(t) < 4L^2M^3$$

for every $t \geqslant t_0$. Thus

$$\mu | x(t; t_0 , x_0) |^2 \leqslant V^*(t) < 4L^2M^3,$$

which proves that the solutions with $| x_0 | < 2ML$ are bounded for $t \geqslant t_0$ and that $| x(t; t_0 , x_0) | \leqslant KL$. Because of uniform asymptotic stability it follows that all the solutions are bounded, and the lemma is proved.

According to this lemma and to the preliminary considerations which we have made, it follows that *if the trivial solution of system* (2) *is asymptotically stable, then system* (1) *admits a unique periodic solution, asymptotically stable.*

Theorem 3.4. *Consider system* (1) *with $A(t)$ and $f(t)$ almost periodic. If the trivial solution of system* (2) *is uniformly asymptotically stable, then* *system* (1) *admits a unique, almost-periodic solution, uniformly asymptotically stable, which verifies an estimate of the form*

$$| x(t) | \leqslant K \sup | f(t) |.$$

Proof. It follows from the preceding lemma that there exists a bounded solution $u(t)$. From

$$\dot{u}(t) = A(t)u(t) + f(t),$$
$$\dot{u}(t+\tau) = A(t+\tau)u(t+\tau) + f(t+\tau)$$

we obtain

$$\dot{u}(t+\tau) - \dot{u}(t) = A(t)[u(t+\tau) - u(t)] + [A(t+\tau) - A(t)]u(t+\tau) + f(t+\tau) - f(t).$$

Let $M_1 = \sup | u(t) | + 1$, τ an $(\epsilon/2M_1K)$-almost period for A and f; K is the constant, depending only on system (2), whose existence followed from the lemma.

Let $y(t)$ be the solution of system (2) with

$$y(0) = u(\tau) - u(0), \qquad v(t) = u(t+\tau) - u(t) - y(t).$$

We have $v(0) = 0$ and

$$\begin{aligned} \dot{v}(t) = \dot{u}(t+\tau) - \dot{u}(t) - \dot{y}(t) &= A(t)[u(t+\tau) - u(t)] \\ &\quad + [A(t+\tau) - A(t)]u(t+\tau) + f(t+\tau) - f(t) - A(t)y(t) \\ &= A(t)v(t) + [A(t+\tau) - A(t)]u(t+\tau) + f(t+\tau) - f(t). \end{aligned}$$

According to the lemma, we will have

$$\begin{aligned} | v(t)| &\leqslant K \sup| [A(t+\tau) - A(t)]u(t+\tau) + f(t+\tau) - f(t)| \\ &\leqslant K(\sup| A(t+\tau) - A(t)| \sup| u(t+\tau)| + \sup| f(t+\tau) - f(t)|) \\ &\leqslant K\left(\frac{\epsilon}{2M_1K} \sup| u(t+\tau)| + \frac{\epsilon}{2M_1K}\right) = K\frac{\epsilon}{2K} = \frac{\epsilon}{2}. \end{aligned}$$

Consequently, $| u(t+\tau) - u(t) - y(t) | < \epsilon/2$ for $t \geqslant 0$.

Since the trivial solution of system (2) is uniformly asymptotically stable, we have

$$|y(t)| \leqslant Be^{-\alpha t}| y(0) | < 2M_1Be^{-\alpha t}.$$

There exists $T > 0$ such that if $t > T$ we have

$$|y(t)| < \frac{\epsilon}{2}.$$

Then, for $t > T$, we will have

$$|u(t+\tau) - u(t)| < \frac{\epsilon}{2} + \frac{\epsilon}{2} = \epsilon.$$

It follows that for given $\epsilon > 0$ there exist quantities $l(\epsilon)$ and $T(\epsilon)$ such that in every interval of length l there exists a number τ with the property that $|u(t+\tau) - u(t)| < \epsilon$ for $t > T$.

This means, however, that $u(t)$ is an asymptotically almost-periodic function. Then, on the strength of the fundamental Fréchet theorem we have

$$u(t) = x_0(t) + \omega(t),$$

where $x_0(t)$ is almost periodic and

$$\lim_{t\to\infty} \omega(t) = 0.$$

We have

$$\dot{x}_0(t) + \dot{\omega}(t) = A(t)x_0(t) + A(t)\omega(t) + f(t).$$

But $A(t)\omega(t)$ has the limit zero and $A(t)x_0(t) + f(t)$ is almost periodic; on the basis of the fundamental Fréchet theorem of decomposition, it follows that

$$\dot{x}_0(t) = A(t)x_0(t) + f(t);$$

hence $x_0(t)$ is an almost-periodic solution of system (1). From

$$|u(t)| \leqslant K \sup |f|$$

we obtain

$$|x_0(t)| \leqslant ML + |\omega(t)|.$$

Let $\epsilon > 0$; from

$$\lim_{t\to\infty} \omega(t) = 0$$

it follows that there exists a $T > 0$ such that for $t > T$ we have

$$|\omega(t)| < \frac{\epsilon}{2}.$$

It follows that

$$|x_0(t)| \leqslant ML + \frac{\epsilon}{2},$$

for $t > T$. Let now t be arbitrary; there exists an $\epsilon/2$–almost period such that $t + \tau > T$. Then $|x_0(t + \tau)| \leqslant ML + (\epsilon/2)$ and

$$|x_0(t + \tau) - x_0(t)| < \frac{\epsilon}{2};$$

hence

$$|x_0(t)| \leqslant ML + \epsilon.$$

Since $\epsilon > 0$ was arbitrary, it follows that

$$|x_0(t)| \leqslant ML.$$

The theorem is thus completely proved.

3.3. Quasi-Linear Systems

Passing now to the study of nonlinear systems, we shall first consider the simplest case of quasi-linear systems of the form

$$\frac{dx}{dt} = A(t)x + f(x, t), \tag{4}$$

where $A(t)$ is a periodic matrix and $f(x, t)$ is periodic with respect to t with the same period ω as $A(t)$.

We will suppose that the linear system

$$\frac{dx}{dt} = A(t)x$$

does not admit any periodic solutions of period ω other than the trivial solution. In this case we have seen that there exists a matrix $G(t, s)$ such that the unique periodic solution of the nonhomogeneous system

$$\frac{dx}{dt} = A(t)x + g(t)$$

may be written in the form

$$x(t) = \int_0^\omega G(t, s)g(s)ds.$$

We form the nonlinear integral equation

$$x(t) = \int_0^\omega G(t, s) f[x(s), s]ds. \tag{5}$$

Any continuous solution of this equation represents a periodic solution of the system, since if we take into account the expression of the matrix $G(t, s)$, the integral equation becomes

$$x(t) = U(t)[E - U(\omega)]^{-1} \int_0^\omega C(\omega, s) f[x(s), s]ds + \int_0^t C(t, s) f[x(s), s]ds$$

and thus

$$\frac{dx(t)}{dt} = A(t)U(t)[E - U(\omega)]^{-1} \int_0^\omega C(\omega, s) f[x(s), s]ds + f[x(t), t] + \int_0^t A(t)C(t, s) f[x(s), s]ds = A(t)x(t) + f[x(t), t].$$

Conversely, if $x_0(t)$ is a periodic solution of system (4), it may be considered as a solution of the linear system

$$\frac{dx}{dt} = A(t)x + f[x_0(t), t]$$

and this periodic solution is unique and is represented by the formula

$$x_0(t) = \int_0^\omega G(t, s) f[x_0(s), s]ds;$$

hence $x_0(t)$ is a solution of the integral equation (5).

It follows that the problem of finding the periodic solutions of the system of differential equations considered is equivalent to the finding of the solutions of a nonlinear integral equation. To prove the existence of the solution of this equation we shall use a fixed-point method.

Consider the Banach space of the vector functions, continuous and periodic, of period ω, with the norm

$$\| x(t) \| = \max_{0 \leqslant t \leqslant \omega} | x(t) |.$$

Define in this space the operator

$$\Omega[x(t)] = \int_0^\omega G(t, s) f[x(s), s]ds$$

which maps this space in itself. Indeed, from what precedes, we already know that $\Omega[x(t)]$ is the periodic solution of the linear system

$$\frac{dy}{dt} = A(t)y + f[x(t), t],$$

and hence is a continuous and periodic function of period ω.

The integral equation may be written

$$x(t) = \Omega[x(t)].$$

Hence its solutions are those points of the space which are transformed in themselves by the operator Ω, which is to say they are the fixed points of operator Ω. Thus the problem of proving the existence of periodic solutions for the considered system of differential equations is reduced to that of proving the existence of the fixed points of operator Ω. The simplest fixed-point theorem is provided by the so-called *contraction principle*, which holds in every complete metric space. Namely, if an operator maps a sphere of the space in itself and in addition contracts all distances, then the operator admits a fixed point and this fixed point is unique. The condition of the contraction of distances is written

$$\rho[\Omega(x), \Omega(y)] \leqslant \mu\rho(x, y) \qquad (0 < \mu < 1).$$

The contraction principle represents, as it is known, an abstract form of the method of successive approximations.

Let us suppose that for all x_1 and x_2 we have the relation

$$| f(x_1, t) - f(x_2, t) | \leqslant \beta(t) | x_1 - x_2 |, \qquad \int_0^\omega \beta(s)ds < \frac{q}{M}$$

$$(q < 1, M = \sup_{0\leqslant t, s\leqslant\omega} | G(t, s) |).$$

We have

$$\begin{aligned} | \Omega[x_1(t)] - \Omega[x_2(t)] | &= \left| \int_0^\omega G(t, s)\{ f[x_1(s), s] - f[x_2(s), s]\}ds \right| \\ &\leqslant \int_0^\omega | G(t, s) | \, | f[x_1(s), s] - f[x_2(s), s] | ds \\ &\leqslant \int_0^\omega | G(t, s)\beta(s) | \, x_1(s) - x_2(s)| ds \\ &\leqslant M \| x_1 - x_2 \| \int_0^\omega \beta(s)ds < M \frac{q}{M} \| x_1 - x_2 \| = q \| x_1 - x_2 \|; \end{aligned}$$

hence Ω is a contraction.

We deduce that Ω has a unique fixed point, and thus the system considered admits a unique periodic solution.

The conditions imposed on the function f are very strong; it is required that this function be Lipschitzian in the whole space, for example, that its partial derivatives be bounded in the whole space. It is therefore desirable to replace this condition by a local Lipschitz condition. For this purpose let us put

$$f(0, t) = g(t), \qquad F(x, t) = f(x, t) - f(0, t).$$

System (4) then takes the form

$$\frac{dx}{dt} = A(t)x + g(t) + F(x, t).$$

The integral equation equivalent to the system becomes

$$x(t) = \int_0^{\omega} G(t, s)g(s)ds + \int_0^{\omega} G(t, s)F[x(s), s]ds.$$

But $\int_0^{\omega} G(t, s)g(s)ds$ represents the unique periodic solution of the system

$$\frac{dx}{dt} = A(t)x + g(t);$$

let us denote this solution by $\phi(t)$. The integral equation (5) is thus written

$$x(t) = \phi(t) + \int_0^{\omega} G(t, s)F[x(s), s]ds.$$

Let us suppose that there exists a number q with $0 < q < 1$ such that in the sphere $\| x - \phi \| \leqslant L$ with $L \geqslant q/(1 - q) \| \phi \|$, the function F verifies the condition

$$| F(x_1 , t) - F(x_2 , t) | < \beta(t) | x_1 - x_2 |, \qquad \int_0^{\omega} \beta(s)ds < \frac{q}{M}.$$

Then the operator Ω maps the sphere $\| x - \phi \| < L$ into itself and is in this sphere a contraction; hence the system admits a unique periodic solution in the sphere $\| x - \phi \| \leqslant L$.

Indeed, let $x(t)$ be such that $\| x - \phi \| \leqslant L$. We have

$$
\begin{aligned}
| \Omega[x(t)] - \phi(t) | &= \left| \int_0^\omega G(t, s)F[x(s), s]ds \right| \leqslant M \int_0^\omega | F[x(s), s] | ds \\
&\leqslant M \int_0^\omega \beta(s) | x(s) | ds \leqslant M \| x \| \int_0^\omega \beta(s) ds < q \| x \| \\
&= q \| x - \phi + \phi \| \leqslant q \| x - \phi \| + q \| \phi \| \\
&\leqslant qL + q \| \phi \| \leqslant qL + q \frac{1-q}{q} L = L;
\end{aligned}
$$

hence $\|\Omega(x) - \phi \| \leqslant L$. The fact that Ω is a contraction is seen as above.

If we replace the contraction principle by a more powerful fixed-point theorem, we may replace the condition that f be Lipschitzian by other weaker conditions. Further on we shall use the Schauder theorem under the following form: If the operator Ω maps a sphere of the Banach space in itself and in addition is completely continuous (compact), then Ω admits at least one fixed point. We recall that an operator is said to be completely continuous if it maps any bounded set in a relative compact set. In the Banach space of the continuous vectorial functions, periodic of period ω, the condition that a set be compact is given by the theorem of Arzelà; it is sufficient that this set be formed by uniformly bounded and equicontinuous functions.

Let us show that the operator Ω considered above is completely continuous. If $\| x \| \leqslant \alpha$, it follows that $\| \Omega(x) \| = \sup | \int_0^\omega G(t, s) f[x(s), s] ds | \leqslant M\omega L$, where $L = \sup_{|x| \leqslant \alpha,\, t \in [0,\omega]} | f(x, t) |$; hence the set of functions $\{\Omega(x)\}$ is uniformly bounded. On the other hand, the functions $x(t)$ are in fact differentiable and we have

$$\frac{d}{dt} \Omega(x)(t) = A\Omega(x)(t) + f[x(t), t].$$

Hence

$$\left\| \frac{d}{dt} \Omega(x)(t) \right\| \leqslant \sup_{0 \leqslant t \leqslant \omega} | A(t) | M\omega L + L.$$

Therefore the derivatives of the functions $\Omega(x)(t)$ are uniformly bounded, which shows that these functions are equally continuous. The set $\{\Omega(x)\}$ will be relatively compact if $\| x \| \leqslant \alpha$; hence the operator Ω is completely continuous. In order to deduce the existence of a fixed point it remains to find the conditions which assure that there exists a sphere which is mapped into itself by Ω.

Let $|f(x, t)| \leqslant \beta(|x|)$; *if there exist an* α_0 *such that* $\beta(\alpha_0)/\alpha_0 \leqslant 1/M\omega$, *then the operator* Ω *maps the sphere* $\|x\| \leqslant \alpha_0$ *into itself.*

Indeed, if $\|x\| \leqslant \alpha_0$, we obtain

$$|f(x(t), t)| \leqslant \beta(\alpha_0) \quad \text{and} \quad \|\Omega(x)\| \leqslant M\omega\beta(\alpha_0) \leqslant M\omega \frac{\alpha_0}{M\omega} = \alpha_0 .$$

In particular, if there exist β *and* K *such that in the whole space* $|f(t, x)| \leqslant \beta|x| + K$ *and* $\beta < 1/M\omega$, *then* $\beta(\alpha) = \beta\alpha + K$, $\beta(\alpha)/\alpha = \beta + (K/\alpha)$, $\lim_{\alpha\to\infty} \beta(\alpha)/\alpha = \beta < 1/M\omega$ *and there exists an* α_0 *such that* $\beta(\alpha_0)/\alpha_0 \leqslant 1/M\omega$.

It follows that *if* $|f(t, x)| \leqslant \beta|x| + K$ *and* $\beta < 1/M\omega$, *then system* (4) *admits at least a periodic solution of period* ω.

We shall state now a result which allows certain applications in the theory of nonlinear servomechanisms.

Theorem 3.5. *Consider the system*

$$\frac{dx}{dt} = A(t)x + \lambda e(t) + F(x, t), \qquad \lambda > 0.$$

Suppose $A(t)$ *and* $e(t)$ *are periodic of period* ω; *the linear system* $dx/dt = A(t)x$ *has no other periodic solutions of period* ω *than the trivial solution;* $F(x, t)$ *is periodic in* t *of period* ω; $|F(x, t)| \leqslant L$ *for all* x *and* t; *and* $|F(x_1, t) - F(x_2, t)| < B|x_1 - x_2|$ *for all* x_1, x_2, *and* t. *Suppose in addition that there exists an* $r_0 > 0$ *such that for* $|x_1| \geqslant r_0$, $|x_2| \geqslant r_0$ *we have*

$$|F(x_1, t) - F(x_2, t)| \leqslant \beta|x_1 - x_2|, \qquad \beta < \frac{1}{M\omega} \qquad (M = \sup|G(t, s)|).$$

Finally, suppose that there exists an $\eta > 0$ *such that*

$$\text{mes}\, E = \text{mes}\{t \in [0, \omega], |\phi(t)| < \eta\} < \frac{1 - M\omega\beta}{MB},$$

$\phi(t)$ *being the unique periodic solution of the system* $dx/dt = A(t)x + e(t)$. *Under these conditions, the system admits for* $\lambda > \lambda_0 = (r_0 + ML\omega)/\eta$ *a unique periodic solution of period* ω.

Remark. The hypothesis $|F(x, t)| \leqslant L$ is sufficient to allow us to deduce, on the basis of the preceding considerations, the existence of the periodic solution for every λ. Therefore the essential fact in the theorem we are proving is *the uniqueness* of the periodic solution for $\lambda > \lambda_0$. As far as the hypotheses are concerned, they differ from those of the result based upon the contraction principle in that it is required that the function F admit a small Lipschitz constant only for $|x| > r_0$ and, in exchange, a supplementary condition is imposed on the solution $\phi(t)$. We stress the fact that in the conditions of the theorem, uniqueness is obtained only for $\lambda > \lambda_0$.

Proof. The periodic solutions of period ω of the system verify the integral equation

$$x(t) = \lambda\phi(t) + \int_0^{\omega} G(t, s)F[x(s), s]ds.$$

Therefore, for all periodic solutions we have

$$|x(t) - \lambda\phi(t)| \leqslant L\omega M;$$

hence

$$|x(t)| \geqslant \lambda|\phi(t)| - L\omega M.$$

For $t \in [0, \omega] - E_\eta = CE_\eta$ it will follow that $|x(t)| \geqslant \lambda\eta - L\omega M > r_0$ if $\lambda > r_0$. If x_1 and x_2 are two periodic solutions of period ω, we have

$$\begin{aligned} x_1(t) - x_2(t) &= \int_0^{\omega} G(t, s)\{F[x_1(s), s] - F[x_2(s), s]\}ds \\ &= \int_{E_\eta} G(t, s)\{F[x_1(s), s] - F[x_2(s), s]\}ds \\ &\quad + \int_{CE_\eta} G(t, s)\{F[x_1(s), s] - F[x_2(s), s]\}ds; \end{aligned}$$

hence

$$|x_1(t) - x_2(t)| \leqslant MB\| x_1 - x_2 \| \operatorname{mes} E_\eta + \omega M\beta\| x_1 - x_2 \|,$$

since $\operatorname{mes} CE_\eta \leqslant \omega$, and on CE_η we have $|x_1(t)| > r_0$, $|x_2(t)| > r_0$. Thus

$$\| x_1 - x_2 \| \leqslant M(B \operatorname{mes} E_\eta + \omega\beta)\| x_1 - x_2 \|.$$

From

$$\operatorname{mes} E_\eta < \frac{1 - M\omega\beta}{MB}$$

we obtain

$$MB \operatorname{mes} E_\eta + M\omega\beta < 1.$$

The inequality obtained implies $\| x_1 - x_2 \| = 0$; hence $x_1 = x_2$. The theorem is thus proved.

Theorem 3.6. *If to the conditions of the preceding theorem we add the condition that the trivial solution of the system*

$$\frac{dy}{dt} = A(t)y$$

be uniformly asymptotically stable, hence that $| y(t; t_0, y_0)| \leqslant Ke^{-\alpha(t-t_0)}| y_0 |$, *and in addition*

$$\beta < \min\left\{\frac{\alpha}{K}, \frac{1}{M\omega}\right\}$$

and

$$\operatorname{mes}\{t \in [0, \omega], | \phi(t)| = 0\} = 0,$$

then there exists a λ_0 *such that for* $\lambda > \lambda_0$ *the unique periodic solution is uniformly asymptotically stable.*

Proof. Let $\mu > 0$ arbitrary, $\tau > (\ln K + BK\mu)/(\alpha - K\beta)$; then

$$q = Ke^{BK\mu}e^{-(\alpha-K\beta)\tau} < 1.$$

Let N be the least natural number such that $N\omega \geqslant \tau$. Since the set of points in which $\phi(t)$ is zero has measure zero, it follows that there exists an $\eta > 0$ such that

$$\operatorname{mes}\{t \in [t_0, t_0 + N\omega], | \phi(t)| < \eta\} < \mu.$$

Indeed, the function $\phi(t)$ being periodic, we have for every $t_0 \geqslant 0$,

$$\operatorname{mes}\{t \in [t_0, t_0 + N\omega], | \phi(t)| = 0\} = 0.$$

But

$$\{t \in [t_0, t_0 + N\omega], | \phi(t)| = 0\} = \bigcap_{i=0}^{\infty} \{t \in [t_0, t_0 + N\omega], | \phi(t)| < \eta_i\},$$

where η_i is a monotone-decreasing sequence convergent to zero. It follows that

$$\lim_{i\to\infty} \operatorname{mes}\{t \in [t_0, t_0 + N\omega], | \phi(t)| < \eta_i\} = 0;$$

hence there exists an $\eta > 0$ such that

$$\operatorname{mes}\{t \in [t_0, t_0 + N\omega], |\phi(t)| < \eta\} < \mu,$$

η depending only on μ and not on t_0 (since the measure of the translate of a set is the same as that of the given set, and $\{t \in [t_0, t_0 + N\omega], |\phi(t)| < \eta_i\}$ is the translate with t_0 of the set $\{t \in [0, N\omega], |\phi(t)| < \eta_i\}$ due to the periodicity of the function ϕ).

For η thus found we take

$$\lambda_0 = \frac{2r_0 + LM\omega}{\eta}.$$

Put

$$F_\eta^t = \{s \in [t_0, t], |\phi(s)| < \eta\}.$$

For $0 \leqslant t_0 \leqslant t \leqslant t_0 + N\omega$ we have $\operatorname{mes} F_\eta^t < \mu$. Let $x_0(t)$ be the unique periodic solution of the system, which exists for $\lambda > \lambda_0$ according to the preceding theorem. From the relation

$$x_0(t) = \lambda\phi(t) + \int_0^\omega G(t, s)F[x_0(s), s]ds$$

we obtain

$$\| x_0(t) - \lambda\phi(t)\| < LM\omega,$$

hence

$$| x_0(t)| \geqslant \lambda| \phi(t)| - LM\omega.$$

From this we deduce that for $s \in [t_0, t] - F_\eta^t = CF_\eta^t$ we will have $| x_0(s)| \geqslant \lambda\eta - LM\omega \geqslant 2r_0$. Let $x(t)$ be a solution of the system and

$$y_0 = x(t_0) - x_0(t_0), \qquad y(t) = x(t) - x_0(t).$$

We have

$$\frac{dy(t)}{dt} = A(t)y(t) + F[y(t) + x_0(t), t] - F[x_0(t), t].$$

It follows that

$$\begin{aligned} y(t) &= C(t, t_0)y_0 + \int_{t_0}^t C(t, s)\{F[y(s) + x_0(s), s] - F[x_0(s), s]\}ds \\ &= C(t, t_0)y_0 + \int_{F_\eta^t} C(t, s)\{F[y(s) + x_0(s), s] - F[x_0(s), s]\}ds \\ &\quad + \int_{CF_\eta^t} C(t, s)\{F[y(s) + x_0(s), s] - F[x_0(s), s]\}ds. \end{aligned}$$

Let

$$K^* = e^{(\alpha - K\beta)\tau}, \qquad |y_0| \leqslant \frac{r_0}{K^*}.$$

Since $K^* > 1$ there exists an interval beyond t_0 for which $|y(s)| < r_0$; we have

$$|y(s) + x_0(s)| \geqslant |x_0(s)| - |y(s)|.$$

Hence for the values of s for which $|y(s)| < r_0$ and which belong to CF^t_η we will have

$$|y(s) + x_0(s)| \geqslant 2r_0 - r_0 = r_0 .$$

It follows that for $0 \leqslant t_0 \leqslant t \leqslant t_0 + \tau \leqslant t_0 + N\omega$ we will have

$$|y(t)| \leqslant Ke^{-\alpha(t-t_0)}|y_0| + BK \int_{F^t_\eta} e^{-\alpha(t-s)}|y(s)|ds + K\beta \int_{CF^t_\eta} e^{-\alpha(t-s)}|y(s)|ds$$

if for $t_0 \leqslant s < t$ we have $|y(s)| < r_0$.

Putting

$$u(t) = |y(t)|e^{\alpha t},$$

the inequality may be written

$$u(t) \leqslant Ke^{\alpha t_0}|y_0| + \int_{F^t_\eta} BKu(s)ds + \int_{CF^t_\eta} \beta Ku(s)ds.$$

Consider the measurable function

$$k(s) = \begin{cases} BK & \text{for } s \in F^t_\eta, \\ \beta K & \text{for } s \in CF^t_\eta . \end{cases}$$

The preceding inequality becomes

$$u(t) \leqslant Ke^{\alpha t_0}|y_0| + \int_{t_0}^{t} k(s)u(s)ds.$$

From this we deduce

$$u(t) \leqslant Ke^{\alpha t_0}|y_0| \exp\left[\int_{t_0}^{t} k(s)ds\right] = Ke^{\alpha t_0}|y_0| \exp\left[\int_{F^t_\eta} BK\,ds\right] \exp\left[\int_{CF^t_\eta} \beta K\,ds\right]$$

$$\leqslant Ke^{\alpha t_0}|y_0|e^{BK\mu}e^{\beta K(t-t_0)}.$$

Hence

$$| y(t)| < Ke^{BK\mu}| y_0 |e^{-(\alpha-K\beta)(t-t_0)},$$

whence

$$| y(t)| \leqslant Ke^{2K\mu}| y_0 | = qK^*| y_0 | \leqslant qr_0$$

for every $t_0 \leqslant t \leqslant t_0 + \tau$. This shows that the inequality $| y(t)| < r_0$ is maintained in the whole interval $t_0 \leqslant t \leqslant t_0 + \tau$. Hence in this interval we have

$$| y(t)| \leqslant qK^*| y_0 |e^{-(\alpha-K\beta)(t-t_0)}.$$

In particular,

$$| y(t_0 + \tau)| \leqslant qK^*| y_0 |e^{-(\alpha-K\beta)\tau} = q| y_0 |.$$

Since the constant q does not depend on t_0, we can take $t_0 + \tau$ as an initial moment and we deduce that

$$| y(t_0 + 2\tau)| \leqslant q| y(t_0 + \tau)| \leqslant q^2| y_0 |.$$

By induction we obtain

$$| y(t_0 + n\tau)| \leqslant q^n| y_0 |.$$

Now let $t \geqslant 0$. There exists an n such that

$$n\tau \leqslant t - t_0 < (n + 1)\tau.$$

Hence

$$| y(t)| \leqslant qK^*| y(t_0 + n\tau)| \leqslant qK^*q^n| y_0 |.$$

From

$$n + 1 > \frac{t - t_0}{\tau}, \qquad q < 1$$

we obtain

$$q^{n+1} < q^{(t-t_0)/\tau} = \exp\left(\frac{t - t_0}{\tau} \ln q\right),$$

Taking $\alpha^* = -\ln q/\tau$ we deduce

$$| y(t)| \leqslant K^*e^{-\alpha^*(t-t_0)}| y_0 |,$$

which shows that the solution $x_0(t)$ is exponentially stable, and the theorem is thus proved.

Let us observe that if

$$\lambda \geqslant \frac{mr_0 + LM\omega}{\eta}, \qquad m \geqslant 2,$$

the asymptotic stability will be assured if

$$| y_0 | \leqslant \frac{(m-1)r_0}{K^*};$$

hence the domain of attraction can be arbitrarily large on the condition that λ be sufficiently large.

Applications. 1. Consider the system

$$\ddot{x} + A\dot{x} + Bx = \begin{cases} M(t)[\lambda e(t) + C\dot{x} + Dx] & \text{for } |\lambda e(t) + C\dot{x} + Dx| \leqslant 1, \\ \dfrac{M(t)[\lambda e(t) + C\dot{x} + Dx]}{|\lambda e(t) + C\dot{x} + Dx|} & \text{for } |\lambda e(t) + C\dot{x} + Dx| \geqslant 1, \end{cases}$$

where A, B, C, D are constant quadratic matrices, of order n, $M(t)$ is a quadratic matrix of order n, periodic of period ω, with a continuous derivative, $\lambda > 0$.

Suppose the following conditions verified:

(a) The matrices C and D commute with A and B.

(b) The real parts of the roots of equations

$$\det(\lambda^2 E + A\lambda + B) = 0, \qquad \det(C^{-1}D + E\lambda) = 0$$

are negative; E is, as usual, the unit matrix.

(c) $e(t)$ is periodic, of period ω; it admits a continuous derivative of the second order and

$$\text{mes}\{t \in [0, \omega], |e(t)| = 0\} = 0.$$

Then there exists a λ_0 such that for $\lambda > \lambda_0$ the system admits a unique periodic solution and this solution is asymptotically stable; its domain of attraction increases with λ and tends to infinity when $\lambda \to \infty$.

Proof. Let

$$g(u) = \begin{cases} u & \text{for } |u| \leqslant 1, \\ \dfrac{u}{|u|} & \text{for } |u| \geqslant 1. \end{cases}$$

Consider the auxiliary system

$$\dot{x} = -C^{-1}Dx + C^{-1}y - \lambda C^{-1}e(t),$$
$$\dot{y} = -Ay + z + CM(t)g(y) + \lambda(\dot{e}(t) + Ae(t)),$$
$$\dot{z} = -By + DM(t)g(y) + \lambda Be(t).$$

This system verifies all the conditions of the preceding theorem. The corresponding linear system is

$$\dot{x} = -C^{-1}Dx + C^{-1}y, \qquad = -Ay + z, \qquad \dot{z} = -By.$$

Its matrix is

$$\begin{pmatrix} -C^{-1}D & C^{-1} & 0 \\ 0 & -A & E \\ 0 & -B & 0 \end{pmatrix};$$

the eigenvalues of this matrix will be those of the matrix

$$\begin{pmatrix} -A & E \\ -B & 0 \end{pmatrix}$$

and those of the matrix $-C^{-1}D$.

Since the roots of the equation

$$\det(C^{-1}D + \lambda E) = 0$$

have negative real parts, the matrix $-C^{-1}D$ is Hurwitzian. The equation

$$\det \begin{pmatrix} -A - \lambda E & E \\ -B & -\lambda E \end{pmatrix} = 0$$

can also be written

$$\det \begin{pmatrix} -A - \lambda E & E \\ -B - A\lambda - \lambda^2 E & 0 \end{pmatrix} = 0;$$

hence $\det(\lambda^2 E + \lambda A + B) = 0$. Thus, according to the hypotheses, the matrix

$$\begin{pmatrix} -A & E \\ -B & 0 \end{pmatrix}$$

is likewise Hurwitzian. It follows that the trivial solution of the linear system of first approximation is asymptotically stable.

Consider now the linear nonhomogeneous system

$$\dot{x} = -C^{-1}Dx + C^{-1}y - C^{-1}e(t),$$
$$\dot{y} = -Ay + z + (\dot{e}(t) + Ae(t)),$$
$$\dot{z} = -By + Be(t).$$

This system admits a periodic solution $x = 0$, $y = e(t)$, $z = 0$. Owing to the properties of the homogeneous system, this periodic solution is unique; according to the hypothesis made with respect to the function $e(t)$, the periodic solution verifies the condition of the preceding theorem. It remains, therefore, to verify the properties of the nonlinear terms. The first group of equations does not contain such terms. The terms from the last two groups are of the form $CM(t)g(y)$ and $DM(t)g(y)$. Since $|g(u)| \leqslant 1$, the boundedness condition is verified.

Further, if $|u_1| \leqslant 1$, $|u_2| \leqslant 1$, we have

$$|g(u_1) - g(u_2)| = |u_1 - u_2|.$$

If $1 \leqslant |u_1| \leqslant u_2$, let $u_3 = (|u_1|/|u_2|)u_2$; then

$$|g(u_1) - g(u_2)| = \left|\frac{u_1}{|u_1|} - \frac{u_2}{|u_2|}\right| = \frac{1}{|u_1|}\left|u_1 - \frac{|u_1|}{|u_2|}u_2\right| = \frac{1}{|u_1|}|u_1 - u_3|$$
$$\leqslant \frac{1}{|u_1|}|u_1 - u_2|.$$

If $|u_1| < 1 < |u_2|$, then

$$|g(u_1) - g(u_2)| = \left|u_1 - \frac{u_2}{|u_2|}\right| < |u_1 - u_2|.$$

It follows that for all u_1 and u_2 we have

$$|g(u_1) - g(u_2)| \leqslant |u_1 - u_2|;$$

hence g is Lipschitzian. If $|u_2| \geqslant |u_1| \geqslant r_0$, we have

$$|g(u_1) - g(u_2)| \leqslant \frac{1}{|u_1|}|u_1 - u_2| \leqslant \frac{1}{r_0}|u_1 - u_2|;$$

hence if r_0 is sufficiently large, the Lipschitz constant in region $r \geqslant r_0$ may be taken arbitrarily small. We deduce that all the conditions of the preceding theorem are fulfilled and hence for $\lambda > \lambda_0$ there exists a unique periodic solution of the system and this solution is exponentially stable. The system initially given may be written

$$\dot{x} = y, \qquad \dot{y} = -Bx - Ay + \varphi(x, y, t),$$

where

$$\varphi(x, y, t) = \begin{cases} M(t)[\lambda e(t) + Cy + Dx] & \text{for} \quad |\lambda e(t) + Cy + Dx| \leqslant 1, \\ \dfrac{M(t)[\lambda e(t) + Cy + Dx]}{|\lambda e(t) + Cy + Dx|} & \text{for} \quad |\lambda e(t) + Cy + Dx| \geqslant 1. \end{cases}$$

It is obvious that φ is bounded and since the matrix of the linear system

$$\dot{x} = y, \qquad \dot{y} = -Bx - Ay$$

is Hurwitzian, it follows that the given system admits a periodic solution of period ω. In order to deduce the uniqueness and stability of this solution we will show that every solution of the given system verifies the auxiliary system. Since the periodic solution of the auxiliary system is unique, the periodic solution of the given system, which exists, will be unique. From the asymptotic stability of the periodic solution of the auxiliary system will also follow the asymptotic stability of the periodic solution for the given system.

Let $x(t)$ be any solution of the given equation. Put

$$y(t) = \lambda e(t) + C\dot{x}(t) + Dx(t).$$

We have

$$\ddot{x} + A\dot{x} + Bx = M(t)g(y(t)).$$

For $|u| \neq 1$, the function $g(u)$ is differentiable; hence for the values t for which $|y(t)| \neq 1$ we have

$$\dddot{x} + A\ddot{x} + B\dot{x} = M(t)\frac{\partial g}{\partial y}\dot{y} + \dot{M}g(y).$$

We deduce

$$\begin{aligned} \ddot{y} + A\dot{y} + By &= \lambda\ddot{e} + C\dddot{x} + D\ddot{x} + A(\lambda\dot{e} + C\ddot{x} + D\dot{x}) + B(\lambda e + C\dot{x} + Dx) \\ &= \lambda(\ddot{e} + A\dot{e} + Be) + C(\dddot{x} + A\ddot{x} + B\dot{x}) + D(\ddot{x} + A\dot{x} + Bx) \\ &= \lambda(\ddot{e} + A\dot{e} + Be) + C\left(M(t)\frac{\partial g}{\partial y}\dot{y} + \dot{M}g(y)\right) + DMg(y). \end{aligned}$$

Let us put

$$z(t) = \dot{y}(t) + Ay(t) - CM(t)g(y(t)) - \lambda(\dot{e}(t) + Ae(t)).$$

We obtain

$$\begin{aligned}\dot{z}(t) &= \ddot{y}(t) + A\dot{y}(t) - C\dot{M}(t)g(y(t)) - CM(t)\frac{\partial g}{\partial y}\dot{y}(t) - \lambda(\ddot{e}(t) + A\dot{e}(t)) \\ &= -By(t) + \lambda(\ddot{e}(t) + A\dot{e}(t) + Be(t)) + CM(t)\frac{\partial g}{\partial y}\dot{y}(t) + C\dot{M}(t)g(y(t)) \\ &\quad + DM(t)g(y(t)) - C\dot{M}(t)g(y(t)) - \lambda(\ddot{e}(t) + A\dot{e}(t)) - CM(t)\frac{\partial g}{\partial y}\dot{y}(t).\end{aligned}$$

Hence

$$\dot{z}(t) = -By(t) + \lambda Be(t) + DM(t)g(y(t)).$$

We have showed that if $x(t)$ is any solution of the given system, the functions $x(t)$, $y(t) = \lambda e(t) + C\dot{x}(t) + Dx(t)$, $z(t) = \dot{y}(t) + Ay(t) - CM(t)g(y)t)) - \lambda(\dot{e}(t) + Ae(t))$ form a solution of the auxiliary system. With this, the proof is completely carried out.

2. Consider the system

$$\dot{x} = A(t)x + \sum_{i=1}^{m} k^i(t)f(\sigma_i) + \lambda e(t),$$

where $A(t)$ is a quadratic matrix, continuous and periodic of period ω, $k^i(t)$ are vector functions, continuous and periodic of period ω, and $f(u)$ is a scalar function of a real variable defined by

$$f(u) = \begin{cases} 1 & \text{for } |u| \geqslant 1, \\ u & \text{for } |u| \leqslant 1, \end{cases}$$

and $\sigma_i = (\beta^i(t), x) + \lambda\eta_i(t)$, where the $\beta^i(t)$ are periodic vectors, of period ω, with continuous first derivatives, the η_i are scalar functions, periodic of period ω, with continuous first derivatives, and $e(t)$ is periodic of period ω, with a continuous derivative.

Suppose the following conditions:

(a) There exists a determinant of order m of the matrix of vectors $\beta^i(t)$ which is different from zero for all t.

(b) The system $\dot{x} = A(t)x$ is such that the trivial solution is uniformly asymptotically stable.

(c) If $\phi_i(t)$ are the components of the unique periodic solution of period ω of system $dx/dt = A(t)x + e(t)$, we have for $i = 1, 2, \ldots, m$,

$$\text{mes}\left\{t \in [0, \omega], \left|\eta_i(t) + \sum_{k=1}^{n} \beta_k^i \phi_k(t)\right| = 0\right\} = 0.$$

In these conditions there exists $\lambda_0 > 0$ such that for $\lambda \geqslant \lambda_0$ the given system admits a unique periodic solution of period ω and this solution is exponentially stable.

Proof. Suppose that the determinant formed by the first m rows and m columns of the matrix of vectors $\beta^i(t)$ is different from zero. Consider the nonsingular matrix

$$B(t) = \begin{pmatrix} \beta_1^1(t) & \beta_2^1(t) & \cdots & \beta_m^1(t) & \beta_{m+1}^1(t) & \cdots & \beta_n^1(t) \\ \beta_1^2(t) & \beta_2^2(t) & \cdots & \beta_m^2(t) & \beta_{m+1}^2(t) & \cdots & \beta_n^2(t) \\ & & & \cdots & & & \\ \beta_m^1(t) & \beta_m^2(t) & \cdots & \beta_m^m(t) & \beta_{m+1}^m(t) & \cdots & \beta_n^m(t) \\ 0 & 0 & \cdots & 0 & 1 & \cdots & 0 \\ \vdots & & & & \vdots & & \vdots \\ 0 & 0 & & 0 & 0 & & 1 \end{pmatrix},$$

the vector

$$\eta(t) = \begin{pmatrix} \eta_1(t) \\ \vdots \\ \eta_m(t) \\ 0 \\ \vdots \\ 0 \end{pmatrix},$$

and the linear transformation $y = B(t)x + \lambda\eta(t)$. We have

$$y_1 = \sigma_1, \qquad y_2 = \sigma_2, \dots, y_m = \sigma_m, \qquad y_{m+1} = x_{m+1}, \dots, y_n = x_n,$$

$$\begin{aligned} \dot{y} &= \dot{B}x + B\dot{x} + \lambda\dot{\eta} = \dot{B}B^{-1}(y - \lambda\eta) + B(Ax + \sum k^i f(\sigma_i) + \lambda e) + \lambda\dot{\eta} \\ &= \dot{B}B^{-1}y - \lambda\dot{B}B^{-1}\eta + BAB^{-1}(y - \lambda\eta) + \lambda Be + \lambda\dot{\eta} + \sum Bk^i f(\sigma_i) \\ &= (BAB^{-1} + \dot{B}B^{-1})y + \lambda Be(t) + \lambda\dot{\eta}(t) - \lambda(\dot{B}B^{-1} + BAB^{-1})\eta(t) \\ &\qquad + B\sum_{i=1}^{m} k^i(t) f(y_i). \end{aligned}$$

This system fulfills all the conditions of Theorem 3.6. Indeed, the linear system

$$\frac{dz}{dt} = (BAB^{-1} + \dot{B}B^{-1})z$$

is obtained from $dx/dt = A(t)x$ through the transformation $z = B(t)x$ and has the trivial solution uniformly asymptotically stable.

The linear nonhomogeneous system

$$\dot{y} = (BAB^{-1} + \dot{B}B^{-1})y + Be(t) + \dot{\eta}(t) - (BAB^{-1} + \dot{B}B^{-1})\eta(t)$$

admits the periodic solution $\eta(t) + B\phi(t)$ and, according to the hypothesis, this solution is zero on a set of measure zero. The nonlinear terms are given by $B \sum k^i f(y_i)$ and it is obvious that they are bounded, Lipschitzian, and that if $|y_i| \geqslant 1$ for $i = 1, 2, \ldots, m$, the Lipschitzian constant is zero. It follows that the system in y admits a unique periodic solution, asymptotically stable.

If $y(t)$ is this solution, then

$$x(t) = B^{-1}(t)[y(t) - \lambda\eta(t)]$$

is the periodic solution of the given system and we immediately see that it is likewise unique and asymptotically stable.

3.4. Systems Containing a Small Parameter

A very important method from the practical viewpoint in the study of nonlinear systems is the so-called *method of the small parameter*. Nonlinear elements very often occur in equations multiplied by a small parameter. This gives rise to the idea that they can be neglected and that we can study only the equations which are obtained for the zero value of the parameter. This must, however, be justified, and the theory precisely states the cases when it is permitted, indicating at the same time the new phenomena which appear from the consideration of nonlinear terms.

Consider a system of the form

$$\frac{dx}{dt} = X_0(x, t) + \epsilon X_1(x, t, \epsilon), \tag{6}$$

where X_0 and X_1 are periodic with respect to t of period ω and verify the usual regularity conditions (we will assume that they admit continuous partial derivatives). For $\epsilon = 0$ we obtain the system

$$\frac{dx}{dt} = X_0(x, t) \tag{7}$$

which we will call the *generating system*. We suppose that the generating system admits a periodic solution $x_0(t)$; we will call this solution the *generating solution*. The problem consists in stating some conditions which assure that there exists an $\epsilon_0 > 0$ such that if $|\epsilon| < \epsilon_0$ system (6) admits a periodic solution $x(t, \epsilon)$ with the property that

$$\lim_{\epsilon \to 0} x(t, \epsilon) = x_0(t),$$

hence a solution for which $x_0(t)$ represents a good approximation for $|\epsilon|$ sufficiently small.

Let $x(t, p, \epsilon)$ be the solution of system (6) with $x(0, p, \epsilon) = \text{p}$. The condition that this solution be periodic is $x(\omega, p, \epsilon) = x(0, p, \epsilon)$, i.e. $x(\omega, p, \epsilon) - p = 0$. Observe that $x(t, p, 0) = x_0(t, p)$, where $x_0(t, p)$ is the solution of system (7) with $x_0(0, p) = \text{p}$. Let $f(p, \epsilon) = x(\omega, p, \epsilon) - p$.

We find that equation $f(p, \epsilon) = 0$ is verified by the point $(p_0, 0)$, where $p_0 = x_0(0)$, since the generating system admits the periodic solution $x_0(t)$. From the implicit function theorem it follows that if $\det(\partial f/\partial p) \neq 0$ in point $(p_0, 0)$, then there exists an $\epsilon_0 > 0$ such that for $|\epsilon| < \epsilon_0$ there exists a quantity $p(\epsilon)$ continuous, with $p(0) = 0$ and $f[p(\epsilon), \epsilon] = 0$. The solution $x(t, p(\epsilon), \epsilon)$ of the system will be the desired periodic solution $x(t, \epsilon)$.

It remains thus to find the significance of the condition $det(\partial f/\partial p) \neq 0$ in the point $(p_0, 0)$. Observe that $\partial f/\partial p = (\partial/\partial p)x(\omega, p, \epsilon) - E$, E being the unit matrix. It follows from here that $\det(\partial f/\partial p) \neq 0$ in the point $(p_0, 0)$ is equivalent to the requirement that the matrix $(\partial/\partial p)x(\omega, p, \epsilon)$ for $\epsilon = 0, p = p_0$ does not admit the eigenvalue 1. Further, $(\partial/\partial p)x(\omega, p, \epsilon)$ for $\epsilon = 0, p = p_0$ coincides with $(\partial/\partial p)x(\omega, p, 0)$ for $p = p_0$; therefore with $(\partial/\partial p)x(t, p, 0)$ for $t = \omega$, $p = p_0$; that is, $(\partial/\partial p)\, x_0\, (t, p)$ for $t = \omega, p = p_0$.

It follows from this that the existence of the periodic solution for $|\epsilon| < \epsilon_0$ depends only on the generating system (7). From

$$\frac{dx_0(t, p)}{dt} = X_0[x_0(t, p), t]$$

we obtain

$$\frac{\partial}{\partial p}\frac{\partial x_0(t, p)}{dt} = \frac{\partial}{\partial p} X_0[x_0(t, p), t] = \frac{\partial}{\partial x} X_0[x_0(t, p), t] \frac{\partial}{\partial p} x_0(t, p);$$

hence

$$\frac{d}{dt}\frac{\partial}{\partial p} x_0(t, p) = \frac{\partial}{\partial x} X_0[x_0(t, p), t] \frac{\partial}{\partial p} x_0(t, p).$$

It follows that the matrix $(\partial/\partial p)x_0(t, p_0)$ is a matrix of solutions of the system

$$\frac{du}{dt} = \frac{\partial}{\partial x} X_0[x_0(t), t]u \tag{8}$$

(*the variational system corresponding to the generating solution*).

Since $x_0(0, p) = p$, it follows that $(\partial/\partial p)x_0(t, p)$ for $t = 0$ is just E; hence $(\partial/\partial p)x_0(t, p_0)$ is a fundamental matrix of solutions of the variational system. Since $x_0(t)$ is periodic of period ω, the matrix $(\partial/\partial x)X_0[x_0(t), t]$ is periodic of period ω. The matrix $(\partial/\partial p)x_0(t, p)$ for $p = p_0$, $t = \omega$ is just the monodromy matrix of the linear system (8). The condition that this matrix does not have the eigenvalue 1 is equivalent with the request that the variational system does not have a periodic solution of period ω. Thus we have obtained

Theorem 3.7. *If the variational system corresponding to the generating solution has no other periodic solution of period ω than the trivial solution, then there exists an $\epsilon_0 > 0$ such that for $|\epsilon| < \epsilon_0$ system (6) admits a unique periodic solution $x(t, \epsilon)$ with the property*

$$\lim_{\epsilon\to 0} x(t, \epsilon) = x_0(t),$$

and this solution depends continuously on ϵ.

An important particular case is the one in which the generating system is linear, hence the case of systems of the form

$$\frac{dx}{dt} = A(t)x + P(t) + \epsilon X(x, t, \epsilon).$$

System (8) coincides in this case with $du/dt = A(t)u$, and the theorem shows that if the generating solution represents a forced oscillation in the case of nonresonance, then for $|\epsilon|$ sufficiently small the nonlinear system admits a unique periodic solution whose first approximation is the generating solution.

Consider now the case where the variational system (8) has periodic solutions of period ω; then the adjoint system of system (8) has the same number of linearly independent periodic solutions of period ω. Denote by $W(t)$ the matrix whose rows are these solutions.

Suppose that system (6) admits a periodic solution $x(t, \epsilon)$ such that

$$\lim_{\epsilon\to 0} x(t, \epsilon) = x_0(t).$$

Let

$$y(t, \epsilon) = x(t, \epsilon) - x_0(t).$$

We deduce that

$$\begin{aligned}\frac{d}{dt} y(t, \epsilon) &= X_0[x(t, \epsilon), t] + \epsilon X_1[x(t, \epsilon), t, \epsilon] - X_0[x_0(t), t] \\ &= \frac{\partial}{\partial x} X_0[x_0(t), t]y(t, \epsilon) + Y_0[y(t, \epsilon), t] + \epsilon X_1[y(t, \epsilon) + x_0(t), t, \epsilon],\end{aligned}$$

where $Y_0(0, t) \equiv 0$.

Since $y(t, \epsilon)$ is periodic, it follows from here that the system

$$\frac{du}{dt} = \frac{\partial}{\partial x} X_0[x_0(t), t]u + Y_0[y(t, \epsilon), t] + \epsilon X_1[y(t, \epsilon) + x_0(t), t, \epsilon]$$

admits a periodic solution. On the basis of Theorem 3.2 we obtain

$$\int_0^\omega W(s)\{Y_0[y(s, \epsilon), s] + \epsilon X_1[y(s, \epsilon) + x_0(s), s, \epsilon]\}ds = 0.$$

From here it follows that

$$\int_0^\omega W(s)X_1[x_0(s), s, 0]ds = 0.$$

Indeed, if it were not so, we would have

$$\left| \int_0^\omega W(s)X_1[x_0(s), s, 0]ds \right| = c > 0.$$

From $\lim_{\epsilon\to 0} y(s, \epsilon) = 0$ and from the continuity of function X_1, it follows that there exists an $\epsilon_0 > 0$ such that for $|\epsilon| < \epsilon_0$ we have

$$\left| \int_0^\omega W(s)X_1[y(s, \epsilon) + x_0(s), s, \epsilon]ds \right| > \frac{c}{2}.$$

If X_1 is differentiable with respect to ϵ, then $x(t, \epsilon)$ is differentiable with respect to ϵ; hence $y(t, \epsilon)$ is differentiable with respect to ϵ and $|y(t, \epsilon)| < L|\epsilon|$ for $t \in [0, \omega]$. From the differentiability of $X_0(x, t)$ with respect to x follows

$$|Y_0[y(s, \epsilon), s]| = o(|y(s, \epsilon)|) = o(\epsilon).$$

Thus we obtain

$$\left| \epsilon \int_0^\omega W(s)X_1[y(s, \epsilon) + x_0(s), s, \epsilon]ds \right| > \frac{c}{2}\epsilon$$

and

$$\left| \int_0^\omega W(s)Y_0[y(s, \epsilon), s]ds \right| = o(\epsilon),$$

which is contradictory, since the two functions are equal.

We have thus proved the following

Proposition. *If system* (8) *admits periodic solutions of period* ω *and if system* (6) *admits a periodic solution* $x(t, \epsilon)$ *such that* $\lim_{\epsilon\to 0} x(t, \epsilon) = x_0(t)$, *then*

$$\int_0^\omega W(s)X_1[x_0(s), s, 0]ds = 0,$$

$W(t)$ *being the matrix whose rows are the periodic solutions of the adjoint system of system* (8).

If the generating solution belongs to a family of periodic solutions depending on a number of parameters, we are within the conditions of the proposition, since the derivatives of the solutions with respect to the parameters are periodic solutions of system (8).

The condition from the proposition allows us to find those values of the parameters for which the corresponding solution is effectively the first approximation of a periodic solution of system (6).

We will now prove the above proposition in a slightly different way; this new proof will allow us to investigate further the case in which the generating solution belongs to a family of solutions depending on a number of parameters.

Let $U(t)$ be the fundamental matrix of solutions of system (8) and l_j the initial vectors of the periodic solutions of the adjoint system of system (8); we have $l_j\{U(\omega) - E\} = 0$. If ρ_j are the initial vectors of the periodic solutions of system (8), we have

$$[U(\omega) - E]\rho_j = 0 \qquad (j = n - k + 1, ..., n).$$

Now consider vectors $l_1, ..., l_{n-k}$ and $\rho_1, ..., \rho_{n-k}$ such that the systems of vectors l_i and ρ_i $(i = 1, ..., n)$. be linearly independent. Let S be the matrix whose rows are l_i and T the matrix whose columns are ρ_i. We have

$$S[U(\omega) - E]T = \begin{pmatrix} \Delta & 0 \\ 0 & 0 \end{pmatrix}.$$

If system (8) admits exactly k linearly independent periodic solutions, then the matrix $U(\omega) - E$ has the rank $n - k$; hence det $\Delta \neq 0$. The condition that the solution $x(t, p, \epsilon)$ of system (6) be periodic is $x(\omega, p, \epsilon) - p = 0$. We may write

$$x(\omega, p, \epsilon) = x(\omega, p_0, 0) + \frac{\partial x(\omega, p_0, 0)}{\partial p}(p - p_0) + \epsilon\frac{\partial x(\omega, p_0, 0)}{\partial \epsilon}$$
$$+ o(|\epsilon| + |p - p_0|).$$

Since $x(\omega, p_0, 0) = p_0$, the periodicity condition is

$$\left\{\frac{\partial x(\omega, p_0, 0)}{\partial p} - E\right\}(p - p_0) + \epsilon \frac{\partial x(\omega, p_0, 0)}{\partial \epsilon} + o(|\epsilon| + |p - p_0|) = 0.$$

But we have seen that that

$$\frac{\partial x(\omega, p_0, 0)}{\partial p} = U(\omega);$$

hence the periodicity condition is

$$[U(\omega) - E](p - p_0) + \epsilon \frac{\partial x(\omega, p_0, 0)}{\partial \epsilon} + o(|\epsilon| + |p - p_0|) = 0.$$

Let us calculate $\partial x(\omega, p_0, 0)/\partial \epsilon$. We have

$$\frac{d}{dt}\frac{\partial}{\partial \epsilon} x(t, p, \epsilon) = \frac{\partial}{\partial \epsilon}\frac{d}{dt} x(t, p, \epsilon) = \frac{\partial}{\partial \epsilon} X_0[x(t, p, \epsilon), t] + \frac{\partial}{\partial \epsilon} \epsilon X_1[x(t, p, \epsilon), t, \epsilon]$$

$$= \frac{\partial X_0[x(t, p, \epsilon), t]}{\partial x} \frac{\partial}{\partial \epsilon} x(t, p, \epsilon) + X_1[x(t, p, \epsilon), t, \epsilon]$$

$$+ \epsilon \frac{\partial}{\partial \epsilon} X_1[x(t, p, \epsilon), t, \epsilon].$$

From this, for $\epsilon = 0, p = p_0$, we obtain

$$\frac{d}{dt}\frac{\partial x(t, p_0, 0)}{\partial \epsilon} = \frac{\partial X_0(x_0(t), t)}{\partial x}\frac{\partial x(t, p_0, 0)}{\partial \epsilon} + X_1[x_0(t), t, 0];$$

hence $\partial x(t, p_0, 0)/\partial \epsilon$ verifies the system

$$\frac{dz}{dt} = \frac{\partial X_0[x_0(t), t]}{\partial x} z + X_1[x_0(t), t, 0]$$

and the initial condition $z(0) = 0$, since $x(0, p, \epsilon) = p$ and

$$\frac{\partial}{\partial \epsilon} x(0, p, \epsilon) = 0.$$

It follows from this, on the basis of the variation-of-constants formula, that

$$\frac{\partial x(t, p_0, 0)}{\partial \epsilon} = U(t) \int_0^t U^{-1}(s) X_1[x_0(s), s, 0] ds;$$

hence

$$\frac{\partial x(\omega, p_0, 0)}{\partial \epsilon} = U(\omega) \int_0^\omega U^{-1}(s) X_1[x_0(s), s, 0] ds.$$

Since the vectors l_i are linearly independent, the periodicity condition may be written under the equivalent form

$$l_i[U(\epsilon) - E](p - p_0) + \epsilon l_i \frac{\partial x(\omega, p_0, 0)}{\partial \epsilon} + o(|\epsilon| + |p - p_0|) = 0$$
$$(i = 1, ..., n - k),$$

$$l_j[U(\omega) - E](p - p_0) + \epsilon l_j \frac{\partial x(\omega, p_0, 0)}{\partial \epsilon} + o(|\epsilon| + |p - p_0|) = 0$$
$$(j = n - k + 1, ..., n).$$

But $l_j[U(\omega) - E] = 0$; hence the second group of equations is

$$\epsilon l_j \frac{\partial x(\omega, p_0, 0)}{\partial \epsilon} + o(|\epsilon| + |p - p_0|) = 0.$$

We seek the solution $p(\epsilon)$ in the form

$$p(\epsilon) - p_0 + \epsilon \sum_{i=1}^{n-k} \beta_i(\epsilon) \rho_i .$$

The system of equations becomes

$$\epsilon \sum_j l_i[U(\omega) - E]\rho_j \beta_j(\epsilon) + \epsilon l_i \frac{\partial x(\omega, p_0, 0)}{\partial \epsilon} + o(|\epsilon| + |p - p_0|) = 0,$$
$$(i = 1, ..., n - k),$$

$$\epsilon l_j \frac{\partial x(\omega, p_0, 0)}{\partial \epsilon} + o(|\epsilon| + |p - p_0|) = 0 \qquad (j = n - k + 1, ..., n).$$

But $|p - p_0| = O(\epsilon)$ and the equations are

$$\sum_j l_i[U(\omega) \quad E]\rho_j \beta_j + l_i \frac{\partial x(\omega, p_0, 0)}{\partial \epsilon} + O(|\epsilon|) = 0 \qquad (i = 1, ..., n - k),$$

$$l_j \frac{\partial x(\omega, p_0, 0)}{\partial \epsilon} + O(|\epsilon|) = 0 \qquad j = (n - k + 1, ..., n). \tag{9}$$

In order that this system admits solutions it is necessary in the first place that

$$l_j \frac{\partial x(\omega, p_0, 0)}{\partial \epsilon} = 0 \qquad (j = n - k + 1, ..., n),$$

which leads to

$$l_j U(\omega) \int_0^\omega U^{-1}(s) X_1[x_0(s), s, 0] ds = 0;$$

hence

$$\int_0^\omega l_j U^{-1}(s) X_1[x_0(s), s, 0] ds = 0$$

or

$$\int_0^\omega W(s) X_1[x_0(s), s, 0] ds = 0.$$

In addition, it is necessary that the system

$$\sum_j l_i[U(\omega) - E]\rho_j \beta_j + l_i \frac{\partial x(\omega, p_0, 0)}{\partial \epsilon} = 0$$

has solutions. Since the matrix of this system is just Δ and $\det \Delta \neq 0$, the system always has solutions.

Suppose now that solution $x_0(t)$ belongs to a family of periodic solutions, of period ω, depending on k parameters; we denote this family by $x_0(t, \alpha)$. Then

$$\frac{\partial x_0(t, \alpha)}{\partial \alpha_i} \qquad (i = 1, 2, ..., k)$$

will be linearly independent periodic solutions of system (8), if the k parameters are independent.

Suppose that system (8) has no other independent periodic solutions, hence that it has exactly k independent periodic-solutions. Then we can repeat the above reasoning starting from any solution $x_0(t, \alpha)$ and we obtain the necessary condition for the existence of a periodic solution of period ω, $x(t, \epsilon, \alpha)$, of system (6), such that

$$\lim_{\epsilon \to 0} x(t, \epsilon, \alpha) = x_0(t, \alpha)$$

under the form

$$P(\alpha) \equiv \int_0^\omega W_\alpha(s) X_1[x_0(s, \alpha), s, 0] ds = 0.$$

Suppose that the equation $P(\alpha) = 0$ admits a solution $\alpha = \alpha_0$ such that $\partial P(\alpha)/\partial \alpha$ for $\alpha = \alpha_0$ is nonsingular. We show that in this case system (6) admits a periodic solution of period ω, $x(t, \epsilon)$, such that

$$\lim_{\epsilon \to 0} x(t, \epsilon) = x_0(t, \alpha_0).$$

The system of equations (9) is verified for $\epsilon = 0$, $\alpha = \alpha_0$ by values $\beta = \beta_0$ given by

$$\sum_j l_i[U_{\alpha_0}(\omega) - E]\rho_j\beta_j + l_i \frac{\partial x(\omega, p_0, 0)}{\partial \epsilon} = 0.$$

The Jacobian of system (9) with respect to β and α for $\epsilon = 0$, $\alpha = \alpha_0$, $\beta = \beta_0$ is equal to

$$\det \begin{pmatrix} \Delta & \Delta_1 \\ 0 & \dfrac{\partial P(\alpha_0)}{\partial \alpha} \end{pmatrix} = \det \Delta \det \frac{\partial P(\alpha_0)}{\partial \alpha},$$

and in our hypotheses it is not zero. From the implicit-function theorem there exists an $\epsilon_0 > 0$ and functions $\alpha(\epsilon)$, $\beta(\epsilon)$ defined for $|\epsilon| < \epsilon_0$, verifying system (9) and such that $\alpha(0) = \alpha_0$, $\beta(0) = \beta_0$.

Putting

$$p(\epsilon) = p_0(\alpha(\epsilon)) + \epsilon \sum_{i=1}^{n-k} \beta_i(\epsilon)\rho_i[\alpha(\epsilon)]$$

the solution $x(t, p(\epsilon), \epsilon)$ will be periodic of period ω and for $\epsilon \to 0$ it becomes

$$x_0(t, p_0(\alpha_0)) = x_0(t, \alpha_0).$$

We have thus proved the following theorem:

Theorem 3.8. *If system* (7) *admits a family of periodic solutions* $x_0(t, \alpha)$ *of period* ω, *such that the corresponding variational system admits for every* α *exactly k independent periodic solutions of period* ω, *then for every* α_0 *such that*

$$P(\alpha_0) = 0, \qquad \det \frac{\partial P(\alpha_0)}{\partial \alpha} \neq 0,$$

where

$$P(\alpha) \equiv \int_0^{\omega} W_\alpha(s) X_1[x_0(s, \alpha), s, 0]\, ds,$$

there exists a periodic solution $x(t, \epsilon)$ *of system* (6), *of period* ω, *such that* $\lim_{\epsilon \to 0} x(t, \epsilon) = x_0(t, \alpha_0)$.

Applications. 1. An important particular case is that of the equation

$$\ddot{x} + n^2 x + f(t) = \epsilon F(t, x, \dot{x}, \epsilon),$$

where f and F are periodic with respect to t of period 2π. Here the variational system is $\ddot{x} + n^2x = 0$ and has solutions periodic of period $2\pi/n$, hence also of period 2π. The function $f(t)$ is supposed such that the generating equation $\ddot{x} + n^2x + f(t) = 0$ has a periodic solution of period 2π. Then the solutions of the generating system are periodic of period 2π and form a family with two parameters,

$$x_0 = \varphi(t) + M_0 \cos nt + N_0 \sin nt.$$

We have

$$U(t) = \begin{pmatrix} \frac{1}{\sqrt{n}} \cos nt & \frac{1}{\sqrt{n}} \sin nt \\ -\sqrt{n} \sin nt & \sqrt{n} \cos nt \end{pmatrix}, \quad U^{-1}(t) = \begin{pmatrix} \sqrt{n} \cos nt & -\frac{1}{\sqrt{n}} \sin nt \\ \sqrt{n} \sin nt & \frac{1}{\sqrt{n}} \cos nt \end{pmatrix},$$

$$X_1[x_0(s, \alpha), s, 0] = \binom{0}{F},$$

$$F = F[s, \varphi(s) + M_0 \cos ns + N_0 \sin ns, \dot{\varphi}(s) - M_0 n \sin ns + N_0 n \cos ns, 0].$$

The equations which determine M_0 and N_0 are

$$\int_0^{2\pi} \frac{1}{\sqrt{n}} \sin nsF[s, x_0(s), \dot{x}_0(s), 0]ds = 0,$$

$$\int_0^{2\pi} \frac{1}{\sqrt{n}} \cos nsF[s, x_0(s), \dot{x}_0(s), 0]ds = 0;$$

hence

$$P(M_0, N_0) \equiv \int_0^{2\pi} F[s, \varphi(s) + M_0 \cos ns + N_0 \sin ns, \dot{\varphi}(s) - M_0 n \sin ns + N_0 n \cos ns, 0] \sin ns\, ds = 0,$$

$$Q(M_0, N_0) \equiv \int_0^{2\pi} F[s, \varphi(s) + M_0 \cos ns + N_0 \sin ns, \dot{\varphi}(s) - M_0 n \sin ns + N_0 n \cos ns, 0] \cos ns\, ds = 0,$$

$$\frac{\partial(P, Q)}{\partial(M_0, N_0)} \neq 0.$$

2. Consider the equation

$$\ddot{x} + \frac{1}{n^2} x + f(t) = \epsilon F[t, x, \dot{x}, \epsilon].$$

The variational system has no other solutions of period 2π than the trivial solution; hence for $|\epsilon|$ sufficiently small there exists a unique periodic solution of period 2π. At the same time, all the solutions of the generating system are periodic with period $2n\pi$. The functions f and F having period 2π also have period $2n\pi$. Hence in the neighborhood of the solutions of the generating systems which verify relations from Theorem 3.8, there may appear, for $|\epsilon|$ sufficiently small, periodic solutions of period $2n\pi$ which do not have period 2π. These types of oscillations are called *subharmonic oscillations*, and the phenomenon described above has been called by Mandelstam and Papalexi, who discovered it in 1932, resonance of the nth kind.

Before closing this section, let us make some remarks on the stability of the periodic solution of system (6) in the simplest case. Suppose that the trivial solution of system (8) is asymptotically stable; then, obviously system (8) has no other periodic solutions than the trivial one, and on the strength of Theorem 3.7 system (6) admits a unique periodic solution $x(t, \epsilon)$ with

$$\lim_{\epsilon\to 0} x(t, \epsilon) = x_0(t).$$

Let us perform in system (6) the change of variables $y = x - x(t, \epsilon)$. We obtain

$$\begin{aligned}
\frac{dy}{dt} &= \frac{dx}{dt} - \frac{dx(t, \epsilon)}{dt} \\
&= X_0[y + x(t, \epsilon), t] + \epsilon X_1[y + x(t, \epsilon), t, \epsilon] - X_0[x(t, \epsilon), t] - \epsilon X_1[x(t, \epsilon), t, \epsilon] \\
&= \frac{\partial X_0[x(t, \epsilon), t]}{\partial x} y + o(|y|) + \epsilon \frac{\partial X_1[x(t, \epsilon), t, \epsilon]}{\partial x} y + o(|y|) \\
&= \frac{\partial X_0[x_0(t), t]}{\partial x} y + \left[\frac{\partial X_0[x(t, \epsilon), t]}{\partial x} - \frac{\partial X_0[x_0(t), t]}{\partial x}\right] y \\
&\qquad + \epsilon \frac{\partial X_1[x(t, \epsilon), t, \epsilon]}{\partial x} y + o(|y|).
\end{aligned}$$

For sufficiently small $|\epsilon|$ and $|y|$ we have

$$\left|\left[\frac{\partial X_0[x(t, \epsilon), t]}{\partial x} - \frac{\partial X_0[x_0(t), t]}{\partial x}\right] y + \epsilon \frac{\partial X_1[x(t, \epsilon), t, \epsilon]}{\partial x} y + o(|y|)\right| < \beta |y|$$

with β however small; since by virtue of the hypothesis the trivial solution of system (8) is asymptotically stable [system (8) being a linear system with periodic coefficients, the solution is uniformly asymptotically stable, hence exponentially stable], it follows that we may apply the fundamental theorem of stability of the first approximation and we deduce that the trivial solution of the system in y is asymptotically stable. We have thus stated the following

Proposition. *If the trivial solution of the variational system* (8) *is asymptotically stable, then for* $|\epsilon|$ *sufficiently small system* (6) *admits a unique periodic solution* $x(t, \epsilon)$ *with the property that*

$$\lim_{\epsilon\to 0} x(t, \epsilon) = x_0(t)$$

and this solution is asymptotically stable.

3.5. The Method of Averaging

In the following pages we shall present some particular cases of the general method elaborated by N. M. Krylov and N. N. Bogoliubov, known under the name *method of averaging*. This method is also applied in the problem of almost-periodic solutions.

Suppose that the generating system (7) has all the solutions periodic of period ω. Let $x_0(t, h)$ be the general solution of the generating system. Perform the change of variables $x = x_0(t, z)$. We obtain

$$\frac{dx}{dt} = \frac{\partial x_0(t, z)}{\partial t} + \frac{\partial x_0(t, z)}{\partial z}\frac{dz}{dt}$$

$$= X_0[x_0(t, z), t] + \epsilon X_1[x_0(t, z), t, \epsilon].$$

However,

$$\frac{\partial x_0(t, z)}{\partial t} = X_0[x_0(t, z), t],$$

and the fact that $x_0(t, h)$ is the general solution of system (7) shows that the matrix $\partial x_0(t, z)/\partial z$ has an inverse; hence

$$\frac{dz}{dt} = \epsilon Z(t, z, \epsilon), \tag{10}$$

where

$$Z(t, z, \epsilon) = \left[\frac{\partial x_0(t, z)}{\partial z}\right]^{-1} X_1[x_0(t, z), t, \epsilon].$$

Let

$$Z_0(z, \epsilon) = \frac{1}{\omega}\int_0^{\omega} Z(t, z, \epsilon)dt$$

and let ζ^0 be a solution of the equation $Z_0(z, 0) = 0$. Perform the change of variables $z = \zeta^0 + b$.

We obtain the system

$$\frac{db}{dt} = \epsilon B(t, b, \epsilon),$$

where $B(t, b, \epsilon) = Z(t, \zeta^0 + b, \epsilon)$; hence $B(t, b, \epsilon)$ has the same regularity properties as Z and is periodic in t of period ω. Let

$$B_0(b, \epsilon) = \frac{1}{\omega}\int_0^{\omega} B(t, b, \epsilon)dt.$$

We obviously have $B_0(0, 0) = 0$.

Let

$$B^*(t, b, \epsilon) = B(t, b, \epsilon) - B_0(b, \epsilon);$$

we obtain

$$\frac{1}{\omega}\int_0^{\omega} B^*(t, b, \epsilon)dt = 0.$$

Let

$$B_\eta^*(t, b, \epsilon) = \int_{-\infty}^{t} e^{-\eta(t-s)}B^*(s, b, \epsilon)ds = \int_0^{\infty} e^{-\eta\sigma}B^*(t - \sigma, b, \epsilon)d\sigma$$

$$= \sum_{n=0}^{\infty} e^{-n\eta\omega}\int_{n\omega}^{(n+1)\omega} B^*(t - \sigma, b, \epsilon)e^{-\eta(\sigma-n\omega)}\, d\sigma$$

$$= \sum_{n=0}^{\infty} e^{-n\eta\omega}\int_0^{\omega} e^{-\eta s}B^*(t - s, b, \epsilon)ds$$

$$= \frac{1}{1 - e^{-\eta\omega}}\int_0^{\omega} e^{-\eta s}B^*(t - s, b, \epsilon)ds.$$

Let

$$B^{**}(\sigma, b, \epsilon) = \int_0^{\sigma} B^*(\xi, b, \epsilon)d\xi.$$

We have

$$B_\eta^*(t, b, \epsilon) = \frac{1}{1 - e^{-\eta\omega}} \int_0^\omega e^{-\eta s} B^*(t - s, b, \epsilon) ds$$

$$= \frac{-1}{1 - e^{-\eta\omega}} \int_t^{t-\omega} e^{-\eta t} e^{\eta\sigma} B^*(\sigma, b, \epsilon) d\sigma$$

$$= \frac{e^{-\eta t}}{1 - e^{-\eta\omega}} \int_{t-\omega}^t e^{\eta\sigma} B^*(\sigma, b, \epsilon) d\sigma = \frac{e^{-\eta t}}{1 - e^{-\eta\omega}} \int_{t-\omega}^t e^{\eta\sigma} dB^{**}$$

$$= \frac{e^{-\eta t}}{1 - e^{-\eta\omega}} \{e^{\eta t} B^{**}(t, b, \epsilon) - e^{\eta(t-\omega)} B^{**}(t - \omega, b, \epsilon)\}$$

$$- \frac{\eta e^{-\eta t}}{1 - e^{-\eta\omega}} \int_{t-\omega}^t e^{\eta\sigma} B^{**}(\sigma, b, \epsilon) d\sigma$$

$$= B^{**}(t, b, \epsilon) - \frac{\eta e^{-\eta t}}{1 - e^{-\eta\omega}} \int_{t-\omega}^t e^{\eta\sigma} B^{**}(\sigma, b, \epsilon) d\sigma$$

$$= B^{**}(t, b, \epsilon) - \frac{\eta}{1 - e^{-\eta\omega}} \int_0^\omega e^{-\eta s} B^{**}(t - s, b, \epsilon) ds.$$

Since $B^*(t, b, \epsilon)$ has the mean value zero, it follows that $B^{**}(t, b, \epsilon)$ is periodic, hence bounded. Thus we obtain the evaluation

$$| B_\eta^*(t, b, \epsilon)| \leqslant M + M \frac{\eta}{1 - e^{-\eta\omega}} \int_0^\omega e^{-\eta s}\, ds = 2M.$$

Perform the change of variables $b = h + \epsilon B_\eta^*(t, h, \epsilon)$. We obtain

$$\frac{dh}{dt} + \epsilon \frac{\partial B_\eta^*}{\partial t} + \epsilon \frac{\partial B_\eta^*}{\partial b} \frac{dh}{dt} = \epsilon B = \epsilon B_0 + \epsilon B^*,$$

$$B_0(h + \epsilon B_\eta^*, \epsilon) = B_0(h, \epsilon) + O(\epsilon) = B_0(h, 0) + O(\epsilon) = Hh + B_1(h) + O(\epsilon),$$

where

$$H = \frac{\partial}{\partial b} B_0(0, 0), \qquad | B_1(h)| \leqslant \mu | h |^2.$$

From

$$B_0(b, \epsilon) = \frac{1}{\omega} \int_0^\omega B(t, b, \epsilon) dt = \frac{1}{\omega} \int_0^\omega Z(t, \zeta^0 + b, \epsilon) dt = Z_0(\zeta^0 + b, \epsilon)$$

it follows that

$$H = \frac{\partial Z_0(\zeta^0, 0)}{\partial z}.$$

Further, we have

$$B^*(t, h + \epsilon B^*_\eta, \epsilon) = B^*(t, h, \epsilon) + O(\epsilon)$$

and

$$\frac{\partial B^*_\eta}{\partial t} = B^* - \eta B^*_\eta .$$

It follows that

$$\left(E + \epsilon \frac{\partial B^*_\eta}{\partial b}\right) \frac{dh}{dt} = \epsilon Hh + \epsilon B_1(h) + \epsilon B^*(t, h, \epsilon)$$
$$- \epsilon B^*(t, h, \epsilon) + \epsilon\eta B^*_\eta(t, h, \epsilon) + \epsilon O(\epsilon).$$

We take $\eta = \epsilon$; from $| B^*_\eta | < 2M$ we obtain

$$\eta B^*_\eta(t, h, \epsilon) = O(\epsilon);$$

hence the system becomes

$$\left(E + \epsilon \frac{\partial B^*_\eta}{\partial b}\right) \frac{dh}{dt} = \epsilon Hh + \epsilon B_1(h) + \epsilon O(\epsilon).$$

However,

$$\frac{\partial B^*_\eta}{\partial b} = \int_{-\infty}^{t} e^{-\eta(t-s)} \frac{\partial B^*}{\partial b}\, ds;$$

$\partial B^*/\partial b$ is as B^*, periodic of period ω, and has the mean value zero, hence $\partial B^*_\eta/\partial b$ is, as B^*_η, bounded. It follows that $\epsilon(\partial B^*_\eta/\partial b) = O(\epsilon)$; hence

$$\left(E + \epsilon \frac{\partial B^*_\eta}{\partial b}\right)^{-1} = E + O(\epsilon).$$

We finally obtain

$$\frac{dh}{dt} = \epsilon Hh + \epsilon B_1(h) + \epsilon O(\epsilon).$$

Perform the change of independent variables $\tau = \epsilon t$. The system becomes

$$\frac{dh}{d\tau} = Hh + B_1(h) + O(\epsilon), \tag{11}$$

where terms $O(\epsilon)$ are periodic in τ of period $\epsilon\omega$. Suppose that the eigenvalues of matrix H have real parts different from zero. In this case the system $dh/d\tau = Hh$ cannot have any kind of periodic solutions different from the trivial one. The Green's matrix corresponding to the periodicity conditions $h(0) = h(\epsilon\omega)$ is

$$G(t, s) = e^{Ht}[E - e^{\epsilon H\omega}]^{-1}e^{-Hs} = e^{H(t-s)}[E - e^{\epsilon\omega H}]^{-1} \qquad (0 \leqslant s \leqslant t \leqslant \epsilon\omega),$$

$$G(t, s) = e^{H(t-\epsilon\omega-s)}[E - e^{\epsilon\omega H}]^{-1} \qquad (0 \leqslant t < s \leqslant \epsilon\omega).$$

It follows that we have $|G(t, s)| \leqslant M/\epsilon$, since $[E - e^{\epsilon\omega H}]^{-1}$ admits such an evaluation. System (11) will have a periodic solution of period $\epsilon\omega$ if the integral equation

$$h(\tau) = \int_0^{\epsilon\omega} G(\tau, s)[B_1(h(s)) + O(\epsilon)]ds$$

has a solution. Let $\Omega(h)$ be the operator defined by

$$\Omega(h) = \int_0^{\epsilon\omega} G(\tau, s)[B_1(h(s)) + O(\epsilon)]ds;$$

for $\| h \| < l$ we have

$$|\Omega(h)(t)| \leqslant \epsilon\omega \frac{M}{\epsilon}(\beta\| h \| + N\epsilon);$$

if $\beta < 1/2\omega M$ and $\epsilon < l/2\omega MN$ we will have $\| \Omega(h) \| < l$; hence Ω maps the sphere $\| h \| < l$ into itself. Likewise we see that

$$|\Omega(h_1) - \Omega(h_2)| \leqslant \epsilon\omega \frac{M}{\epsilon}(\beta\| h_1 - h_2 \| + N_1\epsilon\| h_1 - h_2 \|)$$

and that if ϵ is sufficiently small, Ω is a contraction.

We deduce that for $|\epsilon|$ sufficiently small Ω admits a unique fixed point, to which corresponds a periodic solution of period $\epsilon\omega$, unique, of system (11); this solution for $\epsilon \to 0$ tends to the trivial solution $h = 0$.

Returning to the independent variable t we deduce the existence of a solution $h(t, \epsilon)$, periodic of period ω, unique, which for $\epsilon \to 0$ tends to the trivial solution $h = 0$.

Taking into account the changes of variables performed, we deduce the existence of a periodic solution of period ω, $b(t, \epsilon)$, which for $\epsilon \to 0$ tends to zero, and hence the existence of a periodic solution $z(t, \epsilon)$ of system (10) which for $\epsilon \to 0$ tends to ζ^0. Finally, there follows the existence of a periodic solution $x(t, \epsilon) = x_0(t, z(t, \epsilon))$, of period ω, of system (6), which for $\epsilon \to 0$ tends to $x_0(t, \zeta^0)$.

In addition, if the eigenvalues of matrix H have negative real parts, it is obvious, as previously, that the solution $h(\tau, \epsilon)$ is asymptotically stable; hence the solution $x(t, \epsilon)$ will be asymptotically stable. Let us observe in conclusion that the request that H does not have purely imaginary eigenvalues may be replaced by the weaker one that det $H \neq 0$. For, if H has no zero eigenvalues, for ϵ sufficiently small, the system $dx/dt = Hx$ cannot have periodic solutions of period $\epsilon\omega$. We have thus proved the following theorem:

Theorem 3.9. *If the general solution $x_0(t, h)$ of the generating system (7) is periodic of period ω, and ζ^0 is a solution of the equation*

$$Z_0(z, 0) = 0$$

such that

$$\det \frac{\partial Z_0(\zeta^0, 0)}{\partial z} \neq 0,$$

where

$$Z_0(z, 0) = \frac{1}{\omega} \int_0^\omega \left(\frac{\partial x_0(t, z)}{\partial z} \right)^{-1} X_1[x_0(t, z), t, 0] dt,$$

then for ϵ sufficiently small there exists a unique periodic solution of period ω of system (6) with the property that $\lim_{\epsilon \to 0} x(t, \epsilon) = x_0(t, \zeta^0)$.

If the eigenvalues of the matrix $\partial Z_0(\zeta^0, 0)/\partial z$ have negative real parts, this solution is asymptotically stable.

Remark. The theorem's affirmation, with the exception of the conclusion on stability, follows from Theorem 3.8, since if the general solution of system (7) is periodic, of period ω, then system (8) has n linearly independent periodic solutions of period ω, and the matrix W coincides with $[\partial x_0/\partial z]^{-1}$. The interest of the method of averaging lies in the fact that it can also be applied to much more general cases, in particular to the problem of almost-periodic solutions. To formulate a result relative to almost-periodic solutions we need a lemma due to N. N. Bogoliubov.

Lemma. *Let $f(t, x)$ be a function defined for real t and $x \in E$, where E is a compact set in a metric space. Suppose that in any point of E we have*

$$\lim_{T \to \infty} \frac{1}{T} \int_t^{t+T} f(s, x) ds = 0$$

uniformly with respect to, t, and in addition there exists M and λ such that

$$|f(t, x)| < M, \qquad |f(t, x') - f(t, x'')| \leqslant \lambda \rho(x', x'');$$

from here follows that the limit is uniform not only with respect to t but also with respect to (t, x). Let

$$f_\eta(t, x) = \int_{-\infty}^t e^{-\eta(t-\tau)} f(\tau, x) d\tau$$

Then

$$|f_\eta(t, x)| \leqslant \frac{\zeta(\eta)}{\eta} \qquad \textit{for} \quad -\infty < t < \infty,\ x \in E,$$

where $\lim_{\eta\to 0} \zeta(\eta) = 0$.

The conditions of the lemma are verified in particular if $f(t, x)$ is almost periodic with respect to t, uniform with respect to x, and has the mean value zero.

Proof. We have

$$f_\eta(t, x) = \int_0^\infty e^{-\eta\tau} f(t - \sigma, x) d\sigma$$
$$= \sum_{n=0}^\infty e^{-n\eta T} \int_{nT}^{(n+1)T} f(t - \sigma, x) e^{-\eta(\sigma - nT)}\, d\sigma$$

Further

$$|f_\eta(t, x)| = \left| \sum_{n=0}^\infty e^{-n\eta T} \int_{nT}^{(n+1)T} f(t - \sigma, x) e^{-\eta(\sigma - nT)} + f(t - \sigma, x) - f(t - \sigma, x)] d\sigma \right|$$

$$= \left| \sum_{n=0}^\infty e^{-n\eta T} \int_{nT}^{(n+1)T} f(t - \sigma, x) d\sigma \right.$$

$$\left. - \sum_{n=0}^\infty e^{-n\eta T} \int_{nT}^{(n+1)T} f(t - \sigma, x)[1 - e^{-\eta(\sigma - nT)}] d\sigma \right|$$

$$\leqslant \sum_{n=0}^\infty e^{-n\eta T} \left| \int_{nT}^{(n+1)T} f(t - \sigma, x) d\sigma \right|$$

$$+ M \sum_{n=0}^\infty e^{-n\eta T} \int_{nT}^{(n+1)T} (1 - e^{-\eta(\sigma - nT)}) d\sigma$$

$$= \sum_{n=0}^\infty e^{-n\eta T} \left| \int_{nT}^{(n+1)T} f(t - \sigma, x) d\sigma \right| + M \sum_{n=0}^\infty e^{-n\eta T} \int_0^T (1 - e^{-\eta s}) ds$$

$$= \sum_{n=0}^\infty e^{-n\eta T} \left| \int_{nT}^{(n+1)T} f(t - \sigma, x) ds \right| + M \frac{1}{1 - e^{-\eta T}} \left(T + \frac{1}{\eta} (e^{-\eta T} - 1) \right)$$

$$= \sum_{n=0}^\infty e^{-n\eta T} \left| \int_{nT}^{(n+1)T} f(t - \sigma, x) d\sigma \right| + \frac{MT}{1 - e^{-\eta T}} - \frac{M}{\eta}$$

$$= \sum_{n=0}^\infty e^{-n\eta T} \left| \int_{nT}^{(n+1)T} f(t - \sigma, x) d\sigma \right| + \frac{\zeta_1(\eta)}{\eta},$$

where we have set

$$\frac{\zeta_1(\eta)}{\eta} = M\left(\frac{T}{1 - e^{-\eta T}} - \frac{1}{\eta}\right).$$

We have

$$e^{-\eta T} = 1 - \eta T + o(\eta);$$

hence

$$1 - e^{-\eta T} = \eta T + o(\eta)$$

and

$$\frac{\zeta_1(\eta)}{\eta} = M\left(\frac{T}{\eta T + o(\eta)} - \frac{1}{\eta}\right) = M\frac{T\eta - \eta T + o(\eta)}{\eta(T\eta + o(\eta))}.$$

We obtain

$$\zeta_1(\eta) = M\frac{o(\eta)}{\eta T + o(\eta)};$$

hence

$$\lim_{\eta\to 0} \zeta_1(\eta) = 0.$$

According to the hypotheses,

$$\left|\frac{1}{T}\int_t^{t+T} f(s, x)ds\right| \leqslant \epsilon(T), \qquad \lim_{T\to\infty} \epsilon(T) = 0.$$

It follows that

$$|f_\eta(t, x)| \leqslant T\epsilon(T)\frac{1}{1 - e^{-\eta T}} + \frac{\zeta_1(\eta)}{\eta}.$$

We choose T as the function of η defined by the equation $1 - e^{-\eta T} = \epsilon(T)$.

When $\eta \to 0$, we have $\eta T(\eta) \to 0$; indeed, if T is bounded, the relation is evident, and if $T \to \infty$ we obtain $\epsilon(T) \to 0$; hence $\eta T \to 0$. Set $\eta T(\eta) = \zeta_2(\eta)$ and deduce

$$|f_\eta(t, x)| \leqslant \frac{\zeta_2(\eta)}{\eta} + \frac{\zeta_1(\eta)}{\eta},$$

where $\zeta_2(\eta) \to 0$ and $\zeta_1(\eta) \to 0$. The lemma is thus proved.

Let us now consider system (6), supposing that X_0 and X_1 are almost periodic in t, uniformly with respect to the other arguments. We likewise suppose that the general solution $x_0(t, h)$ of system (7) is almost periodic in t, uniformly with respect to h.

We perform again the change of variables $x = x_0(t, z)$ and obtain system (10), where this time $Z(t, z, \epsilon)$ is almost periodic in t, uniformly with respect to the other arguments. Let

$$Z_0(z, \epsilon) = \lim_{T\to\infty} \frac{1}{T} \int_0^T Z(t, z, \epsilon)dt$$

and let ζ^0 be a solution of the equation $Z_0(z, 0) = 0$. Perform the change of variables $z = \zeta^0 + b$. We obtain the system

$$\frac{db}{dt} = \epsilon B(t, b, \epsilon),$$

where $B(t, b, \epsilon)$ has the same regularity properties as Z and is almost periodic in t, uniformly with respect to the other arguments. Let

$$B_0(b, \epsilon) = \lim_{T\to\infty} \frac{1}{T} \int_0^T B(t, b, \epsilon)dt;$$

we have $B_0(0, 0) = 0$. Setting

$$B^*(t, b, \epsilon) = B(t, b, \epsilon) - B_0(b, \epsilon)$$

we obtain

$$\lim_{T\to\infty} \frac{1}{T} \int_0^T B^*(t, b, \epsilon)dt = 0.$$

By virtue of the lemma, we deduce that $| B_\eta^* | \leqslant \zeta(\eta)/\eta$.

We perform the change of variables $b = h + \epsilon B_\eta^*$ and obtain, choosing $\eta = \epsilon$, the system

$$\frac{dh}{dt} = \epsilon Hh + \epsilon B_1(h) + \epsilon \Gamma(t, h, \epsilon), \tag{12}$$

where Γ is almost periodic in t, uniformly with respect to the other arguments, and $| \Gamma | \leqslant \gamma(\epsilon)$, $| \partial\Gamma/\partial h | < \gamma(\epsilon)$ with $\lim_{\epsilon\to 0} \gamma(\epsilon) = 0$.

Suppose that the eigenvalues of matrix H have negative real parts; we will prove that for $0 < \epsilon < \epsilon_0$ the system (12) has a unique almost-periodic solution, which for $\epsilon \to 0$ tends to zero. Consider the system

$$\frac{dy}{dt} = Hy \tag{$*$}$$

and form the function

$$V(y) = \int_0^\infty |y(t, y)|^2 \, dt + \frac{1}{\epsilon} \sup_{\sigma \geqslant 0} | y(\sigma, y)|^2,$$

where $y(t, y)$ is the solution of system (*) with $y(0, y) = y$. We have

$$\frac{1}{\epsilon} | y |^2 \leqslant V(y) \leqslant \frac{K_1}{\epsilon} | y |^2,$$

since

$$| y(t, y)| \leqslant Ke^{-\epsilon\alpha t},$$

$$| V(y_1) - V(y_2)| \leqslant \frac{L_0}{\epsilon} (| y_1 | + | y_2 |)| y_1 - y_2 |,$$

$$\limsup_{h\to 0+} \frac{V[y(t + h, y_0)] - V[y(t, y_0)]}{h} \leqslant -| y(t, y_0)|^2.$$

Using this function, we deduce as in the proof of Theorem 3.4 that the system

$$\frac{dh}{dt} = \epsilon Hh + f(t)$$

admits for every almost-periodic f a unique almost-periodic solution $h_0(t)$, for which we have the evaluation

$$| h_0(t)| \leqslant \frac{L}{\epsilon} \sup | f |.$$

Let $h_0(t)$ be the almost-periodic solution of the system

$$\frac{dh}{dt} = \epsilon Hh + \epsilon \Gamma(t, 0, \epsilon).$$

We have

$$| h_0(t)| \leqslant \frac{L}{\epsilon} \epsilon\gamma(\epsilon) = L\gamma(\epsilon).$$

Let $h_k(t)$ be the almost-periodic solution of the system

$$\frac{dh}{dt} = \epsilon Hh + \epsilon B_1(h_{k-1}(t)) + \epsilon\Gamma(t, h_{k-1}(t), \epsilon).$$

We suppose, inductively, that $| h_{k-1}(t)| < 2L\gamma(\epsilon)$. Then

$$| B_1(h_{k-1}(t))| < 4\mu L^2\gamma^2(\epsilon);$$

hence

$$| h_k(t)| < \frac{L}{\epsilon}\epsilon\{4\mu L^2\gamma^2(\epsilon) + \gamma(\epsilon)\} = L\gamma(\epsilon)[4\mu L^2\gamma(\epsilon) + 1].$$

For ϵ sufficiently small we obtain $\gamma(\epsilon) < 1/4\mu L^2$ and hence

$$| h_k(t)| < 2L\gamma(\epsilon);$$

on the basis of induction it follows that for all k we have the stated estimate. Now let.

$$l_k(t) = h_k(t) - h_{k-1}(t).$$

We have

$$\begin{aligned}\frac{dl_{k+1}(t)}{dt} &= \frac{dh_{k+1}}{dt} - \frac{dh_k}{dt} = \epsilon H h_{k+1}(t) + \epsilon B_1(h_k(t))\\ &\quad + \epsilon\Gamma(t, h_k(t), \epsilon) - \epsilon H h_k(t) - \epsilon B_1(h_{k-1}(t)) - \epsilon\Gamma(t, h_{k-1}(t), \epsilon)\\ &= \epsilon H l_{k+1}(t) + \epsilon[B_1(h_k(t)) - B_1(h_{k-1}(t))]\\ &\quad + \epsilon[\Gamma(t, h_k(t), \epsilon) - \Gamma(t, h_{k-1}(t), \epsilon)].\end{aligned}$$

We have

$$| B_1(u) - B_1(v)| \leqslant \mu(| u | + | v |)| u - v |;$$

hence

$$| B_1(h_k(t)) - B_1(h_{k-1}(t))| \leqslant 4\mu L\gamma(\epsilon) \sup | l_k |.$$

It follows that

$$| l_{k+1}(t)| \leqslant \frac{L}{\epsilon}\epsilon\{4\mu L\gamma(\epsilon) \sup | l_k | + \gamma(\epsilon) \sup | l_k |\} \leqslant L_1\gamma(\epsilon) \sup | l_k |,$$

from which, for $\gamma(\epsilon) < 1/L_1$, follows the uniform convergence of the sequence of successive approximations to an almost-periodic solution of system (12). Taking into account the estimates of the successive approximations, we deduce that this solution tends to zero as $\epsilon \to 0$. But then, taking into account the changes of variables performed, we deduce the existence of a unique almost-periodic solution, asymptotically stable, $x(t, \epsilon)$, with the property that $\lim_{\epsilon\to 0} x(t, \epsilon) = x_0(t, \zeta^0)$. We have thus obtained the following theorem:

Theorem 3.10. *If in system (6) the functions X_0 and X_1 are almost periodic in t, uniformly with respect to the other arguments, and the general solution $x_0(t, h)$ of system (7) is almost periodic in t, uniformly with respect to h, and ζ^0 is a solution of the equation $Z_0(z, 0) = 0$ such that the eigen-*

values of matrix $\partial Z_0(\zeta^0, 0)/\partial z$ have negative real parts, then for ϵ sufficiently small there exists a unique almost-periodic solution of system (6) with the property

$$\lim_{\epsilon\to 0} x(t, \epsilon) = x_0(t, \zeta^0).$$

Here

$$Z_0(z, 0) = \lim_{T\to\infty} \frac{1}{T} \int_0^T \left(\frac{\partial x_0(t, z)}{\partial z}\right)^{-1} X_1[x_0(t, z), t, 0]dt.$$

3.6. Topological Methods

By using some topological methods, strong results can be obtained in the theory of systems with a small parameter, in which the conditions imposed on the generating system are very general and have an intrinsic character.

Theorem 3.11. *If the generating system (7) admits a periodic solution $x_0(t)$, asymptotically stable, then for $|\epsilon|$ sufficiently small system (6) admits a periodic solution $x(t, \epsilon)$ with the property that*

$$\lim_{\epsilon\to 0} x(t, \epsilon) = x_0(t).$$

Proof. We depend upon the following theorem of F. Browder. Let X be a Banach space, S and S_1 open and convex sets in X, S_0 closed and convex, $S_0 \subset S_1 \subset S$, f a compact mapping of S in X; suppose that there exists a natural number m such that f^m is defined on S_1, $f^j(S_0) \subset S_1$ for $0 \leqslant j \leqslant m$, $f^m(S_1) \subset S_0$; f then has a fixed point in S_0. We shall apply this theorem in the particular case where X is the n-dimensional Euclidean space; in this case it will be sufficient that f be continuous.

Let $x(t, p, \epsilon)$ be the general solution of system (6) with $x(0, p, \epsilon) = p$. We consider the transformation $f(p, \epsilon) = x(\omega, p, \epsilon)$ and prove that it fulfills all the conditions of the Browder theorem, if ϵ is sufficiently small; it will follow that for ϵ sufficiently small there exists a fixed point, and from $x(\omega, p, \epsilon) = p$ it follows that the corresponding solution is periodic. We will continue the proof taking $x_0(t) \equiv 0$, since we obtain this case by a simple change of variables. Since system (7) is periodic, the asymptotic stability is uniform; hence there exists a $\delta_0 > 0$ and two functions $\delta(\eta)$ and $T(\eta)$ such that $|p| < \delta(\eta)$ implies $|x_0(t, p)| < \eta$ for $t \geqslant 0$ and $|p| < \delta_0$, $t > T(\eta)$ implies $|x_0(t, p)| < \eta$.

Let $\delta_1 = \delta(\alpha/2)$, $0 < \eta < \min\{\delta_0, \delta(\frac{1}{2}\delta_1)\}$, $T = T[\frac{1}{2}\delta(\frac{1}{2}\eta)]$, m the least natural number such that $m\omega > T$. Let S be the sphere $|p| < \delta_1$.

Then $| x_0(t, p)| < \alpha/2$ for $p \in S, t \geqslant 0$. If $| \epsilon |$ is sufficiently small, we will have $| x(t, p, \epsilon)| < \alpha$ for $p \in S, 0 \leqslant t \leqslant m\omega$, on the basis of the continuity theorem of the solution with respect to the parameter. From this follows that for $p \in S$ we have $| f(p, \epsilon)| < \alpha$. From this also follows that the solutions $x(t, p, \epsilon)$ are defined if $p \in S$; hence the operator f and its iterates f^j $(j = 1, ..., m)$ are defined on S. Let S_1 be the sphere $| p | < \eta$ and S_0 the sphere $| \varphi | < \frac{3}{4}\delta(\frac{1}{2}\eta)$. For $| p | < \eta, t \geqslant 0$, we have $| x_0(t, p)| < \frac{1}{2}\delta_1$, since $\eta < \delta(\frac{1}{2}\delta_1)$; for $| \epsilon |$ sufficiently small we obtain $| x(t, p, \epsilon)| < \delta_1$, for $0 \leqslant t \leqslant m\omega$; hence $f^j(S_1) \subset S\,(j = 1, ..., m)$. For $| p | \leqslant \frac{3}{4}\delta(\frac{1}{2}\eta)$, $t \geqslant 0$, we have $| x_0(t, p)| < \frac{1}{2}\eta$; hence for $| \epsilon |$ sufficiently small $| x(t, p, \epsilon)| < \eta$ if $| p | \leqslant \frac{3}{4}\delta(\frac{1}{2}\eta)$, $0 \leqslant t \leqslant m\omega$, which shows that $f^j(S_0) \subset S_1$ for $0 \leqslant j \leqslant m$.

From $\eta < \delta_0$ it follows that for $p \in S_1$, $t > T$, we have $| x_0(t, p) | < \frac{1}{2}\delta(\frac{1}{2}\eta)$; hence for $| \epsilon |$ sufficiently small we obtain $| x(m\omega, p, \epsilon)| \leqslant \frac{3}{4}\delta(\frac{1}{2}\eta)$ if $p \in S_1$; i.e., $f^m(S_1) \subset S_0$.

It follows that all the conditions of the Browder theorem are verified; hence the existence of a fixed point in S_0 is proved. It is obvious that S_0 can be chosen arbitrarily small, but then ϵ should be taken small. This means that the solution whose existence we have proved tends to zero when $\epsilon \to 0$. The theorem is thus completely proved.

Theorem 3.12. *Let X_0 be analytic*:

$$X_0(x, t) = X_0^{(m)}(x, t) + X_0^{(m+1)}(x, t) + \cdots, \qquad m \geqslant 2,$$

where $X_0^{(k)}$ are forms of degree k in the coordinates of x; suppose that the field $\int_0^\omega X_0^{(m)}(x, t)dt$ has the point $x = 0$ as an isolated singular point. If the index of point $x = 0$ in the vector field $\int_0^\omega X_0^{(m)}(x, t)dt$ is different from zero, then for $| \epsilon |$ sufficiently small system (6) *admits a periodic solution of period ω which for $\epsilon \to 0$ tends to zero.*

Proof. Consider the system

$$\frac{dx}{dt} = X_0^{(m)}(x, t) + X_0^{(m+1)}(x, t) + \cdots.$$

Its general solution is

$$x = A_1(t)x_0 + A_2(t, x_0) + \cdots + A_k(t, x_0) + \cdots,$$

where the $A_k(t, x_0)$ are vectors whose coordinates are forms of degree k with respect to the coordinates of x_0, with coefficients functions of t.

By substituting in the system we obtain

$$\frac{dA_1}{dt}x_0 + \frac{\partial A_2}{\partial t} + \cdots + \frac{\partial A_k}{\partial t} + \cdots$$
$$= X_0^{(m)}(A_1x_0 + A_2 + \cdots + A_k + \cdots, t) + \cdots.$$

We obtain the relations

$$\frac{dA_1}{dt} = 0, \qquad \frac{\partial A_2}{\partial t} = 0, \cdots, \frac{\partial A_m}{\partial t} = X_0^{(m)}(A_1x_0, t), \cdots,$$

$$A_1(0) = E, \qquad A_2(0, x_0) \equiv \cdots \equiv A_m(0, x_0) \equiv 0.$$

This yields

$$A_1 = E, \qquad A_2 \equiv \cdots A_{m-1} \equiv 0, \qquad A_m(t, x_0) = \int_0^t X_0^{(m)}(x_0, t)dt.$$

We deduce that the general solution of system (7) is of the form

$$x(t) = x_0 + \int_0^t X_0^{(m)}(x_0, t)dt + \cdots,$$

where the unwritten terms are of higher degree in the coordinates of x_0.

Consider the vector field

$$u(x_0) \equiv x(\omega) - x_0 = \int_0^\omega X_0^{(m)}(x_0, t)dt + \cdots.$$

This field has $x_0 = 0$ as an isolated singular point since this is supposed for the field $\int_0^\omega X_0^{(m)}(x_0, t)dt$. Since the index of point $x_1 = 0$ in the field $\int_0^\omega X_0^{(m)}(x_0, t)dt$ is different from zero, it follows that the index of point $x_0 = 0$ in the field $u(x_0)$ is different from zero. Let us also consider the field $u_\epsilon(x_0) = x(\omega, x_0, \epsilon) - x_0$; we have $\lim_{\epsilon\to 0} x(\omega, x_0, \epsilon) = x(\omega, x_0, 0)$; hence for $|\epsilon|$ sufficiently small the rotation of the field $u_\epsilon(x_0)$ on a sphere containing the origin will be equal to that of the field $u(x_0)$. Since the index of the origin in the field $u(x_0)$ is different from zero, it follows that if the sphere is small enough, the rotation of the field $u_\epsilon(x_0)$ on this sphere will be different from zero. However, then the field $u_\epsilon(x_0)$ will have in the interior of the sphere a singular point, hence a point for which $u_\epsilon(x_0) = 0$, namely, $x(\omega, x_0, \epsilon) = x_0$; this point corresponds to a periodic solution. The theorem is thus proved.

Remark. If the point $x = 0$ is asymptotically stable for system (7), its index in the field $x(k\omega) - x_0$ is, for k sufficiently large, equal to ± 1;

hence its index in the field $\int_0^{k\omega} X_0^{(m)} dt$ is different from zero. However,

$$\int_0^{k\omega} X_0^{(m)}\, dt = k \int_0^{\omega} X_0^{(m)}\, dt$$

and the condition in the statement is verified. Thus we find a particular case of Theorem 3.11.

Theorem 3.13. *If system* (7) *does not explicitly depend on* t, *if* $X_0(x)$ *admits in* $x = 0$ *an isolated singular point which is not a limit point of periodic solutions with period* $\omega' \leqslant \omega$, *and if the index of the point* $x = 0$ *in the field* $X_0(x)$ *is different from zero, then for* $|\epsilon|$ *sufficiently small system* (7) *admits a periodic solution of period* ω, *which for* $\epsilon \to 0$ *tends to zero.*

Proof. As in the case of the preceding theorem, we will show that the rotation of the field $u_\epsilon(x_0)$ is different from zero on a sufficiently small sphere whose center is in the origin, showing that the index of the origin in the field $u(x_0)$ is different from zero. Therefore we will prove that the index of the origin in the field $u(x)$ coincides with the index in the field $X_0(x)$. We define the field $W(x_0, \tau) \equiv (1/\omega\tau)[x(\omega\tau, x_0, 0) - x_0]$ for $\tau \neq 0$, $W(x_0, 0) = X_0(x_0)$. Since $(d/dt)x(t, x_0, 0)$ for $t = 0$ is $X_0(x_0)$, it follows that $\lim_{\tau\to 0} W(x_0, \tau) = W(x_0, 0)$; hence the field $W(x_0, \tau)$ depends continuously on τ. The field $W(x_0, \tau) \neq 0$, $0 \leqslant \tau \leqslant 1$, on a small enough sphere whose center is in the origin, since we have supposed that the origin is not a limit point of periodic solutions with period $\omega' \leqslant \omega$, and hence $x(\omega\tau, x_0, 0) \neq x_0$ for $0 \leqslant \tau \leqslant 1$. The field $W(x_0, \tau)$ represents a continuous deformation of the field $X_0(x_0)$ in the field $(1/\omega)u(x_0)$. Since $W(x_0, \tau) \neq 0$, it follows that the index of the origin is the same in both fields. The theorem is thus proved.

3.7. Autonomous Systems

The problem of periodic solutions presents certain particularities in case the functions X_0 and X_1 do not explicitly depend on t, since in this case the periodic solutions of systems (6) and (7) have, in general, different periods. In the following section we will present the complete theory of autonomous systems containing a small parameter, by following the geometric method systematically used by M. Urabe.

Consider the system

$$\frac{dx}{dt} = X(x). \tag{13}$$

Suppose that this system admits a periodic solution $x = u(t)$ of period ω. It follows on the basis of the uniqueness theorem that $X[u(t)] \neq 0$ for all t. Denote $\bar{X} = X[u(t)]/|X[u(t)]|$. If $n \geqslant 3$ and if X verifies a local Lipschitz condition, the curve $x = \bar{X}(t)$ does not cover the whole unit sphere. Hence there exists a unitary vector e_1, such that $\bar{X}(t)$ does not coincide with $-e_1$ for any value of t. Starting from the constant vector e_1, we construct an orthogonal and normed system of vectors $e_1, e_2, \ldots, e_n$. Denote $\cos\theta_i = \bar{X}(t)e_i$ and form the vectors

$$\xi_\nu = e_\nu - \frac{\cos\theta_\nu}{1+\cos\theta_1}(e_1 + \bar{X}), \nu = 2, 3, \ldots, n.$$

Since $\bar{X}(t)$ does not coincide anywhere with $-e_1$, it follows that $1 + \cos\theta_1 \neq 0$. The vectors ξ_ν are periodic functions of t, of period ω, and have the same regularity properties as $\bar{X}(t)$. The vectors $(\bar{X}(t), \xi_2, \xi_3, \ldots, \xi_n)$ form an orthogonal, normed system. Let us verify this:

$$(\xi_\nu, \bar{X}) = \left(e_\nu - \frac{\cos\theta_\nu}{1+\cos\theta_1}(e_1+\bar{X}), \bar{X}\right)$$

$$= (e_\nu, \bar{X}) - \frac{\cos\theta_\nu}{1+\cos\theta_1}[(e_1, \bar{X}) + (\bar{X}, \bar{X})]$$

$$= \cos\theta_\nu - \frac{\cos\theta_\nu}{1+\cos\theta_1}(\cos\theta_1 + 1) = 0,$$

$$(\xi_\nu, \xi_\mu) = \left(e_\nu - \frac{\cos\theta_\nu}{1+\cos\theta_1}e_1 - \frac{\cos\theta_\nu}{1+\cos\theta_1}\bar{X}, \xi_\mu\right)$$

$$= \left(e_\nu - \frac{\cos\theta_\nu}{1+\cos\theta_1}e_1, \xi_\mu\right)$$

$$= \left(e_\nu - \frac{\cos\theta_\nu}{1+\cos\theta_1}e_1, e_\mu - \frac{\cos\theta_\mu}{1+\cos\theta_1}e_1 - \frac{\cos\theta_\mu}{1+\cos\theta_1}\bar{X}\right)$$

$$= \delta_{\mu\nu} - \frac{\cos\theta_\mu\cos\theta_\nu}{1+\cos\theta_1} + \frac{\cos\theta_\nu\cos\theta_\mu}{(1+\cos\theta_1)^2} + \frac{\cos\theta_\nu\cos\theta_\mu\cos\theta_1}{(1+\cos\theta_1)^2}$$

$$= \delta_{\mu\nu}.$$

In the case $n = 2$, let $\bar{X} = \begin{pmatrix}\bar{X}^1\\ \bar{X}^2\end{pmatrix}$; we take $\xi_2 = \begin{pmatrix}-\bar{X}^2\\ \bar{X}^1\end{pmatrix}$ and system $(\bar{X}, \xi_2)$ is orthogonal and normed.

It follows that *to the periodic solution $u(t)$ has been attached an orthogonal and normed system of vectors, having as one of the vectors $\bar{X}$ (the unitary vector of the tangent to curve $x = u(t)$), formed by periodic vectors of period ω, with the same regularity properties as $\bar{X}(t)$.*

With the help of this orthogonal, normed system we perform the change of variables given by the relation

$$x = u(\theta) + S(\theta)y,$$

$S(\theta)$ being the matrix whose columns are vectors $\xi_\nu(\theta)$; θ is a scalar and y a vector of dimension $n-1$. We verify that the relations which define the change of variables are invertible in the neighborhood of the curve $x = u(t)$. We have

$$\left.\frac{\partial(x^1, x^2, \ldots, x^n)}{\partial(y^1, \ldots, y^{n-1}, \theta)}\right|_{y=0} = \det\,(S(\theta), X[u(\theta)]),$$

where we have denoted by (S, X) the matrix whose $n-1$ columns are formed by the columns of matrix S, and whose last column is X. Further,

$$\begin{aligned}\det\,(S(\theta), X[u(\theta)]) &= \det\,(S(\theta), |\,X[u(\theta)]|\bar{X}[u(\theta)])\\ &= |\,X[u(\theta)]|\det\,(S(\theta), \bar{X}[u(\theta)]) = |\,X[u(\theta)]| \neq 0.\end{aligned}$$

We have used the fact that the system $(\xi_2, \ldots, \xi_n, \bar{X})$ is orthogonal and normed; hence the determinant of matrix $(S(\theta), \bar{X}(\theta))$ is 1. We obtain

$$\frac{\partial(x^1, \ldots, x^n)}{\partial(y^1, \ldots, y^{n-1}, \theta)} \neq 0$$

and the transformation is locally invertible. By this change of variables the curve $x = u(t)$ becomes $y = 0$, $\theta = t$. Let us examine the form taken in the new variables by system (13). We have

$$\frac{dx}{dt} = \frac{du(\theta)}{d\theta}\frac{d\theta}{dt} + \frac{dS(\theta)}{d\theta}\frac{d\theta}{dt}y + S(\theta)\frac{dy}{dt} = X[u(\theta) + S(\theta)y];$$

hence

$$X[u(\theta)]\frac{d\theta}{dt} + \frac{d\theta}{dt}\frac{dS(\theta)}{d\theta}y + S(\theta)\frac{dy}{dt} = X[u(\theta) + S(\theta)y]. \tag{14}$$

Multiplying this relation by $X^*[u(\theta)]$ and taking into account the fact that $X^*S = 0$, we obtain

$$\frac{d\theta}{dt}\left(|\,X[u(\theta)]|^2 + X^*[u(\theta)]\frac{dS(\theta)}{d\theta}y\right) = X^*[u(\theta)]X[u(\theta) + S(\theta)y].$$

For $|\,y\,|$ sufficiently small, the coefficient of $d\theta/dt$ is not zero; hence in the neighborhood of the curve $x = u(t)$ we obtain

$$\frac{d\theta}{dt} = \frac{X^*[u(\theta)]X[u(\theta) + S(\theta)y]}{|\,X[u(\theta)]|^2 + X^*[u(\theta)][dS(\theta)/d\theta]y}.$$

Multiplying relation (14) by $\xi^*(\theta)$ and taking into account the orthogonality properties, we obtain

$$\frac{d\theta}{dt}\xi^*_\mu \frac{dS}{d\theta} y + \frac{dy^\mu}{dt} = \xi^*_\mu X[u(\theta) + S(\theta)y];$$

hence

$$\frac{dy^\mu}{dt} = \xi^*_\mu(\theta) X[u(\theta) + S(\theta)y] - \frac{X^*[u(\theta)]X[u(\theta) + S(\theta)y]}{|X[u(\theta)]|^2 + X^*[u(\theta)][dS(\theta)/d\theta]y} \xi^*_\mu(\theta) \frac{dS(\theta)}{d\theta} y.$$

Finally, system (13) is replaced by a system of the form

$$\frac{dy}{dt} = Y(\theta, y), \qquad \frac{d\theta}{dt} = \Theta(\theta, y),$$

where we immediately see that Y and Θ are periodic in θ with period ω, that they verify the relations $\Theta(\theta, 0) \equiv 1$, $Y(\theta, 0) \equiv 0$, and that they have the same regularity property as $X(x)$.

Now form the system

$$\frac{dy}{d\theta} = \frac{1}{\Theta(\theta, y)} Y(\theta, y). \tag{15}$$

The function $Y(\theta, y)/\Theta(\theta, y)$ is periodic in θ of period ω and has for $|y|$ sufficiently small the same regularity properties as X, since from $\Theta(\theta, 0) \equiv 1$ it follows that for $|y|$ sufficiently small $\Theta(\theta, y) \neq 0$. Let us emphasize the first linear approximation in this system. We have

$$X[u(\theta) + S(\theta)y] = X[u(\theta)] + \frac{\partial X[u(\theta)]}{\partial x} S(\theta)y + O(|y|^2);$$

hence

$$x^*[u(\theta)]X[u(0) + S(\theta)y] = |X[u(\theta)]|^2 + X^*[u(\theta)]A(\theta)S(\theta)y + O(|y|^2),$$

where we have set $A(\theta) = \partial X[u(\theta)]/\partial x$. We obtain

$$\frac{1}{X^*[u(\theta)]X[u(\theta) + S(\theta)y]} = \frac{1}{|X[u(\theta)]|^2} \frac{1}{1 + \dfrac{X^*[u(\theta)]A(\theta)S(\theta)y}{|X[u(\theta)]|^2} + o(|y|)}$$

$$= \frac{1}{|X[u(\theta)]|^2}\left\{1 - \frac{X^*[u(\theta)]A(\theta)S(\theta)y}{|X[u(\theta)]|^2} + o(|y|)\right\}.$$

Further,

$$\frac{1}{\Theta(\theta, y)} = \left\{| X[u(\theta)]|^2 + X^*[u(\theta)] \frac{dS(\theta)}{d\theta} y\right\} \frac{1}{| X[u(\theta)]|^2}$$

$$\times \left\{1 - \frac{X^*[u(\theta)]A(\theta)S(\theta)y}{| X[u(\theta)]|^2} + o(| y |)\right\}$$

$$= 1 + O(| y |),$$

$$Y^\mu(\theta, y) = \xi_\mu^*(\theta)X[u(\theta) + S(\theta)y] - \Theta(\theta, y)\xi_\mu^*(\theta) \frac{dS(\theta)}{dt} y;$$

hence

$$\frac{1}{\Theta(\theta, y)} Y^\mu(\theta, y)$$

$$= \frac{1}{\Theta(\theta, y)} \xi_\mu^*(\theta)\{X[u(\theta)] + A(\theta)S(\theta)y + o(| y |)\} - \xi_\mu^*(\theta) \frac{dS(\theta)}{d\theta} y$$

$$= \{1 + O(| y |)\}\{\xi_\mu^*(\theta)A(\theta)S(\theta)y + o(| y |)\} - \xi_\mu^*(\theta) \frac{dS(\theta)}{d\theta} y.$$

It follows that

$$\frac{dy^\mu}{d\theta} = \xi_\mu^*(\theta) \left(A(\theta)S(\theta) - \frac{dS(\theta)}{d\theta}\right) y + o(| y |).$$

System (15) is thus written

$$\frac{dy}{d\theta} = B(\theta)y + o(| y |),$$

where the elements $b_{\mu\nu}$ of the matrix $B(\theta)$ are given by

$$b_{\mu\nu}(\theta) = \xi_\mu^*(\theta) \left(A(\theta)\xi_\nu(\theta) - \frac{d\xi_\nu}{d\theta}\right)$$

and are periodic functions of θ with period ω.

We will call the system

$$\frac{dy}{d\theta} = B(\theta)y$$

the system in normal variations. Let us consider the system

$$\frac{dv}{d\theta} = A(\theta)v,$$

i.e., the variational system corresponding to the solution $u(\theta)$. We write the vector v in the normal orthogonal system $(\bar{X}, \xi_2, ..., \xi_n)$:

$$v(\theta) = p(\theta)X[u(\theta)] + \sum_{\nu=2}^{n} p^{\nu}(\theta)\xi_{\nu}(\theta).$$

We seek the equations which are verified by $p^{\mu}(\theta)$. We have

$$\frac{dv}{d\theta} = \frac{dp}{d\theta} X[u(\theta)] + pA(\theta)\frac{du}{d\theta} + \sum_{\nu=2}^{n} p^{\nu}\frac{d\xi_{\nu}}{d\theta} + \frac{dp^{\nu}}{d\theta}\xi_{\nu}$$

$$= ApX[u(\theta)] + \sum_{\nu=2}^{n} p^{\nu}(\theta)A(\theta)\xi_{\nu}(\theta).$$

Since

$$\frac{du}{d\theta} = X[u(\theta)],$$

we obtain

$$\frac{dp}{d\theta} X[u(\theta)] + \sum_{\nu=2}^{n} p^{\nu}\frac{d\xi_{\nu}}{d\theta} + \frac{dp^{\nu}}{d\theta}\xi_{\nu} = \sum_{\nu=2}^{n} p^{\nu}A(\theta)\xi_{\nu}.$$

Multiplying by ξ_{μ}^{*} we obtain

$$\frac{dp^{\mu}}{d\theta} = \xi_{\mu}^{*}\sum_{\nu=2}^{n}\left(A(\theta)\xi_{\nu}(\theta) - \frac{d\xi_{\nu}(\theta)}{d\theta}\right)p^{\nu} = \sum_{\nu=2}^{n} b_{\mu\nu}(\theta)p^{\nu}.$$

We have thus reached the conclusion that *the normal components p^{ν} of variations v verify the system in normal variations.*

Let us observe that from

$$\frac{du}{d\theta} = X[u(\theta)]$$

follows

$$\frac{d}{dt}\frac{du}{d\theta} = A(\theta)\frac{du}{d\theta};$$

hence

$$\frac{du}{d\theta} = X[u(\theta)]$$

is a solution of the variational system.

Let $\phi(\theta)$ be a fundamental matrix of solutions for the variational system whose first column is formed by the solution $X[u(\theta)]$. We have

$$\phi(\theta) = U(\theta)C,$$

where $U(\theta)$ is the matrix of solutions with $U(0) = E$. From this,

$$\phi(\theta + \omega) = U(\theta + \omega)C = U(\theta)U(\omega)C = U(\theta)CC^{-1}U(\omega)C = \phi(\theta)K,$$

where $K = C^{-1}U(\omega)C$; since K is similar to the monodromy matrix $U(\omega)$, its eigenvalues are precisely the multipliers of the variational system. Let $v_2, ..., v_n$ be the solutions different from $X[u(\theta)]$ which form the matrix ϕ. We write these solutions in the normal orthogonal system $(\bar{X}, \xi_2, ..., \xi_n)$;

$$v_\nu = p_\nu X[u(\theta)] + \sum_\mu p_\nu^\mu \xi_\mu .$$

The relation

$$\phi(\theta + \omega) = \phi(\theta)K$$

becomes

$$X[u(\theta + \omega)] = X[u(\theta)]k_1^1 + \sum_{\mu=2}^{n} v_\mu(\theta)k_1^\mu ,$$

$$v_\nu(\theta + \omega) = X[u(\theta)]k_\nu^1 + \sum_{\mu=2}^{n} v_\mu(\theta)k_\nu^\mu .$$

Taking $\theta = 0$ and passing to the basis $(\bar{X}, \xi_2, ..., \xi_n)$, we obtain

$$p_\nu(\omega)X[u(\omega)] + \sum_\mu p_\nu^\mu(\omega)\xi_\mu(\omega)$$

$$= X[u(0)]k_\nu^1 + \sum_{\mu=2}^{n} [p_\mu(0)X[u(0)] + \sum_k p_\mu^k(0)\xi_k(0)]k_\nu^\mu .$$

However,

$$u(\omega) = u(0), \qquad \xi_\mu(\omega) = \xi_\mu(0);$$

hence

$$X[u(0)] = X[u(0)]k_1^1 + \sum_{\mu=2}^{n} v_\mu(0)k_1^\mu ,$$

$$p_\nu(\omega)X[u(0)] + \sum_\mu p_\nu^\mu(\omega)\xi_\mu(0)$$

$$= X[u(0)]k_\nu^1 + \sum_{\mu=2}^{n} \left[p_\mu(0)X[u(0)] + \sum_k p_\mu^k(0)\xi_k(0)\right] k_\nu^\mu .$$

The vectors $X[u(0)]$, $\xi_2(0), ..., \xi_n(0)$ are linearly independent; $X[u(0)]$, $v_2(0), ..., v_n(0)$ are also linearly independent.

Thus

$$k_1^1 = 1, \qquad k_1^\mu = 0,$$

$$p_\nu(\omega) = k_\nu^1 + \sum_{\mu=2}^{n} k_\nu^\mu p_\mu(0), \qquad p_\nu^k(\omega) = \sum_\mu k_\nu^\mu p_\mu^k(0).$$

We have $\det(p_\nu^\mu(0)) \neq 0$; indeed, if the determinant were zero, there would exist constants c^ν not all zero such that $\Sigma_\nu c^\nu p_\nu^\mu = 0$; hence

$$\sum_\nu c^\nu v_\nu(0) = \sum_\nu c^\nu p_\nu(0) X[u(0)] + \sum_{\nu,\mu} c^\nu p_\nu^\mu(0) \xi_\mu(0)$$

$$= \sum_\nu c^\nu p_\nu(0) X[u(0)],$$

and $c^\nu = 0$, $\Sigma_\nu c^\nu p_\nu(0) = 0$, which is contradictory.

The functions $v_\nu(\theta)$ are solutions of the variational system; hence, as we have already seen it, their normal components $p_\nu^\mu(\theta)$ are solutions of the system in normal variations. Since $\det p_\nu^\mu(0) \neq 0$, it follows that $p_\nu^\mu(\theta)$, $\nu = 2, \ldots, n$, $\mu = 2, \ldots, n$ represents a fundamental matrix of solutions for the system in normal variations. Let $P(\theta)$ be this matrix and let us denote by K_2 the matrix $(k_\nu^\mu)_{\nu=2,\ldots,n/\mu=2,\ldots,n}$. The relation $p_\nu^\mu(\omega) = \Sigma_\lambda p_\lambda^\mu(0) k_\nu^\lambda$ is written $P(\omega) = P(0)K_2$ and shows that the eigenvalues of matrix K_2 are precisely the multipliers of the system in normal variations. Since $k_1^1 = 1$, $k_1^\mu = 0$, the matrix K will have the form

$$K = \begin{pmatrix} 1 & K_1 \\ 0 & K_2 \end{pmatrix}.$$

We have obtained the following result: *The multipliers of the system in normal variations are obtained from the multipliers of the variational system by eliminating the multiplier equal to* 1 (which corresponds to the periodic solution $X[u(\theta)]$).

We can now prove a stability theorem of the periodic solution $u(t)$. This theorem has been proved for the first time by Andronov and Witt.

Theorem 3.14. *If* $(n - 1)$ *multipliers of the variational system corresponding to the periodic solution* $x = u(t)$ *are situated in the interior of the unit circle, then the periodic solution* $x = u(t)$ *is orbitally stable; this means that if* $x(t)$ *is another solution of system* (13) *for which* $x(t_0)$ *is close enough to the curve* $x = u(t)$, *then there exists a real number* c, *such that*

$$\lim_{t\to\infty} [x(t) - u(t + c)] = 0.$$

Proof. If $(n - 1)$ multipliers of the variational system are situated in the interior of the unit circle, it follows that the multipliers of the system in normal variations are situated in the interior of the unit circle; hence the trivial solution of the system in normal variations is uniformly asymptotically stable. Therefore, on the basis of the theorem of stability of the first approximation, the trivial solution of system (15) is uniformly asymptotically stable. However, for $|y(0)|$ sufficiently small, we then have $\lim_{\theta\to\infty} y(\theta) = 0$. Thus from the relation

$$x[t(\theta)] = u(\theta) + S(\theta)y(\theta)$$

we deduce

$$\lim_{\theta\to\infty} (x[t(\theta)] - u(\theta)) = 0.$$

Let $0 < \theta' < \theta''$; we have

$$[t(\theta'') - \theta''] - [t(\theta') - \theta'] = \int_{\theta'}^{\theta''} \left(\frac{dt}{d\theta} - 1\right) d\theta = \int_{\theta'}^{\theta''} \left(\frac{1}{\Theta(\theta, y)} - 1\right) d\theta$$

$$= \int_{\theta'}^{\theta''} (1 + O(|y|) - 1)d\theta = \int_{\theta'}^{\theta''} O(|y|)d\theta.$$

However,

$$|y(\theta)| \leqslant ke^{-\alpha\theta};$$

hence

$$O(|y|) \leqslant Me^{-\alpha\theta}.$$

From this follows

$$|[t(\theta'') - \theta''] - [t(\theta') - \theta']| \leqslant M \int_{\theta'}^{\theta} e^{-\alpha\theta}\, d\theta < M \int_{\theta'}^{\infty} e^{-\alpha\theta}\, d\theta = \frac{M}{\alpha} e^{-\alpha\theta'}.$$

For θ' sufficiently large, $[t(\theta'') - \theta''] - [t(\theta') - \theta']$ can be taken arbitrarily small; hence $\lim_{\theta\to\infty} [t(\theta) - \theta]$ exists; let θ_0 be this limit.

On the other hand,

$$x[t(\theta)] - x(\theta + \theta_0) = \int_{\theta+\theta_0}^{t(\theta)} X[x(\alpha)]d\alpha;$$

hence

$$|x[t(\theta)] - x(\theta + \theta_0)| \leqslant |t(\theta) - (\theta + \theta_0)| \sup |X[x(\alpha)]|.$$

However, if $|y(0)| < \delta_0$, from the stability of the trivial solution of system (15), it follows that $|y(\theta)| < 1$ for $\theta \geqslant 0$; hence $|x[t(\theta)]|$ is bounded, therefore $|X[x(\alpha)]|$ is bounded. Since

$$\lim_{\theta\to\infty} [t(\theta) - (\theta + \theta_0)] = \lim_{\theta\to\infty} [t(\theta) - \theta - \theta_0] = 0,$$

it follows that

$$\lim\, (x[t(\theta)] - x(\theta + \theta_0)) = 0.$$

Since we also have

$$\lim_{\theta\to\infty} (x[t(\theta)] - u(\theta)) = 0,$$

it follows that

$$\lim_{\theta\to\infty} [x(\theta + \theta_0) - u(\theta)] = 0.$$

Setting $\theta + \theta_0 = t$, $c = -\theta_0$, the result obtained above is written

$$\lim_{t\to\infty} [x(t) - u(t + c)] = 0,$$

and the theorem is thus proved.

3.8. Autonomous Systems Containing a Small Parameter

Consider now the perturbed system

$$\frac{dx}{dt} = Z(x, \epsilon), \tag{16}$$

where Z is continuously differentiable and $Z(x, 0) = X(x)$. Suppose as above that system (13) admits a periodic solution $x = u(t)$ of period ω. Consider the system of vectors $\bar{X}(t), \xi_2(t), \ldots, \xi_n(t)$ and perform in system (16) the change of variables $x = u(\theta) + S(\theta)y$. We obtain a system of the form

$$\frac{dy}{dt} = Y(\theta, y, \epsilon), \qquad \frac{d\theta}{dt} = \Theta(\theta, y, \epsilon), \qquad Y(\theta, 0, 0) \equiv 0, \qquad \Theta(\theta, 0, 0) \equiv 1.$$

Form the system

$$\frac{dy}{d\theta} = \frac{1}{\Theta(\theta, y, \epsilon)} Y(\theta, y, \epsilon).$$

We obtain, by the same calculations as in the preceding section,

$$\Theta(\theta, y, \epsilon) = \frac{X^*[u(\theta)]Z[u(\theta) + S(\theta)y, \epsilon)}{|X[u(\theta)]|^2 + X^*[u(\theta)][dS(\theta)/d\theta]y},$$

$$Y^\mu(\theta, y, \epsilon) = \xi_\mu^*(\theta)Z[u(\theta) + S(\theta)y, \epsilon] - \Theta(\theta, y, \epsilon)\xi_\mu^*(\theta)\frac{dS(\theta)}{d\theta}y.$$

Further,

$$Z[u(\theta) + S(\theta)y, \epsilon]$$

$$= Z[u(\theta), 0] + \frac{\partial Z[u(\theta), 0]}{\partial x} S(\theta)y + \epsilon \frac{\partial Z[u(\theta), 0]}{\partial \epsilon} + o(|y| + |\epsilon|)$$

$$= X[u(\theta)] + A(\theta)S(\theta)y + \epsilon \frac{\partial Z[u(\theta), 0]}{\partial \epsilon} + o(|y| + |\epsilon|).$$

Therefore,

$$\xi_\mu^*(\theta)Z[u(\theta) + S(\theta)y, \epsilon] = \xi_\mu^*(\theta)A(\theta)S(\theta)y + \epsilon\xi_\mu^*(\theta)\frac{\partial Z[u(\theta), 0]}{\partial \epsilon} + o(|y| + |\epsilon|).$$

Taking into account the fact that

$$\Theta(\theta, y, \epsilon) = 1 + O(|y|) + O(|\epsilon|),$$

we obtain

$$\frac{dy^\mu}{d\theta} = \xi_\mu^*(\theta)\left[A(\theta)S(\theta) - \frac{dS(\theta)}{d\theta}\right] y + \epsilon\xi_\mu^*(\theta)\frac{\partial Z[u(\theta), 0]}{\partial \epsilon} + o(|y| + |\epsilon|).$$

Finally,

$$\frac{dy}{d\theta} = B(\theta)y + \epsilon\eta(\theta) + o(|y| + |\epsilon|), \tag{17}$$

where

$$\eta^\mu(\theta) = \xi_\mu^*(\theta)\frac{\partial Z[u(\theta), 0]}{\partial \epsilon}.$$

Theorem 3.15. *If system* (13) *admits a periodic solution* $x = u(t)$ *of period* ω, *such that the corresponding variational system admits a single multiplier equal to* 1, *then for* $|\epsilon|$ *sufficiently small system* (16) *admits a unique periodic solution* $x = x(t, \epsilon)$, *of period* $\omega + O(\epsilon)$, *with the property that* $\lim_{\epsilon\to 0} x(t, \epsilon) = u(t)$. *If, in addition, no one of the multipliers, with the exception of the one equal to* 1, *is a root of the unit, system* (16) *does not admit in the neighborhood of solution* $u(t)$ *solutions of period* $p\omega + O(\epsilon)$. *If the multipliers different from* 1 *are situated in the interior of the unit circle, then the periodic solution of system* (16) *is orbitally stable.*

Proof. Let $y(\theta, c, \epsilon)$ be the solution of system (17) with $y(0, c, \epsilon) = c$. The function $y(\theta, c, \epsilon)$ is continuously differentiable with respect to c and ϵ; since $y(\theta, 0, 0) = 0$, we may write

$$y(\theta, c, \epsilon) = G(\theta)c + r(\theta)\epsilon + o(|c| + |\epsilon|).$$

Substituting in system (17), we obtain

$$\frac{dG(\theta)}{d\theta}c + \frac{dr(\theta)}{d\theta}\epsilon + o(|c| + |\epsilon|)$$
$$= B(\theta)[G(\theta)c + r(\theta)\epsilon + o(|c| + |\epsilon|)] + \epsilon\eta(\theta) + o(|c| + |\epsilon|).$$

It follows that

$$\frac{dG(\theta)}{d\theta} = B(\theta)G(\theta), \qquad \frac{dr(\theta)}{d\theta} = B(\theta)r(\theta) + \eta(\theta),$$
$$G(0) = E, \qquad r(0) = 0.$$

Consequently, $G(\theta)$ is a fundamental matrix of the system in normal variations, and $r(\theta)$ is a solution of the nonhomogeneous system, given by the formula

$$r(\theta) = G(\theta)\int_0^\theta G^{-1}(s)\eta(s)ds.$$

The solution $y(\theta, c, \epsilon)$ is periodic of period $p\omega$ if and only if

$$y = (p\omega, c, \epsilon) = y(0, c, \epsilon) = c.$$

However,

$$y(p\omega, c, \epsilon) = G(p\omega)c + r(p\omega)\epsilon + o(|c| + |\epsilon|).$$

Therefore, we may write the periodicity condition in the form

$$[G(p\omega) - E]c + r(p\omega)\epsilon + o(|c| + |\epsilon|) = 0.$$

If

$$\det [G(p\omega) - E] \neq 0,$$

there exists for $|\epsilon| < \epsilon_0$ a function $c(\epsilon)$ continuously differentiable, with $c(0) = 0$ and such that

$$[G(p\omega) - E]c(\epsilon) + r(p\omega)\epsilon + o(|c(\epsilon)| + |\epsilon|) \equiv 0.$$

The solution $y(\theta, c(\epsilon), \epsilon)$ is a periodic solution of period $p\omega$ of system (17) which for $\epsilon \to 0$ tends to zero. To this periodic solution corresponds a solution

$$x[t(\theta)] = u(\theta) + S(\theta)y(\theta, c(\epsilon), \epsilon)$$

of system (16); the curve $x = x[t(\theta)]$ is a closed curve in a neighborhood of $x = u(\theta)$, and for $\epsilon \to 0$ it tends to this one. The period ω_p' of solution $x(t)$ will be given by

$$t(p\omega) - t(0) = \int_0^{p\omega} \frac{dt}{d\theta}d\theta = \int_0^{p\omega} \frac{d\theta}{\Theta(\theta, y, \epsilon)} = \int_0^{p\omega} (1 + O(|y|) + O(|\epsilon|)d\theta$$
$$= p\omega + O(|y| + |\epsilon|) = p\omega + O(|\epsilon|),$$

since $|y| = O(|\epsilon|)$.

Since $G(\theta)$ is a fundamental matrix of the system in normal variations, we have $G(p\omega) = G^p(\omega)$; hence if $G(\omega)$ has an eigenvalue equal to 1, then $G(p\omega)$ has an eigenvalue equal to 1, and if $\det(G(\omega) - E) = 0$, then $\det(G(p\omega) - E) = 0$. It follows from this that if $\det[G(p\omega) - E] \neq 0$, then we also have $\det[G(\omega) - E] \neq 0$; hence there exists in the neighborhood of the solution $u(\theta)$ a periodic solution of period $\omega + O(\epsilon)$ of system (16). However, if $\det[G(p\omega) - E] \neq 0$, the periodic solution solution $y(\theta, c(\epsilon), \epsilon)$ is unique of period $p\omega$ and therefore it coincides with that of period ω. If $\det[G(\omega) - E] \neq 0$ but there exists p such that $\det[G(p\omega) - E] = 0$, then for this p there may exist solutions $y(\theta, c(\epsilon), \epsilon)$ of period $p\omega$ which do not also admit the period ω. The condition that $\det[G(\omega) - E] \neq 0$ is the condition that the multipliers of the system in normal variations are not equal to 1, hence the condition that the system in variations does admit a single multiplier equal to 1.

It remains to prove the assertion relative to the stability of the solution. We have

$$A(t, \epsilon) = \frac{\partial Z[x(t, \epsilon), \epsilon]}{\partial x} = \frac{\partial Z[u(t) + O(\epsilon), \epsilon]}{\partial x}$$

$$= \frac{\partial Z[u(t), 0]}{\partial x} + O(\epsilon) = \frac{\partial X[u(t)]}{\partial x} + O(\epsilon)$$

$$= A(t) + O(\epsilon).$$

According to the hypothesis, the system

$$\frac{dv}{dt} = A(t)v$$

has its multipliers in the interior of the unit circle, with the exception of that equal to 1. Since the multipliers depend continuously on the monodromy matrix, and this continuously depends on the coefficients of the system, it follows that for $|\epsilon|$ sufficiently small the multipliers of the system

$$\frac{dv}{dt} = A(t, \epsilon)v,$$

with the exception of that equal to 1, will be situated in the interior of the unit circle. The orbital stability of the periodic solution $x(t, \epsilon)$ is deduced now on the basis of Theorem 3.14. The theorem is thus completely proved.

Now consider the case where system (13) admits a periodic solution $x = u(t)$ of period ω_0, such that all its neighboring solutions are also periodic; in case $n \geqslant 3$ we will assume that the periods of these solutions are bounded. Let x_0 be a point on the closed curve C_0 given by $x = u(t)$ and Π be the normal hyperplane to C_0 in x_0. According to the hypothesis, every trajectory which crosses Π in a neighboring point of x_0 is closed, and, conversely, every closed trajectory from the neighborhood of C_0 crosses Π in a point in the neighborhood of x_0. Let $\omega(x)$ be the period of such a trajectory $\omega(x_0) = \omega_0$. We prove that we can choose the periods such that the function $\tilde{\omega}(x)$, which for any x in a neighborhood of x_0 is a period of the trajectory which passes through x, is continuous in x_0. The trajectories we have considered are given by the solutions of system (15).

In conformity with the hypothesis, the solutions of this system, for $|y|$ sufficiently small, will be periodic functions of θ with period $p\omega_0$; indeed, any solution of this kind corresponds to a solution of system (13) situated in the neighborhood of the curve $x = u(t)$, periodic of period

$$t(p\omega_0) - t(0) = \int_0^{p\omega_0} \frac{d\theta}{\Theta(\theta, y)},$$

and conversely, if the solution $x(t)$ is periodic of period ω, it means that this solution,

$$\theta(t + \omega) = \theta(t) + p\omega_0, \qquad y(t + \omega) = y(t),$$

which shows that $y(\theta)$ is periodic of period $p\omega_0$. We have

$$t(p\omega_0) - t[(p-1)\omega_0] - \omega_0 = \int_{(p-1)\omega_0}^{p\omega_0} \left[\frac{1}{\Theta(\theta, y)} - 1\right] d\theta = \int_{(p-1)\omega_0}^{p\omega_0} O(|y|)d\theta.$$

From this it follows that for $H > 0$ sufficiently small, there exists $R > 0$ such that if $|y| < H$ we have

$$|t(p\omega_0) - t((p-1)\omega_0) - \omega_0| < R \max |y|.$$

If $n = 2$, from the general properties of the systems in the plane, it follows that the only possible case is $p = 1$; hence $\omega(x) = t(\omega_0) - t(0)$ and

$$|\omega(x) - \omega_0| < R \max |y|.$$

Hence $\omega(x)$ is continuous for $x = x_0$. Now let $n \geqslant 3$, $\omega(x) = t(p\omega_0) - t(0)$.

We have

$$\begin{aligned} \omega(x) - p\omega_0 = {} & [t(p\omega_0) - t((p-1)\omega_0) - \omega_0] \\ & + [t((p-1)\omega_0) - t((p-2)\omega_0) - \omega_0] \\ & + \cdots + [t(\omega_0) + t(0) - \omega_0]. \end{aligned}$$

It follows that

$$|\omega(x) - p\omega_0| \leqslant pR \max |y|;$$

hence

$$\omega(x) - p\omega_0 \geqslant -pR \max |y|, \qquad \omega(x) \geqslant p[\omega_0 - R \max |y|].$$

For $|y|$ sufficiently small,

$$\omega_0 - R \max |y| > 0.$$

Since we have supposed that periods $\omega(x)$ are bounded,

$$p < \frac{M}{\omega_0 - R \max |y|};$$

hence the set of the integers p is bounded. Let S_p be the set of points x situated in the hyperplane Π in the neighborhood of x and such that the period of the solution which passes through x be close to $p\omega_0$, and let L be the least common multiple of numbers p. For $x \in S_p$ we will take

$$\tilde{\omega}(x) = \frac{L}{p}\,\omega(x);$$

obviously, $\tilde{\omega}(x)$ is also a period for the solution which passes through x. We have

$$|\tilde{\omega}(x) - L\omega_0| = \frac{L}{p}\,|\omega(x) - p\omega_0| < \frac{L}{p}\,\bar{\epsilon};$$

for $\epsilon > 0$ arbitrary, we choose $\bar{\epsilon}$ such that $(L/p)\bar{\epsilon} < \epsilon$ and then we choose the neighborhood of x_0 small enough so that $|\omega(x) - p\omega_0| < \bar{\epsilon}$. Taking into account that $\omega(x_0) = x_0$, hence that $x_0 \in S_1$, it follows that

$$\tilde{\omega}(x_0) = L\omega_0 = L\omega(x_0).$$

Hence

$$|\tilde{\omega}(x) - \tilde{\omega}(x_0)| < \epsilon$$

if x is in a small enough neighborhood of x_0, which shows that $\tilde{\omega}$ is continuous in point x_0. We will say that the period $\tilde{\omega}(x)$ is an *universal period.* In what follows we will consider only universal periods.

Let $y(\theta, \alpha)$ be the solution of system (15) with $y(0, \alpha) = \alpha$; if ω_0 is a universal period of C_0, for $|\alpha|$ sufficiently small, the solutions $y(\theta, \alpha)$ are all periodic of period ω_0; therefore $y(\omega_0, \alpha) = \alpha$. The closed curves in the neighborhood of the curve C_0 may be written

$$x(t) = u(\theta) + S(\theta)y(\theta, \alpha);$$

Denote by C_α the curve corresponding to the solution $y(\theta, \alpha)$. Supposing that $t(0) = 0$ we have

$$t(\theta, \alpha) = \int_0^\theta \frac{d\theta}{\Theta(\theta, y(\theta, \alpha))}$$

and the universal period ω_α is given by

$$\omega_\alpha = t(\omega_0 , \alpha).$$

If we write system (15) in the form

$$\frac{dy}{d\theta} = W(\theta, y), \tag{18}$$

system (17) can be written

$$\frac{dy}{d\theta} = W(\theta, y) + \epsilon W_1(\theta, y, \epsilon). \tag{19}$$

The general solution $y(\theta, \alpha)$ of system (18) is, for $|\alpha|$ sufficiently small, periodic in θ with period ω_0. For the study of the periodic solutions of period ω_0 of systems (19) we may use Theorem 3.9.

In case the solution $u(t)$ of system (13) belongs to a family of periodic solutions depending on $k + 1$ parameters, supposing again that the periods are bounded, we will deduce the existence of an universal period. System (18) will have a family of periodic solutions of period ω_0, depending on k parameters, and for the study of periodic solutions of period ω_0 of system (19) we can use Theorem 3.8.

Applications. 1. Suppose $n = 2$ and consider the system

$$\frac{dx}{dt} = X(x, y), \qquad \frac{dy}{dt} = Y(x, y),$$

x, y being scalar. Let $x = \varphi(t), y = \psi(t)$ be a periodic solution of this system. The normed orthogonal system attached to this curve is formed by the vectors

$$\begin{pmatrix} \dfrac{X[\varphi(t), \psi(t)]}{R} \\[2ex] \dfrac{Y[\varphi(t), \psi(t)]}{R} \end{pmatrix}, \qquad \begin{pmatrix} -\dfrac{Y[\varphi(t), \psi(t)]}{R} \\[2ex] \dfrac{X[\varphi(t), \psi(t)]}{R} \end{pmatrix} \qquad (R = \sqrt{X^2 + Y^2}).$$

The matrix $A(\theta)$ of the coefficients of the variational system is

$$A(\theta) = \begin{pmatrix} \dfrac{\partial X[\varphi(\theta), \psi(\theta)]}{\partial x} & \dfrac{\partial X[\varphi(\theta), \psi(\theta)]}{\partial y} \\ \dfrac{\partial Y[\varphi(\theta), \psi(\theta)]}{\partial x} & \dfrac{\partial Y[\varphi(\theta), \psi(\theta)]}{\partial y} \end{pmatrix}.$$

From this follows

$$A(\theta) \begin{pmatrix} -\dfrac{Y}{R} \\ \dfrac{X}{R} \end{pmatrix} = \begin{pmatrix} \dfrac{\partial X}{\partial x} & \dfrac{\partial X}{\partial y} \\ \dfrac{\partial Y}{\partial x} & \dfrac{\partial Y}{\partial y} \end{pmatrix} \begin{pmatrix} -\dfrac{Y}{R} \\ \dfrac{X}{R} \end{pmatrix} = \frac{1}{R} \begin{pmatrix} -\dfrac{\partial X}{\partial x} Y + \dfrac{\partial X}{\partial y} X \\ -\dfrac{\partial Y}{\partial x} Y + \dfrac{\partial Y}{\partial y} X \end{pmatrix}.$$

The scalar product of $(-Y/R\ X/R)$ and the vector $A(\theta)\,(-Y/R\ X/R)$ is equal to

$$\frac{1}{R^2} \left(\frac{\partial X}{\partial x} Y^2 - \frac{\partial X}{\partial y} XY - \frac{\partial Y}{\partial x} XY + \frac{\partial Y}{\partial y} X^2 \right),$$

and the scalar product of the unitary vector $(-Y/R\ X/R)$ and its derivative is zero; hence

$$b(\theta) = \frac{1}{R^2} \left(\frac{\partial X}{\partial x} Y^2 - \frac{\partial X}{\partial y} XY - \frac{\partial Y}{\partial x} XY + \frac{\partial Y}{\partial y} X^2 \right).$$

Further, we have

$$\frac{d}{d\theta} \ln R = \frac{1}{2} \frac{d}{d\theta} \ln R^2 = \frac{1}{2} \frac{dR^2/d\theta}{R^2} = \frac{1}{R^2} (X\dot{X} + Y\dot{Y}).$$

However,

$$\dot{X} = \frac{\partial X}{\partial x} X + \frac{\partial X}{\partial y} Y, \qquad \dot{Y} = \frac{\partial Y}{\partial x} X + \frac{\partial Y}{\partial y} Y;$$

hence

$$\frac{d}{d\theta} \ln R = \frac{1}{R^2} \left(\frac{\partial X}{\partial x} X^2 + \frac{\partial X}{\partial y} XY + \frac{\partial Y}{\partial x} XY + \frac{\partial Y}{\partial y} Y^2 \right).$$

It follows that

$$b(\theta) + \frac{d}{d\theta} \ln R = \frac{1}{R^2} \left(\frac{\partial X}{\partial x} (X^2 + Y^2) + \frac{\partial Y}{\partial y} (X^2 + Y^2) \right) = \frac{\partial X}{\partial x} + \frac{\partial Y}{\partial y},$$

and that

$$b(\theta) = \frac{\partial X}{\partial x} + \frac{\partial Y}{\partial y} - \frac{d}{d\theta} \ln \sqrt{X^2 + Y^2}.$$

The system in normal variations is the equation

$$\frac{dv}{d\theta} = b(\theta)v,$$

whose solution with $v(0) = 1$ is

$$v(\theta) = \exp\left[\int_0^\theta \left(\frac{\partial X}{\partial x} + \frac{\partial Y}{\partial y}\right) d\theta - \int_0^\theta \frac{d}{d\theta} \sqrt{X^2 + Y^2}\, d\theta\right] = \frac{\sqrt{X_0^2 + Y_0^2}}{\sqrt{X^2 + Y^2}} e^{h(\theta)},$$

where

$$h(\theta) = \int_0^\theta \left[\frac{\partial X[\varphi(t), \psi(t)]}{\partial x} + \frac{\partial Y[\varphi(t), \psi(t)]}{\partial y}\right] dt.$$

The condition of orbital stability is given by $h(\omega) < 0$. If $h(\omega) \neq 0$, in the neighborhood of the periodic solution we have considered, there appears a periodic solution of the perturbed system.

2. Consider the case where $X(x) = Ax$, A being a constant matrix which has two purely imaginary eigenvalues. Suppose that matrix A is of the third order and that it has the eigenvalues i, $-i$, a. Through a linear transformation with constant coefficients, A can be brought to the form

$$\begin{pmatrix} a & 0 & 0 \\ 0 & 0 & -1 \\ 0 & 1 & 0 \end{pmatrix}$$

We will suppose from the beginning that it has this form.

In this case, system (13) will be written

$$\frac{dx^1}{dt} = ax^1, \qquad \frac{dx^2}{dt} = -x^3, \qquad \frac{dx^3}{dt} = x^2$$

and it admits the fundamental matrix of solutions

$$\begin{pmatrix} e^{at} & 0 & 0 \\ 0 & \cos t & -\sin t \\ 0 & \sin t & \cos t \end{pmatrix}.$$

Let

$$e_1 = \begin{pmatrix} 1 \\ 0 \\ 0 \end{pmatrix}, \qquad e_2 = \begin{pmatrix} 0 \\ 1 \\ 0 \end{pmatrix}, \qquad e_3 = \begin{pmatrix} 0 \\ 0 \\ 1 \end{pmatrix}.$$

Consider the solution

$$u(t, \alpha) = \alpha(\cos t\, e_2 + \sin t\, e_3).$$

We have

$$X[u(t, \alpha)] = \dot{u}(t, \alpha) = \alpha(-\sin t\, e_2 + \cos t\, e_3), \qquad |X[u(t, \alpha)]| = |\alpha|,$$

$$\bar{X}[u(t, \alpha)] = -\sin t\, e_2 + \cos t\, e_3\,,$$

$$\cos \theta_1 = 0, \qquad \cos \theta_2 = -\sin t, \qquad \cos \theta_3 = \cos t,$$

$$\begin{aligned} \xi_2 &= e_2 + \sin t(e_1 - \sin t\, e_2 + \cos t\, e_3) \\ &= \sin t\, e_1 + \cos^2 t\, e_2 + \sin t \cos t\, e_3\,, \\ \xi_3 &= e_3 - \cos t(e_1 - \sin t\, e_2 + \cos t\, e_3) \\ &= -\cos t\, e_1 + \sin t \cos t\, e_2 + \sin^2 t\, e_3\,. \end{aligned}$$

Let

$$Z(x, \epsilon) = Ax + \epsilon X_1(x, \epsilon).$$

We will have

$$\begin{aligned} \Theta(\theta, y, \epsilon) &= \frac{X^*[u(\theta)]Z[u(\theta) + S(\theta)y, \epsilon]}{|X[u(\theta)]|^2 + X^*[u(\theta)][dS(\theta)/d\theta]y} \\ &= \frac{X^*[u(\theta)](X[u(\theta) + S(\theta)y] + \epsilon X_1[u(\theta) + S(\theta)y, \epsilon])}{|X[u(\theta)]|^2 + X^*[u(\theta)][dS(\theta)/d\theta]y}\,. \end{aligned}$$

However,

$$S(\theta) = \begin{pmatrix} \sin\theta & -\cos\theta \\ \cos^2\theta & \sin\theta\cos\theta \\ \sin\theta\cos\theta & \sin^2\theta \end{pmatrix},$$

$$\frac{dS(\theta)}{d\theta} = \begin{pmatrix} \cos\theta & \sin\theta \\ -2\sin\theta\cos\theta & \cos^2\theta - \sin^2\theta \\ \cos^2\theta - \sin^2\theta & 2\sin\theta\cos\theta \end{pmatrix},$$

$$\begin{aligned} X^*[u(\theta)]\frac{dS(\theta)}{d\theta} &= (0 \quad -\alpha\sin\theta \quad \alpha\cos\theta)\begin{pmatrix} \cos\theta & \sin\theta \\ -2\sin\theta\cos\theta & \cos^2\theta - \sin^2\theta \\ \cos^2\theta - \sin^2\theta & 2\sin\theta\cos\theta \end{pmatrix} \\ &= (\alpha\sin\theta\sin 2\theta + \alpha\cos\theta\cos 2\theta, -\alpha\sin\theta\cos 2\theta + \alpha\cos\theta\sin 2\theta) \\ &= (\alpha\cos\theta \quad \alpha\sin\theta) = \alpha(\cos\theta \quad \sin\theta); \end{aligned}$$

hence the denominator in the expression of $\Theta(\theta, y, \epsilon)$ is $\alpha^2 + \alpha(y_2\cos\theta + y_3\sin\theta)$. The numerator is of the form

$$\begin{aligned} &X^*[u(\theta)](Au(\theta) + AS(\theta)y + \epsilon X[u(\theta) + S(\theta)y, 0] + o(\epsilon)) \\ &\quad = |X[u(\theta)]|^2 + X^*[u(\theta)]AS(\theta)y + \epsilon X^*[u(\theta)]X_1[u(\theta) + S(\theta)y, 0] + o(\epsilon). \end{aligned}$$

We have

$$X^*[u(\theta)]A = (0 \quad -\alpha\sin\theta \quad \alpha\cos\theta)\begin{pmatrix} a & 0 & 0 \\ 0 & 0 & -1 \\ 0 & 1 & 0 \end{pmatrix} = (0 \quad \alpha\cos\theta \quad \alpha\sin\theta),$$

$$X^*[u(\theta)]AS(\theta) = (0 \qquad \alpha\cos\theta \qquad \alpha\sin\theta)\begin{pmatrix} \sin\theta & -\cos\theta \\ \cos^2\theta & \sin\theta\cos\theta \\ \sin\theta\cos\theta & \sin^2\theta \end{pmatrix}$$

$$= (\alpha\cos\theta \qquad \alpha\sin\theta),$$

$$X^*[u(\theta)]AS(\theta)y = \alpha(y_2\cos\theta + y_3\sin\theta).$$

Thus,

$$\Theta(\theta, y, \epsilon)$$

$$= \frac{\alpha^2 + \alpha(y_2\cos\theta + y_3\sin\theta) + \epsilon X^*[u(\theta)]X_1[u(\theta) + S(\theta)y, 0] + o(\epsilon)}{\alpha^2 + \alpha(y_2\cos\theta + y_3\sin\theta)}$$

$$= 1 + \epsilon\frac{X^*[u(\theta)]X[u(\theta) + S(\theta)y, 0]}{\alpha^2 + \alpha(y_2\cos\theta + y_3\sin\theta)} + o(\epsilon).$$

Further,

$$Y^\mu(\theta, y, \epsilon) = \xi_\mu^*(\theta)Z[u(\theta) + S(\theta)y, \epsilon] - \Theta(\theta, y, \epsilon)\xi_\mu^*(\theta)\frac{dS(\theta)}{dt}y;$$

hence

$$\frac{Y^\mu(\theta, y, \epsilon)}{\Theta(\theta, y, \epsilon)}$$

$$= \frac{\xi_\mu^*(\theta)[X[u(\theta)] + AS(\theta)y + \epsilon X_1[u(\theta) + S(\theta)y, 0] + o(\epsilon)]}{\Theta(\theta, y, \epsilon)} - \xi_\mu^*(\theta)\frac{dS(\theta)}{d\theta}y$$

$$= \frac{\xi_\mu^*(\theta)AS(\theta)y + \epsilon\xi_\mu^*(\theta)X_1[u(\theta) + S(\theta)y, 0] + o(\epsilon)}{\Theta(\theta, y, \epsilon)} - \xi_\mu^*(\theta)\frac{dS(\theta)}{d\theta}y.$$

We have

$$AS(\theta) = \begin{pmatrix} a & 0 & 0 \\ 0 & 0 & -1 \\ 0 & 1 & 0 \end{pmatrix}\begin{pmatrix} \sin\theta & -\cos\theta \\ \cos^2\theta & \sin\theta\cos\theta \\ \sin\theta\cos\theta & \sin^2\theta \end{pmatrix}$$

$$= \begin{pmatrix} a\sin\theta & -a\cos\theta \\ -\sin\theta\cos\theta & -\sin^2\theta \\ \cos^2\theta & \sin\theta\cos\theta \end{pmatrix},$$

$$\xi_2^*(\theta)AS(\theta) = (\sin\theta \qquad \cos^2\theta \qquad \sin\theta\cos\theta)\begin{pmatrix} a\sin\theta & -a\cos\theta \\ -\sin\theta\cos\theta & -\sin^2\theta \\ \cos^2\theta & \sin\theta\cos\theta \end{pmatrix}$$

$$= (a\sin^2\theta \qquad -a\sin\theta\cos\theta),$$

$$\xi_3^*(\theta)AS(\theta) = (-\cos\theta \quad \sin\theta\cos\theta \quad \sin^2\theta)\begin{pmatrix} a\sin\theta & -a\cos\theta \\ -\sin\theta\cos\theta & -\sin^2\theta \\ \cos^2\theta & \sin\theta\cos\theta \end{pmatrix}$$
$$= (-a\sin\theta\cos\theta \quad a\cos^2\theta),$$

$$\xi_2^*(\theta)\frac{dS(\theta)}{d\theta} = (\sin\theta \quad \cos^2\theta \quad \sin\theta\cos\theta)\begin{pmatrix} \cos\theta & \sin\theta \\ -\sin 2\theta & \cos 2\theta \\ \cos 2\theta & \sin 2\theta \end{pmatrix} = (0 \quad 1),$$

$$\xi_3^*(\theta)\frac{dS(\theta)}{d\theta} = (-\cos\theta \quad \sin\theta\cos\theta \quad \sin^2\theta)\begin{pmatrix} \cos\theta & \sin\theta \\ -\sin 2\theta & \cos 2\theta \\ \cos 2\theta & \sin 2\theta \end{pmatrix} = (-1 \quad 0).$$

It follows that

$$\frac{Y^2(\theta, y, \epsilon)}{\Theta(\theta, y, \epsilon)}$$
$$= y_3 + \frac{a\sin\theta(y_2\sin\theta - y_3\cos\theta) + \epsilon\xi_2^*(\theta)X_1[u(\theta) + S(\theta)y, 0] + o(\epsilon)}{1 + \epsilon\dfrac{X^*[u(\theta)]X_1[u(\theta) + S(\theta)y, 0]}{\alpha^2 + \alpha(y_2\cos\theta + y_3\sin\theta)} + o(\epsilon)},$$

$$\frac{Y^3(\theta, y, \epsilon)}{\Theta(\theta, y, \epsilon)}$$
$$= -y_2 + \frac{a\cos\theta(-y_2\sin\theta + y_3\cos\theta) + \epsilon\xi_3^*(\theta)X_1[u(\theta) + S(\theta)y, 0] + o(\epsilon)}{1 + \epsilon\dfrac{X^*[u(\theta)]X_1[u(\theta) + S(\theta)y, 0]}{\alpha^2 + \alpha(y_2\cos\theta + y_3\sin\theta)} + o(\epsilon)}.$$

From here,

$$\frac{Y^2(\theta, y, \epsilon)}{\Theta(\theta, y, \epsilon)}$$
$$= y_3 + [a\sin\theta(y_2\sin\theta - y_3\cos\theta) + \epsilon\xi_2^*(\theta)X_1[u(\theta) + S(\theta)y, 0] + o(\epsilon)]$$
$$\times \left[1 - \epsilon\frac{X^*[u(\theta)]X_1[u(\theta) + S(\theta)y, 0]}{\alpha^2 + \alpha(y_2\cos\theta + y_3\sin\theta)} + o(\epsilon)\right]$$

$$= y_3 + a\sin\theta(y_2\sin\theta - y_3\cos\theta) + \epsilon\xi_2^*(\theta)X_1[u(\theta) + S(\theta)y, 0]$$
$$-\epsilon\frac{a\sin\theta(y_2\sin\theta - y_3\cos\theta)}{\alpha^2 + \alpha(y_2\cos\theta + y_3\sin\theta)}X^*[u(\theta)]X_1[u(\theta) + S(\theta)y, 0] + o(\epsilon)$$

$$= y_2\sin^2\theta + y_3(1 - a\sin\theta\cos\theta)$$
$$+ \epsilon\left[\xi_2^*(\theta) - \frac{a\sin\theta(y_2\sin\theta - y_3\cos\theta)}{\alpha^2 + \alpha(y_2\cos\theta + y_3\sin\theta)}X^*[a(\theta)]\right]$$
$$\times X_1[u(\theta) + S(\theta)y, 0] + o(\epsilon),$$

$$\frac{Y^3(\theta, y, \epsilon)}{\Theta(\theta, y, \epsilon)}$$

$$= -y_2 + a\cos\theta(-y_2\sin\theta + y_3\cos\theta) + \epsilon\xi_3^*(\theta)X_1[u(\theta) + S(\theta)y, 0]$$

$$-\epsilon\frac{a\cos\theta(-y_2\sin\theta + y_3\cos\theta)}{\alpha^2 + \alpha(y_2\cos\theta + y_3\sin\theta)}X^*[u(\theta)]X_1[u(\theta) + S(\theta)y, 0] + o(\epsilon)$$

$$= -y_2(1 + a\sin\theta\cos\theta) + y_3 a\cos^2\theta$$

$$+\epsilon\left[\xi_3^*(\theta) - \frac{a\cos\theta(-y_2\sin\theta + y_3\cos\theta)}{\alpha^2 + \alpha(y_2\cos\theta + y_3\sin\theta)}X^*[u(\theta)]\right]$$

$$\times X_1[u(\theta) + S(\theta)y, 0] + o(\epsilon).$$

We have

$$\left[\xi_2^*(\theta) - \frac{a\sin\theta(y_2\sin\theta - y_3\cos\theta)}{\alpha^2 + \alpha(y_2\cos\theta + y_3\sin\theta)}X^*[u(\theta)]\right]X_1[u(\theta) + S(\theta)y, 0]$$

$$= X_1^1[u(\theta) + S(\theta)y, 0]\sin\theta + X_1^2[u(\theta) + S(\theta)y, 0]$$

$$\times\left[\cos^2\theta + \frac{a\sin\theta(y_2\sin\theta - y_3\cos\theta)}{\alpha^2 + \alpha(y_2\cos\theta + y_3\sin\theta)}\alpha\sin\theta\right] + X_1^3[u(\theta) + S(\theta)y, 0]$$

$$\times\left[\sin\theta\cos\theta - \frac{a\sin\theta(y_2\sin\theta - y_3\cos\theta)}{\alpha^2 + \alpha(y_2\cos\theta + y_3\sin\theta)}\alpha\cos\theta\right]$$

$$= X_1^1[u(\theta) + S(\theta)y, 0]\sin\theta + X_1^2[u(\theta) + S(\theta)y, 0]$$

$$\times\frac{\alpha\cos^2\theta + y_2\cos^3\theta + y_3\cos^2\theta\sin\theta + ay_2\sin^3\theta - ay_3\sin^2\theta\cos\theta}{\alpha + y_2\cos\theta + y_3\sin\theta}$$

$$+ X_1^3[u(\theta) + S(\theta)y, 0]$$

$$\times\frac{\alpha\sin\theta\cos\theta + y_2\sin\theta\cos^2\theta + y_3\sin^2\theta\cos\theta - ay_2\sin^2\theta\cos\theta + ay_3\sin\theta\cos^2\theta}{\alpha + y_2\cos\theta + y_3\sin\theta}$$

$$= X_1^1[u(\theta) + S(\theta)y, 0]\sin\theta + X_1^2[u(\theta) + S(\theta)y, 0]$$

$$\times\frac{\alpha\cos^2\theta + y_2(\cos^3\theta + a\sin^3\theta) + y_3\sin\theta\cos\theta(\cos\theta - a\sin\theta)}{\alpha + y_2\cos\theta + y_3\sin\theta}$$

$$+ X_1^3[u(\theta) + S(\theta)y, 0]$$

$$\times\frac{\alpha\sin\theta\cos\theta + y_2\sin\theta\cos\theta(\cos\theta - a\sin\theta) + y_3\sin\theta\cos\theta(\sin\theta + a\cos\theta)}{\alpha + y_2\cos\theta + y_3\sin\theta}.$$

Likewise,

$$\left[\xi_3^*(\theta) - \frac{a\cos\theta(-y_2\sin\theta + y_3\cos\theta)}{\alpha^2 + \alpha(y_2\cos\theta + y_3\sin\theta)} X^*[u(\theta)]\right] X_1[u(\theta) + S(\theta)y, 0]$$

$$= -X_1^1[u(\theta) + S(\theta)y, 0]\cos\theta + X_1^2[u(\theta) + S(\theta)y, 0]$$

$$\times \left[\sin\theta\cos\theta + \frac{a\cos\theta(-y_2\sin\theta + y_3\cos\theta)}{\alpha^2 + \alpha(y_2\cos\theta + y_3\sin\theta)}\alpha\sin\theta\right]$$

$$+ X_1^3[u(\theta) + S(\theta)y, 0]\left[\sin^2\theta - \frac{a\cos\theta(-y_2\sin\theta + y_3\cos\theta)}{\alpha^2 + \alpha(y_2\cos\theta + y_3\sin\theta)}\alpha\cos\theta\right]$$

$$= -X_1^1[u(\theta) + S(\theta)y, 0]\cos\theta + X_1^2[u(\theta) + S(\theta)y, 0]$$

$$\times \frac{\alpha\sin\theta\cos\theta + y_2\sin\theta\cos\theta(\cos\theta - a\sin\theta) + y_3\sin\theta\cos\theta(\sin\theta + a\cos\theta)}{\alpha + y_2\cos\theta + y_3\sin\theta}$$

$$+ X_1^3[u(\theta) + S(\theta)y, 0]$$

$$\times \frac{\alpha\sin^2\theta + y_2\sin\theta\cos\theta(\sin\theta + a\cos\theta) + y_3(\sin^3\theta - a\cos^3\theta)}{\alpha + y_2\cos\theta + y_3\sin\theta}.$$

It follows that

$$\frac{dy_2}{dt} = y_2 a\sin^2\theta + y_3(1 - a\sin\theta\cos\theta)$$

$$+ \epsilon\Bigg\{X_1^1[u(\theta) + S(\theta)y, 0]\sin\theta + X_1^2[u(\theta) + S(\theta)y, 0]$$

$$\times \frac{\alpha\cos^2\theta + y_2(\cos^3\theta + a\sin^3\theta) + y_3\sin\theta\cos\theta(\cos\theta - a\sin\theta)}{\alpha + y_2\cos\theta + y_3\sin\theta}$$

$$+ X_1^3[u(\theta) + S(\theta)y, 0]$$

$$\times \frac{\alpha\sin\theta\cos\theta + y_2\sin\theta\cos\theta(\cos\theta - a\sin\theta) + y_3\sin\theta\cos\theta(\sin\theta + a\cos\theta)}{\alpha + y_2\cos\theta + y_3\sin\theta}\Bigg\} + o(\epsilon),$$

$$\frac{dy_3}{dt} = -y_2(1 - a\sin\theta\cos\theta) + y_3 a\cos^2\theta$$

$$+ \epsilon\Bigg\{-X_1^1[u(\theta) + S(\theta)y, 0]\cos\theta + X_1^2[u(\theta) + S(\theta)y, 0]$$

$$\times \frac{\alpha\sin\theta\cos\theta + y_2\sin\theta\cos\theta(\cos\theta - a\sin\theta) + y_3\sin\theta\cos\theta(\sin\theta + a\cos\theta)}{\alpha + y_2\cos\theta + y_3\sin\theta}$$

$$+ X_1^3[u(\theta) + S(\theta)y, 0]$$

$$\times \frac{\alpha\sin^2\theta + y_2\sin\theta\cos\theta(\sin\theta + a\cos\theta) + y_3(\sin^3\theta - a\cos^3\theta)}{\alpha + y_2\cos\theta + y_3\sin\theta}\Bigg\} + o(\epsilon).$$

We have thus obtained the explicit form of system (19). System (18) is, in this case,

$$\frac{dy_2}{d\theta} = y_2 a \sin^2\theta + y_3(1 - a\sin\theta\cos\theta),$$

$$\frac{dy_3}{d\theta} = -y_2(1 + a\sin\theta\cos\theta) + y_3\, a\cos^2\theta.$$

In order to obtain a fundamental matrix of solution of this system, let us observe that it coincides with the system in normal variations; hence its solutions will be the normal components of the solutions of the variational system, which in this case is $dx/dt = Ax$. Thus we write the solutions of this system in the basis formed by the vectors $(\bar{X}, \xi_2, \xi_3)$. We have

$$e^{a\theta}e_1 = p_1^1\bar{X} + p_1^2\xi_2 + p_1^3\xi_3,$$

$$\cos\theta\, e_2 + \sin\theta\, e_3 = p_2^1\bar{X} + p_2^2\xi_2 + p_2^3\xi_3,$$

$$-\sin\theta\, e_2 + \cos\theta e_3 = p_3^1\bar{X} + p_3^2\xi_2 + p_3^3\xi_3.$$

From the last relation we obtain

$$-\sin\theta = -p_3^1\sin\theta + p_3^2\cos^2\theta + p_3^3\sin\theta\cos\theta,$$

$$\cos\theta = p_3^1\cos\theta + p_3^2\sin\theta\cos\theta + p_3^3\sin^2\theta,$$

$$0 = p_3^2\sin\theta - p_3^3\cos\theta.$$

Therefore,

$$p_3^1 = \frac{\begin{vmatrix} -\sin\theta & \cos^2\theta & \sin\theta\cos\theta \\ \cos\theta & \sin\theta\cos\theta & \sin^2\theta \\ 0 & \sin\theta & -\cos\theta \end{vmatrix}}{\begin{vmatrix} \sin\theta & \cos^2\theta & \sin\theta\cos\theta \\ \cos\theta & \sin\theta\cos\theta & \sin^2\theta \\ 0 & \sin\theta & -\cos\theta \end{vmatrix}} = 1, \qquad p_3^2 = 0, \qquad p_3^3 = 0.$$

The other relations yield

$$e^{a\theta} = p_1^2\sin\theta - p_1^3\cos\theta,$$

$$0 = -p_1^1\sin\theta + p_2^2\cos^2\theta + p_1^3\sin\theta\cos\theta,$$

$$0 = p_1^1\cos\theta + p_1^2\sin\theta\cos\theta + p_1^3\sin^2\theta,$$

$$\cos\theta = -p_2^1\sin\theta + p_2^2\cos^2\theta + p_2^3\sin\theta\cos\theta,$$

$$\sin\theta = p_2^1\cos\theta + p_2^2\sin\theta\cos\theta + p_2^3\sin^2\theta,$$

$$0 = p_2^2\sin\theta - p_2^3\cos\theta.$$

Both systems have the same determinant (the same as the determinant of the preceding system); the columns of this determinant are the components of vectors $\bar{X}$, ξ_2, ξ_3 in the basis e_1, e_2, e_3, and since these vectors form an orthogonal and normed system, the determinant is equal to 1. It follows that

$$p_1^2 = e^{a\theta}\sin\theta, \qquad p_1^3 = -e^{a\theta}\cos\theta, \qquad p_2^2 = \cos\theta, \qquad p_2^3 = \sin\theta;$$

hence system (18) admits the fundamental matrix of solutions

$$G(\theta) = \begin{pmatrix} \cos\theta & -e^{a\theta}\sin\theta \\ \sin\theta & e^{a\theta}\cos\theta \end{pmatrix},$$

hence the family of periodic solutions of period 2π,

$$y_2 = \beta\cos\theta, \qquad y_3 = \beta\sin\theta.$$

The adjoint system has the fundamental matrix

$$G^{-1}(\theta) = \begin{pmatrix} \cos\theta & \sin\theta \\ -e^{-a\theta}\sin\theta & e^{-a\theta}\cos\theta \end{pmatrix}$$

and the periodic solution of the same form.

We will apply Theorem 3.8 to system (19). We have to compute $P(\gamma)$. We have

$$S(\theta)y = \begin{pmatrix} \sin\theta & -\cos\theta \\ \cos^2\theta & \sin\theta\cos\theta \\ \sin\theta\cos\theta & \sin^2\theta \end{pmatrix}\begin{pmatrix} \beta\cos\theta \\ \beta\sin\theta \end{pmatrix} = \begin{pmatrix} 0 \\ \beta\cos\theta \\ \beta\sin\theta \end{pmatrix},$$

$$u(\theta) + S(\theta)y = (\alpha+\beta)\begin{pmatrix} 0 \\ \cos\theta \\ \sin\theta \end{pmatrix} = \gamma\begin{pmatrix} 0 \\ \cos\theta \\ \sin\theta \end{pmatrix},$$

$$y_2\cos\theta + y_3\sin\theta = \beta,$$

$$\begin{aligned} &y_2\sin\theta\cos\theta(\cos\theta - a\sin\theta) + y_3\sin\theta\cos\theta(\sin\theta + a\cos\theta) \\ &\quad = \beta\sin\theta\cos^2\theta(\cos\theta - a\sin\theta) + \beta\sin^2\theta\cos\theta(\sin\theta + a\cos\theta) \\ &\quad = \beta\sin\theta\cos\theta(\cos^2\theta - a\sin\theta\cos\theta + \sin^2\theta + a\sin\theta\cos\theta) \\ &\quad = \beta\sin\theta\cos\theta, \end{aligned}$$

$$\begin{aligned} &y_2\sin\theta\cos\theta\,(\sin\theta + a\cos\theta) + y_3(\sin^3\theta - a\cos^3\theta) \\ &\quad = \beta\sin\theta\cos^2\theta(\sin\theta + a\cos\theta) + \beta\sin\theta(\sin^3\theta - a\cos^3\theta) \\ &\quad = \beta(\sin^2\theta\cos^2\theta + a\sin\theta\cos^3\theta + \sin^4\theta - a\sin\theta\cos^3\theta) = \beta\sin^2\theta, \end{aligned}$$

$$
\begin{aligned}
y_2(\cos^3\theta + a\sin^3\theta) &+ y_3 \sin\theta\cos\theta(\cos\theta - a\sin\theta)\\
&= \beta\cos\theta(\cos^3\theta + a\sin^3\theta) + \beta\sin^2\theta\cos\theta(\cos\theta - a\sin\theta)\\
&= \beta(\cos^4\theta + a\cos\theta\sin^3\theta + \sin^2\theta\cos^2\theta - a\sin^3\theta\cos\theta) = \beta\cos^2\theta,
\end{aligned}
$$

$$
\begin{aligned}
y_2 \sin\theta\cos\theta(\cos\theta - a\sin\theta) &+ y_3\sin\theta\cos\theta(\sin\theta + a\cos\theta)\\
&= \beta\sin\theta\cos^2\theta(\cos\theta - a\sin\theta) + \beta\sin^2\theta\cos\theta(\sin\theta + a\cos\theta)\\
&= \beta\sin\theta\cos\theta(\cos^2\theta - a\sin\theta\cos\theta + \sin^2\theta + a\sin\theta\cos\theta)\\
&= \beta\sin\theta\cos\theta.
\end{aligned}
$$

It follows that in system (19) the terms in ϵ, written for the generating solution $y_2 = \beta\cos\theta$, $y_3 = \beta\sin\theta$ become

$$
\begin{aligned}
&X_1^1(0, \gamma\cos\theta, \gamma\sin\theta, 0)\sin\theta + X_1^2(0, \gamma\cos\theta, \gamma\sin\theta, 0)\cos^2\theta\\
&\quad + X_1^3(0, \gamma\cos\theta, \gamma\sin\theta, 0)\sin\theta\cos\theta - X_1^1(0, \gamma\cos\theta, \gamma\sin\theta, 0)\cos\theta\\
&\quad + X_1^2(0, \gamma\cos\theta, \gamma\sin\theta, 0)\sin\theta\cos\theta + X_1^3(0, \gamma\cos\theta, \gamma\sin\theta, 0)\sin^2\theta.
\end{aligned}
$$

It follows that

$$
\begin{aligned}
P(\gamma) \equiv \int_0^{2\pi} &\{(X_1^1\sin\theta + X_1^2\cos^2\theta + X_1^3\sin\theta\cos\theta)\cos\theta\\
&+ (-X_1^1\cos\theta + X_1^2\sin\theta\cos\theta + X_1^3\sin^2\theta)\sin\theta\}d\theta\\
\equiv \int_0^{2\pi} &\{X_1^2[0, \gamma\cos\theta, \gamma\sin\theta, 0]\cos\theta + X_1^3[0, \gamma\cos\theta, \gamma\sin\theta, 0]\sin\theta\}d\theta.
\end{aligned}
$$

Through this, Theorem 3.8 gives the complete solution of the problem. The application we have considered could be treated in a simpler way,[‡] but we wanted specifically to give an example of effective computation on the basis of the method which has been theoretically presented above.

3.9. Periodic Solutions of the Second Kind

In the study of some electromechanical systems, after some simplifying hypotheses, the same mathematical problem is reached as appears in

[‡] A treatment of some general systems containing the above-mentioned case as a particular case is to be found in a paper of E. A. Coddington and N. Levinson.

the study of the pendulum with linear friction, under the action of a constant moment. The equation has the form

$$I\frac{d^2\vartheta}{dt^2} + b\frac{d\vartheta}{dt} + mga\sin\vartheta = M_0$$

and is a particular case of the systems (if we denote $d\vartheta/dt = z$)

$$\frac{d\vartheta}{dt} = \phi(\vartheta, z), \qquad \frac{dz}{dt} = F(\vartheta, z),$$

where the function ϕ and F are periodic with respect to ϑ with period 2π.

An important role is played in the study of these systems by solutions of the form

$$z(t) = \varphi(t), \qquad \vartheta(t) = \omega t + \psi(t),$$

where φ, ψ are periodic with period $T = 2N\pi/\omega$. Indeed, let us observe that

$$z(t + T) = z(t), \qquad \vartheta(t + T) = \omega\left(t + \frac{2N\pi}{\omega}\right) + \psi(t + T) = \vartheta(t) + 2N\pi.$$

Owing to the angular character of the variable ϑ, the state of the system does not change when ϑ is replaced by $\vartheta + 2N\pi$; hence we may consider that $z(t + T)$, $\vartheta(t + T)$ correspond to the same state of the system as $z(t)$, $\vartheta(t)$. This justifies the fact that the solutions of the form considered above are assimilated with the periodic solutions of the system and are called periodic solutions of the second kind.

The geometrical meaning of these facts is the following: By putting into correspondence the states of the system and the points of a phase space, we see that for the systems considered, due to the periodicity with respect to ϑ, the corresponding phase space is a cylinder. The periodic solutions of the second kind correspond to some closed curves situated on this cylinder, which surround the cylinder; the curves are closed since when t varies with T, the point $(\vartheta(t), z(t))$ returns in the same point of the cylinder, and they surround the cylinder, since when t varies with T, ϑ varies a multiple of 2π.

In the following pages we will consider systems of a general form, whose particular cases are those mentioned above and we will emphasize a stability theorem of periodic solutions of the second kind, analogous to the Andronov-Witt theorem, as well as a theory of the systems containing a small parameter.

Consider an autonomous system of the form $\dot{x} = f(x)$, where $f(x + 2\pi p) = f(x)$, p being a vector with some components equal to 1 and the other components zero. This means that f is periodic of period 2π with respect to a part of the components of vector x.

Suppose that the system admits a periodic solution of the second kind:

$$u(t) = \omega tp + \psi(t),$$

where ψ is periodic of period $T = 2\pi N/\omega$; this means that

$$u(t + T) = \left(t + \frac{2\pi N}{\omega}\right) p + \psi(t + T) = u(t) + 2\pi Np;$$

hence those components of u with respect to which f is periodic vary with a multiple of 2π, while the others remain unchanged. It follows from here that $f[u(t)]$ is periodic in t of period T:

$$f[u(t + T)] = f[u(t) + 2\pi Np] = f[u(t)].$$

Using the formulas of M. Urabe we form the orthogonal normed system attached to the curve $u(t)$; let $\xi_1, \xi_2, \ldots, \xi_n$ be the vectors of this system, where we have denoted $\xi_1 = f[u(t)]/|f[u(t)]|$. Taking into account the construction carried out above, all the vectors ξ_k will be periodic of period T.

As in the study of periodic solutions of autonomous systems, we perform the change of variables $x = u(\theta) + S(\theta)y$ and we obtain a system of the form

$$\frac{dy}{dt} = Y(\theta, y), \qquad \frac{d\theta}{dt} = \Theta(\theta, y),$$

where

$$\Theta = \frac{(f[u(\theta) + S(\theta)y], f[u(\theta)])}{|f[u(\theta)]|^2 + \sum_{\nu=2}^{n} (f[u(\theta)], (d\xi_\nu/d\theta))y^\nu},$$

$$Y_\mu = (\xi_\mu, f[u(\theta) + S(\theta)y]) - \sum_{\nu=2}^{n} \left(\xi_\nu, \frac{d\xi_\nu}{d\theta} y^\nu\right) \Theta.$$

From these formulas we see that Y and Θ are periodic in θ with period T; hence the system in normal variations is a linear system with periodic coefficients of period T.

The variational system corresponding to the solution $u(t)$ has the matrix $A(t) = f_x'[u(t)]$, and since f_x' has the same properties of partial periodicity as f, it follows that $A(t)$ is likewise periodic in t of period T. The variational system

$$\frac{dv}{dt} = A(t)v$$

admits the solution

$$v = \frac{du}{dt} = \omega p + \frac{d\psi}{dt}$$

periodic in t of period T. Thus it admits in any case a multiplier equal to 1. Repeating the calculations carried out in the case where $u(t)$ was periodic, we deduce that the other multipliers of the variational system coincide with the multipliers of the system in normal variations.

Thus we deduce

Theorem 3.14.′ *If $(n - 1)$ multipliers of the variational system corresponding to the periodic solution of the second kind, $u(t)$, are in the interior of the unit circle, this solution is orbitally stable; this means that if $x(t_0)$ is close enough to the curve $x = u(t)$, there exists c such that*

$$\lim_{t\to\infty} [x(t) - u(t + c)] = 0.$$

This theorem has been stated by O. Vejvoda.

Let us now consider a system with a small parameter of the form

$$\frac{dx}{dt} = f(x, \epsilon), \qquad f(x + 2\pi p, \epsilon) = f(x, \epsilon),$$

and suppose that for $\epsilon = 0$ the system admits a periodic solution of the second kind, $u(t)$. Considering again the system of vectors $\xi_1, \ldots, \xi_n$ attached to this solution and performing the change of variables

$$x = u(\theta) + S(\theta)y$$

we obtain a system of the form

$$\frac{dy}{dt} = Y(\theta, y, \epsilon), \qquad \frac{d\theta}{dt} = \Theta(\theta, y, \epsilon).$$

As in the case where u is periodic, we pass to the system

$$\frac{dy}{dt} = \frac{Y(\theta, y, \epsilon)}{\Theta(\theta, y, \epsilon)} = B(\theta)y + \epsilon\eta(\theta) + o(|\, y \,| + |\, \epsilon \,|)$$

and by the usual methods it becomes obvious that if the variational system corresponding to the solution $u(t)$ has $(n - 1)$ multipliers different from 1, there exists a solution $y(\theta, \epsilon)$ periodic in θ of period T with

$$\lim_{\epsilon\to 0} y(\theta, \epsilon) = 0.$$

To this solution corresponds a solution of the initial system, of the form

$$x(t, \epsilon) = u[\theta(t, \epsilon)] + S[\theta(t, \epsilon)]y[\theta(t, \epsilon), \epsilon].$$

From

$$\frac{d\theta}{dt} = \Theta(\theta, y, \epsilon) = 1 + O(|\, y \,| + |\, \epsilon \,|)$$

we obtain

$$t(T) - t(0) = \int_0^T \frac{dt}{d\theta}\, d\theta = \int_0^T (1 + O(|\, y \,| + |\, \epsilon \,|))d\theta = T + \epsilon \tilde{T}(\epsilon),$$

since $y(\theta, \epsilon) = O(\epsilon)$.

We deduce from here that if t varies with $T + \epsilon\tilde{T}(\epsilon)$, θ varies with T and thus

$$\begin{aligned} x[t + T + \epsilon\tilde{T}(\epsilon), \epsilon] &= u[\theta(t, \epsilon) + T] + S[\theta(t, \epsilon) + T]y[\theta(t, \epsilon) + T, \epsilon] \\ &= u[\theta(t, \epsilon)] + 2\pi Np + S[\theta(t, \epsilon)]y[\theta(t, \epsilon), \epsilon] \\ &= x[\theta(t, \epsilon)] + 2\pi Np. \end{aligned}$$

From the fact that the solution $x(t, \epsilon)$ which we have obtained verifies the relation

$$x(t + T^*(\epsilon), \epsilon) = x(t, \epsilon) + 2\pi Np,$$

it follows that

$$x(t, \epsilon) = \frac{2\pi N}{T^*(\epsilon)}\, pt + \psi(t, \epsilon)$$

with

$$\psi(t + T^*(\epsilon), \epsilon) = \psi(t, \epsilon).$$

To this purpose, it suffices to verify that the difference $x(t, \epsilon) - [2\pi N/T^*(\epsilon)]pt$ is periodic, with period $T^*(\epsilon)$. We have

$$\begin{aligned} x(t + T^*, \epsilon) - \frac{2\pi N}{T^*(\epsilon)}\, p(t + T^*) &= x(t, \epsilon) + 2\pi Np - \frac{2\pi N}{T^*}\, pt - 2\pi Np \\ &= x(t, \epsilon) - \frac{2\pi N}{T^*}\, pt, \end{aligned}$$

and the property is proved. We have thus obtained

Theorem 3.15′. *If for $\epsilon = 0$ the system $\dot{x} = f(x, \epsilon)$ admits a periodic solution of the second kind, $u(t)$, such that the corresponding variational system has a single multiplier equal to 1, then for $|\, \epsilon \,|$ sufficiently small* *the system admits a unique periodic solution of the second kind, $x(t, \epsilon)$ with the property*

$$\lim_{\epsilon \to 0} x(t, \epsilon) = u(t).$$

If, in addition, none of the multipliers, with the exception of that equal to 1, is a root of unity, the system does not admit in the neighborhood of the curve $x = u(t)$ other solutions which are closed curves in phase space, except $x(t, \epsilon)$. If the multipliers different from 1 are in the interior of the unit circle, the periodic solution of the second kind $x(t, \epsilon)$ is orbitally stable.

In the same way one can study the cases where the variational system has several multipliers equal to 1, e.g., the cases when there exists a family of periodic solutions of the second kind. All this amounts to the study of periodic solutions of the system

$$\frac{dy}{d\theta} = B(\theta)y + \epsilon\eta(\theta) + o(|\, y \,| + |\, \epsilon \,|),$$

which is carried out by the usual methods.

3.10. A Method of Successive Approximations

We shall present below a method of study of some difficult cases from the theory of nonlinear systems containing a small parameter, elaborated by L. Cesari and representing the synthesis of a whole cycle of works of L. Cesari and of his co-workers. A system of differential equations of the form

$$\frac{dy}{dt} = A(\epsilon)y + \epsilon q(y, t, \epsilon) \tag{20}$$

is considered and the following conditions are assumed to be fulfilled:

(a) There exist numbers $\omega > 0$, $\delta > 0$, $\epsilon_0 > 0$, and integers $0 \leqslant \nu \leqslant n$, a_j, b_j, with $b_j > 0, j = 1, ..., \nu$, such that the n eigenvalues $\rho_j(\epsilon)$ of the matrix A are continuous functions of ϵ for $0 \leqslant \epsilon \leqslant \epsilon_0$ and verify the relations

$$\rho_j(0) = i\frac{a_j}{b_j}\omega \qquad (j = 1, ..., \nu)$$

$$\left| \rho_j(0) - \frac{im\omega}{b_0} \right| > \delta > 0 \qquad \text{for} \quad j = \nu + 1, ..., n, \; m = 0, \pm 1, \pm 2, ...,$$

where b_0 is a common multiple of the number $b_1, ..., b_\nu$. In addition, we will suppose that $A(\epsilon)$ is a diagonal matrix.

(*b*) There exists an $R > 0$ and a function $\psi(t) > 0$ integrable in every finite interval, such that $|y_l| \leqslant R$, $-\infty < t < \infty$ implies

$$|q_j(y, t, \epsilon)| \leqslant \psi_j(t) \qquad (j = 1, ..., n)$$

and for $\zeta > 0$ there exists a $\xi > 0$ such that $|y'_l|, |y''_l| \leqslant R$, $0 \leqslant \epsilon' \leqslant \epsilon'' \leqslant \epsilon_0$, $|y'_l - y''_l| \leqslant \xi$, $|\epsilon' - \epsilon''| \leqslant \xi$ implies

$$|q_j(y', t, \epsilon') - q_j(y'', t, \epsilon'')| \leqslant \zeta\psi(t).$$

In addition, $q(t, y, \epsilon)$ is periodic in t of period $2\pi/\omega$.

(c)

$$|q_j(y', t, \epsilon) - q_j(y'', t, \epsilon)| \leqslant \psi(t) \sum_{l=1}^{n} |y'_l - y''_l| \qquad (j = 1, 2, ..., n).$$

The results obtained will be applied to systems of the form

$$\begin{aligned} \frac{d^2u_j}{dt^2} + 2\alpha_j \frac{du_j}{dt} + \sigma_j^2 u_j &= \epsilon f_j\left(u, v, \frac{du}{dt}, t, \epsilon\right) \qquad (j = 1, ..., \mu) \\ \frac{dv_j}{dt} + \beta_j v_j &= \epsilon f_j\left(u, v, \frac{du}{dt}, t, \epsilon\right) \qquad (j = \mu + 1, ..., n). \end{aligned} \tag{21}$$

Suppose $\alpha_j^2 < \sigma_j^2$, $j = 1, 2, ..., \mu$; put $\gamma_j = \sqrt{\sigma_j^2 - \alpha_j^2}$ and $\rho_{j1}(\epsilon) = -\alpha_j + i\gamma_j$, $\rho_{j2}(\epsilon) = -\alpha_j - i\gamma_j$. We order the first μ equations so that for $\omega > 0$ we have

$$\alpha_j(0) = 0, \qquad \sigma_j(0) = \frac{a_j}{b_j}\omega, \qquad a_j > 0, b_j > 0 \qquad (j = 1, 2, ..., \lambda)$$

and

$$\rho_{j1}(0) \neq \frac{im\omega}{b_0}, \qquad \rho_{j2}(0) \neq \frac{im\omega}{b_0} \qquad (j = \lambda + 1, ..., \mu, m = 0, \pm 1, \pm 2, ...).$$

The last $(n - \mu)$ equations will be ordered so that $\beta_j(0) \neq 0$ for $j = \mu + 1, ..., r$ and $\beta_j(0) = 0$ for $j = r + 1, ..., n$, $\mu \leqslant r \leqslant n$. Suppose that the functions f_j verify conditions (b) and (c) with respect to the variables $(u, v, du/dt)$.

Introduce the new variables $y_1, ..., y_N$, $N = n + \mu$, putting

$$y_{2j-1} = -\rho_{j2}u_j + \frac{du_j}{dt} \qquad (j = 1, ..., \mu),$$

$$y_{2j} = \rho_{j1}u_j - \frac{du_j}{dt} \qquad (j = 1, ..., \mu),$$

$$y_{\mu+j} = v_j \qquad (j = \mu + 1, ..., n).$$

We obtain

$$u_j = \frac{1}{2i\gamma_j}(y_{2j-1} + y_{2j}), \frac{du_j}{dt} = \frac{1}{2i\gamma_j}(\rho_{j1}y_{2j-1} + \rho_{j2}y_{2j}) \qquad (j = 1, ..., \mu)$$

$$\frac{dy_{2j-1}}{dt} = -\rho_{j2}\frac{du_j}{dt} + \frac{d^2u_j}{dt^2} = -\rho_{j2}\frac{du_j}{dt} - 2\alpha_j\frac{du_j}{dt} - \sigma_j^2u_j + \epsilon q_{2j-1}(y, t, \epsilon)$$

$$= \rho_{j1}\frac{du_j}{dt} - \sigma_j^2u_j + \epsilon q_{2j-1}(y, t, \epsilon)$$

$$= \rho_{j1}y_{2j-1} + (\rho_{j2}\rho_{j1} - \sigma_j^2)u_j + \epsilon q_{2j-1};$$

hence

$$\frac{dy_{2j-1}}{dt} = \rho_{j1}y_{2j-1} + \epsilon q_{2j-1}(y, t, \epsilon).$$

Further,

$$\frac{dy_{2j}}{dt} = \rho_{j1}\frac{du_j}{dt} - \frac{d^2u_j}{dt^2} = \rho_{j1}\frac{du_j}{dt} + 2\alpha_j\frac{du_j}{dt} + \sigma_j^2u_j - \epsilon f_j$$

$$= -\rho_{j2}\frac{du_j}{dt} + \sigma_j^2u_j + \epsilon q_{2j} = \rho_{j2}(y_{2j} - \rho_{j1}u_j) + \sigma_j^2u_j + \epsilon q_{2j}$$

$$= \rho_{j2}y_{2j} + \epsilon q_{2j}(y, t, \epsilon),$$

$$\frac{dy_{\mu+j}}{dt} = -\beta_j y_{\mu+j} + \epsilon q_{\mu+j}.$$

System (21) is thus transformed in a system of the form (20). To the first ν equations of system (20) correspond the first 2λ and last $(n - r)$ equations of the transformed system. The numbers $\rho_j(0), j = 1, ..., \nu$ are here $i\tau_1, -i\tau_1, ..., i\tau_\lambda, -i\tau_\lambda, 0, ..., 0$, where 0 is repeated $(n - r)$ times, and $\tau_j = (a_j/b_j)\omega$.

Let us observe that for $\epsilon = 0$, system (20) admits the family of solutions depending on ν parameters:

$$y_j = c_je^{\rho_j(0)t} \qquad (j = 1, ..., \nu, y_j = 0, j = \nu + 1, ..., n).$$

But

$$e^{\rho_j(0)t} = e^{i(a_j/b_j)\omega t}$$

is a periodic function of t with period $2\pi b_j/\omega$; hence the solutions considered are periodic functions of t with period $2\pi b_0/\omega$, where b_0, as above, is the least common multiple of numbers $b_j, j = 1, ..., \nu$.

We are thus in the conditions of Theorem 3.8. The conditions of existence of a periodic solution of period $2\pi b_0/\omega$ can be obtained with the help of this general theorem. We will, however, study this problem independently of Theorem 3.8, with the help of L. Cesari's method, which can be applied in other cases, too. This method also makes available a technique of approximative computation, through successive approximations, of the periodic solution.

We will begin by some preparatory notions. Consider the family C_ω of functions $f(t)$, $-\infty < t < \infty$, which are finite sums of functions of the form $e^{\sigma t}\varphi(t)$, σ being a complex number and φ a complex-valued function, periodic in t of period $T = 2\pi/\omega$ integrable in $[0, T]$. Evidently C_ω is an additive class. If φ has the Fourier series

$$\varphi \sim \sum_{m=-\infty}^{+\infty} c_m e^{im\omega t},$$

then the series

$$\sum_{m=-\infty}^{+\infty} c_m e^{(im\omega+\sigma)t}$$

is called the series associate to the function f.

The mean value $\mathfrak{M}[f]$ *is defined by* $\mathfrak{M}[f] = c_m$ *if* $im\omega + \sigma = 0$ *and* $\mathfrak{M}[f] = 0$ *if there does not exist an* m *with* $im\omega + \sigma = 0$. *For every* $f \in C_\omega$, $\mathfrak{M}[f]$ *is defined and represents a linear functional on* C_ω. *For vector functions* $\mathfrak{M}[f]$ *is the vector with components* $\mathfrak{M}[f_j]$.

If $f \in C_\omega$, *a primitive* F *of* f *belongs to* C_ω *if and only if* $\mathfrak{M}[f] = 0$; *if* $\mathfrak{M}[f] = 0$, *there exists a primitive* F *unique, belonging to* C_ω *and such that* $\mathfrak{M}[F] = 0$. *This primitive will be denoted by* $\int f(t)dt$.

If $f = e^{(\alpha+i\beta)t}\varphi$ and $\mathfrak{M}[f] = 0$, $\varphi \sim \sum c_m e^{im\omega t}$, then

$$\int f(t)dt = e^{(\alpha+i\beta)t}\phi, \qquad \phi = \sum \frac{c_m}{\alpha + i\beta + im\omega} e^{im\omega t}.$$

For every constant $V \geqslant T$, there exists an $N(\sigma, T, V)$ such that

$$|F(t)| \leqslant N \int_0^T |\varphi(u)|\, du \qquad (0 \leqslant t \leqslant V).$$

For $\sigma \not\equiv 0 \pmod{\omega i}$,

$$F(t) = \frac{1}{e^{\sigma T} - 1} \int_t^{t+T} f(u)du,$$

and for $\sigma \equiv 0 \pmod{\omega i}$, $F(t) = 1/T \int_t^{t+T} uf(u)du$.

If $\sigma + im\omega \neq 0$ for $m = 0, \pm 1, \ldots$, and $0 < \delta \leqslant \min |\sigma + im\omega|$, $0 < \delta \leqslant \omega$, let σ' be such that $|\sigma - \sigma'| \leqslant \delta/2, f = e^{\sigma t}\varphi, f' = e^{\sigma' t}\varphi$, $V \geqslant T$. Then the unique primitives F, F', which have the mean value zero, verify the relation

$$|F(t) - F'(t)| \leqslant |\sigma' - \sigma| N' \int_0^T |\varphi(u)|\, du \qquad (0 \leqslant t \leqslant V).$$

Indeed, we have

$$F(t) = \frac{1}{e^{\sigma T} - 1} \int_t^{t+T} e^{\sigma u}\varphi(u) du, \qquad F'(t) = \frac{1}{e^{\sigma' T} - 1} \int_t^{t+T} e^{\sigma' u}\varphi(u) du;$$

hence

$$F(t) - F'(t) = \int_t^{t+T} \left[\frac{e^{\sigma u}}{e^{\sigma T} - 1} - \frac{e^{\sigma' u}}{e^{\sigma' T} - 1}\right] \varphi(u) du$$

$$= \frac{1}{(e^{\sigma T} - 1)(e^{\sigma' T} - 1)} \int_t^{t+T} (e^{\sigma u} e^{\sigma' T} - e^{\sigma' u} e^{\sigma T} - e^{\sigma u} + e^{\sigma' u})\varphi(u) du$$

$$= \frac{1}{(e^{\sigma T} - 1)(e^{\sigma' T} - 1)} \int_t^{t+T} \{e^{\sigma' T}[1 - e^{(\sigma' - \sigma)(u - T)}] + [e^{(\sigma' - \sigma)u} - 1]\} \times e^{\sigma u}\varphi(u) du,$$

from which immediately follows the foregoing evaluation.

Lemma. *If A is a constant matrix with eigenvalues $\rho_1, \ldots, \rho_n$, and f is a periodic vector with period $T = 2\pi/\omega$, and if there exists a $\delta > 0$ such that $|im\omega + \rho_j| \geqslant \delta > 0$ for every $m = 0, \pm 1. \pm 2, \ldots$, then the system $dy/dt = Ay + f$ has a unique periodic solution, of period T, and this solution statisfies the estimate*

$$|y_j(t)| \leqslant N \sum_{k=1}^{n} \int_0^T |f_k(t)|\, dt.$$

Proof. It may be assumed that A is triangular, since there always exists a linear transformation which leads to this form. The last equation of the system then has the form

$$\dot{y}_n = \rho_n y_n + f_n(t)$$

and admits the unique periodic solution

$$y_n(t) = e^{\rho_n t} \int e^{-\rho_n t} f_n(t) dt;$$

we have

$$|y_n(t)| \leqslant MN \int_0^T |f_n(t)|\, dt.$$

The next-to-last equation has the form

$$\dot{y}_{n-1} = \rho_{n-1}y_{n-1} + a_{n-1,n}\, y_n(t) + f_{n-1}(t)$$

and admits the unique periodic solution given by the formula

$$y_{n-1}(t) = e^{\rho_{n-1}t}\int e^{-\rho_{n-1}t}[a_{n-1,n}\, y_n(t) + f_{n-1}(t)]dt.$$

The procedure is repeated, and thus lemma is proved.

Given the numbers c_j, $j = 1, ..., \nu$, consider the set Ω of the continuous vector functions, periodic of the period $T = 2\pi b_0/\omega$ whose first ν components have the form

$$\varphi_j(t) = e^{i\tau_j t}[c_j + \varphi_j^*(t)], \qquad \mathfrak{M}[\varphi_j^*] = 0.$$

Consider the transformation defined by the relations

$$\psi_j(t) = c_j e^{i\tau_j t} + \epsilon e^{i\tau_j t}\int e^{-i\tau_j t}\{q_j[\varphi(t), t, \epsilon] - d_j\varphi_j(t)\}dt \qquad (j = 1, 2, ..., \nu)$$

$$\psi_j(t) = \epsilon e^{\rho_j t}\int e^{-\rho_j t}q_j[\varphi(t), t, \epsilon]dt \qquad (j = \nu + 1, ..., n)$$

where the numbers d_j are defined by the relations

$$c_j d_j = \mathfrak{M}[e^{-i\tau_j t}q_j(\varphi(t), t, \epsilon)] \qquad (j = 1, ..., \nu).$$

Observe that $e^{-\rho_j t}q_j[\varphi(t), t, \epsilon], j = \nu + 1, ..., n,$ are of the class $C_{\omega'}$, with $| - \rho_j + (im\omega/b_0) | > \delta > 0$, $\omega' = \omega/b_0$; hence they have the mean value zero.

We see immediately that the functions ψ_j are continuous and periodic of period T. Taking into account the relations which define d_j and the fact that $\mathfrak{M}[e^{-i\tau_j t}\varphi_j] = c_j$, $j = 1, ..., \nu$, it is clear that

$$\mathfrak{M}[e^{-i\tau_j t}\{q_j[\varphi(t), t, \epsilon] - d_j\varphi_j(t)\}] = 0$$

and we immediately deduce that

$$\mathfrak{M}[\psi_j(t)e^{-i\tau_j t}] = c_j \qquad (j = 1, ..., \nu).$$

It follows that the transformation considered maps Ω into itself.

We introduce in Ω the norm

$$\| \varphi \| = \max | \varphi_j(t)|$$

and Ω becomes a complete metric space. Let

$$z(t) = (c_1 e^{-i\tau_1 t}, ..., c_\nu e^{-i\tau_\nu t}, 0, ..., 0)$$

and Ω_0 be the sphere $\| \psi - z \| \leqslant r$. Let R be the number which intervenes in the hypotheses stated with respect to the functions q_j, and ψ be the function which intervenes in these same hypotheses; let $K > 0$ be such that $\int_0^T \psi(t)dt \leqslant KT$.

If $\max | c_j | \leqslant r_2 < R$ and $r = R - r_2$, for $\varphi \in \Omega_0$, we have

$$\| \varphi \| \leqslant \| z \| + r \leqslant r + r_2 = R,$$

and from

$$c_j d_j = \frac{1}{T} \int_0^T e^{-i\tau_j t} q_j[\varphi(t), t, \epsilon]dt$$

we obtain the estimate

$$| d_j | \leqslant \frac{1}{| c_j | T} \int_0^T \psi(u)du;$$

if $r_1 \leqslant | c_j |$, it follows that

$$| d_j | \leqslant \frac{K}{r_1};$$

hence

$$\begin{aligned} | \psi_j(t) - z_j(t)| &\leqslant N\epsilon \int_0^T \{| q_j[\varphi(u), u, \epsilon]| + | d_j | \, | \varphi_j(u)|\}du \\ &\leqslant N\epsilon \left[KT + \frac{TKR}{r_1}\right] \qquad \text{for} \quad j = 1, ..., \nu. \end{aligned}$$

For $j = \nu + 1, ..., n$ we have

$$| \psi_j(t) - z_j(t)| = | \psi_j(t)| \leqslant \epsilon HN \int_0^T | q_j[\varphi(u), u, \epsilon]du \leqslant \epsilon HNKT,$$

where $H = e^{\gamma T}$, $\gamma = \max | \operatorname{Re} \rho_j | \; (j = \nu + 1, ..., n)$. It follows that if ϵ is sufficiently small, we have $| \psi_j - z_j | < r$; hence the transformation considered maps the sphere Ω_0 into itself.

We shall show that for ϵ sufficiently small, the transformation is a contraction. We have

$$| d_j^1 - d_j^2 | \leqslant \frac{1}{| c_j | T} \sum_{l=1}^{n} \int_0^T \psi(u) | \varphi_l^1(u) - \varphi_l^2(u) | \, du \leqslant \frac{nK}{r_1} \| \varphi^1 - \varphi^2 \|,$$

$$| \psi_j^1 - \psi_j^2 | \leqslant N\epsilon \int_0^T \{ | q_j[\varphi^1(u), u, \epsilon] - q_j[\varphi^2(u), u, \epsilon] |$$

$$+ | d_j^1 | \, | \varphi_j^1(u) - \varphi_j^2(u) | + | d_j^1 - d_j^2 | \, | \varphi_j^2(u) | \} du$$

$$\leqslant N\epsilon \int_0^T \Big\{ \psi(t) \sum_{l=1}^{n} | \varphi_l^1(u) - \varphi_l^2(u) | + | d_j^1 | \, | \varphi_j^1(u) - \varphi_j^2(u) |$$

$$+ R \frac{nK}{r_1} \| \varphi^1 - \varphi^2 \| \Big\} du \leqslant \epsilon N \Big\{ KTn \| \varphi^1 - \varphi^2 \|$$

$$+ \frac{KT}{r_1} \| \varphi^1 - \varphi^2 \| + \frac{nKRT}{r_1} \| \varphi^1 - \varphi^2 \| \Big\} \leqslant \epsilon NM \| \varphi^1 - \varphi^2 \|$$

$$\text{for} \quad j = 1, \ldots, \nu,$$

$$| \psi_j^1 - \psi_j^2 | \leqslant \epsilon NHnKT \| \varphi^1 - \varphi^2 \| \qquad (j = \nu + 1, \ldots, n)$$

From this we see that if ϵ is small enough, the transformations is a contraction. It thus admits a fixed point in Ω_0. Let $y_j(t)$ be this fixed point. We have

$$y_j(t) = c_j e^{i\tau_j t} + \epsilon e^{i\tau_j t} \int e^{-i\tau_j t} \{ q_j[y(t), t, \epsilon] - d_j y_j(t) \} dt \qquad (j = 1, \ldots, \nu),$$

$$y_j(t) = \epsilon e^{\rho_j(\epsilon) t} \int e^{-\rho_j(\epsilon) t} q_j[y(t), t, \epsilon] dt \qquad (j = \nu + 1, \ldots, n).$$

We obtain

$$\frac{dy_j}{dt} = i\tau_j c_j e^{i\tau_j t} + i\tau_j \epsilon e^{i\tau_j t} \int e^{-i\tau_j t} \{ q_j[y(t), t, \epsilon] - d_j y_j(t) \} dt$$

$$+ \epsilon e^{i\tau_j t} e^{-i\tau_j t} \{ q_j[y(t), t, \epsilon] - d_j y_j(t) \}$$

$$= i\tau_j y_j + \epsilon q_j[y(t), t, \epsilon] - \epsilon d_j y_j(t) \qquad (j = 1, \ldots, \nu)$$

$$\frac{dy_j}{dt} = \epsilon \rho_j(\epsilon) e^{\rho_j(\epsilon) t} \int e^{-\rho_j(\epsilon) t} q_j[y(t), t, \epsilon] dt + \epsilon e^{\rho_j(\epsilon) t} e^{-\rho_j(\epsilon) t} q_j[y(t), t, \epsilon]$$

$$= \rho_j(\epsilon) y_j + \epsilon q_j[y(t), t, \epsilon] \qquad (j = \nu + 1, \ldots, n).$$

We deduce from this that the functions y_j satisfy system (20) if the supplementary conditions

$$\frac{ia_j}{b_j}\omega - \epsilon d_j = \rho_j(\epsilon) \qquad (j = 1, 2, ..., \nu) \qquad (*)$$

are fulfilled.

The solution $y(t)$ of system (20) and the equations (*) can be obtained by the following procedure of successive approximations:

$$y^{(0)}(t) = z(t),$$

$$y_j^{(m)}(t) = z_j(t) + \epsilon e^{i\tau_j t}\int e^{-i\tau_j t}\{q_j[y^{(m-1)}(t), t, \epsilon] - d_j^{(m-1)}y^{(m-1)}(t)\}dt \ (j = 1, ..., \nu),$$

$$y_j^{(m)}(t) = \epsilon e^{\rho_j(\epsilon)t}\int e^{-\rho_j(\epsilon)t}q_j[y^{(m-1)}(t), t, \epsilon]dt \qquad (j = \nu + 1, ..., n),$$

$$d_j^{(m-1)}c_j = \mathfrak{M}[e^{-i\tau_j t}q_j(y^{(m-1)}(t), t, \epsilon)] \qquad (j = 1, ..., \nu).$$

The relations (*) can be put under a more effective form. Indeed, we have

$$y_j = z_j + O(\epsilon), \qquad \rho_j(\epsilon) = \frac{ia_j}{b_j}\omega + \epsilon\sigma_j + o(\epsilon).$$

The relations (*) become

$$\epsilon\sigma_j + \epsilon d_j + o(\epsilon) = 0$$

or

$$\sigma_j + d_j + O(\epsilon) = 0.$$

On the other hand,

$$d_j = \frac{1}{c_j T}\int_0^T e^{-i\tau_j u}q_j[y(u), u, \epsilon]du = \frac{1}{c_j T}\int_0^T e^{-i\tau_j u}q_j[z(u), u, 0]du + O(\epsilon).$$

Hence the relations of the condition become

$$\sigma_j + \frac{1}{c_j T}\int_0^T e^{-i\tau_j u}q_j[z(u), u, 0]du + O(\epsilon) = 0.$$

Let

$$P_j(c_1, ..., c_\nu) \equiv \sigma_j + \frac{1}{c_j T}\int_0^T e^{-i\tau_j u}q_j[z(u), u, 0]du$$

$$z_j(u) = \begin{cases} c_j e^{i\tau_j u} & (j = 1, ..., \nu), \\ 0 & (j = \nu + 1, ..., n). \end{cases}$$

If $P_j(c_1^0, ..., c_\nu^0) = 0$ and $\partial(P_1, ..., P_\nu)/\partial(c_1, ..., c_\nu) \neq 0$ for $c_j = c_j^0$, then, on the basis of the implicit-function theorem, there exist quantities $c_j(\epsilon)$ which verify relations (*); hence there exists a periodic solution of period $T = 2\pi b_0/\omega$ of system (20).

We have finally obtained the following theorem:

Theorem 3.16. *We consider system* (20) *and suppose the conditions* (a), (b), (c) *satisfied. If*

$$\rho_j(\epsilon) = \frac{ia_j}{b_j}\omega + \epsilon\sigma_j + o(\epsilon) \qquad (j = 1, ..., \nu),$$

and if $c_1^0, ..., c_\nu^0$ *verify the conditions*

$$P_j(c_1^0, ..., c_\nu^0) = 0, \qquad \frac{\partial(P_1, ..., P_\nu)}{\partial(c_1, ..., c_\nu)} \neq 0$$

for $c_j = c_j^0$, *where*

$$P_j(c_1, ..., c_\nu) \equiv \sigma_j + \frac{1}{c_j T}\int_0^T e^{-i\tau_j u} q_j[z(u), u, 0]du,$$

$$z_j(u) = \begin{cases} c_j e^{i\tau_j u} \ (\tau_j = a_j/b_j), & (j = 1, ..., \nu), \\ 0 & (j = \nu + 1, ..., n), \end{cases}$$

then system (20) *admits a periodic solution* $y_j(t, \epsilon)$ *of period* T *with the property*

$$y_j(t, \epsilon) = z_j(t) + O(\epsilon).$$

Different conditions may be obtained from this theorem for systems of the form (21).

3.11. Periodic Perturbations of Autonomous Systems

With the view of studying the periodic perturbations of autonomous systems, we shall first give some general propositions in connection with the existence of invariant periodic surfaces for some classes of systems.

Consider a system of the form

$$\dot{\theta} = \Theta(t, \theta, y) \qquad \dot{y} = Y(t, \theta, y) \tag{22}$$

where Θ and Y are periodic in t with period T and in θ with period ω. We have the relations

$$\begin{aligned} \theta(t; \theta_0 + \omega, y_0) &= \theta(t; \theta_0, y_0) + \omega \\ y(t; \theta_0 + \omega, y_0) &= y(t; \theta_0, y_0) \end{aligned} \tag{23}$$

Indeed, from the periodicity of Θ and Y with respect to θ it follows that we have on both sides solutions of system (22), and these solutions coincide for $t = 0$.

The periodicity with respect to t entails the validity of the relations

$$\begin{aligned} \theta(t + T; \theta_0, y_0) &= \theta(t; \theta(T; \theta_0, y_0), y(T; \theta_0, y_0)), \\ y(t + T; \theta_0, y_0) &= y(t; \theta(T; \theta_0, y_0), y(T; \theta_0, y_0)). \end{aligned} \tag{24}$$

Let $\alpha : R \to R^{n-1}$ be continuous and periodic, of period ω. Consider for every fixed $t \geqslant 0$ the function $\rho_t^\alpha : R \to R$ defined by $\rho_t^\alpha(\sigma) = \theta(t; \sigma, \alpha(\sigma))$.

Suppose that for all fixed $t \geqslant 0$ and α, *the function* ρ_t^α *has an inverse and denote this inverse by* σ_t^α.

For every natural N define the mapping T_N by

$$(T_N\alpha)(\rho) = y(NT; \sigma_{NT}^\alpha(\rho), \alpha[\sigma_{NT}^\alpha(\rho)]).$$

Lemma 1. $T_{N+1}\alpha = T_N(T_1 \alpha)$ *for all* N; *hence* $T_N\alpha = T_1^N \alpha$.

Proof. From (24) we obtain

$$\begin{aligned} \theta((N + 1)T; \theta_0, \alpha(\theta_0)) &= \theta(NT; \theta(T; \theta_0, \alpha(\theta_0)), y(T; \theta_0, \alpha(\theta_0))), \\ y((N + 1)T; \theta_0, \alpha(\theta_0)) &= y(NT; \theta(T; \theta_0, \alpha(\theta_0)), y(T; \theta_0, \alpha(\theta_0))). \end{aligned} \tag{25}$$

Let us put $\theta(T; \theta_0, \alpha(\theta_0)) = \rho_1$; it follows that $\theta_0 = \sigma_T^\alpha(\rho_1)$ and

$$y(T; \theta_0, \alpha(\theta_0)) = y(T; \sigma_T^\alpha(\rho_1), \alpha[\sigma_T^\alpha(\rho_1)]) = (T_1\alpha)(\rho_1).$$

Let $\beta = T_1\alpha_1$. From the first equation of (25) follows

$$\theta((N + 1)T; \theta_0, \alpha(\theta_0)) = \theta(NT; \rho_1, \beta(\rho_1)) = \rho_{NT}^\beta(\rho_1);$$

hence $\rho_{N+1}^\alpha(\theta_0) = \rho_{NT}^\beta(\rho_1)$. Taking $\theta_0 = \sigma_{(N+1)T}^\alpha(\rho)$ it follows that $\rho = \rho_{NT}^\beta(\rho_1)$; hence $\rho_1 = \sigma_{NT}^\beta(\rho)$.

Using the second equation of (25) we further deduce that

$$\begin{aligned} (T_{N+1}\alpha)(\rho) &= y((N + 1)T; \sigma_{(N+1)T}^\alpha(\rho), \alpha[\sigma_{(N+1)T}^\alpha(\rho)]) \\ &= y(NT; \rho_1, \beta(\rho_1)) = y(NT; \sigma_{NT}^\beta(\rho), \beta(\sigma_{NT}^\beta(\rho)]) \\ &= (T_N\beta)(\rho); \end{aligned}$$

hence $T_{N+1}\alpha = T_N\beta = T_N(T_1\alpha)$.

Consequence. If there exists a natural N for which T_N admits a unique fixed point α_0, then α_0 is also a fixed point for T_1. Indeed, $T_N T_1\alpha_0 =$

$T_{N+1}\alpha_0 = T_1 T_N \alpha_0 = T_1\alpha_0$; hence $T_1\alpha_0$ is a fixed point of T_N and from the uniqueness of the fixed point it follows that $\alpha_0 = T_1\alpha_0$.

Lemma 2. $\rho_t^\alpha(\sigma + \omega) = \rho_t^\alpha(\sigma) + \omega$, $\sigma_t^\alpha(\rho + \omega) = \sigma_t^\alpha(\rho) + \omega$.

Proof. We have

$$\rho_t^\alpha(\sigma + \omega) = \theta(t; \sigma + \omega, \alpha(\sigma + \omega)) = \theta(t; \sigma + \omega, \alpha(\sigma)) = \theta(t; \sigma, \alpha(\sigma)) + \omega$$
$$= \rho_t(\sigma) + \omega.$$

From $\rho_t^\alpha(\sigma + \omega) = \rho_t^\alpha(\sigma) + \omega$ follows $\rho_t^\alpha[\sigma_t^\alpha(\rho) + \omega] = \rho_t^\alpha[\sigma_t^\alpha(\rho)] + \omega = \rho + \omega$; hence $\sigma_t^\alpha(\rho_t^\alpha[\sigma_t^\alpha(\rho) + \omega]) = \sigma_t^\alpha(\rho + \omega)$, and $\sigma_t^\alpha(\rho + \omega) = \sigma_t^\alpha(\rho) + \omega$.

Lemma 3. *$T_N\alpha$ is a periodic function.*

Proof.

$$\begin{aligned}(T_N\alpha)(\rho + \omega) &= y(NT; \sigma_{NT}^\alpha(\rho + \omega), \alpha[\sigma_{NT}^\alpha(\rho + \omega)])\\ &= y(NT; \sigma_{NT}^\alpha(\rho) + \omega, \alpha[\sigma_{NT}^\alpha(\rho) + \omega])\\ &= y(NT; \sigma_{NT}^\alpha(\rho) + \omega, \alpha[\sigma_{NT}^\alpha(\rho)])\\ &= y(NT; \sigma_{NT}^\alpha(\rho), \alpha[\sigma_{NT}^\alpha(\rho)]) = (T_N\alpha)(\rho).\end{aligned}$$

Lemma 4. *$T_N\alpha$ is continuous.*

Proof. This follows automatically from the continuity of σ_{NT}^α and from the theorem of continuity with respect to initial conditions.

Define the function $\Sigma(t, \theta)$ by the relation $\Sigma(t, \theta) = y(t; \sigma_t^\alpha(\theta), \alpha[\sigma_t^\alpha(\theta)]$. The function Σ is defined for $t \geqslant 0$ and θ real and has values in R^{n-1}.

Lemma 5. $\Sigma(0, \theta) = \alpha(\theta)$.

Proof. $\Sigma(0, \theta) = y(0; \sigma_0^\alpha(\theta), \alpha[\sigma_0^\alpha(0)] = \alpha[\sigma_0^\alpha(\theta)]$. However, $\rho_0^\alpha(\sigma) = \theta(0; \sigma, \alpha(\sigma)) = \sigma$; hence $\sigma_0^\alpha(\rho) = \rho$. It follows that $\Sigma(0, \theta) = \alpha(\theta)$.

Lemma 6. If $y_0 = \alpha(\theta_0)$, *then* $\Sigma(t, \theta(t; \theta_0, y_0)) = y(t; \theta_0, y_0)$; hence Σ is an invariant surface.

Proof. $\Sigma(t, \theta(t; \theta_0, y_0)) = y(t; \sigma_t^\alpha(\theta(t; \theta_0, y_0)), \alpha[\sigma_t^\alpha(\theta(t; \theta_0, y_0))])$. However, $\theta(t; \theta_0, y_0) = \theta(t; \theta_0, \alpha(\theta_0)) = \rho_t^\alpha(\theta_0)$; hence $\sigma_t^\alpha(\theta(t; \theta_0, y_0)) = \sigma_t^\alpha[\rho_t^\alpha(\theta_0)] = \theta_0$ and $\Sigma(t, \theta(t; \theta_0, y_0)) = y(t; \theta_0, \alpha(\theta_0)) = y(t; \theta_0, y_0)$.

Lemma 7. $\Sigma(t, \theta + \omega) = \Sigma(t, \theta)$.

Proof.

$$\begin{aligned}\Sigma(t, \theta + \omega) &= y(t; \sigma_t^\alpha(\theta + \omega), \alpha[\sigma_t^\alpha(\theta + \omega)]) \\ &= y(t; \sigma_t^\alpha + \omega, \alpha[\sigma_t^\alpha(\theta) + \omega]) = y(t; \sigma_t^\alpha(\theta) + \omega, \alpha[\sigma_t^\alpha(\theta)]) \\ &= y(t; \sigma_t^\alpha(\theta), \alpha[\sigma_t^\alpha(\theta)]) = \Sigma(t, \theta).\end{aligned}$$

Lemma 8. *If* $T_1\alpha = \alpha$, *then* $\Sigma(t + T, \theta) = \Sigma(t, \theta)$.

Proof. If $T_1\alpha = \alpha$ we have $\alpha(\rho) = y(T; \sigma_T^\alpha(\rho), \alpha[\sigma_T^\alpha(\rho)])$; hence

$$\alpha(\rho_T^\alpha(\sigma)) = y(T; \sigma_T^\alpha(\rho_T^\alpha(\sigma)), \alpha[\sigma_T^\alpha(\rho_T^\alpha(\sigma))]) = y(T; \sigma, \alpha(\sigma)).$$

On the other hand, $\theta(t + T; \theta_0, y_0) = \theta(t; \theta(T; \theta_0, y_0), y(T; \theta_0, y_0))$. If $y_0 = \alpha(\theta_0)$ we have $\theta(T; \theta_0, y_0) = \rho_T^\alpha(\theta_0)$, $y(T; \theta_0, y_0) = y(T; \theta_0, \alpha(\theta_0)) = \alpha[\rho_T^\alpha(\theta_0)]$; hence

$$\theta(t + T; \theta_0, y_0) = \theta(t; \rho_T^\alpha(\theta_0), \alpha[\rho_T^\alpha(\theta_0)]) = \rho_t^\alpha(\rho_T^\alpha(\theta_0)).$$

It follows that $\rho_{t+T}^\alpha(\theta_0) = \rho_t^\alpha[\rho_T^\alpha(\theta_0)]$. For $\theta_0 = \sigma_{t+T}^\alpha(\rho_0)$ we obtain $\rho_0 = \rho_t^\alpha[\rho_T^\alpha(\sigma_{t+T}^\alpha(\rho_0))]$; i.e., $\sigma_t^\alpha(\rho_0) = \rho_T^\alpha(\sigma_{t+T}^\alpha(\rho_0))$; hence $\sigma_{t+T}^\alpha(\rho_0) = \sigma_T^\alpha[\sigma_t^\alpha(\rho_0)]$. From this follows

$$\begin{aligned}\Sigma(t + T, \theta) &= y(t + T; \sigma_{t+T}^\alpha(\theta), \alpha[\sigma_{t+T}^\alpha(\theta)]) \\ &= y(t; \theta(T; \sigma_{t+T}^\alpha(\theta), \alpha[\sigma_{t+T}^\alpha(\theta)]), y(T; \sigma_{t+T}^\alpha(\theta), \alpha[\sigma_{t+T}^\alpha(\theta)])) \\ &= y(t; \rho_T^\alpha(\sigma_{t+T}^\alpha(\theta)), \alpha[\rho_T^\alpha(\sigma_{t+T}^\alpha(\theta))]) = y(t; \sigma_t^\alpha(\theta), \alpha[\sigma_t^\alpha(\theta)]) = \Sigma(t, \theta).\end{aligned}$$

Definition. *If* $\Sigma(t, \theta)$ *has the properties stated in Lemmas* 6, 7, and 8 *we say that* $y = \Sigma(t, \theta)$ *is an invariant periodic surface of system* (22).

It follows that to prove the existence of an invariant periodic surface we have to prove that for fixed $t \geqslant 0$ and α, the function $\rho_t^\alpha : R \to R$ admits an inverse and then that there exists a natural number N such that the mapping T_N admits a unique fixed point.

Consider a system of the form

$$\frac{dx}{dt} = X_0(x) + \epsilon X_1(t, x, \epsilon), \tag{26}$$

where X_1 is periodic with respect to t of period T, and suppose that the generating system

$$\frac{dx}{dt} = X_0(x)$$

admits a periodic solution $x = u(t)$, of period ω, with the property that the corresponding variational system has $(n - 1)$ multipliers situated in the interior of the unit circle.

By performing the change of variables defined by the orthogonal normed system $(\bar{X}_0, \xi_2, \ldots, \xi_n)$ we obtain a system of the form

$$\frac{d\theta}{dt} = \Theta_0(\theta, y) + \epsilon\Theta_1(t, \theta, y, \epsilon),$$
$$\frac{dy}{dt} = Y_0(\theta, y) + \epsilon Y_1(t, \theta, y, \epsilon), \tag{27}$$

where $\Theta_0, \Theta_1, Y_0, Y_1$ are periodic in θ with period ω, and Θ_1, Y_1 are also periodic in t with period T,

$$\Theta_0(\theta, 0) \equiv 1, \qquad Y_0(\theta, 0) \equiv 0.$$

The system $dz/dt = B(t)z$, $B(t) = \partial Y_0(t, 0)/\partial y$, has the multipliers in the interior of the unit circle; hence its zero solution is uniformly asymptotically stable.

We will prove that for $|\epsilon|$ sufficiently small, system (27) admits an invariant periodic surface. Consider the space of functions $\alpha : R \to R^{n-1}$ periodic of period ω, with the norm $\|\alpha\| = \sup_{\sigma\subset[0,\omega]} |\alpha(\sigma)|$. Consider the closed set formed by the functions with $\|\alpha\| \leqslant K|\epsilon|$, $|\alpha(\sigma_1) - \alpha(\sigma_2)| \leqslant L|\epsilon| |\sigma_1 - \sigma_2|$, L, K conveniently chosen. Let N be such that $|G(NT + \sigma)G^{-1}(\sigma)| < \frac{1}{2}$, where G is a fundamental matrix of solutions of the system $dz/dt = B(t)z$. The existence of such an N is assured by the uniform asymptotic stability of the zero solution of this system.

We will prove that for $|\epsilon|$ sufficiently small and α chosen in the set considered above, ρ_t^α has an inverse; T_N maps this set in itself and represents a contraction; hence it admits a unique fixed point. Denoting in the usual way the solutions of system (27), we obviously have

$$\theta(t, \theta_0, 0, 0) = t + \theta_0, \qquad y(t, \theta_0, 0, 0) \equiv 0,$$

hence

$$\frac{\partial\theta}{\partial\theta_0}(t, \theta_0, 0, 0) = 1, \qquad \frac{\partial y}{\partial\theta_0}(t, \theta, 0, 0) = 0,$$

and from direct considerations of continuity,

$$\frac{\partial\theta}{\partial\theta_0}(t, \sigma, \alpha(\sigma), \epsilon) = 1 + O(|\epsilon|), \qquad \frac{\partial y}{\partial y_0}(t, \sigma, \alpha(\sigma), \epsilon) = O(|\epsilon|)$$
$$(\sigma \leqslant t \leqslant \sigma + NT).$$

On the other hand, a direct computation leads to

$$\frac{\partial y}{\partial y_0}(t, \theta_0, 0, 0) = G(t + \theta_0)G^{-1}(\theta_0),$$
$$\frac{\partial \theta}{\partial y_0}(t, \theta_0, 0, 0) = \int_0^t \frac{\partial \Theta_0(t + \theta_0, 0)}{dy} G(t + \theta_0)G^{-1}(\theta_0)dt,$$

which shows that

$$\left|\frac{\partial y}{\partial y_0}(t, \theta_0, 0, 0)\right| < \tfrac{1}{2}, \qquad \frac{\partial \theta}{\partial y_0}(t, \theta_0, 0, 0) = O(1).$$

From direct considerations of continuity we deduce

$$\left|\frac{\partial y}{\partial y_0}(t, \sigma, \alpha(\sigma), \epsilon)\right| < \tfrac{1}{2} + O(|\epsilon|), \qquad \frac{\partial \theta}{\partial y_0}(t, \sigma, \alpha(\sigma), \epsilon) = O(1)$$
$$(\sigma \leqslant t \leqslant \sigma + NT).$$

To prove that ρ_t^α has an inverse $(0 \leqslant t \leqslant NT)$, we will show that $\theta(t, \sigma, \alpha(\sigma), \epsilon)$ is monotone-increasing. We have, for $\sigma_1 > \sigma_2$,

$$\begin{aligned}
&\theta(t, \sigma_1, \alpha(\sigma_1), \epsilon) - \theta(t, \sigma_2, \alpha(\sigma_2), \epsilon)\\
&= \frac{\partial \theta}{\partial \theta_0}(t, \sigma^*, \alpha^*, \epsilon)(\sigma_1 - \sigma_2) + \frac{\partial \theta}{\partial y_0}(t, \sigma^*, \alpha^*, \epsilon)[\alpha(\sigma_1) - \alpha(\sigma_2)]\\
&= [1 + O(|\epsilon|)](\sigma_1 - \sigma_2) + O(1)[\alpha(\sigma_1) - \alpha(\sigma_2)] > \tfrac{1}{2}(\sigma_1 - \sigma_2) - ML|\epsilon|(\sigma_1 - \sigma_2)\\
&= (\tfrac{1}{2} - ML|\epsilon|)(\sigma_1 - \sigma_2) > 0
\end{aligned}$$

if $|\epsilon|$ is small enough; hence ρ_t^α is monotone-increasing.

Let $\beta = T_N\alpha$. We have

$$\beta(\rho) = y(NT; \sigma_{NT}^\alpha(\rho), \alpha[\sigma_{NT}^\alpha(\rho)], \epsilon)$$

$$\begin{aligned}
|\beta(\rho)| &= |y(NT; \sigma_{NT}^\alpha(\rho), \alpha[\sigma_{NT}^\alpha(\rho)], \epsilon) - y(NT; \sigma_{NT}^\alpha(\rho), 0, 0)|\\
&= \left|\frac{\partial y}{\partial y_0}(NT; \sigma_{NT}^\alpha(\rho), 0, 0)\alpha[\sigma_{NT}^\alpha(\rho)] + \frac{\partial y}{\partial \epsilon}\epsilon + o(|\alpha| + |\epsilon|)\right|\\
&\leqslant \tfrac{1}{2}K|\epsilon| + K_1|\epsilon| + o(|\epsilon|);
\end{aligned}$$

$K_1 = \sup |(\partial y/\partial \epsilon)(NT, \sigma_{NT}^\alpha(\rho), 0, 0)|$ does not depend on K. Thus, choosing this quantity large enough, we will have $|\beta(\rho)| \leqslant K|\epsilon|$. Further,

$$\begin{aligned}
&|\beta(\rho_1) - \beta(\rho_2)|\\
&\qquad \leqslant |y(NT, \sigma_{NT}^\alpha(\rho_1), \alpha[\sigma_{NT}^\alpha(\rho_1)], \epsilon) - y(NT, \sigma_{NT}^\alpha(\rho_2), \alpha[\sigma_{NT}^\alpha(\rho_2)], \epsilon)|\\
&\qquad \leqslant K_2|\epsilon|\,|\sigma_{NT}^\alpha(\rho_1) - \sigma_{NT}^\alpha(\rho_2)| + (\tfrac{1}{2} + O(|\epsilon|))|\alpha[\sigma_{NT}^\alpha(\rho_1)] - \alpha[\sigma_{NT}^\alpha(\rho_2)]|\\
&\qquad \leqslant \{K_2|\epsilon| + (\tfrac{1}{2} + O(|\epsilon|)L|\epsilon|\}|\sigma_{NT}^\alpha(\rho_1) - \sigma_{NT}^\alpha(\rho_2)|.
\end{aligned}$$

From

$$\begin{aligned}\rho_1 - \rho_2 &= \theta(NT; \sigma_{NT}^{\alpha}(\rho_1), \alpha[\sigma_{NT}^{\alpha}(\rho_1)], \epsilon) - \theta(NT, \sigma_{NT}^{\alpha}(\rho_2), \alpha[\sigma_{NT}^{\alpha}(\rho_2)], \epsilon)\\ &= \frac{\partial\theta}{\partial\theta_0}(NT, \sigma^*, \alpha^*, \epsilon)[\sigma_{NT}^{\alpha}(\rho_1) - \sigma_{NT}^{\alpha}(\rho_2)]\\ &\quad + \frac{\partial\theta}{\partial y_0}(NT, \sigma^*, \alpha^*, \epsilon)(\alpha[\sigma_{NT}^{\alpha}(\rho_1)] - \alpha[\sigma_{NT}^{\alpha}(\rho_2)]),\end{aligned}$$

we obtain

$$| \sigma_{NT}^{\alpha}(\rho_1) - \sigma_{NT}^{\alpha}(\rho_2)| < (1 + O(| \epsilon |))| \rho_1 - \rho_2 |.$$

Consequently,

$$| \beta(\rho_1) - \beta(\rho_2)| \leqslant \{K_2| \epsilon | + (\tfrac{1}{2} + O(| \epsilon |))L| \epsilon |\}(1 + O(| \epsilon |))| \rho_1 - \rho_2 |.$$

Since K_2 is independent of L, it follows that for L large enough we have $| \beta(\rho_1) - \beta(\rho_2)| \leqslant L| \epsilon || \rho_1 - \rho_2 |$; hence T_N maps the closed set considered into itself.

Now let $\beta_1 = T_N\alpha_1$, $\beta_2 = T_N\alpha_2$. We have

$$\begin{aligned}| \beta_1 - \beta_2 | &= | y(NT; \overset{\alpha_1}{\sigma}_{NT}(\rho), \alpha_1[\overset{\alpha_1}{\sigma}_{NT}(\rho)], \epsilon) - y(NT; \overset{\alpha_2}{\sigma}_{NT}(\rho), \alpha_2[\overset{\alpha_2}{\sigma}_{NT}(\rho)], \epsilon)|\\ &\leqslant K_2| \epsilon | | \overset{\alpha_1}{\sigma}_{NT}(\rho) - \overset{\alpha_2}{\sigma}_{NT}(\rho)| + (\tfrac{1}{2} + O(| \epsilon |))| \alpha_1[\overset{\alpha_1}{\sigma}_{NT}(\rho)] - \alpha_1[\overset{\alpha_2}{\sigma}_{NT}(\rho)]|\\ &\quad + (\tfrac{1}{2} + O(| \epsilon |))| \alpha_1[\overset{\alpha_2}{\sigma}_{NT}(\rho)] - \alpha_2[\overset{\alpha_2}{\sigma}_{NT}(\rho)]|\\ &\quad + o(| \overset{\alpha_1}{\sigma}_{NT}(\rho) - \overset{\alpha_2}{\sigma}_{NT}(\rho)| + \| \alpha_1 - \alpha_2 \|)\\ &\leqslant \{K_2| \epsilon | + (\tfrac{1}{2} + O(| \epsilon |))L| \epsilon |\}| \overset{\alpha_1}{\sigma}_{NT}(\rho) - \overset{\alpha_2}{\sigma}_{NT}(\rho)|\\ &\quad + (\tfrac{1}{2} + o(| \epsilon |))\| \alpha_1 - \alpha_2 \| + o(| \overset{\alpha_1}{\sigma}_{NT}(\rho) - \overset{\alpha_2}{\sigma}_{NT}(\rho)| + \| \alpha_1 - \alpha_2 \|).\end{aligned}$$

On the other hand, from

$$\theta(NT; \overset{\alpha_1}{\sigma}_{NT}(\rho), \alpha_1[\overset{\alpha_1}{\sigma}_{NT}(\rho)], \epsilon) - \theta(NT; \overset{\alpha_2}{\sigma}_{NT}(\rho), \alpha_2[\overset{\alpha_2}{\sigma}_{NT}(\rho)], \epsilon) \equiv 0$$

follows

$$\begin{aligned}&[1 + O(| \epsilon |)][\overset{\alpha_1}{\sigma}_{NT}(\rho) - \overset{\alpha_2}{\sigma}_{NT}(\rho)] + O(1)(\alpha_1[\overset{\alpha_1}{\sigma}_{NT}(\rho)] - \alpha_2[\overset{\alpha_2}{\sigma}_{NT}(\rho)])\\ &\quad + o(| \overset{\alpha_1}{\sigma}_{NT}(\rho) - \overset{\alpha_2}{\sigma}_{NT}(\rho)| + | \alpha_1[\overset{\alpha_1}{\sigma}_{NT}(\rho)] - \alpha_2[\overset{\alpha_2}{\sigma}_{NT}(\rho)]|) \equiv 0;\end{aligned}$$

hence

$$| \overset{\alpha_1}{\sigma}_{NT}(\rho) - \overset{\alpha_2}{\sigma}_{NT}(\rho)| \leqslant K_3\| \alpha_1 - \alpha_2 \|,$$

from which follows

$$|\beta_1 - \beta_2| \leqslant K_4|\epsilon| \, \|\alpha_1 - \alpha_2\| + (\tfrac{1}{2} + O(|\epsilon|))\|\alpha_1 - \alpha_2\| + o(\|\alpha_1 - \alpha_2\|.$$

We deduce

$$\|\beta_1 - \beta_2\| \leqslant \tfrac{2}{3}\|\alpha_1 - \alpha_2\|,$$

which shows that T_N is a contraction for $|\epsilon|$ sufficiently small. It follows that T_N admits a unique fixed point; hence for $|\epsilon|$ sufficiently small, system (27) admits an invariant periodic surface.

Taking into account the property of invariant periodic surfaces expressed in Lemma 6, it follows that $\theta(t; \theta_0, \alpha(\theta_0), \epsilon)$ is the solution of the equation

$$\frac{d\theta}{dt} = \Theta_0(\theta, \Sigma(t, \theta, \epsilon)) + \epsilon\Theta_1(t, \theta, \Sigma(t, \theta, \epsilon), \epsilon) = f(t, \theta, \epsilon) \qquad (28)$$

The properties of invariant periodic surfaces from Lemmas 7 and 8 show that f is periodic in t with period T and in θ with period ω.

For the system in x we obtain the family of solutions

$$x(t; \theta_0, \epsilon) = u(\theta(t; \theta_0, \alpha(\theta_0), \epsilon)) + S[\theta(t; \theta_0, \alpha(\theta_0), \epsilon)] \Sigma(t, \theta(t; \theta_0, \alpha(\theta_0), \epsilon), \epsilon) \qquad (29)$$

which forms the variety $x = H(t, \theta, \epsilon)$, $H(t, \theta, \epsilon) = u(\theta) + S(\theta)\Sigma(t, \theta, \epsilon)$. Hence $H(t, \theta, \epsilon)$ is periodic in t with period T and in θ with period ω.

Observe that

$$\theta(t + T; \theta_0, \alpha(\theta_0), \epsilon) = \theta(t; \theta(T; \theta_0, \alpha(\theta_0), \epsilon), y(T; \theta_0, \alpha(\theta_0), \epsilon), \epsilon).$$

If we let $\theta_1 = \theta(T; \theta_0, \alpha(\theta_0), \epsilon)$, we have

$$y(T; \theta_0, \alpha(\theta_0), \epsilon) = \Sigma(T; \theta_1, \epsilon) = \Sigma(0; \theta_1, \epsilon) = \alpha(\theta_1) \qquad \text{(Lemma 5)}$$

Hence

$$\theta(t + T; \theta_0, \alpha(\theta_0), \epsilon) = \theta(t; \theta_1, \alpha(\theta_1), \epsilon).$$

It follows that

$$x(t + T; \theta_0, \epsilon) = u(\theta(t; \theta_1, \alpha(\theta_1), \epsilon) + S(\theta(t; \theta_1, \alpha(\theta_1), \epsilon)) \Sigma(t, \theta(t; \theta_1, \alpha(\theta_1), \epsilon), \epsilon).$$

For the solutions of this family we have

$$x_0 = u(\theta_0) + S(\theta_0)\Sigma(0, \theta_0, \epsilon) = u(\theta_0) + S(\theta_0)\alpha(\theta_0).$$

Every point of the surface $x = H(t, \theta, \epsilon)$ is situated on a solution of this family; indeed, let t_0 and θ be given. Since ρ_i^α has an inverse there exists a θ_0 such that $\theta = \theta(t_0; \theta_0, \alpha(\theta_0), \epsilon)$. Consider the solution of the system which for $t = 0$ coincides with $u(\theta_0) + S(\theta_0)\alpha(\theta_0)$. This solution will be given by formula (29) and will therefore be equal to $H(t_0, \theta, \epsilon)$ for $t = t_0$.

We obtain finally

Theorem 3.17. *For* $|\epsilon|$ *sufficiently small, system* (26) *admits a family of solutions which forms the surface* $x = H(t, \theta, \epsilon)$, *where* H *is periodic in* t *with period* T *and in* θ *with period* ω. *For* $\epsilon = 0$ *this surface reduces to the curve* $u(t)$.

The determination of this family of solutions is reduced to finding the function $\alpha(\sigma)$, invariant with respect to the transformation T_N, to the construction of the invariant periodic surface $y = \Sigma(t, \theta, \epsilon)$, and then to the solution of equation (28).

3.12. Singular Perturbations

We shall now study some problems relative to systems containing small parameters multiplying the derivatives. These problems will be called problems of *singular perturbation.*

Consider the system

$$\frac{dx}{dt} = f(t, x, y, \epsilon), \qquad \epsilon\frac{dy}{dt} = g(t, x, y, \epsilon). \tag{30}$$

Suppose that f and g are, respectively, periodic or almost periodic with respect to t, and admit the usual hypotheses of regularity. For $\epsilon = 0$ we obtain the system

$$\frac{dx}{dt} = f(t, x, y, 0), \qquad g(t, x, y, 0) = 0 \tag{31}$$

Suppose that system (31) admits a periodic or an almost-periodic solution $u(t)$, $v(t)$, respectively, such that the matrix $g'_y[t, u(t), v(t), 0]$ is nonsingular for every t. Set

$$U(t) = (g'_y[t, u(t), v(t), 0])^{-1} g'_x[t, u(t), v(t), 0].$$

In the following pages f'_x, f'_y, f'_ϵ will be the derivatives of the function f in point $[t, u(t), v(t), 0]$, and g'_y, g'_x, the derivatives of the function g in the same point.

Perform in system (30) the change of variables

$$\xi = x - u(t), \qquad \eta = y - v(t) + U(t)\xi.$$

We obtain

$$\frac{d\xi}{dt} = f[t, \xi + u(t), \eta + v(t) - U(t)\xi, \epsilon] - f[t, u(t), v(t), 0],$$

$$\frac{d\eta}{dt} = \frac{1}{\epsilon} g[t, \xi + u(t), \eta + v(t) - U(t)\xi, \epsilon] - \frac{dv(t)}{dt} + \frac{dU(t)}{dt}\xi + U(t)\frac{d\xi}{dt}.$$

From this follows

$$\frac{d\xi}{dt} = f_x'\xi(t) + f_y'[\eta - U(t)\xi] + \epsilon f_\epsilon' + F[t, \xi, \eta, \epsilon],$$

$$\epsilon \frac{d\eta}{dt} = g_x'\xi + g_y'[\eta - U(t)\xi] + \epsilon \left[g_\epsilon' - \frac{dy}{dt}\right] + G(t, \xi, \eta, \epsilon).$$

Set

$$A_1(t) = f_x' - f_y'U, \qquad A_2(t) = f_y', \qquad Q(t) = g_y'.$$

The system obtained is written

$$\begin{aligned} \frac{d\xi}{dt} &= A_1\xi + A_2\eta + \epsilon f_\epsilon' + F(t, \xi, \eta, \epsilon), \\ \epsilon \frac{d\eta}{dt} &= Q\eta + \epsilon \left(g_\epsilon' - \frac{dv}{dt}\right) + G(t, \xi, \eta, \epsilon), \end{aligned} \tag{32}$$

where

$$| F | = O(| \xi |^2 + | \eta |^2 + \epsilon^2), \qquad | G | = O(| \xi |^2 + | \eta |^2 + \epsilon^2).$$

In addition, F and G are Lipschitzian with an arbitrary small constant if $| \xi |, | \eta |, | \epsilon |$ are small enough.

Suppose that $(Q + Q^*)/2 \leqslant - \mu E$, $\mu > 0$; this implies in particular the previous hypothesis of the nonsingularity of matrix Q. In addition, Q^{-1} is then bounded. The coefficients A_1, A_2, Q and the functions f_ϵ', $g_\epsilon' - (dv/dt)$, F, G are respectively, periodic or, almost periodic.

We will finally suppose that the linear system

$$\frac{d\xi}{dt} = A_1\xi \tag{33}$$

has the trivial solution uniformly asymptotically stable. Under these conditions we prove that system (32) admits, respectively, a unique periodic or almost-periodic solution, which for $\epsilon \to 0$ tends to zero.

To this end we consider the operator which attaches respectively, to the periodic or almost-periodic functions $\alpha(t)$, $\beta(t)$, respectively the unique periodic or almost-periodic solution of the system

$$\begin{aligned} \frac{d\xi}{dt} &= A_1\xi + A_2\eta + \epsilon f_\epsilon' + F[t, \alpha(t), \beta(t), \epsilon], \\ \epsilon \frac{d\eta}{dt} &= Q\eta + \epsilon \left[g_\epsilon' - \frac{dv}{dt}\right] + G[t, \alpha(t), \beta(t), \epsilon]. \end{aligned} \tag{34}$$

From the second equation (34) we first determine respectively, the periodic or almost-periodic solution $\eta(t)$, which is substituted in the first equation.

The conditions imposed on the matrix Q assure the existence of this solution, and the condition imposed on system (33) assures, respectively, the existence of a periodic or almost-periodic solution which satisfies the estimate

$$|\xi| \leqslant K_1[K_2 \sup|\eta| + K_3|\epsilon| + O(|\alpha|^2 + |\beta|^2 + \epsilon^2)] \qquad \text{(Theorem 3.4).}$$

Let $\|\alpha\| \leqslant K|\epsilon|$, $\|\beta\| \leqslant K'|\epsilon|$. It follows that

$$|G[t, \alpha(t), \beta(t), \epsilon]| \leqslant L\epsilon^2.$$

We have

$$\epsilon\left(\eta, \frac{d\eta}{dt}\right) = (\eta, Q\eta) + \epsilon\left(\eta, g_\epsilon' - \frac{dv}{dt}\right) + (\eta, G);$$

hence, supposing that $\epsilon > 0$,

$$\epsilon \frac{1}{2}\frac{d}{dt}|\eta|^2 \leqslant -\mu|\eta|^2 + \epsilon|\eta|M + |\eta|L\epsilon^2.$$

Setting $|\eta|^2 = v^2$, we deduce that

$$v\frac{dv}{dt} \leqslant -\frac{\mu}{\epsilon}v^2 + vM + vL\epsilon,$$

i.e.,

$$\frac{dv}{dt} \leqslant -\frac{\mu}{\epsilon}v + M + \epsilon L.$$

From this we obtain the inequality

$$v \leqslant \frac{\epsilon}{\mu}(M + \epsilon L);$$

hence

$$|\eta| \leqslant \frac{\epsilon}{\mu}(M + \epsilon L).$$

Choosing K' large enough and ϵ small enough, we deduce that

$$|\eta| \leqslant K'\epsilon.$$

Further, from the first equation (34) we have

$$|\xi| \leqslant K_1(K_2K'\epsilon + K_3\epsilon + L_1\epsilon^2).$$

Choosing K large enough and ϵ small enough, we have

$$|\xi| \leqslant K|\epsilon|.$$

Consequently, the operator maps the set $\|\alpha\| \leqslant K\epsilon$, $\|\beta\| \leqslant K'\epsilon$ into itself. Let us show that the operator is a contraction on this set, for ϵ sufficiently small.

Let $\alpha_1, \beta_1, \alpha_2, \beta_2$, be given, $\xi_1, \eta_1, \xi_2, \eta_2$ be the corresponding images, $\gamma = \xi_1 - \xi_2$, $\delta = \eta_1 - \eta_2$. We have

$$\frac{d\gamma}{dt} = A_1\gamma + A_2\delta + F[t, \alpha_1(t), \beta_1(t), \epsilon] - F[t, \alpha_2(t), \beta_2(t), \epsilon],$$

$$\epsilon\frac{d\delta}{dt} = Q\delta + G[t, \alpha_1(t), \beta_1(t), \epsilon] - G[t, \alpha_2(t), \beta_2(t), \epsilon].$$

It follows, as above, that

$$\|\delta\| \leqslant L_2\epsilon(\|\alpha_1 - \alpha_2\| + \|\beta_1 - \beta_2\|)$$

and then that

$$\|\gamma\| \leqslant L_3\epsilon(\|\alpha_1 - \alpha_2\| + \|\beta_1 - \beta_2\|),$$

which shows that the operator is, for ϵ sufficiently small, a contraction.

We deduce the existence of a unique fixed point in the region $\|\alpha\| \leqslant K\epsilon$, $\|\beta\| \leqslant K'\epsilon$; hence, respectively, of a periodic or almost-periodic solution of system (32), of the form

$$\xi(t) = \epsilon\xi^*(t, \epsilon), \qquad \eta(t) = \epsilon\eta^*(t, \epsilon).$$

We have obtained

Theorem 3.18. *If system* (31) *admits, respectively, a periodic or almost-periodic solution* $u(t)$, $v(t)$ *such that* $(Q + Q^*)/2) \leqslant -\mu E$, *and if the trivial solution of system* (33) *is uniformly asymptotically stable, system* (30) *admits, respectively, for* $0 < \epsilon < \epsilon_0$ *a unique periodic or almost-periodic solution* $[x(t, \epsilon), y(t, \epsilon)]$ *of the form*

$$x(t, \epsilon) = u(t) + \epsilon\xi^*(t, \epsilon),$$

$$y(t, \epsilon) = v(t) + \epsilon\eta^*(t, \epsilon) - \epsilon U(t)\xi^*(t, \epsilon).$$

Remark. In the case of periodic solutions, the condition imposed on system (33) may be weakened, by requiring only that it does not admit periodic solutions of the period considered, different from the trivial solution.

Likewise, the condition imposed on the matrix Q can be weakened by requiring, for example, that for every t it admits eigenvalues with negative real parts $\leqslant -\alpha$. This condition can be weakened even more, but it leads to completely noneffective requirements.

We shall now consider only the periodic case and will suppose that the system obtained for $\epsilon = 0$ admits a family of periodic solutions depending on the parameters $c_1, c_2, \ldots, c_k$.

Denote by c the vector $(c_1, c_2, \ldots, c_k)$ of the parameters. In this case system (33) admits periodic solutions. Indeed, from

$$\frac{du(t,c)}{dt} = f[t, u(t,c), v(t,c), 0],$$

$$g[t, u(t,c), v(t,c), 0] \equiv 0,$$

we obtain

$$\frac{d}{dt}\frac{\partial u(t,c)}{\partial c} = f'_x \frac{\partial u(t,c)}{\partial c} + f'_y \frac{\partial v(t,c)}{\partial c},$$

$$g'_x \frac{\partial u(t,c)}{\partial c} + g'_y \frac{\partial v(t,c)}{\partial c} = 0;$$

hence

$$\frac{\partial v(t,c)}{\partial c} = -U(t)\frac{\partial u(t,c)}{\partial c}.$$

It follows that

$$\frac{d}{dt}\frac{\partial u(t,c)}{\partial c} = [f'_x - f'_y U(t)]\frac{\partial u(t,c)}{\partial c} = A_1(t)\frac{\partial u(t,c)}{\partial c}.$$

Consequently, the periodic functions $\partial u(t,c)/\partial c$ are solutions of system (33). According to Theorem 3.2, the adjoint system of system (33) admits the same number of independent periodic solutions, which we will denote by $q_1(t,c), \ldots, q_k(t,c)$. Suppose that for a value c_0 of the parameter, system (32) admits a periodic solution of the form

$$\xi(t,\epsilon) = \epsilon\xi^*(t,\epsilon), \qquad \eta(t,\epsilon) = \epsilon\eta^*(t,\epsilon).$$

Then ξ^* and η^* verify the system

$$\frac{d\xi^*(t,\epsilon)}{dt} = A_1(t)\xi^*(t,\epsilon) + A_2(t)\eta^*(t,\epsilon) + f'_\epsilon + \epsilon F^*,$$

$$\epsilon\frac{d\eta^*(t,\epsilon)}{dt} = Q(t)\eta^*(t,\epsilon) + g'_\epsilon - \frac{dv}{dt} + \epsilon G^*.$$

Taking Theorem 3.2 into account we have

$$\int_0^{\omega} q_j(t, c_0)\{A_2(t)\eta^*(t, \epsilon) + f'_\epsilon + \epsilon F^*\}dt = 0 \qquad (j = 1, 2, ..., k).$$

Let $\eta^{**}(t) = \lim_{\epsilon\to 0} \eta^*(t, \epsilon)$. It follows that

$$\int_0^{\omega} q_j(t, c_0)\{A_2(t)\eta^{**}(t) + f'_\epsilon\}dt = 0 \quad (j = 1, 2, ..., k).$$

To compute η^{**} let us consider the system

$$\epsilon \frac{d\eta}{dt} = Q(t)\eta.$$

Let $U(t, s, \epsilon)$ be the fundamental matrix of this system. From the hypotheses $(Q + Q^*)/2 \leqslant - \mu E$ follows the inequality

$$| U(t, s, \epsilon)| \leqslant Be^{-(\mu/\epsilon))t-s)}.$$

The periodic solution $\eta^*(t, \epsilon)$ may be written in the form

$$\eta^*(t, \epsilon) = \int_{-\infty}^{t} \frac{1}{\epsilon} U(t, s, \epsilon) \left[g'_\epsilon - \frac{dv}{ds} + \epsilon G^*\right] ds.$$

We have

$$\left| \int_{-\infty}^{t} U(t, s, \epsilon)G^* \, ds \right| \leqslant M \int_{-\infty}^{t} e^{-(\mu/\epsilon))t-s)} \, ds = M \frac{\epsilon}{\mu};$$

hence

$$\lim_{\epsilon\to 0} \int_{-\infty}^{t} U(t, s, \epsilon)G^* \, ds = 0.$$

It follows that

$$\eta^{**}(t) = \lim_{\epsilon\to 0} \frac{1}{\epsilon} \int_{-\infty}^{t} U(t, s, \epsilon) \left(g'_\epsilon - \frac{dv}{ds}\right) ds.$$

Further,

$$\frac{1}{\epsilon} \left| \int_{-\infty}^{t-\sqrt{\epsilon}} U(t, s, \epsilon) \left(g'_\epsilon - \frac{dv}{ds}\right) ds \right| \leqslant \frac{M_1}{\epsilon} e^{-(\mu/\epsilon)t} \frac{\epsilon}{\mu} e^{(\mu/\epsilon)s} \Big|_{-\infty}^{t-\sqrt{\epsilon}} = \frac{M_1}{\mu} e^{-\mu/\sqrt{\epsilon}};$$

hence

$$\lim_{\epsilon\to 0} \frac{1}{\epsilon} \int_{-\infty}^{t-\sqrt{\epsilon}} U(t, s, \epsilon) \left(g'_\epsilon - \frac{dv}{ds}\right) ds = 0.$$

Consequently, we have

$$\eta^{**}(t) = \lim_{\epsilon\to 0} \frac{1}{\epsilon} \int_{t-\sqrt{\epsilon}}^{t} U(t, s, \epsilon) \left(g_\epsilon' - \frac{dv}{ds}\right) ds,$$

$$\frac{1}{\epsilon} \int_{t-\sqrt{\epsilon}}^{t} U(t, s, \epsilon) \left(g_\epsilon' - \frac{du}{ds}\right) ds = -\frac{1}{\epsilon} \int_{t-\sqrt{\epsilon}}^{t} -U(t, s, \epsilon)Q(s)Q^{-1}(s) \left(g_\epsilon' - \frac{dv}{ds}\right) ds$$

$$= -\int_{t-\sqrt{\epsilon}}^{t} \frac{d}{ds} U(t, s, \epsilon)Q^{-1}(s) \left(g_\epsilon' - \frac{dv}{ds}\right) ds$$

$$= -U(t, s, \epsilon)Q^{-1}(s)\left(g_\epsilon' - \frac{dv}{ds}\right)\Big|_{t-\sqrt{\epsilon}}^{t} + \int_{t-\sqrt{\epsilon}}^{t} U(t, s, \epsilon) \frac{d}{ds} Q^{-1}(s)\left(g_\epsilon' - \frac{dv}{ds}\right) ds$$

$$= -Q^{-1}(t) \left(g_\epsilon' - \frac{dv}{dt}\right) + U(t, t - \sqrt{\epsilon}, \epsilon)Q^{-1}(t - \sqrt{\epsilon}) \left(g_\epsilon' - \frac{dv}{ds}\right)_{s=t-\sqrt{\epsilon}}$$

$$+ \int_{t-\sqrt{\epsilon}}^{t} U(t, s, \epsilon) \frac{d}{ds} Q^{-1}(s) \left(g_\epsilon' - \frac{dv}{ds}\right) ds.$$

For $\epsilon \to 0$, the last integral evidently tends to zero. Since

$$| U(t, t - \sqrt{\epsilon}, \epsilon)| \leqslant Be^{-(\mu/\epsilon)\sqrt{\epsilon}}$$

it also follows that the second term tends to zero. We finally obtain

$$\eta^{**}(t) = -Q^{-1}(t) \left[g' - \frac{dv}{dt}\right].$$

Theorem 3.19. *Suppose that system* (31) *admits a family of periodic solutions of period* ω, $[u(t, c), v(t, c)]$, *and that for the solution which corresponds to the value* $c = c_0$, *we have* $(Q + Q^*)/2 \leqslant -\mu E$. *If system* (30) *admits a periodic solution of period* ω *of the form*

$$x(t, \epsilon) = u(t, c_0) + \epsilon\xi^*(t, \epsilon), y(t, \epsilon) = v(t, c_0) + \epsilon\eta^*(t, \epsilon) - \epsilon U(t)\xi^*(t, \epsilon),$$

then

$$\int_0^\omega q_j(t, c_0) \left\{A_2(t, c_0)Q^{-1}(t, c_0) \left[g_\epsilon' - \frac{dv(t, c_0)}{dt}\right] - f_\epsilon'\right\} dt = 0 \qquad (j = 1, 2, ..., k),$$

for all periodic solutions $q_j(t, c_0)$ *of period* ω *of the adjoint system of system* (33).

We shall now study the problem of singular perturbations of autonomous systems of the form

$$\frac{dx}{dt} = f(x, y, \epsilon), \qquad \epsilon\frac{dy}{dt} = g(x, y, \epsilon). \tag{35}$$

For $\epsilon = 0$ we obtain the system

$$\frac{dx}{dt} = f(x, y, 0), \qquad g(x, y, 0) = 0.$$

Suppose that for $x \in D$ there exists a function $\varphi(x)$ such that

$$g(x, \varphi(x), 0) \equiv 0.$$

Consider the system

$$\frac{dx}{dt} = f[x, \varphi(x), 0] \qquad (x \in D). \tag{36}$$

Suppose that this system admits in D a periodic or almost-periodic solution, $u(t)$, respectively. Consider the orthogonal normed system $\xi_1, \xi_2, \ldots, \xi_l$ attached to this solution, where

$$\xi_1 = \frac{f[u(t), \varphi(u(t)), 0]}{|f[u(t), \varphi(u(t)), 0]|}.$$

From the construction of the vectors $\xi_1, \ldots, \xi_l$ it follows that they are respectively, periodic or almost periodic in t.

Perform in system (35) the change of variables

$$x = u(\theta) + S(\theta)z,$$

the new variables being θ and z, and S the matrix whose columns are vectors $\xi_2, \ldots, \xi_l$. We obtain a system of the form

$$\frac{d\theta}{dt} = \Theta(\theta, z, y, \epsilon),$$

$$\frac{dz}{dt} = Z(\theta, z, y, \epsilon),$$

$$\epsilon\frac{dy}{dt} = g[u(\theta) + S(\theta)z, y, \epsilon].$$

For $\epsilon = 0, z = 0, y = \varphi[u(\theta)]$, we have $\Theta = 1$; hence for y in the neighborhood of $\varphi[u(\theta)]$, and for small z and ϵ, we have $\Theta \neq 0$. We may therefore take θ as an independent variable and we obtain

$$\frac{dz}{dt} = \frac{Z(\theta, z, y, \epsilon)}{\Theta(\theta, z, y, \epsilon)}, \qquad \epsilon\frac{dy}{d\theta} = \frac{g[u(\theta) + S(\theta)z, y, \epsilon]}{\Theta(\theta, z, y, \epsilon)}.$$

We have thus obtained, respectively, a periodic or an almost-periodic system of the form

$$\frac{dz}{d\theta} = F(\theta, z, y, \epsilon), \qquad \epsilon \frac{dy}{d\theta} = Y(\theta, z, y, \epsilon),$$

as in Theorem 3.18.

For $\epsilon = 0$ we obtain

$$g[u(\theta) + S(\theta)z, y, 0] = 0,$$

which admits the solution

$$z = 0, \qquad y = \varphi[u(\theta)]$$

because

$$g(u(\theta), \varphi[u(\theta)], 0) \equiv 0$$

and

$$Z(\theta, 0, \varphi[u(\theta)], 0) \equiv 0.$$

We further have,

$$Y_z'(\theta, 0, \varphi[u(\theta)], 0) = \frac{g_x' S(\theta)\Theta - g\Theta_z'}{\Theta^2}\Bigg|_{\substack{z=0\\ y=\varphi[u(0)]\\ \epsilon=0}}$$

$$= g_x'(u(\theta), \varphi[u(\theta)], 0)S(\theta),$$

$$Y_y'(\theta, 0, \varphi[u(\theta)], 0) = \frac{g_y'\Theta - g\Theta_y'}{\Theta^2}\Bigg|_{\substack{z=0\\ y=\varphi[u(0)]\\ y=0}} = g_y'(u(\theta), \varphi[u(\theta)], 0).$$

It follows that

$$U(\theta) = (g_y'[u(\theta), \varphi[u(\theta)], 0])^{-1} g_x'[u(\theta, \varphi[u(\theta)], 0] S(\theta),$$

$$Q(\theta) = g_y'(u(\theta), \varphi[u(\theta)], 0).$$

We compute:

$$A_1(\theta) = F_z'(\theta, 0, \varphi[u(0)], 0) - F_y'(\theta, 0, \varphi[u(\theta)], 0)U(\theta),$$

$$F_z'(\theta, 0, \varphi[u(\theta)], 0) = \frac{Z_z'\Theta - Z\Theta_z'}{\Theta^2}\Bigg|_{\substack{z=0\\ y=\varphi[u(\theta)]\\ \epsilon=0}} = Z_\epsilon' - Z\Theta_z'\Bigg|_{\substack{z=0\\ y=\varphi[u(\theta)]\\ \epsilon=0}}$$

$$F_y'(\theta, 0, \varphi[u(\theta)], 0) = \frac{Z_y'\Theta - Z\Theta_y'}{\Theta^2}\Bigg|_{\substack{z=0\\ y=\varphi[u(\theta)]\\ \epsilon=0}} = Z_y' - Z\Theta_y'\Bigg|_{\substack{z=0\\ y=\varphi[u(\theta)]\\ \epsilon=0}}$$

System (36) is written in the new variables

$$\frac{d\theta}{dt} = \Theta(\theta, z, \varphi[u(\theta) + S(\theta)z], 0),$$

$$\frac{dz}{dt} = Z(\theta, z, \varphi[u(\theta) + S(\theta)z], 0);$$

hence

$$\frac{dz}{d\theta} = \frac{Z(\theta, z, \varphi[u(\theta) + S(\theta)z], 0)}{\Theta(\theta, z, \varphi[u(\theta) + S(\theta)z], 0)}.$$

The matrix of the system of normal variations is obtained by taking the derivative with respect to z in the point $z = 0$. We deduce

$$B(\theta) = \frac{[Z_z' + Z_y'\varphi_x'S(\theta)]\Theta - Z[\Theta_z' + \Theta_y'\varphi_x'S(\theta)]}{\Theta^2}\Bigg|_{z=0}$$

$$= Z_z' - Z_y'(g_y')^{-1}g_x'S(\theta) - Z\Theta_z' + Z\Theta_y'(g_y')^{-1}g_x'S(\theta)|_{z=0}$$

$$= (Z_z' - Z\Theta_z')_{z=0} - (Z_y' - Z\Theta_y')_{z=0}U = F_z' - F_y'U;$$

hence

$$B(\theta) = A_1(\theta).$$

If we suppose that the solution of the system of normal variations is uniformly asymptotically stable [which signifies in the periodic case that the variational system corresponding to solution $u(t)$ has all the multipliers except one in the interior of the unit circle], the conditions of Theorem 3.18 are fulfilled.

Theorem 3.20. *If system* (36) *admits, respectively, a periodic or an almost-periodic solution, $u(t)$, situated in D such that $(Q + Q^*)/2 \leqslant -\mu E$, where $Q = g_y'(u(t), \varphi[u(t)], 0)$, and if, in addition, the trivial solution of the corresponding system of normal variations is uniformly asymptotically stable, then for* $0 < \epsilon < \epsilon_0$ *system* (35) *admits, respectively, a unique periodic or an almost-periodic solution, which for* $\epsilon = 0$ *reduces to* $(u(t), \varphi[u(t)])$.

It is sufficient to observe that from the hypotheses of the theorem, on the basis of Theorem 3.18, follows the existence of a solution $z(\theta, \epsilon)$, $y(\theta, \epsilon)$ of the form

$$z(\theta, \epsilon) = \epsilon\xi^*(\theta, \epsilon), \qquad y(\theta, \epsilon) = \varphi[u(\theta)] + O(\epsilon),$$

which leads to a solution of the form

$$x = u(\theta) + \epsilon S(\theta)\xi^*(\theta, \epsilon), \qquad y(\theta, \epsilon) = \varphi[u(\theta)] + O(\epsilon).$$

NOTES

The proof of Theorem 3.3 follows [47]. Theorem 3.4 was given for the first time in [48]. The proof in the text is adapted from the proof given for systems with delayed argument in [49]. More general results in this sense are to be found in [50]. The results relative to quasi-linear systems have been published in [51]. The theory of systems containing a small parameter with numerous applications is presented in monograph [52](see also [4] and [5]). The method of averaging, in its most general form, has been presented by N. N. Bogoliubov in [53]. A detailed exposition of the method is to be found in [54]. The results of Section 3.6 have been published in [55] and [56]. The theorem of F. Browder is given in [57]. The theory of autonomous systems follows [58]. The result of E. A. Coddington and N. Levinson mentioned in Section 3.8 can be found in [4]. The theorem of Andronov and Witt for periodic solutions of the second kind has been given in [59]. The proof in the text is new. The method of L. Cesari is that given in [60]. The results of section 3.11 can be found in [61]. See also [104]. Theorem 3.18 has been given in a more general formulation for the case of periodic solutions in [62], and for the case of almost-periodic solutions in [63]. Theorem 3.19 is new. Theorem 3.20 for the almost-periodic case is new. The proof for the periodic case is new, although the result was given in [64].

For further references on the theory of oscillations and on the theory of stability see the book of L. Cesari [105]. See also the book of J. K. Hale [106].

CHAPTER 4

Systems with Time Lag

In many circumstances the duration of the transmission of the action cannot be neglected. This is the reason why the forces intervening in the system depend at every moment on the state of the system not only at the time considered but also on previous times. In the following paragraph we shall outline some qualitative problems of the theory of systems with time lag.

4.1. The Existence Theorem. General Properties

Let us consider a system of the form

$$\frac{dx(t)}{dt} = f[t, x(t), x(t-\tau)], \tag{1}$$

where $\tau > 0$; we suppose that f is continuous in all arguments. For such a system the solution is constructed by a "step-by-step-method," in the following way. Given a function $\varphi_0(t)$ continuous on $[t_0 - \tau, t_0]$, we form the system

$$\frac{dx}{dt} = f[t, x, \varphi_0(t-\tau)] \qquad (t_0 \leqslant t \leqslant t_0 + \tau)$$

and consider a solution of this system determined by the initial condition $x(t_0) = \varphi(t_0)$. Let $\varphi_1(t)$ be this solution, which exists by virtue of continuity hypotheses. If this solution is defined on the whole segment $[t_0, t_0 + \tau]$, we form the new system

$$\frac{dx}{dt} = f[t, x, \varphi_1(t-\tau)], \qquad (t_0 + \tau \leqslant t \leqslant t_0 + 2\tau)$$

and consider a solution of this system determined by the initial condition $x(t_0 + \tau) = \varphi_1(t_0 + \tau)$. Let $\varphi_2(t)$ be this solution. In general, assuming that $\varphi_{k-1}(t)$ is defined on the interval $[t_0 + (k-2)\tau, t_0 + (k-1)\tau]$, we form the system

$$\frac{dx}{dt} = f[t, x, \varphi_{k-1}(t-\tau)] \qquad (t_0 + (k-1)\tau \leqslant t \leqslant t_0 + k\tau)$$

and we consider a solution of this system with

$$x(t_0 + (k - 1)\tau) = \varphi_{k-1}[t_0 + (k - 1)\tau],$$

which is denoted by $\varphi_k(t)$. A solution of system (1), $x(t)$, defined by the initial function $\varphi_0(t)$ will be given by the relations $x(t) = \varphi_k(t)$ for $t \in [t_0 + (k - 1)\tau, t_0 + k\tau]$, $k = 0, 1, \ldots$. The function $x(t)$ is obviously continuous; as a consequence of its construction, the function $x(t)$ is differentiable in the interior points of intervals $[t_0 + (k - 1)\tau, t_0 + k\tau]$, $k \geqslant 1$. It is also obvious that $x(t)$ is differentiable and has a continuous derivative at the points $t_0 + k\tau$, $k \geqslant 1$. At the point t_0, only the right derivative exists.

If $f(t, x, y)$ verifies a Lipschitz condition with respect to x, whatever y is, then there exists a single solution which coincides with φ_0 in $[t_0 - \tau, t_0]$, since the functions $\varphi_k(t)$ are uniquely determined, and every solution coincides with $\varphi_k(t)$ in $[t_0 + (k - 1)\tau, t_0 + k\tau]$.

System (1) represents the simplest type of system with time lag. Other situations are also possible, in which the values of the function $x(t)$ appear with different time lags, and finally where these time lags depend on t. Thus we can consider systems of the form

$$\frac{dx(t)}{dt} = f[t, x(t), x(t - \tau_1(t)), x(t - \tau_2(t)), \ldots, x(t - \tau_m(t))].$$

We suppose for such systems that $\tau_j(t) \geqslant 0$ and we consider the set E_{t_0} constituted by values $t - \tau_j(t)$, $t \geqslant t_0$, which are smaller than or equal to t_0. The initial function φ_0 is given in a set E_{t_0}.

More generally, we may consider systems of the form

$$\frac{dx(t)}{dt} = f[t, x(t + s)], \tag{2}$$

where for every fixed t the components of vector f are functionals defined on the set of continuous functions given in $[-\tau, 0]$, $\tau > 0$. The function f therefore depends upon the whole behavior of function x on $[t - \tau, t]$. We will suppose the given initial function φ continuous in $[t_0 - \tau, t_0]$. We consider the metric space of continuous functions, given in $[t_0 - \tau, t_0 + h]$ with $h > 0$ sufficiently small, with the distance being defined by the usual norm of uniform convergence, that is, $\| u \| = \sup_{t_0 - \tau \leqslant t \leqslant t_0 + h} | u(t)|$; the subset of the functions in this space which coincide with φ in $[t_0 - \tau, t_0]$ obviously form a complete subspace. Let $A[u]$ be the operator defined in this complete subspace through the relations

$$A[u] = \begin{cases} \varphi(t_0) + \int_{t_0}^{t} f[\sigma, u(\sigma + s)]d\sigma & (\text{for } t_0 \leqslant t \leqslant t_0 + h), \\ \varphi(t) & (\text{for } t_0 - \tau \leqslant t \leqslant t_0). \end{cases}$$

It is obvious that the operator A maps the subspace considered into itself. We will suppose that f verifies a condition of the Lipschitz type and we will prove that A is a contraction. We have

$$|A[u_1] - A[u_2]| = \left| \int_{t_0}^{t} \{f[\sigma, u_1(\sigma + s)] - f[\sigma, u_2(\sigma + s)]\} d\sigma \right|$$

$$\leqslant \int_{t_0}^{t} |f[\sigma, u_1(\sigma + s)] - f[\sigma, u_2(\sigma + s)]| \, d\sigma \quad \text{for } t_0 \leqslant t \leqslant t_0 + h,$$

$$A[u_1] - A[u_2] \equiv 0 \qquad \text{for } t_0 - \tau \leqslant t \leqslant t_0 .$$

If we suppose that

$$|f(t, \varphi_1) - f(t, \varphi_2)| < L \| \varphi_1 - \varphi_2 \|$$

for φ_1, φ_2 in a neighborhood of $\varphi(t_0 + s)$, then, for h sufficiently small and u_1, u_2 in this neighborhood, it will follow that $A[u_1]$ and $A[u_2]$ are in the same neighborhood and in addition that

$$|A[u_1] - A[u_2]| \leqslant hL \| u_1 - u_2 \|.$$

Hence for h sufficiently small, A is a contraction. It follows under these conditions that A admits a fixed point and that this point is unique. If $x(t)$ is the fixed point of the operator A, we have

$$x(t) = \varphi(t) \qquad \text{for} \quad t \in [t_0 - \tau, t_0]$$

and

$$x(t) = \varphi(t_0) + \int_{t_0}^{t} f[\sigma, x(\sigma + s)] d\sigma \qquad \text{for} \quad t_0 \leqslant t \leqslant t_0 + h;$$

hence

$$\frac{dx(t)}{dt} = f[t, x(t + s)]$$

and $x(t)$ is a solution of system (2).

In this way, if f verifies a condition of the Lipschitz type, the theorem of existence and uniqueness is proved for general systems of the form (2). As in the case of systems of ordinary differential equations, this theorem has a local character.

We will denote by $x(t; t_0, \varphi)$, as in the case of systems of ordinary differential equations, the solution of system (2) defined for $t \geqslant t_0 - \tau$, which coincides with the initial function φ on $[t_0, t_0 - \tau]$.

Supposing that the Lipschitz-type condition is verified, let us prove the fundamental inequality‡

$$| x(t; t_0, \varphi_1) - x(t; t_0, \varphi_2)| \leqslant \| \varphi_1 - \varphi_2 \| e^{L(t-t_0)} \tag{3}$$

‡ The proof below reproduces the one carried out by N. N. Krasovski.

For $t = t_0$ the inequality is obviously verified. We assume that it is not verified for all t for which the solutions are defined and let t_1 be the upper bound of points t for which the inequality occurs. We have

$$|x(t_1; t_0, \varphi_1) - x(t_1; t_0, \varphi_2)| = \|\varphi_1 - \varphi_2\| e^{L(t_1 - t_0)}$$

and for every n there exists a t_n satisfying $t_1 < t_n < t_1 + (1/n)$ such that

$$|x(t_n; t_0, \varphi_1) - x(t_n; t_0, \varphi_2)| > \|\varphi_1 - \varphi_2\| e^{L(t_n - t_0)}.$$

We obtain

$$\frac{1}{t_n - t_1}\{|x(t_n; t_0, \varphi_1) - x(t_n; t_0, \varphi_2)| - |x(t_1; t_0, \varphi_1) - x(t_1; t_0, \varphi_2)|\}$$
$$> \frac{1}{t_n - t_1}[e^{L(t_n - t_0)} - e^{L(t_1 - t_0)}] \|\varphi_1 - \varphi_2\|;$$

hence

$$\limsup_{h \to 0+} \frac{1}{h}\{|x(t_1 + h; t_0, \varphi_1) - x(t_1 + h; t_0, \varphi_2)| - |x(t_1; t_0, \varphi_1) - x(t_1; t_0, \varphi_2)|\}$$
$$\geqslant L e^{L(t_1 - t_0)} \|\varphi_1 - \varphi_2\| = L|x(t_1; t_0, \varphi_1) - x(t_1; t_0, \varphi_2)|. \qquad (*)$$

From system (2) we obtain

$$\left|\frac{dx(t; t_0, \varphi_1)}{dt} - \frac{dx(t; t_0, \varphi_2)}{dt}\right|$$
$$= |f[t, x(t + s; t_0, \varphi_1)] - f[t, x(t + s; t_0, \varphi_2)]|$$
$$\leqslant L \sup_{-\tau \leqslant s \leqslant 0} |x(t + s; t_0, \varphi_1) - x(t + s; t_0, \varphi_2)|;$$

hence

$$\left|\frac{dx(t_1; t_0, \varphi_1)}{dt} - \frac{dx(t_1; t_0, \varphi_2)}{dt}\right|$$
$$\leqslant L \sup_{-\tau \leqslant s \leqslant 0} |x(t_1 + s; t_0, \varphi_1) - x(t_1 + s; t_0, \varphi_2)| \leqslant L\|\varphi_1 - \varphi_2\| e^{L(t_1 - t_0)}$$
$$= L|x(t_1; t_0, \varphi_1) - x(t_1; t_0, \varphi_2)|,$$

since for $s \leqslant 0$ we have $t_1 + s \leqslant t_1$, and the inequality (3) is verified.

However, we obviously have

$$\limsup_{h \to 0+} \frac{1}{h}\{|u(t_1 + h)| - |u(t_1)|\} \leqslant \left|\frac{du(t_1)}{dt}\right|;$$

hence

$$\limsup_{h\to 0+} \frac{1}{h}\{| x(t_1+ h; t_0 , \varphi_1) - x(t_1+ h; t_0 , \varphi_2)| - | x(t_1 ; t_0 , \varphi_1) - x(t_1 ; t_0 , \varphi_2)|\}$$
$$< L| x(t_1 ; t_0 , \varphi_1) - x(t_1 ; t_0 , \varphi_2)|,$$

which contradicts the inequality $(*)$. The existence of t_1 is contradictory, hence inequality (3) is valid for all values of t for which the solutions are defined.

Under the same conditions, let us also consider the system

$$\frac{du(t)}{dt} = f[t, u(t + s)] + g[t, u(t + s)]. \tag{4}$$

We prove the inequality

$$| x(t ; t_0 , \varphi) - u(t; t_0 , \varphi)| \leqslant (e^{L(t-t_0)} - 1) \sup | g(t, u(t + s))| \tag{5}$$

We use the same procedure as above. The inequality (5) is verified for $t = t_0$; let t_1 be the upper bound of the set of values t for which it still holds. We have

$$|x(t_1 ; t_0 , \varphi) - u(t_1 ; t_0 , \varphi)| = (e^{L(t_1-t_0)} - 1) \sup | g(t, u(t + s))|$$

and for every n there exists $t_1 < t_n < t_1 + (1/n)$ such that

$$| x(t_n ; t_0 , \varphi) - u(t_n ; t_0 , \varphi)| > [e^{L(t_n-t_0)} - 1] \sup | g(t, u(t + s))|.$$

We will have

$$\limsup_{h\to 0+} \frac{1}{h}\{| x(t_1 + h; t_0 , \varphi) - u(t_1 + h; t_0 , \varphi)| - | x(t_1 ; t_0 , \varphi) - u(t_1 ; t_0 , \varphi)|\}$$
$$\geqslant Le^{L(t_1-t_0)} \sup | g(t, u(t + s))|. \tag{$**$}$$

On the other hand,

$$\left| \frac{dx(t_1 ; t_0 , \varphi)}{dt} - \frac{du(t_1 ; t_0 , \varphi)}{dt} \right|$$
$$< L \sup_{-\tau\leqslant s\leqslant 0} | x(t_1 + s; t_0 , \varphi) - u(t_1 + s; t_0 , \varphi)| + \sup | g(t, u(t + s))|$$
$$\leqslant L(e^{L(t_1-t_0)} - 1) \sup | g(t, u(t + s))| + \sup | g(t, u(t + s))|$$
$$= Le^{L(t_1-t_0)} \sup | g(t, u(t + s))| + (1 - L) \sup | g(t, u(t + s))|$$
$$< Le^{L(t_1-t_0)} \sup | g(t, u(t + s))|$$

if we assume $L > 1$. It follows that

$$\limsup \frac{1}{h}\{| x(t_1 + h; t_0, \varphi) - u(t_1 + h; t_0, \varphi)| - | x(t_1; t_0, \varphi) - u(t_1; t_0, \varphi)|\}$$
$$< Le^{L(t_1 - t_0)} \sup | g(t, u(t + s))|,$$

which contradicts (**). The existence of t_1 is contradictory and thus inequality (5) is proved for all $t > t_0$ for which solutions (2) and (4) exist.

Let us suppose now that f has components which are differentiable in the sense of Fréchet. Then we could write

$$f[t, x(t + s)] - f[t, x_0(t + s)] = A(t, x(t + s) - x_0(t + s)) + o(\| x - x_0 \|),$$

where $A(t, \varphi)$ is a vector whose components are for every t linear functionals. Hence, on the basis of the Riesz theorem,

$$A(t, \varphi) = \int_{-\tau}^{0} (d_s\eta(t, s))\varphi(s),$$

$\eta(t, s)$ being a matrix which depends on the solution x_0. The linear system

$$\dot{y}(t) = \int_{-\tau}^{0} (d_s\eta(t, s))y(t + s) \tag{6}$$

is called the *variational system* corresponding to system (2) and the solution x_0.

To avoid the inconvenient representation (6) when dealing with general linear systems of this form, we will suppose that y is a row vector and will write

$$\dot{y}(t) = \int_{-\tau}^{0} y(t + s)d_s\eta(t, s). \tag{7}$$

In the case of systems of form (1), supposing that $f(t, u, v)$ is differentiable, the variational system is written

$$\dot{y}(t) = f_u'[t, x_0(t), x_0(t - \tau)]y(t) + f_v'(t, x_0(t), x_0(t - \tau)]y(t - \tau) \tag{7'}$$

Let us suppose that f is differentiable in the above sense and let $x(t; t_0, \varphi_0)$ and $x(t; t_0, \varphi)$ be two solutions of system (2). Setting

$$u(t) = x(t; t_0, \varphi) - x(t; t_0, \varphi_0),$$

we may write

$$\dot{u}(t) = f[t, x(t + s; t_0, \varphi)] - f[t, x(t + s; t_0, \varphi_0)]$$
$$= A(t, u(t + s)) + o(\| u \|).$$

Let $y(t)$ be the solution of the variational system (6) which in $[t_0 - \tau, t_0]$ coincides with $\varphi - \varphi_0$. Then, on the basis of inequality (5) we may write

$$| x(t; t_0, \varphi) - x(t; t_0, \varphi_0) - y(t)| = o(\| x(t; t_0, \varphi) - x(t; t_0, \varphi_0)\|),$$

and also taking into account inequality (3) we obtain

$$| x(t; t_0, \varphi) - x(t; t_0, \varphi_0) - y(t)| = o(\| \varphi - \varphi_0 \|). \tag{8}$$

We shall close these introductory considerations by observing that to a time-lag system of form (2) is attached an operator U_t defined on the space of the functions continuous in $[-\tau, 0]$ through the formula

$$U_t\varphi = x[t + s; 0, \varphi], s \in [-\tau, 0] \qquad (t \geqslant 0).$$

This operator has the following properties:

1. It is continuous for every fixed t; this results from inequality (3).

2. We have $U_0\varphi = \varphi$; hence U_0 is the identical operator.

3. If the system is linear, of forms (6) and (7), respectively, then U_t is a linear operator. Indeed, it follows from the system's linearity that every linear combination of solutions is a solution; hence

$$y(t; t_0, \alpha_1\varphi_1 + \alpha_2\varphi_2) = \alpha_1 y(t; t_0, \varphi_1) + \alpha_2 y(t; t_0, \varphi_2),$$

since both members of the equality contain solutions and these solutions coincide in $[t_0 - \tau, t_0]$.

From the equality written above, it follows that

$$U_t(\alpha_1\varphi_1 + \alpha_2\varphi_2) = \alpha_1 U_t\varphi_1 + \alpha_2 U_t\varphi_2 ;$$

hence U_t is linear.

Relation (8) shows that if (6) is the variational system attached to system (2) and to the solution $x(t; 0, \varphi_0)$ and if we denote by U_t the operator attached to (2) and by V_t the operator attached to system (6), then

$$\| U_t\varphi - U_t\varphi_0 - V_t(\varphi - \varphi_0)\| = o(\| \varphi - \varphi_0 \|).$$

Hence V_t is the Fréchet differential of U_t in point φ_0.

4.2. Stability Theory

We shall now state the fundamental propositions concerning Lyapunov stability for systems with time lag.

Definition. *The solution $x_0(t)$ of system (2) is said to be uniformly stable if for every $\epsilon > 0$ there exists a $\delta(\epsilon) > 0$ such that if $|\varphi(s) - x_0(s)| < \delta$ for $s \in [t_0 - \tau, t_0]$, then $|x(t; t_0, \varphi) - x_0(t)| < \epsilon$ for $t \geqslant t_0$.*

As in the case of systems of ordinary differential equations, the study of the stability of a solution $x_0(t)$ is reduced to the study of the stability of the trivial solution.

Theorem 4.1. *Let us suppose that there exists a functional $V[t, \varphi]$ defined for every t on the sphere $\| \varphi \| \leqslant H$ in the space of the continuous functions defined in $[-\tau, 0]$ with the following properties:*

1. *There exist functions $a(r)$, $b(r)$ continuous, positive, and monotone-increasing, with $a(0) = b(0) = 0$, such that $a(\| \varphi \|) \leqslant V[t, \varphi] \leqslant b(\| \varphi \|)$.*
2. *$V^*(t) = V[t, x(t + s; t_0, \varphi)]$ is a monotone-decreasing function for $t \geqslant t_0$, $(s \in [-\tau, 0])$.*

Then the trivial solution of system (2) is uniformly stable.

Proof. Let $\epsilon > 0$, $\delta(\epsilon) < b^{-1}[a(\epsilon)]$, $t_0 \geqslant 0$, φ be a continuous function on $[t_0 - \tau, t_0]$, $\| \varphi \| < \delta(\epsilon)$. Consider the solution $x(t; t_0, \varphi)$ and form the function

$$V^*(t) = V[t, x(t + s; t_0, \varphi)].$$

According to the hypothesis, this function is monotone-decreasing; hence

$$\begin{aligned} V^*(t) \leqslant V^*(t_0) &= V[t_0, x(t_0 + s; t_0, \varphi)] \\ &= V[t_0, \varphi(t_0 + s)] \leqslant b(\| \varphi \|) < b(\delta(\epsilon)) < a(\epsilon). \end{aligned}$$

From $a(\| x(t + s; t_0, \varphi) \|) < a(\epsilon)$ and the monotonicity of the function $a(r)$, it follows that $\| x(t + s; t_0, \varphi) \| < \epsilon$; hence $| x(t; t_0, \varphi) | < \epsilon$, for $t \geqslant t_0$.

Theorem 4.2. *If the trivial solution of system (2) is uniformly stable, there exists a functional $V[t, \varphi]$ with the properties of the preceding theorem.*

Proof. Let $G(r)$ be a continuous function, positive and monotone-increasing for $r > 0$, $G(0) = 0$. We define the functional $V[t, \varphi]$ by the relation

$$V[t, \varphi] = \sup_{\sigma \geqslant 0} G[\| x(t + \sigma + s; t, \varphi(u - t)) \|] \quad (t - \tau \leqslant u \leqslant t, \ -\tau \leqslant s \leqslant 0).$$

Since for $\sigma = 0$ we have

$$\| x(t + s; t, \varphi(u - t)) \| = \| \varphi(u - t) \| = \| \varphi \|$$

it follows that

$$V[t, \varphi] \geqslant G(\| \varphi \|).$$

From the uniform stability of the trivial solution of system (2) it follows that there exists a function $\delta(\epsilon)$ with the property that $\| \varphi \| < \delta$ implies $| x(t; t_0, \varphi)| < \epsilon$ for $t \geqslant t_0$. As we have shown in Chapter 1, the function $\delta(\epsilon)$ may be chosen monotone-increasing and continuous; hence there exists an inverse function $\epsilon(\delta)$ with the property that $| x(t; t_0, \varphi)| < \epsilon(\| \varphi \|)$, for $t \geqslant t_0 - \tau$ (we suppose in addition, which does not restrict the generality, that $\delta(\epsilon) < \epsilon$). From this it follows that

$$\| x(t + \sigma + s; t, \varphi(u - t))\| < \epsilon(\| \varphi \|);$$

hence

$$V[t, \varphi] < G[\epsilon(\| \varphi \|)].$$

Further,

$$V^*(t) = V[t, x(t + s; t_0, \varphi)] = \sup_{\sigma \geqslant 0} G[\| x(t + \sigma + s; t, x(t + s, t_0, \varphi))\|]$$
$$= \sup_{\sigma \geqslant 0} G[\| x(t + \sigma + s; t_0, \varphi)\|];$$

the solutions $x(u; t, x(t + s; t_0, \varphi))$ and $x(u; t_0, \varphi)$ coincide for $u \geqslant t$, since they coincide for all $t - \tau \leqslant u \leqslant t$.

Let $t_1 > t_2$, $d = t_1 - t_2$. We have

$$V^*(t_1) = \sup_{\sigma \geqslant 0} G[\| x(t_1 + \sigma + s; t_0, \varphi)\|] = \sup_{\sigma \geqslant 0} G[\| x(t_2 + d + \sigma + s; t_0, \varphi)\|]$$
$$= \sup_{\sigma \geqslant d} G[\| x(t_2 + \sigma + s; t_0, \varphi)\|] \leqslant \sup_{\sigma \geqslant 0} G[\| x(t_2 + \sigma + s; t_0, \varphi)\|] = V^*(t_2);$$

hence $V^*(t)$ is monotone-decreasing.

Definition. *The trivial solution of system (2) is called uniformly asymptotically stable if there exists a* $\delta_0 > 0$ *and functions* $\delta(\epsilon)$, $T(\epsilon)$ *such that* $\| \varphi \| < \delta$ *implies* $| x(t; t_0, \varphi)| < \epsilon$ *for* $t \geqslant t_0$ *and* $\| \varphi \| < \delta_0$ *and* $t \geqslant t_0 + T$ *implies* $| x(t; t_0, \varphi)| < \epsilon$.

Theorem 4.3. *Let us suppose that there exists a functional* $V[t, \varphi]$ *defined for every* $t \geqslant 0$ *on the sphere* $\| \varphi \| \leqslant H$ *of the space of the functions continuous in* $[-\tau, 0]$, *with the following properties*:

1. *There exist functions* $a(r)$, $b(r)$, $c(r)$ *continuous, positive, and monotone-increasing for* $r > 0$, $a(0) = b(0) = c(0) = 0$ *such that* $a(\| \varphi \|) \leqslant V[t, \varphi] \leqslant b(\| \varphi \|)$.

2.

$$\limsup_{h\to 0+} \frac{V(t+h, x(t+h+s; t, \varphi)] - V[t, \varphi(t+s)]}{h} \leqslant -c(\|\varphi\|).$$

Then the trivial solution of system (2) *is uniformly asymptotically stable.*

Proof. Let $\delta(\epsilon) < b^{-1}[a(\epsilon)]$, $\|\varphi\| < \delta(\epsilon)$, $V^*(t) = V[t, x(t+s; t_0, \varphi)]$. We have

$$\limsup_{h\to 0+} \frac{V^*(t+h) - V^*(t)}{h}$$

$$= \limsup_{h\to 0+} \frac{V[t+h, x(t+h+s; t_0, \varphi)] - V[t, x(t+s; t_0, \varphi)]}{h}$$

$$= \limsup_{h\to 0+} \frac{V[t+h, x(t+h+s; t_0, \varphi)] - V[t, x(t+s; t_0, \varphi)]}{h}$$

$$\leqslant -c(\|x(t+s; t_0, \varphi)\|) < 0$$

if $\|\varphi\| \neq 0$. From

$$\limsup_{h\to 0+} \frac{V^*(t+h) - V^*(t)}{h} < 0$$

it follows that $V^*(t)$ is monotone-decreasing; thus, as in Theorem 4.1, it follows that $\|x(t; t_0, \varphi)\| < \epsilon$ for $t \geqslant t_0$. Let us observe that since $V^*(t)$ is monotone-decreasing, it is differentiable almost everywhere and thus condition 2 is likewise verified almost everywhere by the derivative of the function V^*.

Let $\delta_0 = \delta(H)$, $T(\epsilon) = b[\delta_0]/c[\delta(\epsilon)]$, $\|\varphi\| < \delta_0$. If for $t \in [t_0, t_0 + T]$ we would have

$$\|x(t+s; t_0, \varphi)\| \geqslant \delta(\epsilon),$$

it would follow that

$$c(\|x(t+s; t_0, \varphi)\|) \geqslant c[\delta(\epsilon)].$$

Hence

$$\limsup_{h\to 0+} \frac{V^*(t+h) - V^*(t)}{h} \leqslant -c[\delta(\epsilon)],$$

from which, on the basis of a well-known result in the theory of functions of real variables,

$$V^*(t) - V^*(t_0) \leqslant -c[\delta(\epsilon)](t - t_0);$$

hence

$$V^*(t) \leqslant V^*(t_0) - c[\delta(\epsilon)](t - t_0)$$
$$\leqslant b(\| \varphi \|) - c[\delta(\epsilon)](t - t_0) \leqslant b(\delta_0) - c[\delta(\epsilon)](t - t_0).$$

From this follows

$$V^*(t_0 + T) < b(\delta_0) - c[\delta(\epsilon)]T = 0,$$

which is a contradiction. It follows that there exists $t' \in [t_0, t_0 + T]$ such that $\| x(t' + s; t_0, \varphi)\| < \delta(\epsilon)$; hence $| x(t; t', x(t' + s; t_0, \varphi))| < \epsilon$ for $t \geqslant t'$. This means, however, that for $t \geqslant t_0 + T$ we have $| x(t; t_0, \varphi)| < \epsilon$, and the theorem is thus proved.

Theorem 4.4. *If the trivial solution of system* (2) *is uniformly asymptotically stable, there exists a functional* $V[t, \varphi]$ *with the properties stated in the preceding theorem.*

Proof. As in the proof of Theorem 1.6, let $G(r)$ be a function with $G(0) = 0$, $G'(0) = 0$, $G'(r) > 0$, $G''(r) > 0$ for $r > 0$. We choose

$$V[t, \varphi] = \sup_{\sigma \geqslant 0} G(\| x(t + \sigma + s; t, \varphi(u - t))\|) \frac{1 + \alpha\sigma}{1 + \alpha}.$$

The proof is continued in the same way as in the case of Theorem 1.6; therefore we shall not repeat it.

Taking into account that f verifies a Lipschitz-type condition and using evaluation (3), we prove as in Theorem 1.6′ that we may choose a function G such that the functional $V[t, \varphi]$ verifies the inequality

$$| V[t, \varphi_1] - V[t, \varphi_2]| \leqslant M\| \varphi_1 - \varphi_2 \|,$$

for $\| \varphi_1 \| < \delta(\delta_0)$, $\| \varphi_2 \| < \delta(\delta_0)$.

Theorem 4.5. *If the trivial solution of the linear system* (6) *or* (7), *respectively, is uniformly asymptotically stable, then it is exponentially stable*; *i.e.*,

$$| y(t; t_0, \varphi)| \leqslant Be^{-\alpha(t-t_0)}\| \varphi \|.$$

Proof. We define the operation U_{t,t_0} by the relation

$$U_{t,t_0}\varphi = y(s; t_0, \varphi) \qquad (t - \tau \leqslant s \leqslant t).$$

This operation maps the space of continuous functions defined in $[t_0 - \tau, t_0]$ in the space of the functions continuous in $[t - \tau, t]$.

This operation is linear, because of the linearity of the system. The fundamental inequality (3) shows that it is also continuous. It follows therefore that it is bounded; hence there exists a quantity $\| U_{t,t} \|$ with the property

$$\sup_{\|\varphi\| \leqslant 1} \| U_{t,t_0}\varphi \| = \| U_{t,t_0} \|.$$

For $\| \varphi \| \leqslant \delta_0$, $t \geqslant t_0 + T$, we have $| y(t; t_0 \varphi,)| < \epsilon$; hence for $t \geqslant t_0 + T + \tau$ it follows that $\| U_{t,t_0} \varphi \| < \epsilon$.

We fix ϵ with $0 < \epsilon < 1$. Let φ_0 be arbitrary with $\| \varphi_0 \| \leqslant 1$; then $\| \delta_0\varphi_0 \| \leqslant \delta_0$; hence $\| U_{t,t_0}\delta_0\varphi_0 \| < \epsilon$ for $t \geqslant t_0 + T + \tau$ and $\| U_{t,t_0}\varphi_0 \| < \epsilon/\delta_0$. Since φ_0 is arbitrary with $\| \varphi_0 \| \leqslant 1$, we will have $\| U_{t,t_0} \| \leqslant \epsilon/\delta_0$ for $t \geqslant t_0 + T + \tau$, or $\| U_{t,t_0} \| \leqslant \epsilon$ for $t \geqslant t_0 + T_1 + \tau$, where we have set $T_1(\epsilon) = T(\delta_0\epsilon)$. We have the relation

$$U_{t,t_0}\varphi = U_{t,t_0+T_1+\tau}(U_{t_0+T_1+\tau,t_0}\varphi)$$

which amounts to

$$y(s; t_0, \varphi) = y(s, t_0 + T_1 + \tau; y(u; t_0, \varphi)) \qquad (u \in [t_0 + T_1, t_0 + T_1 + \tau]).$$

From here follows

$$\| U_{t,t_0}\varphi \| \leqslant \| U_{t,t_0+T_1+\tau} \| \cdot \| U_{t_0+T_1+\tau,t_0}\varphi \| \leqslant \epsilon^2 \| \varphi \| \qquad \text{for} \quad t \geqslant t_0 + 2(T_1 + \tau);$$

hence

$$\| U_{t,t_0} \| \leqslant \epsilon^2 \qquad \text{for} \quad t \geqslant t_0 + 2(T_1 + \tau).$$

By induction it follows immediately that $\| U_{t,t_0} \| \leqslant \epsilon^m$ for $t \geqslant t_0 + m(T_1 + \tau)$ and the proof continues using the same procedure as that for systems of ordinary differential equations (Section 1.4).

Theorem 4.4′. *If the trivial solution of the linear system* (6) *or* (7), *respectively, is uniformly asymptotically stable, there exists a functional* $V[t, \varphi]$ *defined for every* $t \geqslant 0$ *in the space of the functions continuous in* $[-\tau, 0]$, *with the following properties*:

1. $\| \varphi \|^2 \leqslant V[t, \varphi] \leqslant K_1 \| \varphi \|^2$.

2. $| V[t, \varphi_1] - V[t, \varphi_2] | \leqslant K_1(\| \varphi_1 \| + \| \varphi_2 \|) \| \varphi_1 - \varphi_2 \|$.

3. $$\limsup_{h \to 0+} \frac{V[t + h, y(t + h + s; t_0, \varphi)] - V[t, y(t + s; t_0, \varphi)]}{h} \leqslant -\| y(t + s; t_0, \varphi) \|^2.$$

Proof. Let

$$V[t, \varphi] = \int_0^\infty \| y(t + u + s; t, \varphi)\|^2 \, du + \sup_{\sigma \geqslant 0} \| y(t + \sigma + s; t, \varphi)\|^2;$$

we recall that $\| \varphi \| = \sup_{-\tau \leqslant s \leqslant 0} | \varphi(s)|$. Owing to exponential stability, the convergence of the integral is assured.

Obviously,

$$V[t, \varphi] \geqslant \sup_{\sigma \geqslant 0} \| y(t + \sigma + s; t, \varphi)\|^2 \geqslant \| \varphi \|^2.$$

From

$$| y(t; t_0, \varphi)| > Be^{-\alpha(t-t_0)} \| \varphi \|$$

we obtain

$$| y(t + u + s; t, \varphi)| \leqslant Be^{-\alpha(u+s)} \| \varphi \|;$$

hence $\| y(t + u + s; t, \varphi)\| \leqslant Be^{\alpha\tau} e^{-\alpha u} \| \varphi \|$; we deduce from this that

$$V[t, \varphi] \leqslant B^2 e^{2\alpha\tau} \int_0^\infty e^{-2\alpha u} \, du + B^2 e^{2\alpha\tau} \| \varphi \|^2 = \left(1 + \frac{1}{2\alpha}\right) B^2 e^{2\alpha\tau} \| \varphi \|^2 = K_1 \| \varphi \|^2.$$

Further,

$$\begin{aligned}
| V[t, \varphi_1] - V[t, \varphi_2]| & \\
\leqslant & \left| \int_0^\infty \| y(t + u + s; t, \varphi_1)\|^2 \, du - \int_0^\infty \| y(t + u + s; t, \varphi_2)\|^2 \, du \right| \\
& + | \sup_{\sigma \geqslant 0} \| y(t + \sigma + s; t, \varphi_1)\|^2 - \sup_{\sigma \geqslant 0} \| y(t + \sigma + s; t, \varphi_2)\|^2 | \\
\leqslant & \int_0^\infty | \| y(t + u + s; t, \varphi_1)\|^2 - \| y(t + u + s; t, \varphi_2)\|^2 | \, du \\
& + \sup_{\sigma \geqslant 0} | \| y(t + \sigma + s; t, \varphi_1)\|^2 - \| y(t + \sigma + s; t, \varphi_2)\|^2 | \\
\leqslant & \int_0^\infty (\| y(t + u + s; t, \varphi_1)\| + \| y(t + u + s; t, \varphi_2)\|) \\
& \times \| y(t + u + s; t, \varphi_1) - y(t + u + s; t, \varphi_2)\| \, du \\
& + \sup_{\sigma \geqslant 0} (\| y(t + \sigma + s; t, \varphi_1)\| + \| y(t + \sigma + s; t, \varphi_2)\|) \\
& \times \sup_{\sigma \geqslant 0} \| y(t + \sigma + s; t, \varphi_1) - y(t + \sigma + s; t, \varphi_2)\| \\
\leqslant & \int_0^\infty Be^{\alpha\tau} e^{-\alpha u} (\| \varphi_1 \| + \| \varphi_2 \|) Be^{\alpha\tau} e^{-\alpha u} \| \varphi_1 - \varphi_2 \| \, du \\
& + Be^{\alpha\tau} (\| \varphi_1 \| + \| \varphi_2 \|) Be^{\alpha\tau} \| \varphi_1 - \varphi_2 \| \\
= & B^2 e^{2\alpha\tau} \left(1 + \frac{1}{2\alpha}\right) (\| \varphi_1 \| + \| \varphi_2 \|) \| \varphi_1 - \varphi_2 \| \\
= & K_1 (\| \varphi_1 \| + \| \varphi_2 \|) \| \varphi_1 - \varphi_2 \|.
\end{aligned}$$

We have

$$V[t, y(t+s; t_0, \varphi)] = \int_0^\infty \| y(t+u+s; t, y(t+s; t_0, \varphi))\|^2\, du$$
$$+ \sup_{\sigma \geqslant 0} \| y(t+\sigma+s; t, y(t+s; t_0, \varphi))\|^2$$
$$= \int_0^\infty \| y(t+u+s; t_0, \varphi)\|^2\, du + \sup_{\sigma \geqslant 0} \| y(t+\sigma+s; t_0, \varphi)\|^2$$
$$= \int_t^\infty \| y(u+s; t_0, \varphi)\|^2\, du + \sup_{\sigma \geqslant 0} \| y(t+\sigma+s; t_0, \varphi)\|^2.$$

We have seen in the proof of Theorem 4.2 that $\sup_{\sigma \geqslant 0} \| y(t+\sigma+s; t_0, \varphi)\|^2$ is a monotone-decreasing function. It follows from this that

$$\limsup_{h\to 0+} \frac{V[t+h, y(t+h+s; t_0, \varphi)] - V[t, y(t+s; t_0, \varphi)]}{h}$$
$$\leqslant \frac{d}{dt}\int_t^\infty \| y(u+s; t_0, \varphi)\|^2\, du = -\| y(t+s; t_0, \varphi)\|^2.$$

The theorem is thus proved.

As in the case of systems of ordinary differential equations this theorem will serve to prove a stability theorem by the first approximation.

Theorem 4.6. *Let us consider the system*

$$\dot{x}(t) = A(t, x(t+s)) + f(t, x(t+s)), \tag{9}$$

where $A(t, x(t+s))$ is for every t a vector whose components are linear functionals in the space of the functions continuous in $[-\tau, 0]$ (with norms bounded as functions of t), and the components of vector f are for every t continuous functionals in the same space, with the property that $| f(t, x(t+s))| < \gamma \| x(t+s)\|$, γ being sufficiently small for $\| x(t+s)\| \leqslant H$. If the trivial solution of the first-approximation linear system

$$\dot{y}(t) = A(t, y(t+s)) \tag{10}$$

is uniformly asymptotically stable, then the trivial solution of system (9) is likewise uniformly asymptotically stable.

Proof. Let $V[t, \varphi]$ be the functional defined for system (10) on the basis of Theorem 4.4′. We consider a solution $x(t; t_0, \varphi)$ of system (9) with $\| \varphi \|$ sufficiently small; let

$$V^*(t) = V[t, x(t+s; t_0, \varphi)].$$

We evaluate

$$\limsup_{h\to 0+} \frac{V^*(t+h) - V^*(t)}{h}.$$

We have

$$\limsup_{h\to 0+} \frac{V^*(t+h) - V^*(t)}{h}$$

$$\leqslant \limsup_{h\to 0+} \frac{V[t+h, y(t+h+s; t, x(t+s; t_0, \varphi))] - V[t, x(t+s; t_0, \varphi)]}{h}$$

$$+ \limsup_{h\to 0+} \frac{V[t+h, x(t+h+s; t, x(t+s; t_0, \varphi)] - V[t+h, y(t+h+s; t, x(t+s; t_0, \varphi))]}{h}$$

$$\leqslant -\| x(t+s; t_0, \varphi)\|^2 + \limsup_{h\to 0+} \frac{|V[t+h, x(t+h+s; t, x(t+s; t_0, \varphi))] - V[t+h, y(t+h+s; t, x(t+s; t_0, \varphi))]|}{h}.$$

We have

$$|V[t+h, x(t+h+s; t, x(t+s; t_0,\varphi))] - V[t+h, y(t+h+s; t, x(t+s; t_0,\varphi))]|$$
$$\leqslant K_1(\| x(t+h+s; t_0, \varphi)\| + \| y(t+h+s; t, x(t+s; t_0, \varphi))\|)$$
$$\times \| x(t+h+s; t, x(t+s; t_0, \varphi)) - y(t+h+s; t, x(t+s; t_0, \varphi))\|.$$

On the other hand, on the basis of the estimate (3) we have

$$\| x(t+h+s; t, x(t+s; t_0, \varphi)) \| \leqslant e^{Lh} \| x(t+s; t_0, \varphi) \|,$$

and on the basis of the estimate (5)

$$\| x(t+h+s; t, x(t+s; t_0, \varphi)) - y(t+h+s; t, x(t+s; t_0, \varphi))\|$$
$$\leqslant (e^{Lh} - 1)\gamma e^{Lh}\| x(t+s; t_0, \varphi)\|.$$

According to the hypothesis made with respect to the linear system, we also have

$$\| y(t+h+s; t, x(t+s; t_0, \varphi))\| \leqslant B\| x(t+s; t_0, \varphi)\|.$$

We obtain

$$|V[t+h, x(t+h+s; t, x(t+s; t_0,\varphi))] - V[t+h, y(t+h+s; t, x(t+s; t_0,\varphi))]|$$
$$\leqslant K_1(e^{Lh} + B)\| x(t+s; t_0, \varphi)\|(e^{Lh} - 1)\gamma e^{Lh}\| x(t+s; t_0, \varphi)\|$$
$$= K_1\gamma(e^{Lh} + B)(e^{Lh} - 1)\| x(t+s; t_0, \varphi)\|^2.$$

From this we have

$$\limsup_{h\to 0+} \frac{\begin{array}{l}|\, V[t+h, x(t+h+s; t, x(t+s; t_0, \varphi))] \\ \qquad -V[t+h, y(t+h+s; t, x(t+s; t_0\ \varphi))]\,|\end{array}}{h}$$

$$\leqslant LK_1\gamma(1+B)\|\, x(t+s; t_0, \varphi)\|^2.$$

It follows that

$$\limsup_{h\to 0+} \frac{V^*(t+h) - V^*(t)}{h}$$
$$\leqslant -\|\, x(t+s; t_0, \varphi)\|^2 + \gamma LK_1(1+B)\|\, x(t+s; t_0, \varphi)\|^2$$
$$= -[1 - \gamma LK_1(1+B)]\|\, x(t+s; t_0, \psi)\|^2.$$

For $\gamma < 1/LK_1(1+B)$ we have

$$\limsup_{h\to 0+} \frac{V^*(t+h) - V^*(t)}{h} \leqslant -\gamma_1\|\, x(t+s; t_0, \varphi)\|^2,$$

which shows, on the basis of Theorem 4.3, that the trivial solution is uniformly asymptotically stable. It is easy to see that the stability is in fact exponential, since from

$$V[t, \varphi] \geqslant \|\, \varphi\,\|^2$$

it follows that

$$V^*(t) \geqslant \|\, x(t+s; t_0, \psi)\|^2$$

and thus that

$$\limsup_{h\to 0+} \frac{V^*(t+h) - V^*(t)}{h} \leqslant -\gamma_1 V^*(t)$$

or

$$\frac{1}{V^*(t)} \limsup_{h\to 0+} \frac{V^*(t+h) - V^*(t)}{h} \leqslant -\gamma_1,$$

from which follows

$$\limsup_{h\to 0+} \frac{\ln V^*(t+h) - \ln V^*(t)}{h} \leqslant -\gamma_1.$$

Hence

$$\ln V^*(t) - \ln V^*(t_0) \leqslant -\gamma_1(t - t_0)$$

from which follows

$$V^*(t) \leqslant V^*(t_0)e^{-\gamma_1(t-t_0)} \leqslant K_1 e^{-\gamma_1(t-t_0)}\| \varphi \|^2$$

and

$$\| x(t + s; t_0 , \varphi)\|^2 \leqslant K_1 e^{-\gamma_1(t-t_0)}\| \varphi \|^2,$$

and the exponential stability is proved.

Theorem 4.7. *Let us again consider system* (9) *and suppose that*

$$| f(t, x(t + s))| < g(t)\| x(t + s)\| \qquad \text{with} \int^{\infty} g(t)dt < \infty.$$

If the trivial solution of system (10) *is uniformly stable, then the trivial solution of system* (9) *is uniformly stable, and if the trivial solution of system* (10) *is uniformly asymptotically stable, then the trivial solution of system* (9) *is uniformly asymptotically stable.*

Proof. If the trivial solution of system (10) is uniformly stable, it follows that $\| y(t; t_0 , \varphi)\| \leqslant M \| \varphi \|$ for $t \geqslant t_0$, since the system is linear.

Let

$$V[t, \varphi] = \sup_{\sigma\geqslant 0} \| y(t + \sigma + s; t, \varphi(u - t))\|.$$

We obviously have

$$\| \varphi \| \leqslant V[t, \varphi] \leqslant M\| \varphi \|,$$

and from

$$\begin{aligned}&\| y(t + \sigma + s; t, \varphi_1)\| - \| y(t + \sigma + s; t, \varphi_2)\| \\ &\qquad \leqslant \| y(t + \sigma + s; t, \varphi_1 - \varphi_2)\| \leqslant M\| \varphi_1 - \varphi_2 \|\end{aligned}$$

follows

$$\| y(t + \sigma + s; t, \varphi_1)\| \leqslant \| y(t + \sigma + s; t, \varphi_2)\| + M\| \varphi_1 - \varphi_2 \|;$$

hence

$$V[t, \varphi_1] \leqslant V[t, \varphi_2] + M\| \varphi_1 - \varphi_2 \|,$$

from which

$$|V[t, \varphi_1] - V[t, \varphi_2]| \leqslant M\| \varphi_1 - \varphi_2 \|.$$

As in the proof of Theorem 4.2 we deduce that $V[t, y(t + s; t_0, \varphi)]$ is monotone-decreasing; hence

$$\limsup_{h\to 0+} \frac{V[t+h, y(t+h+s; t, \varphi)] - V[t, \varphi]}{h} \leqslant 0.$$

As in the preceding theorem we deduce that

$$\| x(t+h+s; t, \varphi) - y(t+h+s; t, \varphi)\| \leqslant g(t)(e^{Lh} - 1)e^{Lh}\| \varphi \|;$$

hence

$$\limsup_{h\to 0+} \frac{V[t+h, x(t+h+s; t, \varphi)] - V[t+h, y(t+h+s; t, \varphi)]}{h} \leqslant MLg(t)\| \varphi \|.$$

We obtain

$$\limsup_{h\to 0+} \frac{V[t+h, x(t+h+s; t, \varphi)] - V[t, \varphi]}{h} \leqslant MLg(t)\| \varphi \| \leqslant MLg(t)V[t, \varphi].$$

Setting

$$V^*(t) = V[t, x(t+s; t_0, \varphi)],$$

we deduce that

$$\frac{1}{V^*(t)} \limsup_{h\to 0+} \frac{V^*(t+h) - V^*(t)}{h} \leqslant MLg(t),$$

$$\limsup_{h\to 0+} \frac{\ln V^*(t+h) - \ln V^*(t)}{h} \leqslant LMg(t);$$

hence

$$\ln V^*(t) - \ln V^*(t_0) \leqslant LM \int_{t_0}^{t} g(t)dt,$$

from which

$$\| x(t+s; t_0, \varphi)\| \leqslant V^*(t) \leqslant V^*(t_0) \exp\left[LM \int_{t_0}^{\infty} g(t)dt\right]$$
$$\leqslant M \exp\left[LM\int_{t_0}^{\infty} g(t)dt\right] \| \varphi \|,$$

and the first assertion of the theorem is thus proved.

If the trivial solution of system (10) is uniformly asymptotically stable, we deduce, as in the preceding theorem,

$$\frac{1}{V^*(t)} \limsup_{h\to 0+} \frac{V^*(t+h) - V^*(t)}{h} \leqslant -\frac{1}{K_1} + Kg(t),$$

from which we obtain

$$\| x(t+s; t_0, \varphi)\|^2 \leqslant V^*(t) \leqslant V^*(t_0) \exp\left[K \int_{t_0}^{\infty} g(t)dt\right] \exp\left[-\frac{1}{K_1}(t-t_0)\right] \|\varphi\|^2,$$

which proves the exponential stability of the trivial solution of system (9). The theorem is thus fully proved.

Similarly to the case of systems of ordinary differential equations, the uniform asymptotic stability implies stability with respect to permanent perturbations.

Theorem 4.8. *If the trivial solution of system* (2) *is uniformly asymptotically stable, then it is also stable with respect to permanent perturbations. This means that for every* $\epsilon > 0$ *there exists* $\eta_1 > 0$ and $\eta_2 > 0$ *with the property that if* $\sup_{\|\varphi\|<\epsilon} | R(t, \varphi)| < \eta_1$ *every solution of the system*

$$\dot{y}(t) = f[t, y(t+s)] + R[t, y(t+s)] \tag{11}$$

with $\|\varphi\| < \eta_2$ *verifies the inequality* $| y(t; t_0, \varphi)| < \epsilon$ *for* $t \geqslant t_0$.

Proof. We have, because of inequality (3),

$$| x(v; t, \varphi)| \leqslant e^{LH}\|\varphi\| \qquad (t \leqslant v \leqslant t+h),$$

and, because of inequality (5),

$$| y(v; t, \varphi) - x(v; t, \varphi)| \leqslant (e^{LH} - 1)\eta_1$$

if

$$| y(v, t, \varphi)| \leqslant e^{LH}\|\varphi\| \qquad \text{and} \qquad t \leqslant v \leqslant t+h.$$

It follows that

$$| y(v; t, \varphi)| \leqslant e^{LH}\|\varphi\| + (e^{LH} - 1)\eta_1$$

and if $\|\varphi\| < \epsilon/2$ and h is sufficiently small, it follows that $\| y(v; t, \epsilon)\| < \epsilon$ and the estimate deduced from (5) is valid. Since the trivial solution of system (2) is uniformly asymptotically stable, there exists a functional $V[t, \varphi]$ with the properties from Theorem 4.4 and

$$| V[t, \varphi_1] - V[t, \varphi_2]| \leqslant M(r)\|\varphi_1 - \varphi_2\| \qquad (\text{for } \|\varphi_1\| < r, \|\varphi_2\| < r).$$

We have

$$\limsup_{h\to 0+} \frac{V[t+h, y(t+h+s; t, \varphi)] - V[t, \varphi]}{h}$$

$$\leqslant \limsup_{h\to 0+} \frac{V[t+h, x(t+h+s; t, \varphi)] - V[t, \varphi]}{h}$$

$$+ \limsup_{h\to 0+} \frac{V[t+h, y(t+h+s; t, \varphi)] - V[t+h, x(t+h+s; t, \varphi)]}{h}$$

$$\leqslant - c(\| \varphi \|) + ML\eta_1 .$$

Let $\epsilon > 0$, $l < a(\epsilon/2)$, $\| \varphi \| < \eta_2 = b^{-1}(l)$, and $\eta_1 < c[b^{-1}(l)]/LM$. We prove that $\| y(t+s; t_0, \varphi)\| < \epsilon$ for $t \geqslant t_0$.

However, if this were not true, there would exist a $t_1 > t_0$ such that $\| y(t_1 + s; t_0, \varphi)\| \geqslant \epsilon$; if, as usual, we set

$$V^*(t) = V[t, y(t+s; t_0, \varphi)]$$

we have

$$V^*(t_1) \geqslant a(\| y(t_1 + s; t_0, \varphi)\|) \geqslant a(\epsilon) > a\left(\frac{\epsilon}{2}\right) > l.$$

On the other hand,

$$V^*(t_0) = V[t_0, \varphi] \leqslant b(\| \varphi \|) < b(\eta_2) = l.$$

It follows, because of the continuity of the function $V^*(t)$, that there exists a t_2 with $t_0 < t_2 < t_1$ such that $V^*(t_2) = l$ and $V^*(t) > l$ for $t > t_2$. From $V^*(t_2) = l$ we obtain

$$b(\| y(t_2 + s; t_0, \varphi)\|) \geqslant V[t_2, y(t_2 + s; t_0, \varphi)] = l \geqslant a(\| y(t_2, + s; t_0, \varphi)\|);$$

hence

$$b^{-1}(l) \leqslant \| y(t_2 + s; t_0, \varphi)\| \leqslant a^{-1}(l) < \frac{\epsilon}{2}.$$

We set $\psi(s) = y(t_2 + s; t_0, \varphi)$. We have

$$\limsup_{h\to 0+} \frac{V^*(t_2 + h) - V^*(t_2)}{h}$$

$$= \limsup_{h\to 0+} \frac{V[t_2 + h, y(t_2 + h + s; t_2, \psi)] - V[t_2, \psi]}{h}$$

$$\leqslant - c(\| \psi \|) + LM\eta_1 \leqslant -c[b^{-1}(l)] + LM\eta_1 < 0.$$

On the other hand, from $V^*(t_2) = l$ and $V^*(t) > l$ for $t > t_2$ follows

$$\limsup_{h\to 0+} \frac{V^*(t_2 + h) - V^*(t_2)}{h} \geqslant 0.$$

We have obtained a contradiction, hence $\| y(t + s; t_0, \varphi)\| < \epsilon$ for $t \geqslant t_0$. The theorem is thus proved.

As in the case of systems of ordinary differential equations we may prove a stability theorem with respect to permanent perturbations bounded in the mean. A series of other theorems may likewise be stated for systems with time lag without modifying the proof.

Theorem 4.9. *Let us suppose that there exists a functional $V[t, \varphi]$ defined as in the preceding theorems, with the following properties:*

1. $a(t, \| \varphi \|) \leqslant V[t, \varphi] \leqslant b(\| \varphi \|)$,

2. $\limsup_{h\to 0+} \dfrac{V[t + h, x(t + h + s; t, \varphi)] - V[t, \varphi]}{h} \leqslant -c(t, \| \varphi \|)$,

3. $|V[t, \varphi_1] - V[t, \varphi_2]| < L\| \varphi_1 - \varphi_2 \|$,

where $b(r)$ is continuous, monotone-increasing for $r > 0$, $b(0) = 0$, and $a(t, r)$, $c(t, r)$ are continuous and with the property that for every pair (α, β) with $0 < \alpha \leqslant \beta < H$, there exists $\theta(\alpha, \beta) \geqslant 0$, $k(\alpha, \beta) > 0$ such that $a(t, r) > k(\alpha, \beta)$, $c(t, r) > k(\alpha, \beta)$ for $\alpha \leqslant r \leqslant \beta$, $t \geqslant \theta(\alpha, \beta)$. Then the trivial solution of system (2) *is uniformly asymptotically stable.*

Theorem 4.10. *We consider the system*

$$\dot{x}(t) = f[t, x(t + s)] + R[t, x(t + s)], \tag{12}$$

where $f[t, 0] \equiv R[t, 0] \equiv 0$, f and R verify a Lipschitz condition, and in addition $\lim_{t\to\infty} R(t, \varphi) = 0$ uniformly with respect to φ for $\| \varphi \| \leqslant H$. Then, if the trivial solution of the system

$$\dot{z}(t) = f[t, z(t + s)]$$

is uniformly asymptotically stable, the trivial solution of system (12) *is likewise uniformly asymptotically stable.*

Theorem 4.11 *We consider the system*

$$\begin{aligned} \dot{x}(t) &= f[t, x(t + s), y(t + s)], \\ \dot{y}(t) &= g[t, x(t + s), y(t + s)], \end{aligned} \tag{13}$$

where $f(t, 0, 0) \equiv g(t, 0, 0) \equiv 0$. *We suppose that the trivial solution of system* (13) *is stable with respect to components* x; *hence that there exists* $\delta(\epsilon) > 0$ *with the property that* $\| \varphi \| < \delta$, $\| \psi \| < \delta$ *implies* $| x(t, t_0, \varphi, \psi)| < \epsilon$ *for* $t \geqslant t_0$. *We suppose, in addition, that the trivial solution of the system*

$$\dot{z}(t) = g[t, 0, z(t + s)]$$

is uniformly asymptotically stable. Then the trivial solution of system (13) *is uniformly stable. If in addition the stability with respect to components* x *is asymptotic, i.e., if there exists* $\delta_0 > 0$ *and* $T_0(\epsilon)$ *such that* $\| \varphi \| < \delta_0$, $\| \psi \| < \delta_0$, $t \geqslant t_0 + T_0$ *implies* $| x(t; t_0, \varphi, \psi)| < \epsilon$, *then the trivial solution of system* (13) *is uniformly asymptotically stable.*

Theorem 4.12. *We consider the system*

$$\begin{aligned} \dot{x}(t) &= f[t, x(t + s), y(t + s)], \\ \dot{y}(t) &= A(t, y(t + s)) + g[t, x(t + s), y(t + s)], \end{aligned} \tag{14}$$

where for $\| \varphi \| < \alpha_0$, $\| \psi \| < \alpha_0$, *we have* $| f(t, \varphi, \psi)| \leqslant K \| \psi \|^{\beta}$, $\beta > 0$, $| g(t, \varphi, \psi)| \leqslant k \| \varphi \|$, k *sufficiently small, and* $A(t, \varphi)$ *is linear. We suppose that the trivial solution of the linear system*

$$\dot{z}(t) = A(t, z(t + s)) \tag{15}$$

is uniformly asymptotically stable. Then the trivial solution of system (14) *is uniformly stable, and, in addition, for every solution for which the initial functions are sufficiently small we have* $y(t) \to 0$, $x(t) \to l$ *for* $t \to \infty$.

Proof. Let $V[t, \varphi]$ be a functional defined for system (15) on the basis of Theorem 4.4′. Taking into account the condition imposed for $g(t, \varphi)$, we deduce, as in the proof of Theorem 4.6, the estimate

$$\limsup_{h \to 0+} \frac{V[t + h, y(t + h + s; t, \varphi, \psi)] - V[t, \varphi, \psi]}{h} \leqslant -[1 - kM] \| \psi \|^2.$$

Setting $V^*(t) = V[t, y(t + s; t_0, \varphi, \psi)]$ we obtain from here, if $\| \varphi \|$, $\| \psi \|$ are sufficiently small (then k is sufficiently small),

$$\limsup_{h \to 0+} \frac{V^*(t + h) - V^*(t)}{h} \leqslant -k_1 V^*(t).$$

From this we immediately deduce

$$\| y(t + s; t_0, \varphi, \psi)\|^2 \leqslant V^*(t) \leqslant V^*(t_0) e^{-k_1(t - t_0)} \leqslant K_1 e^{-k_1(t - t_0)} \| \psi \|^2.$$

Further, from

$$x(t; t_0, \varphi, \psi) = \varphi(t_0) + \int_{t_0}^{t} f[u, x(u+s; t_0, \varphi, \psi), y(u+s; t_0, \varphi, \psi)]du$$

we obtain

$$| x(t; t_0, \varphi, \psi)| \leqslant \| \varphi \| + \int_{t_0}^{t} K\sqrt{K_1^{\beta}}\, e^{-(k_1\beta/2)(u-t_0)}\, du \, \| \psi \|^{\beta},$$

from which the assertion of the theorem follows immediately.

The definition of integral stability for systems with time lag can be formulated in the same way as in the case of systems of ordinary differential equations. Without essential modifications as compared to the proofs given in Chapter 1 we obtain the lemmas and the theorems stated in section 1.8. Here we will give only the formulations of the theorems.

Theorem 4.13. *We suppose that there exists a functional* $V[t, \varphi]$ *defined as in the preceding theorems, with the following properties:*

1. $V[t, \varphi] \geqslant a(\| \varphi \|)$, $V[t, 0] \equiv 0$, $a(r)$ *continuous, monotone-increasing for* $r > 0$, $a(0) = 0$,
2. $| V[t, \varphi_1] - V[t, \varphi_2] | \leqslant K \| \varphi_1 - \varphi_2 \|$,
3.

$$\limsup_{h\to 0+} \frac{V[t+h, x(t+h+s; t_0, \varphi)] - V[t, x(t+s; t_0, \varphi)]}{h} \leqslant g(t)V[t, x(t+s; t_0, \varphi)],$$

where $\int^{\infty} g(t)dt < \infty$, $g(t) \geqslant 0$. *Then the trivial solution of system* (2) *is integrally stable.*

Consequence. *Under the conditions stated in Theorem* 4.7, *the trivial solution of system* (9) *is integrally stable, if the trivial solution of system* (10) *is uniformly stable.*

Theorem 4.14. *If the functional V of the preceding theorem verifies, instead of condition* 3, *the condition*

$$(3') \quad \limsup_{h\to 0+} \frac{V[t+h, x(t+h+s; t_0, \varphi)] - V[t, x(t+s; t_0, \varphi)]}{h} \leqslant -c(\| x(t+s; t_0, \varphi)\|),$$

then the trivial solution of system (2) *is asymptotically integrally stable.*

Consequence. *If the trivial solution of system* (2) (*with the Lipschitz-type condition satisfied*) *is uniformly asymptotically stable, then it is also asymptotically integrally stable. In particular, under the conditions of Theorem 4.7, if the trivial solution of system* (10) *is uniformly asymptotically stable, the trivial solution of system* (9) *is asymptotically integrally stable.*

4.3. Linear Systems with Time Lag

We consider the linear system

$$\dot{x}(t) = A(t)x(t) + B(t)x(t - \tau) \tag{16}$$

We will call the *adjoint system* of system (16) the system with the advanced argument

$$\dot{y}(t) = -y(t)A(t) - y(t + \tau)B(t + \tau), \tag{17}$$

where y is a row vector.

Let $x(t)$ and $y(t)$ be arbitrary solutions of systems (16) and (17), respectively. We denote by (y, x) the function

$$(y, x) = y(t)x(t) + \int_0^t y(t + \alpha)B(t + \alpha)x(t + \alpha - \tau)d\alpha.$$

Then $(d/dt)(y, x) \equiv 0$, hence $(y, x) = \text{const}$. Indeed,

$$(y, x) = y(t)x(t) + \int_t^{t+\tau} y(\alpha)B(\alpha)x(\alpha - \tau)d\alpha$$

and

$$\begin{aligned}\frac{d}{dt}(y, x) &= \dot{y}(t)x(t) + y(t)\dot{x}(t) + y(t + \tau)B(t + \tau)x(t) - y(t)B(t)x(t - \tau)\\ &= -y(t)A(t)x(t) - y(t + \tau)B(t + \tau)x(t) + y(t)A(t)x(t)\\ &\quad + y(t)B(t)x(t - \tau) + y(t + \tau)B(t + \tau)x(t) - y(t)B(t)x(t - \tau) = 0.\end{aligned}$$

Let us now consider the nonhomogeneous system

$$\dot{x}(t) = A(t)x(t) + B(t)x(t - \tau) + f(t). \tag{18}$$

Let $Y(\alpha, t)$ be a matrix which verifies system (17) for $\alpha < t$ (as a function of α) and $Y(t, t) = E$, $Y(\alpha, t) \equiv 0$ for $\alpha > t$. This matrix is easily constructed through the "step-by-step" method. Indeed, for $t - \tau < \alpha < t$, we have

$$\frac{\partial}{\partial \alpha} Y(\alpha, t) = -Y(\alpha, t)A(\alpha), \qquad Y(t, t) = E,$$

since for $\alpha > t - \tau$ we have $\alpha + \tau > t$ and $Y(\alpha + \tau, t) \equiv 0$. It follows from here that in $(t - \tau, t]$ the matrix $Y(\alpha, t)$ is determined by a system of ordinary equations. Further, for $t - 2\tau < \alpha < t - \tau$ we have

$$\frac{\partial}{\partial \alpha} Y(\alpha, t) = -Y(\alpha, t)A(\alpha) - U(\alpha + \tau)B(\alpha + \tau), \qquad Y(t - \tau, t) = U(t - \tau)$$

where we have denoted by $U(\alpha)$ the matrix constructed in the preceding step. The procedure continues in the same way and leads to the desired matrix $Y(\alpha, t)$.

Let us multiply system (18) with the matrix $Y(\alpha, t)$ constructed in this way and integrate with respect to α from σ to t. We obtain

$$\int_\sigma^t Y(\alpha, t)\dot{x}(\alpha)d\alpha = \int_\sigma^t Y(\alpha, t)A(\alpha)x(\alpha)d\alpha + \int_\sigma^t Y(\alpha, t)B(\alpha)x(\alpha - \tau)d\alpha + \int_\sigma^t Y(\alpha, t)f(\alpha)d\alpha.$$

Further, integrating by parts,

$$\begin{aligned} Y(t, t)x(t) - Y(\sigma, t)x(\sigma) - \int_\sigma^t \frac{\partial}{\partial \alpha} Y(\alpha, t)x(\alpha)d\alpha \\ = \int_\sigma^t Y(\alpha, t)A(\alpha)x(\alpha)d\alpha + \int_\sigma^t Y(\alpha, t)B(\alpha)x(\alpha - \tau)d\alpha \\ + \int_\sigma^t Y(\alpha, t)f(\alpha)d\alpha. \end{aligned}$$

Taking into account the equation which is verified by $Y(\alpha, t)$, we obtain

$$\begin{aligned} x(t) = Y(\sigma, t)x(\sigma) - \int_\sigma^t Y(\alpha, t)A(\alpha)x(\alpha)d\alpha \\ - \int_\sigma^t Y(\alpha + \tau, t)B(\alpha + \tau)x(\alpha)d\alpha + \int_\sigma^t Y(\alpha, t)A(\alpha)x(\alpha)d\alpha \\ + \int_\sigma^t Y(\alpha, t)B(\alpha)x(\alpha - \tau)d\alpha + \int_\sigma^t Y(\alpha, t)f(\alpha)d\alpha \end{aligned}$$

$$= Y(\sigma, t)x(\sigma) - \int_{\sigma}^{t} Y(\alpha + \tau, t)B(\alpha + \tau)x(\alpha)d\alpha$$

$$+ \int_{\sigma-\tau}^{t-\tau} Y(\alpha + \tau, t)B(\alpha + \tau)x(\alpha)d\alpha + \int_{\sigma}^{t} Y(\alpha, t)f(\alpha)d\alpha$$

$$= Y(\sigma, t)x(\sigma) + \int_{\sigma-\tau}^{\sigma} Y(\alpha + \tau, t)B(\alpha + \tau)x(\alpha)d\alpha$$

$$- \int_{t-\tau}^{t} Y(\alpha + \tau, t)B(\alpha + \tau)x(\alpha)d\alpha + \int_{\sigma}^{t} Y(\alpha, t)f(\alpha)d\alpha.$$

However, $Y(\alpha + \tau, t) \equiv 0$ for $t - \tau < \alpha \leqslant t$ and we obtain

$$x(t) = Y(\sigma, t)x(\sigma) + \int_{\sigma-\tau}^{\sigma} Y(\alpha + \tau, t)B(\alpha + \tau)x(\alpha)d\alpha + \int_{\sigma}^{t} Y(\alpha, t)f(\alpha)d\alpha.$$

From this formula it is obvious that if $X(t, \sigma)$ is the solution of system (16) which verifies the conditions $X(\sigma, \sigma) = E$, $X(t, \sigma) \equiv 0$ for $t < \sigma$, then $X(t, \sigma) \equiv Y(\sigma, t)$.

We thus obtain the formula

$$x(t) = X(t, \sigma)x(\sigma) + \int_{\sigma-\tau}^{\sigma} X(t, \alpha + \tau)B(\alpha + \tau)x(\alpha)d\alpha + \int_{\sigma}^{t} X(t, \alpha)f(\alpha)d\alpha. \quad (19)$$

Let us now consider system (17). Let $y(t)$ be the solution of this system defined for $t \leqslant \sigma$ by the initial conditions given in $[\sigma, \sigma + \tau]$ and let $X(\alpha, t)$ be the matrix of solutions of system (16) which verifies the conditions $X(t, t) = E$, $X(\alpha, t) = 0$ for $\alpha < t$. We have

$$\int_{t}^{\sigma} \dot{y}(s)X(s, t)ds = - \int_{t}^{\sigma} y(s)A(s)X(s, t)ds - \int_{t}^{\sigma} y(s + \tau)B(s + \tau)X(s, t)ds.$$

Further,

$$y(\sigma)X(\sigma, t) - y(t)X(t, t) - \int_{t}^{\sigma} y(s) \frac{\partial}{\partial s} X(s, t)ds$$

$$= - \int_{t}^{\sigma} y(s)A(s)X(s, t)ds - \int_{t+\tau}^{\sigma+\tau} y(\beta)B(\beta)X(\beta - \tau, t)d\beta.$$

From here we obtain

$$y(t) = y(\sigma)X(\sigma, t) - \int_{t}^{\sigma} y(s)A(s)X(s, t)ds - \int_{t}^{\sigma} y(s)B(s)X(s - \tau, t)ds$$

$$+ \int_{t}^{\sigma} y(s)A(s)X(s, t)ds + \int_{t+\tau}^{\sigma+\tau} y(s)B(s)X(s - \tau, t)ds$$

$$= y(\sigma)X(\sigma, t) + \int_{\sigma}^{\sigma+\tau} y(s)B(s)X(s - \tau, t)ds - \int_{t}^{t+\tau} y(s)B(s)X(s - \tau, t)ds.$$

However, for $t \leqslant s \leqslant t + \tau$ we have $s - \tau < t$ and $X(s - \tau, t) \equiv 0$. Consequently,

$$y(t) = y(\sigma)X(\sigma, t) + \int_{\sigma}^{\sigma+\tau} y(s)B(s)X(s - \tau, t)ds. \tag{20}$$

We shall now consider the same problems for general systems with time lag of the form

$$\dot{x}_i(t) = \sum_{j=1}^{n} \int_{-\infty}^{0} x_j(t + s)d_s\eta_{ij}(t, s) + f_i(t)$$

where

(a) $\eta_{ij}(t, s)$ are defined for $t \geqslant 0$, $-\infty < s < \infty$, $\eta_{ij}(t, s) \equiv 0$ for $s \geqslant 0$.

(b) There exist functions $\tau_{ij}(t) > 0$, $V_{ij}(t) > 0$, *bounded* for $t \geqslant 0$ such that

$$\eta_{ij}(t, s) \equiv \eta_{ij}(t, -\tau_{ij}(t)) \qquad \text{for} \quad s \leqslant -\tau_{ij}(t),$$

$$\bigvee_{s=-\tau_{ij}(t)}^{s=0} \eta_{ij}(t, s) \leqslant V_{ij}(t),$$

where, as usual, $\bigvee_{s=0}^{s=\beta} f(s)$ means the total variation of function f in $[\alpha, \beta]$. We set $\tau = \sup_{i,j,t} \tau_{ij}(t)$.

(c) $\eta_{ij}(t, s)$ are continuous in t, uniformly with respect to s.

From now on we shall write the system in vector form,

$$\dot{x}(t) = \int_{-\infty}^{0} x(t + s)d_s\eta(t, s) + f(t), \tag{21}$$

where $x(t)$ is a row vector. We shall call the *adjoint system* the system

$$\frac{d}{d\alpha}\left[y(\alpha) + \int_{-\tau}^{0} \eta(\alpha - \beta, \beta)y(\alpha - \beta)d\beta\right] \equiv 0, \tag{22}$$

where y is a column vector.

System (21) may also be represented in the form

$$y(\alpha) + \int_{-\tau}^{0} \eta(\alpha - \beta, \beta)y(\alpha - \beta)d\beta \equiv \text{const.}$$

or

$$y(\alpha) + \int_{\alpha}^{\alpha+\tau} \eta(\gamma, \alpha - \gamma)y(\gamma)d\gamma \equiv \text{const.}$$

Then, for fixed σ we have

$$y(\alpha) + \int^{\alpha+\tau} \eta(\gamma, \alpha - \gamma)y(\gamma)d\gamma = y(\sigma) + \int_{\sigma}^{\sigma+\tau} \eta(\gamma, \sigma - \gamma)y(\gamma)d\gamma$$

or

$$y(\alpha) + \int_{\alpha}^{\sigma} \eta(\gamma, \alpha - \gamma)y(\gamma)d\gamma$$
$$= y(\sigma) + \int_{\sigma}^{\sigma+\tau} \eta(\gamma, \sigma - \gamma)y(\gamma)d\gamma - \int_{\sigma}^{\sigma+\tau} \eta(\gamma, \alpha - \gamma)y(\gamma)d\gamma.$$

If the function y is given in $[\sigma, \sigma + \tau]$, then for $\sigma - \tau \leqslant \alpha \leqslant \sigma$ the function

$$y(\sigma) + \int_{\sigma}^{\sigma+\tau} \eta(\gamma, \sigma - \gamma)y(\gamma)d\gamma - \int_{\sigma}^{\alpha+\tau} \eta(\gamma, \alpha - \gamma)y(\gamma)d\gamma$$

is known and we can determine $y(\alpha)$ in the interval $[\sigma - \tau, \sigma]$ from a Volterra-type system of integral equations. If y is known in $[\sigma - \tau, \sigma]$ we may determine it by the same procedure in $[\sigma - 2\tau, \sigma - \tau]$, and thus through the step-by-step method we can obtain for equation (22) a theorem of existence and uniqueness. Let us observe that if the initial function given in $[\sigma, \sigma + \tau]$ is of bounded variation, the solution defined by it will be of bounded variation, and if the initial function is continuous, the solution will also be continuous.

Let us consider in particular the matrix solution of equation (21) defined by condition $Y(\alpha, \sigma) \equiv 0$ for $\sigma < \alpha \leqslant \sigma + \tau$, $Y(\sigma, \sigma) = E$. Then

$$Y(\alpha, \sigma) + \int_{\alpha}^{\alpha+\tau} \eta(\gamma, \alpha - \gamma)Y(\gamma, \sigma)d\gamma = E.$$

We can obtain this matrix by the usual procedure of successive approximations by setting

$$Y_0(\alpha, \sigma) = E, \qquad Y_k(\alpha, \sigma) = E - \int_{\alpha}^{\sigma} \eta(\gamma, \alpha - \gamma)Y_{k-1}(\gamma, \sigma)d\gamma$$

for $\sigma - \tau \leqslant \alpha < \sigma$, and then through the step-by-step method. The matrices $Y_k(\alpha, \sigma)$ are continuous with respect to σ and of bounded variation with respect to α. From the uniform convergence of these successive approximation it follows that $Y(\alpha, \sigma)$ also has these properties.

Now let $x(t)$ be an arbitrary solution of system (21) and $y(t)$ be an arbitrary solution of system (22). Then, for $t \geqslant \sigma$,

$$x(t)y(t) + \int_{t-\tau}^{t} x(s)d_s \int_{t}^{s+\tau} \eta(\gamma, s - \gamma)y(\gamma)d\gamma$$
$$= x(\sigma)y(\sigma) + \int_{\sigma-\tau}^{\sigma} x(s)d_s \int_{\sigma}^{s+\tau} \eta(\gamma, s - \gamma)y(\gamma)d\gamma + \int_{\sigma}^{t} f(\alpha)y(\alpha)d\alpha.$$

Indeed, we successively have

$$\int_\sigma^t \dot{x}(\alpha)y(\alpha)d\alpha + \int_\sigma^t x(\alpha)dy(\alpha) = x(t)y(t) - x(\sigma)y(\sigma)$$

$$= \int_\sigma^t \left[\int_{-\tau}^0 x(\alpha+s)d_s\eta(\alpha, s)\right] y(\alpha)d\alpha - \int_\sigma^t x(\alpha)d_\alpha \int_\alpha^{\alpha+\tau} \eta(\gamma, \alpha-\gamma)y(\gamma)d\gamma$$

$$+ \int_\sigma^t f(\alpha)y(\alpha)d\alpha = \int_\sigma^t \left[\int_{\alpha-\tau}^\alpha x(s)d_s\eta(\alpha, s-\alpha)\right] y(\alpha)d\alpha$$

$$- \int_\sigma^t x(\alpha)d_\alpha \int_\alpha^{\alpha+\tau} \eta(\gamma, \alpha-\gamma)y(\gamma)d\gamma + \int_\sigma^t f(\alpha)y(\alpha)d\alpha$$

$$= \int_{\sigma-\tau}^\sigma x(s)d_s \int_\sigma^{s+\tau} \eta(\alpha, s-\alpha)y(\alpha)d\alpha + \int_\sigma^{t-\tau} x(s)d_s \int_s^{s+\tau} \eta(\alpha, s-\alpha)y(\alpha)d\alpha$$

$$+ \int_{t-\tau}^t x(s)d_s \int_s^t \eta(\alpha, s-\alpha)y(\alpha)d\alpha - \int_\sigma^t x(s)d_s \int_s^{s+\tau} \eta(\alpha, s-\alpha)y(\alpha)d\alpha$$

$$+ \int_\sigma^t f(\alpha)y(\alpha)d\alpha.$$

From this we obtain

$$x(t)y(t) - x(\sigma)y(\sigma) = \int_{\sigma-\tau}^\sigma x(s)d_s \int_\sigma^{s+\tau} \eta(\alpha, s-\alpha)y(\alpha)d\alpha$$

$$- \int_{t-\tau}^t x(s)d_s \int_t^s \eta(\alpha, s-\alpha)y(\alpha)d\alpha - \int_{t-\tau}^t x(s)d_s \int_s^{s+\tau} \eta(\alpha, s-\alpha)y(\alpha)d\alpha$$

$$+ \int_\sigma^t f(\alpha)y(\alpha)d\alpha.$$

This relation may also be written

$$x(t)y(t) - x(\sigma)y(\sigma) = \int_{\sigma-\tau}^\sigma x(s)d_s \int_\sigma^{s+\tau} \eta(\alpha, s-\alpha)y(\alpha)d\alpha$$

$$- \int_{t-\tau}^t x(s)d_s \int_t^{s+\tau} \eta(\alpha, s-\alpha)y(\alpha)d\alpha + \int_\sigma^t f(\alpha)y(\alpha)d\alpha;$$

hence

$$x(t)y(t) + \int_{t-\tau}^t x(s)d_s \int_t^{s+\tau} \eta(\alpha, s-\alpha)y(\alpha)d\alpha = x(\sigma)y(\sigma)$$

$$+ \int_{\sigma-\tau}^\sigma x(s)d_s \int_\sigma^{s+\tau} \eta(\alpha, s-\alpha)y(\alpha)d\alpha + \int_\sigma^t f(\alpha)y(\alpha)d\alpha.$$

In particular, for $f \equiv 0$, it follows from the formula obtained that if we set

$$(y, x) = x(t)y(t) + \int_{t-\tau}^{t} x(s)d_s \int_{t}^{s+\tau} \eta(\gamma, s-\gamma)y(\gamma)d\gamma,$$

we will have $(d/dt)(y, x) \equiv 0$.

Let us again consider the solution $x(t)$ of system (21) and the matrix solution $Y(\alpha, \sigma)$ of system (22). We successively have

$$x(t)Y(t,t) - x(\sigma)Y(\sigma,t) - \int_{\sigma}^{t} x(\alpha)d_\alpha Y(\alpha,t) = \int_{\sigma}^{t} \dot{x}(\alpha)Y(\alpha,t)d\alpha$$

$$= \int_{\sigma}^{t} \left[\int_{-\infty}^{0} x(\alpha+s)d_s\eta(\alpha,s)\right] Y(\alpha,t)d\alpha + \int_{\sigma}^{t} f(\alpha)Y(\alpha,t)d\alpha$$

$$= \int_{\sigma}^{t} \left[\int_{\alpha-\tau}^{\alpha} x(s)d_s\eta(\alpha,s-\alpha)\right] Y(\alpha,t)d\alpha + \int_{\sigma}^{t} f(\alpha)Y(\alpha,t)d\alpha$$

$$= \int_{\sigma-\tau}^{\sigma} x(s)d_s \int_{\sigma}^{s+\tau} \eta(\alpha,s-\alpha)Y(\alpha,t)d\alpha + \int_{\sigma}^{t-\tau} x(s)d_s \int_{s}^{s+\tau} \eta(\alpha,s-\alpha)Y(\alpha,t)d\alpha$$

$$+ \int_{t-\tau}^{t} x(s)d_s \int_{s}^{t} \eta(\alpha,s-\alpha)Y(\alpha,t)d\alpha + \int_{\sigma}^{t} f(\alpha)Y(\alpha,t)d\alpha.$$

From this we obtain

$$x(t) = x(\sigma)Y(\sigma,t) + \int_{\sigma-\tau}^{\sigma} x(s)d_s \int_{\sigma}^{s+\tau} \eta(\alpha,s-\alpha)Y(\alpha,t)d\alpha + \int_{\sigma}^{t} f(\alpha)Y(\alpha,t)d\alpha$$

$$+ \int_{\sigma}^{t} x(\alpha)d_\alpha \left[Y(\alpha,t) + \int_{\alpha}^{\alpha+\tau} \eta(\beta,\alpha-\beta)Y(\beta,t)d\beta\right].$$

However,

$$Y(\alpha,t) + \int_{\alpha}^{\alpha+\tau} \eta(\beta,\alpha-\beta)Y(\beta,t)d\beta = E;$$

hence

$$x(t) = x(\sigma)Y(\sigma,t) + \int_{\sigma-\tau}^{\sigma} x(s)d_s \int_{\sigma}^{s+\tau} \eta(\alpha,s-\alpha)Y(\alpha,t)d\alpha + \int_{\sigma}^{t} f(\alpha)Y(\alpha,t)d\alpha. \tag{23}$$

If the solution $x(t)$ is zero for $t < \sigma$ and if $f \equiv 0$, then

$$x(t) = x(\sigma)Y(\sigma,t).$$

Let $X(t, \sigma)$ be the matrix whose rows are for $t > \sigma$ solutions of systems (21) with $f \equiv 0$ and $X(t, \sigma) \equiv 0$ for $t < \sigma$, $X(\sigma, \sigma) = E$; it will then follow that $X(t, \sigma) = Y(\sigma, t)$.

We have thus finally obtained

$$x(t) = x(\sigma)X(t, \sigma) + \int_{\sigma-\tau}^{\sigma} x(s)d_s \int_{\sigma}^{s+\tau} \eta(\alpha, s-\alpha)X(t, \alpha)d\alpha + \int_{\sigma}^{t} f(\alpha)X(t, \alpha)d\alpha. \tag{23'}$$

Let us now state an analogous formula for system (22). Let $y(\alpha)$ be a solution of system (22) whose initial function is of bounded variation and let $X(\alpha, \gamma)$ be the matrix considered above. We have

$$\int_t^{\sigma} X(\alpha, t)dy(\alpha) = X(\sigma, t)y(\sigma) - X(t, t)y(t) - \int_t^{\sigma} \left[\frac{\partial}{\partial x} X(\alpha, t)\right] y(\alpha)d\alpha.$$

From this

$$y(t) = X(\sigma, t)y(\sigma) + \int_t^{\sigma} X(\alpha, t)d_{\alpha} \left[\int_{-\tau}^{0} \eta(\alpha-\gamma, \gamma)y(\alpha-\gamma)d\gamma\right]$$
$$- \int_t^{\sigma} \left[\int_{-\tau}^{0} X(\alpha+s, t)d_s\eta(\alpha, s)\right] y(\alpha)d\alpha.$$

However,

$$\int_t^{\sigma} \left[\int_{-\tau}^{0} X(\alpha+s, t)d_s\eta(\alpha, s)\right] y(\alpha)d\alpha = \int_t^{\sigma} \left[\int_{\alpha-\tau}^{\alpha} X(\beta, t)d_{\beta}\eta(\alpha, \beta-\alpha)\right] y(\alpha)d\alpha$$
$$= \int_{t-\tau}^{t} X(\beta, t)d_{\beta} \int_t^{\beta+\tau} \eta(\alpha, \beta-\alpha)y(\alpha)d\alpha + \int_t^{\sigma-\tau} X(\beta, t)d_{\beta} \int_{\beta}^{\beta+\tau} \eta(\alpha, \beta-\alpha)y(\alpha)d\alpha$$
$$+ \int_{\sigma-\tau}^{\sigma} X(\beta, t)d_{\beta} \int_{\beta}^{\sigma} \eta(\alpha, \beta-\alpha)y(\alpha)d\alpha.$$

From here it follows that

$$y(t) = X(\sigma, t)y(\sigma) + \int_t^{\sigma} X(\beta, t)d_{\beta} \int_{\beta}^{\beta+\tau} \eta(\alpha, \beta-\alpha)y(\alpha)d\alpha$$
$$- \int_{t-\tau}^{t} X(\beta, t)d_{\beta} \int_t^{\beta+\tau} \eta(\alpha, \beta-\alpha)y(\alpha)d\alpha - \int_t^{\sigma-\tau} X(\beta, t)d_{\beta} \int_{\beta}^{\beta+} \eta(\alpha, \beta-\alpha)y(\alpha)d\alpha$$
$$- \int_{\sigma-\tau}^{\sigma} X(\beta, t)d_{\beta} \int_{\beta}^{\sigma} \eta(\alpha, \beta-\alpha)y(\alpha)d\alpha.$$

It follows from the fact that $X(\beta, t) \equiv 0$ for $\beta < t$ that the second integral is zero and we obtain

$$y(t) = X(\sigma, t)y(\sigma) + \int_{\sigma-\tau}^{\sigma} X(\beta, t)d_{\beta} \int_{\sigma}^{\beta+\tau} \eta(\alpha, \beta-\alpha)y(\alpha)d\alpha \tag{24}$$

Taking this formula into account, we immediately deduce, again, $Y(t, \sigma) = X(\sigma, t)$; hence the formula may be also represented in the form

$$y(t) = Y(t, \sigma)y(\sigma) + \int_{\sigma-\tau}^{\sigma} Y(t, \beta)d_\beta \int_{\sigma}^{\beta+\tau} \eta(\alpha, \beta - \alpha)y(\alpha)d\alpha \tag{24'}$$

Let us also consider systems of the form

$$\dot{x}(t) = x(t)A(t) + \int_{-\infty}^{0} x(t + s)d_s\eta(t, s), \tag{25}$$

in which the term containing the time lag is emphasized.

For system (25) we will call the *adjoint system* the system

$$A(\alpha)y(\alpha) + \frac{d}{d\alpha}\left[y(\alpha) + \int_{\alpha}^{\alpha+\tau} \eta(\gamma, \alpha - \gamma)y(\gamma)d\gamma\right] \equiv 0, \tag{26}$$

which can also be written

$$y(\alpha) + \int_{\alpha}^{\alpha+\tau} \eta(\gamma, \alpha - \gamma)y(\gamma)d\gamma = -\int_{\sigma}^{\alpha} A(\beta)y(\beta)d\beta + y(\sigma)$$
$$+ \int_{\sigma}^{\sigma+\tau} \eta(\gamma, \sigma - \gamma)y(\gamma)d\gamma;$$

hence

$$y(\alpha) + \int_{\alpha}^{\sigma} [\eta(\gamma, \alpha - \gamma) - A(\gamma)]y(\gamma)d\gamma = y(\sigma) + \int_{\sigma}^{\sigma+\tau} \eta(\gamma, \sigma - \gamma)y(\gamma)d\gamma$$
$$- \int_{\sigma}^{\alpha+\tau} \eta(\gamma, \alpha - \gamma)y(\gamma)d\gamma.$$

We see from here that if the solution y is given in $[\sigma, \sigma + \tau]$ we can determine it by successive steps from a system of integral equations of the Volterra type.

Now let $x(t)$ be an arbitrary solution of system (25) and $y(t)$ an arbitrary solution of system (26). Then

$$x(t)y(t) - x(\sigma)y(\sigma) = \int_{\sigma}^{t} \dot{x}(\alpha)y(\alpha)d\alpha + \int_{\sigma}^{t} x(\alpha)dy(\alpha)$$
$$= \int_{\sigma}^{t} x(\alpha)A(\alpha)y(\alpha)d\alpha + \int_{\sigma}^{t} \left[\int_{-\tau}^{0} x(\alpha + s)d_s\eta(\alpha, s)\right] y(\alpha)d\alpha$$
$$- \int_{\sigma}^{t} x(\alpha)A(\alpha)y(\alpha)d\alpha - \int_{\sigma}^{t} x(\alpha)d_\alpha \int_{\alpha}^{\alpha+\tau} \eta(\gamma, \alpha - \gamma)y(\gamma)d\gamma$$

$$= \int_{\sigma-\tau}^{\sigma} x(s)d_s \int_{\sigma}^{s+\tau} \eta(\alpha, s-\alpha)y(\alpha)d\alpha + \int_{\sigma}^{t-\tau} x(s)d_s \int_{s}^{s+\tau} \eta(\alpha, s-\alpha)y(\alpha)d\alpha$$

$$+ \int_{t-\tau}^{t} x(s)d_s \int_{s}^{t} \eta(\alpha, s-\alpha)y(\alpha)d\alpha - \int_{\sigma}^{t} x(s)d_s \int_{s}^{s+\tau} \eta(\gamma, s-\gamma)y(\gamma)d\gamma$$

$$= \int_{\sigma-\tau}^{\sigma} x(s)d_s \int_{\sigma}^{s+\tau} \eta(\alpha, s-\alpha)y(\alpha)d\alpha - \int_{t-\tau}^{t} x(s)d_s \int_{t}^{s+\tau} \eta(\gamma, s-\gamma)y(\gamma)d\gamma.$$

Finally, for $t \geqslant \sigma$, we have

$$x(t)y(t) + \int_{t-\tau}^{t} x(s)d_s \int_{t}^{s+\tau} \eta(\alpha, s-\alpha)y(\alpha)d\alpha$$
$$= x(\sigma)y(\sigma) + \int_{\sigma-\tau}^{\sigma} x(s)d_s \int_{\sigma}^{s+\tau} \eta(\alpha, s-\alpha)y(\alpha)d\alpha. \tag{27}$$

Now let $x(t)$ be the solution of system (25) and the matrix solution $Y(\alpha, \sigma)$ of system (26) be such that $Y(\alpha, \sigma) \equiv 0$ for $\sigma < \alpha \leqslant \sigma + \tau$, $Y(\sigma, \sigma) \equiv E$. From relation (27) we have

$$x(t)Y(t, t) + \int_{t-\tau}^{t} x(s)d_s \int_{t}^{s+\tau} \eta(\alpha, s-\alpha)Y(\alpha, t)d\alpha$$
$$= x(\sigma)Y(\sigma, t) + \int_{\sigma-\tau}^{\sigma} x(s)d_s \int_{\sigma}^{s+\tau} \eta(\alpha, s-\alpha)Y(\alpha, t)d\alpha.$$

However, for $t < \alpha \leqslant s + \tau$ we have $Y(\alpha, t) \equiv 0$ and $Y(t, t) = E$. We obtain

$$x(t) = x(\sigma)Y(\sigma, t) + \int_{\sigma-\tau}^{\sigma} x(s)d_s \int_{\sigma}^{s+\tau} \eta(\alpha, s-\alpha)Y(\alpha, t)d\alpha \tag{28}$$

From here we have, as for system (21), $X(t, \sigma) \equiv Y(\sigma, t)$, where $X(t, \sigma)$ is the solution of system (25) with $X(t, \sigma) \equiv 0$ for $\sigma - \tau \leqslant t < \sigma$, $X(\sigma, \sigma) = E$.

Again using relation (27), we obtain for the solution $y(t)$ of system (26) and the matrix solution $X(t, \sigma)$,

$$X(t, t)y(t) + \int_{t-\tau}^{t} X(s, t)d_s \int_{t}^{s+\tau} \eta(\alpha, s-\alpha)y(\alpha)d\alpha$$
$$= X(\sigma, t)y(\sigma) + \int_{\sigma-\tau}^{\sigma} X(s, t)d_s \int_{\sigma}^{s+\tau} \eta(\alpha, s-\alpha)y(\alpha)d\alpha,$$

and taking into account the relations $X(s, t) \equiv 0$ for $t - \tau \leqslant s < t$, $X(t, t) = E$, we deduce

$$y(t) = X(\sigma, t)y(\sigma) + \int_{\sigma-\tau}^{\sigma} X(s, t)d_s \int^{s+\tau} \eta(\alpha, s-\alpha)y(\alpha)d\alpha. \tag{29}$$

In the following pages we shall establish some properties of general linear systems with time lag. The Stieltjes integral will be used in all these theorems. For readers who are not familiar with this integral, we note that all the proofs could be carried out for systems of the form

$$\dot{x}(t) = A(t)x(t) + \sum_k B_k(t)x(t - \tau_k) + \int_{-\tau}^{0} A(t, s)x(t + s)ds \qquad (*)$$

by the same scheme but using more elementary facts.

The adjoint system is

$$\dot{y}(t) = -y(t)A(t) - \sum_k Y(t + \tau_k)B_k(t + \tau_k) - \int_{-\tau}^{0} y(t - \sigma)A(t - \sigma, \sigma)d\sigma \quad (**)$$

It is easy to prove that

$$\frac{d}{dt}\Big\{y(t)x(t) + \sum_k \int_{t-\tau_k}^{t} y(\alpha + \tau_k)B(\alpha + \tau_k)x(\alpha)d\alpha + \int_{t-\tau}^{t} \Big[\int_{t}^{\alpha+\tau} y(s)A(s, \alpha - s)ds\Big] x(\alpha)d\alpha\Big\} = 0$$

if x is a solution of system (*) and y is a solution of system (**). Indeed, if all functions are continuous, the proof is obvious by differentiation.

More generally, we may use integration by parts:

$$\begin{aligned}
y(t)x(t) - y(\sigma)x(\sigma) &= \int_{\sigma}^{t} \dot{y}(\alpha)x(\alpha)d\alpha + \int_{\sigma}^{t} y(\alpha)\dot{x}(\alpha)d\alpha \\
&= -\int_{\sigma}^{t} y(\alpha)A(\alpha)x(\alpha)d\alpha - \sum_k \int_{\sigma}^{t} y(\alpha + \tau_k)B_k(\alpha + \tau_k)x(\alpha)d\alpha \\
&\quad - \int_{\sigma}^{t} \Big[\int_{-\tau}^{0} y(\alpha - s)A(\alpha - s, s)ds\Big] x(\alpha)d\alpha + \int_{\sigma}^{t} y(\alpha)A(\alpha)x(\alpha)d\alpha \\
&\quad + \sum_k \int_{\sigma}^{t} y(\alpha)B_k(\alpha)x(\alpha - \tau_k)d\alpha + \int_{\sigma}^{t} y(\alpha)d\alpha \int_{-\tau}^{0} A(\alpha, s)x(\alpha + s)ds \\
&= -\sum_k \int_{\sigma}^{t} y(\alpha + \tau_k)B_k(\alpha + \tau_k)x(\alpha)d\alpha - \int_{\sigma}^{t} \Big[\int_{\alpha}^{\alpha+\tau} y(s)A(s, \alpha - s)ds\Big] x(\alpha)d\alpha \\
&\quad + \sum_k \int_{\sigma-\tau_k}^{t-\tau_k} y(\alpha + \tau_k)B_k(\alpha + \tau_k)x(\alpha)d\alpha + \int_{\sigma}^{t} y(\alpha)d\alpha \int_{\alpha-\tau}^{\alpha} A(\alpha, s - \alpha)x(s)ds \\
&= \sum_k \int_{\sigma-\tau_k}^{\sigma} y(\alpha + \tau_k)B_k(\alpha + \tau_k)x(\alpha)d\alpha - \sum_k \int_{t-\tau_k}^{t} y(\alpha + \tau_k)B_k(\alpha + \tau_k)x(\alpha)d\alpha \\
&\quad - \int_{\sigma}^{t} \Big[\int_{\alpha}^{\alpha+\tau} y(s)A(s, \alpha - s)ds\Big] x(\alpha)d\alpha + \int_{\sigma-\tau}^{\sigma} \Big[\int_{\sigma}^{s+\tau} y(\alpha)A(\alpha, s - \alpha)d\alpha\Big] x(s)ds \\
&\quad + \int_{\sigma}^{t-\tau} \Big[\int_{s}^{s+\tau} y(\alpha)A(\alpha, s - \alpha)d\alpha\Big] x(s)ds + \int_{t-\tau}^{t} \Big[\int_{s}^{t} y(\alpha)A(\alpha, s - \alpha)d\alpha\Big] x(s)ds
\end{aligned}$$

$$= \sum_k \int_{\sigma-\tau_k}^{\sigma} y(\alpha+\tau_k)B_k(\alpha+\tau_k)x(\alpha)d\alpha - \sum_k \int_{t-\tau_k}^{t} y(\alpha+\tau_k)B_k(\alpha+\tau_k)x(\alpha)d\alpha$$

$$- \int_{t-\tau}^{t} \left[\int_{\alpha}^{\alpha+\tau} y(s)A(s,\alpha-s)ds\right] x(\alpha)d\alpha + \int_{\sigma-\tau}^{\sigma} \left[\int_{\sigma}^{\alpha+\tau} y(s)A(s,\alpha-s)ds\right] x(\alpha)d\alpha$$

$$+ \int_{t-\tau}^{t} \left[\int_{\alpha}^{t} y(s)A(s,\alpha-s)ds\right] x(\alpha)d\alpha$$

$$= \sum_k \int_{\sigma-\tau_k}^{\sigma} y(\alpha+\tau_k)B_k(\alpha+\tau_k)x(\alpha)d\alpha + \int_{\sigma-\tau}^{\sigma} \left[\int_{\sigma}^{\alpha+\tau} y(s)A(s,\alpha-s)ds\right] x(\alpha)d\alpha$$

$$- \sum_k \int_{t-\tau_k}^{t} y(\alpha+\tau_k)B_k(\alpha+\tau_k)x(\alpha)d\alpha - \int_{t-\tau}^{t} \left[\int_{t}^{\alpha+\tau} y(s)A(s,\alpha-s)ds\right] x(\alpha)d\alpha.$$

From this follows

$$y(t)x(t) + \sum_k \int_{t-\tau_k}^{t} y(\alpha+\tau_k)B_k(\alpha+\tau_k)x(\alpha)d\alpha$$

$$+ \int_{t-\tau}^{t} \left[\int_{t}^{\alpha+\tau} y(s)A(s,\alpha-s)ds\right] x(\alpha)d\alpha$$

$$= y(\sigma)x(\sigma) + \sum_k \int_{\sigma-\tau_k}^{\sigma} y(\alpha+\tau_k)B_k(\alpha+\tau_k)x(\alpha)d\alpha$$

$$+ \int_{\sigma-\tau}^{\sigma} \left[\int_{\sigma}^{\alpha+\tau} y(s)A(s,\alpha-s)ds\right] x(\alpha)d\alpha,$$

and this formula may be used to obtain the fundamental representation formulas for the solutions.

If we take the solution $Y(\alpha, t)$ such that $Y(\alpha, t) \equiv 0$ for $\alpha > t$, $Y(t, t) = E$, we obtain

$$x(t) = Y(\sigma, t)x(\sigma) + \sum_k \int_{\sigma-\tau_k}^{\sigma} Y(\alpha+\tau_k, t)B_k(\alpha+\tau_k)x(\alpha)d\alpha$$

$$+ \int_{\sigma-\tau}^{\sigma} \left[\int_{\sigma}^{\alpha+\tau_k} Y(s,t)A(s,\alpha-s)ds\right] x(\alpha)d\alpha.$$

If we take the solution $X(\alpha, t)$ such that $X(\alpha, t) \equiv 0$ for $\alpha < t$, $X(t, t) = E$, we obtain

$$y(t) = y(\sigma)X(\sigma, t) + \sum_k \int_{\sigma-\tau_k}^{\sigma} y(\alpha+\tau_k)B_k(\alpha+\tau_k)X(\alpha, t)d\alpha$$

$$+ \int_{\sigma-\tau}^{\sigma} \left[\int_{\sigma}^{\alpha+\tau} y(s)A(s,\alpha-s)ds\right] X(\alpha, t)d\alpha$$

$$= y(\sigma)X\ \sigma, t) + \sum_k \int_{\sigma}^{\sigma+\tau_k} y(\alpha)B_k(\alpha)X(\alpha-\tau_k, t)d\alpha$$

$$+ \int_{\sigma}^{\sigma+\tau} y(s)ds \int_{s-\tau}^{\sigma} A(s,\alpha-s)X(\alpha, t)d\alpha.$$

4.4. The Perron Condition for Systems with Time Lag

We shall now state the theorem corresponding to Theorem 1.13 for systems with time lag.

Definition. We will say that the system

$$\dot{x}(t) = \int_{-\infty}^{0} x(t+s)d_s\eta(t,s) \tag{30}$$

verifies the condition of Perron if for every vector function f, continuous and bounded in $t \geqslant 0$, the solution of system (21) defined by the initial function zero in $t \leqslant 0$ is bounded on the semiaxis $t \geqslant 0$.

Theorem 4.15. *If system* (30) *verifies the condition of Perron, then its trivial solution is uniformly asymptotically stable.*

To prove this theorem we shall first state some lemmas.

Lemma 1. *Let $Y(\alpha, t)$ be the matrix of solutions of system*(22)*such that $Y(\alpha, t) = 0$ for $\alpha > t$, $Y(t, t) = E$. If $\int_0^t |Y(\alpha, t)|d\alpha < C$ for $t \geqslant 0$, then $|Y(\alpha, t)| < M$ for $0 \leqslant \alpha \leqslant t$.*

Proof. We have

$$Y(\alpha, t) = E - \int_{\alpha}^{\alpha+\tau} \eta(\gamma, \alpha-\gamma)Y(\gamma, t)d\gamma$$

From this follows

$$|Y(\alpha, t)| \leqslant 1 + \int_{\alpha}^{\alpha+\tau} |\eta(\gamma, \alpha-\gamma)|\,|Y(\gamma, t)|d\gamma$$

$$\leqslant 1 + V\int_{\alpha}^{\alpha+\tau} |Y(\gamma, t)|d\gamma \leqslant 1 + V\int_{\alpha}^{t} |Y(\gamma, t)|d\gamma$$

since if $t < \alpha + \tau$ we have $Y(\gamma, t) \equiv 0$ for $t < \gamma \leqslant \alpha + \tau$.
We obtain

$$|Y(\alpha, t)| \leqslant 1 + V\int_0^t |Y(\gamma, t)|d\gamma = 1 + VC = M,$$

and the lemma is proved.

Let us repeat the proof for systems of the form

$$\dot{x}(t) = A(t)x(t) + \sum_k B_k(t)x(t-\tau_k) + \int_{-\tau}^{0} A(t,s)x(t+s)ds. \tag{$*$}$$

For such systems the equation for $Y(\alpha, t)$ is

$$\frac{\partial}{\partial\alpha} Y(\alpha, t) = -Y(\alpha, t)A(\alpha) - \sum_k Y(\alpha + \tau_k, t)B_k(\alpha + \tau_k) - \int_\alpha^{\alpha+\tau} Y(s, t)A(s, \alpha - s)ds.$$

From here we obtain

$$\begin{aligned} E - Y(\alpha, t) &= -\int_\alpha^t Y(\alpha, t)A(\alpha)d\alpha - \sum_k \int_\alpha^t Y(\alpha + \tau_k, t)B_k(\alpha + \tau_k)d\alpha \\ &\quad - \int_\alpha^t \left[\int_\alpha^{\alpha+\tau} Y(s, t)A(s, \alpha - s)ds\right] d\alpha \\ &= -\int_\alpha^t Y(\alpha, t)A(\alpha)d\alpha - \sum_k \int_\alpha^{t-\tau_k} Y(\alpha + \tau_k, t)B_k(\alpha + \tau_k)d\alpha \\ &\quad - \int_\alpha^{\alpha+\tau} Y(s,t)ds \int_\alpha^s A(s, \beta - s)d\beta - \int_{\alpha+\tau}^t Y(s, t)ds \int_{s-\tau}^s A(s, \beta - s)d\beta \\ &\quad - \int_t^{t+\beta} Y(s, t)ds \int_{s-\tau}^t A(s, \beta - s)d\beta. \end{aligned}$$

The last integral is zero since $Y(s, t) \equiv 0$ for $s > t$, and we have

$$Y(\alpha, t) = E + \int_\alpha^t Y(\beta, t)A(\beta)d\beta + \sum_k \int_{\alpha+\tau_k}^t Y(\beta, t)B_k(\beta)d\beta.$$

It follows that

$$\begin{aligned} |Y(\alpha, t)| &\leqslant 1 + A\int_\alpha^t |Y(\beta, t)|d\beta + \sum_k \int_{\alpha+\tau_k}^t |Y(\beta, t)|d\beta \\ &\quad + L\tau \int_\alpha^{\alpha+\tau} |Y(s, t)|ds + L\tau \int_{\alpha+\tau}^t |Y(s, t)|ds \\ &\leqslant 1 + (A + \sum B_k + L\tau) \int_0^t |Y(s, t)|ds \\ &= 1 + C(A + \sum B_k + L\tau) = M, \end{aligned}$$

where $A = \sup |A(t)|$, $B_k = \sup |B_k(t)|$, $L = \sup_{t\geqslant 0, -\tau\leqslant s\leqslant 0} |A(t, s)|$.

Lemma 2. (Bellman). *If system* (30) *verifies the Perron conditions, there exists a constant C such that*

$$\int_0^t |X(t, \alpha)|d\alpha < C \quad \textit{for} \quad t \geqslant 0.$$

Proof. On the basis of formula (23′) the solution of system (21) defined by the zero initial function is given by the formula

$$x(t) = \int_0^t f(\alpha)X(t, \alpha)d\alpha.$$

The proof continues as in that of Lemma 3, section 1.10.

Proof of Theorem 4.15. If $x(t; t_0, \varphi)$ is the solution of system (30) equal with φ on $[t_0 - \tau, t_0]$, then from (23′) follows

$$x(t; t_0, \varphi) = \varphi(t_0)X(t, t_0) + \int_{t_0-\tau}^{t_0} \varphi(s)d_s \int_{t_0}^{s+\tau} \eta(\alpha, s - \alpha)Y(\alpha, t)d\alpha.$$

From the Perron condition we deduce, by using Lemma 2, that $\int_0^t | X(t, \alpha)|d\alpha < C$; hence by Lemma 1, $| X(t, \alpha)| < M$. We deduce that

$$x(t; t_0, \varphi) = \varphi(t_0)X(t, t_0) + \int_{t_0}^{t_0+\tau} \left[\int_{\alpha-\tau}^{t_0} \varphi(s)d_s\eta(\alpha, s - \alpha)\right] Y(\alpha, t)d\alpha;$$

hence

$$| x(t; t_0, \varphi)| \leqslant M\| \varphi \| + \tau MV\| \varphi \| = M(1 + \tau V)\| \varphi \|,$$

and the zero solution of system (30) is uniformly stable.

It remains to prove that $\lim_{t\to\infty} x(t; t_0, \varphi) = 0$ uniformly with respect to t_0 and φ, in $\| \varphi \| \leqslant h$. For $\sigma \geqslant t_0$ we have

$$\begin{aligned} x(t; t_0, \varphi) &= x(\sigma; t_0, \varphi)X(t, \sigma) + \int_{\sigma-\tau}^{\sigma} x(s; t_0, \varphi)d_s \int_{\sigma}^{s+\tau} \eta(\alpha, s - \alpha)Y(\alpha, t)d\alpha \\ &= x(\sigma; t_0, \varphi)X(t, \sigma) + \int_{\sigma}^{\sigma+\tau} \left[\int_{\alpha-\tau}^{\sigma} x(s; t_0, \varphi)d_s\eta(\alpha, s - \alpha)\right] Y(\alpha, t)d\alpha. \end{aligned}$$

From here we obtain

$$(t - t_0)x(t; t_0, \varphi) = \int_{t_0}^{t} x(t; t_0, \varphi)d\sigma - \int_{t_0}^{t} \left[\int_{\sigma}^{\sigma+\tau} \xi(\sigma, \alpha)Y(\alpha, t)d\alpha\right] d\sigma + \int_{t_0}^{t} x(\sigma; t_0, \varphi)X(t, \sigma)d\sigma,$$

where we have set

$$\xi(\sigma, \alpha) = \int_{\alpha-\tau}^{\sigma} x(s; t_0, \varphi)d_s\eta(\alpha, s - \alpha).$$

Further,

$$\int_{t_0}^{t}\left[\int_{\sigma}^{\sigma+\tau}\xi(\sigma,\alpha)Y(\alpha,t)d\alpha\right]d\sigma = \int_{t_0}^{t_0+\tau}\left[\int_{t_0}^{\alpha}\xi(\sigma,\alpha)d\sigma\right]Y(\alpha,t)d\alpha$$

$$+\int_{t_0+\tau}^{t}\left[\int_{\alpha-\tau}^{\alpha}\xi(\sigma,\alpha)d\sigma\right]Y(\alpha,t)d\alpha+\int_{t}^{t+\tau}\left[\int_{\alpha-\tau}^{t}\xi(\sigma,\alpha)d\sigma\right]Y(\alpha,t)d\alpha.$$

The last integral is zero since $Y(\alpha, t) \equiv 0$ for $\alpha > t$, and we obtain

$$(t-t_0)x(t;t_0,\varphi) = \int_{t_0}^{t_0+\tau}\left[\int_{t_0}^{\alpha}\xi(\sigma,\alpha)d\sigma\right]Y(\alpha,t)d\alpha$$

$$+\int_{t_0+\tau}^{t}\left[\int_{\alpha-\tau}^{\alpha}\xi(\sigma,\alpha)d\sigma\right]Y(\alpha,t)d\alpha.$$

We have $|\ \xi(\sigma, \alpha)| \leqslant V \sup |\ x(s; t_0, \varphi)| \leqslant VM_1 \|\varphi\|$ and

$$\int_{\alpha-\tau}^{\alpha}\xi(\sigma,\alpha)d\sigma = \int_{\alpha-\tau}^{\alpha}\left[\int_{\alpha-\tau}^{\sigma}x(s;t_0,\varphi)d_s\eta(\alpha,s-\alpha)\right]d\sigma$$

$$= \int_{-\tau}^{0}\left[\int_{\alpha-\tau}^{\alpha+\sigma}x(s;t_0,\varphi)d_s\eta(\alpha,s-\alpha)\right]d\sigma$$

$$= \int_{-\tau}^{0}\left[\int_{-\tau}^{\sigma}x(\alpha+s;t_0,\varphi)d_s\eta(\alpha,s)\right]d\sigma;$$

hence

$$\left|\int_{\alpha-\tau}^{\alpha}\xi(\sigma,\alpha)d\sigma\right| \leqslant \tau VM_1\|\varphi\|.$$

From here we obtain

$$(t-t_0)|\ x(t;t_0,\varphi)| \leqslant \tau^2 MVM_1\|\varphi\| + \tau VM_1\|\varphi\|\int_{t_0+\tau}^{t}|\ Y(\alpha,t)|\ d\alpha$$

$$+ M_1\|\varphi\|\int_{t_0}^{t}|\ X(t,\sigma)|\ d\sigma \leqslant \tau VM_1(\tau M + C)\|\varphi\| + M_1C\|\varphi\|;$$

hence

$$|\ x(t;t_0,\varphi)| \leqslant \frac{M_2}{t-t_0}\|\varphi\|,$$

and the theorem is proved.

Let us again prove the theorem for system (*). We have

$$x(t; t_0, \varphi) = Y(t_0, t)x(t_0) + \sum_k \int_{t_0-\tau_k}^{t_0} Y(\alpha + \tau_k, t)B_k(\alpha + \tau_k)\varphi(\alpha)d\alpha$$

$$+ \int_{t_0-\tau}^{t_0} \left[\int_{t_0}^{\alpha+\tau} Y(s, t)A(s, \alpha - s)ds\right] \varphi(\alpha)d\alpha$$

$$= Y(t_0, t)\varphi(t_0) + \sum_k \int_{t_0-\tau_k}^{t_0} Y(\alpha + \tau_k, t)B_k(\alpha + \tau_k)\varphi(\alpha)d\alpha$$

$$+ \int_{t_0}^{t_0+\tau} Y(s, t)ds \int_{s-\tau}^{t_0} A(s, \alpha - s)\varphi(\alpha)d\alpha$$

From here follows

$$| x(t; t_0, \varphi)| \leqslant M\| \varphi \| + \sum_k \tau_k B_k M\| \varphi \| + ML\tau\| \varphi \| = M_1\| \varphi \|.$$

Further, we have, for $\sigma \geqslant t_0$,

$$x(t; t_0, \varphi) = Y(\sigma, t)x(\sigma; t_0, \varphi) + \sum_k \int_{\sigma-\tau_k}^{\sigma} Y(\alpha + \tau_k, t)B_k(\alpha + \tau_k)x(\alpha; t_0, \varphi)\, d\alpha$$

$$+ \int_{\sigma}^{\sigma+\tau} Y(s, t)ds \int_{s-\tau}^{\sigma} A(s, \alpha - s)x(\alpha; t_0, \varphi)d\alpha$$

and

$$(t - t_0)x(t; t_0, \varphi) = \int_{t_0}^{t} x(t; t_0, \varphi)d\sigma = \int_{t_0}^{t} Y(\sigma, t)x(\sigma; t_0, \varphi)d\sigma$$

$$+ \sum_k \int_{t_0}^{t} \left[\int_{\sigma}^{\sigma+\tau_k} Y(\alpha, t)B_k(\alpha)x(\alpha - \tau_k; t_0, \varphi)d\alpha\right] d\sigma$$

$$+ \int_{t_0}^{t} \left[\int_{\sigma}^{\sigma+\tau} Y(s, t)\zeta(s, \sigma)ds\right] d\sigma$$

$$= \int_{t_0}^{t} Y(\sigma, t)x(\sigma; t_0, \varphi)d\sigma + \sum_k \int_{t_0}^{t_0+\tau_k} Y(\alpha, t)B_k(\alpha)x(\alpha - \tau_k; t_0, \varphi)d\alpha \int_{t_0}^{\alpha} d\sigma$$

$$+ \sum_k \int_{t_0+\tau_k}^{t} Y(\alpha, t)B_k(\alpha)x(\alpha - \tau_k; t_0, \varphi)d\alpha \int_{\alpha-\tau_k}^{\alpha} d\sigma$$

$$+ \int_{t_0}^{t_0+\tau} Y(s, t)ds \int_{t_0}^{s} \zeta(s, \sigma)d\sigma + \int_{t_0+\tau}^{t} Y(s, t)ds \int_{s-\tau}^{s} \zeta(s, \sigma)d\sigma$$

$$= \int_{t_0}^{t} Y(\sigma, t)x(\sigma; t_0, \varphi)d\sigma + \sum_k \int_{t_0}^{t_0+\tau_k} (\alpha - t_0)Y(\alpha, t)B_k(\alpha)x(\alpha - \tau_k ; t_0, \varphi)d\alpha$$

$$+ \sum_k \int_{t_0+\tau_k}^{t} \tau_k Y(\alpha, t)B_k(\alpha)x(\alpha - \tau_k ; t_0, \varphi)d\alpha + \int_{t_0}^{t_0+\tau} Y(s, t)ds \int_{t_0}^{s} \zeta(s, \sigma)d\sigma$$

$$+ \int_{t_0+\tau}^{t} Y(s, t)ds \int_{s-\tau}^{s} \zeta(s, \sigma)d\sigma,$$

where we have set

$$\zeta(s, \sigma) = \int_{s-\tau}^{\sigma} A(s, \alpha - s)x(\alpha; t_0, \varphi)d\alpha.$$

We have

$$\int_{t_0}^{s} \zeta(s, \sigma)d\sigma = \int_{t_0}^{s} \left[\int_{s-\tau}^{\sigma} A(s, \alpha - s)x(\alpha; t_0, \varphi)d\alpha\right] d\sigma$$

$$= \int_{s-\tau}^{t_0} A(s, \alpha - s)x(\alpha; t_0, \varphi)d\alpha \int_{t_0}^{s} d\sigma + \int_{t_0}^{s} A(s, \alpha - s)x(\alpha; t_0, \varphi)d\alpha \int_{\alpha}^{s} d\sigma$$

$$= (s - t_0) \int_{s-\tau}^{t_0} A(s, \alpha - s)x(\alpha; t_0, \varphi)d\alpha + \int_{t_0}^{s} (s - \alpha)A(s, \alpha - s)x(\alpha; t_0, \varphi)d\alpha$$

and

$$\int_{s-\tau}^{s} \zeta(s, \sigma)d\sigma = \int_{s-\tau}^{s} \left[\int_{s-\tau}^{\sigma} A(s, \alpha - s)x(\alpha; t_0, \varphi)d\alpha\right] d\sigma$$

$$= \int_{s-\tau}^{s} (s - \alpha)A(s, \alpha - s)x(\alpha; t_0, \varphi)d\alpha.$$

From here we deduce

$$\left| \int_{t_0}^{s} \zeta(s, \sigma)d\sigma \right| \leqslant \tau^2 L M_1 \| \varphi \|,$$

$$\left| \int_{s-\tau}^{s} \zeta(s, \sigma)d\sigma \right| \leqslant \tau^2 L M_1 \| \varphi \|$$

and

$$(t - t_0)| x(t; t_0, \varphi)| \leqslant M_1 C \| \varphi \| + \sum_k \tau_k B_k M_1 C \| \varphi \| + \tau^2 L M_1 C \| \varphi \| = M_2 \| \varphi \|.$$

The theorem is thus proved.

4.5. An Estimate in the Stability Theory of Linear Systems with Time Lag

The following problem is interesting in many practical problems. We consider a system of the form

$$\dot{x}(t) = A(t)x(t) + B(t)x(t - \tau) \tag{31}$$

If the lag τ is small, it is quite natural to suppose that it can be neglected and that we can consider the system of ordinary differential equations

$$\dot{y}(t) = [A(t) + B(t)]y(t). \tag{32}$$

We suppose that the trivial solution of system (32) is uniformly asymptotically stable. We could expect that for τ sufficiently small the trivial solution of system (31) be likewise uniformly asymptotically stable. We will prove in the following pages that this is true and will obtain an estimate of the values τ for which uniform asymptotic stability of the trivial solution of system (31) may be deduced from the corresponding property for the system (32).

We shall use a lemma relative to differential inequalities with time lag which is interesting in itself. Let

$$D_{-}\varphi(t) = \liminf_{h \to 0-} \frac{\varphi(t + h) - \varphi(t)}{h}$$

and let $f(t, u, v)$ be continuous for all (u, v) and $0 \leqslant t < \alpha$, monotone-increasing with respect to v.

Proposition 1. *If* $D_{-}\varphi(t) < f[t, \varphi(t), \sup_{t-\tau \leqslant s \leqslant t} \varphi(s)]$, $D_{-}\psi(t) \geqslant f[t, \psi(t), \sup_{t-\tau \leqslant s \leqslant t} \psi(s)]$ *and* $\varphi(s) < \psi(s)$ *for* $-\tau \leqslant s \leqslant 0$, *then* $\varphi(t) < \psi(t)$ *for* $0 < t < \alpha$.

Proof. Let $\xi = \inf\{t; \varphi(t) \geqslant \psi(t)\}$. We have $\xi > 0$, $\varphi(\xi) = \psi(\xi)$.

For $-\tau \leqslant t < \xi$ it follows that $\varphi(t) < \psi(t)$; hence $\sup_{\xi-\tau \leqslant s \leqslant \xi} \varphi(s) \leqslant \sup_{\xi-\tau \leqslant s \leqslant \xi} \psi(s)$. It follows that $D_{-}\varphi(\xi) < f[\xi, \varphi(\xi), \sup_{\xi-\tau \leqslant s \leqslant \xi} \varphi(s)] \leqslant f[\xi, \psi(\xi), \sup_{\xi-\tau \leqslant s \leqslant \xi} \psi(s)] \leqslant D_{-}\psi(\xi)$. From $\varphi(t) < \psi(t)$ for $t < \xi$ and $\varphi(\xi) = \psi(\xi)$, it follows that $D_{-}\varphi(\xi) \geqslant D_{-}\psi(\xi)$, and the proposition is proved.

Proposition 2. *If* $\dot{\omega}(t) \leqslant f[t, \omega(t), \sup_{t-\tau \leqslant s \leqslant t} \omega(s)]$ *for* $t_0 \leqslant t < t_0 + \alpha$ *and if* $y(t; t_0, \omega)$ *is the solution of the equation*

$$\dot{y}(t) = f[t, y(t), \sup_{t-\tau \leqslant s \leqslant t} y(s)],$$

which in $[t_0 - \tau, t_0]$ *coincides with* ω, *then, supposing that this solution is defined in* $[t_0, t_0 + \alpha)$, *it follows that* $\omega(t) \leqslant y(t; t_0, \omega)$ *for* $t_0 \leqslant t < t_0 + \alpha$.

Proof. Let ϵ_n be a sequence of positive numbers tending monotonically to zero, and y_n be the solution of the equation

$$\dot{y}(t) = f[t, y(t), \sup_{t-\tau \leqslant s \leqslant t} y(s)] + \epsilon_n ,$$

which in $[t_0 - \tau, t_0]$ coincides with $\omega + \epsilon_n$. On the basis of the preceding proposition, $y_{n+1}(t) < y_n(t)$ in $[t_0, t_0 + \alpha)$, and it is easy to see that $\lim_{n\to\infty} y_n(t) = y(t; t_0, \omega)$ [in fact we should stress that in case a uniqueness condition is not satisfied, $y(t; t_0, \omega)$ is the superior solution defined by the initial conditions considered]. On the basis of Proposition 1 we have $\omega(t) < y_n(t)$ for $t \in [t_0, t_0 + \alpha)$; hence $\omega(t) \leqslant y(t; t_0, \omega)$.

Lemma. *If* $\dot{f}(t) \leqslant -\alpha f(t) + \beta \sup_{t-\tau\leqslant\sigma\leqslant t} f(\sigma)$ *for* $t \geqslant t_0$ *and if* $\alpha > \beta > 0$, *then there exists* $\gamma > 0$ *and* $k > 0$ *such that* $f(t) \leqslant ke^{-\gamma(t-t_0)}$ *for* $t \geqslant t_0$.

Proof. It follows on the basis of Proposition 2 that $f(t) \leqslant y(t)$, where $y(t)$ is a solution of the equation

$$\dot{y}(t) = -\alpha y(t) + \beta \sup_{t-\tau\leqslant\sigma\leqslant t} y(\sigma), \tag{$*$}$$

which in $[t_0 - \tau, t_0]$ is greater than f. Let us observe that $y(t) = ke^{-\gamma(t-t_0)}$ is a solution of this equation if $-\gamma = -\alpha + \beta e^{\gamma\tau}$. Indeed,

$$\sup_{t-\tau\leqslant\sigma\leqslant t} y(\sigma) = ke^{\gamma\tau}e^{-\gamma(t-t_0)}$$

and

$$\dot{y}(t) = -\gamma k e^{-\gamma(t-t_0)}.$$

If $\alpha > \beta$, the function $\varphi(z) = -\alpha + \beta e^{z\tau} + z$ is negative for $z = 0$ and tends to infinity when $z \to \infty$; hence there exists a $z = \gamma > 0$ for which the function is equal to zero. It follows that if $\alpha > \beta$, there exists $\gamma > 0$ such that $y(t) = ke^{-\gamma(t-t_0)}$ is a solution of equation ($*$). We have $\inf_{t_0-\tau\leqslant t\leqslant t_0} y(t) = k$; hence by choosing $k > \sup_{t_0-\tau\leqslant t\leqslant t_0} f(t)$, it follows on the basis of Proposition 2 that $f(t) \leqslant ke^{-\gamma(t-t_0)}$, and the lemma is thus proved.

Assuming that the trivial solution of system (32) is uniformly asymptotically stable, there exists a quadratic form $(V(t)y, y)$ whose derivative, by virtue of system (32), is $-(y, y)$. Let $x(t)$ be any solution of system (31). We calculate

$$\frac{d}{dt}(V(t)x(t), x(t)).$$

We have

$$\frac{d}{dt}(V(t)x(t), x(t)) = \left(\frac{dV}{dt}x(t), x(t)\right) + 2\left(V(t)\frac{dx(t)}{dt}, x(t)\right)$$

$$= \left(\frac{dV}{dt}x(t), x(t)\right) + 2(V(t)(A(t)x(t) + B(t)x(t-\tau)), x(t))$$

$$= \left(\frac{dV}{dt}x(t), x(t)\right) + 2(V(t)(A(t) + B(t))x(t), x(t))$$
$$+ 2(V(t)B(t)(x(t-\tau) - x(t)), x(t))$$

$$= -(x(t), x(t)) + 2\left(V(t)B(t)\int_{t-\tau}^{t}\frac{dx(u)}{du}\,du, x(t)\right)$$

$$= -(x(t), x(t)) + 2\left(V(t)B(t)\int_{t-\tau}^{t}[A(u)x(u) + B(u)x(u-\tau)]\,du, x(t)\right).$$

Let

$$L_1 = \sup_t |A(t)|, \qquad L_2 = \sup_t |B(t)|, \qquad L_3 = \sup_t |V(t)B(t)|.$$

We deduce that

$$\frac{d}{dt}(V(t)x(t), x(t)) \leqslant -|x(t)|^2 + 2\tau L_3(L_1 + L_2) \sup_{t-2\tau \leqslant u \leqslant t} |x(u)|\,|x(t)|.$$

Let Λ be the upper bound of the highest eigenvalue of the matrix V, λ the lower bound of the smallest eigenvalue of matrix V. We have

$$\lambda|x(t)|^2 \leqslant (V(t)x(t), x(t)) \leqslant \Lambda|x(t)|^2 \qquad (\lambda > 0).$$

Let us set

$$f^2(t) = (V(t)x(t), x(t)).$$

From

$$\lambda|x(t)|^2 \leqslant f^2(t) \leqslant \Lambda|x(t)|^2$$

we obtain

$$\sqrt{\lambda}|x(t)| \leqslant f(t) \leqslant \sqrt{\Lambda}|x(t)|;$$

hence

$$\sup_{t-2\tau\leqslant s\leqslant t} |x(s)| \leqslant \frac{1}{\sqrt{\lambda}} \sup_{t-2\tau\leqslant s\leqslant t} f(s), \quad |x(t)| \leqslant \frac{1}{\sqrt{\lambda}} f(t) \quad -|x(t)|^2 \leqslant -\frac{1}{\Lambda} f^2(t).$$

We may therefore write

$$\frac{d}{dt} f^2(t) \leqslant -\frac{1}{\Lambda} f^2(t) + 2\tau L_3(L_1+L_2) \frac{1}{\sqrt{\lambda}} \sup_{t-2\tau\leqslant s\leqslant t} f(s) \frac{1}{\sqrt{\lambda}} f(t)$$

and, dividing by $2f(t)$,

$$\frac{df(t)}{dt} \leqslant -\frac{1}{2\Lambda} f(t) + \frac{\tau L_3(L_1+L_2)}{\lambda} \sup_{t-2\tau\leqslant s\leqslant t} f(s).$$

We may apply the lemma, taking

$$\alpha = \frac{1}{2\Lambda}, \qquad \beta = \frac{\tau L_3(L_1+L_2)}{\lambda}.$$

The condition $\alpha > \beta$ leads to

$$\frac{\tau L_3(L_1+L_2)}{\lambda} < \frac{1}{2\Lambda};$$

hence

$$\tau < \frac{\lambda}{\Lambda L_3(L_1+L_2)}.$$

It follows that if

$$\tau < \frac{\lambda}{\Lambda L_3(L_1+L_2)}$$

there exist $\gamma > 0$ and $k > 0$ such that $f(t) < ke^{-\gamma(t-t_0)}$ for $t \geqslant t_0$; hence $|x(t)| \leqslant (k/\sqrt{\lambda})e^{-\gamma(t-t_0)}$ for $t \geqslant t_0$. This shows that the trivial solution of system (31) is uniformly asymptotically stable. Let us observe that by supposing the differentiability of matrices A and B we could have continued the computations taking account of terms of the second degree in τ. This would have lead to improved estimates.

We now study the same problem without making use of the Lyapunov function. Let us consider the system

$$\dot{x}(t) = A(t)x(t) + \sum_{i=1}^{k} B_i(t)x(t-\mu\tau_i) \tag{31'}$$

and the system obtained for $\mu = 0$,

$$\dot{x}(t) = \Big[A(t) + \sum_{i=1}^{k} B_i(t)\Big] x(t). \tag{32'}$$

We suppose that the trivial solution of system (32′) is uniformly asymptotically stable. If $U(t, s)$ is a fundamental matrix of solutions of the system (32′), we have $|U(t, s)| \leqslant Ke^{-\alpha(t-s)}$. Let $x(t)$ be any solution of system (31′). We have

$$x(t) = U(t, 0)x(0) + \sum_{i=1}^{k} U(t, s)B_i(s)[x(s - \mu\tau_i) - x(s)]ds.$$

Let $\tau = \max_i \tau_i$. For $t > 2\mu\tau$ we will write

$$x(t) = U(t, 0)x(0) + \sum_{i=1}^{k} \int_0^{2\mu\tau} U(t, s)B_i(s)[x(s - \mu\tau_i) - x(s)]ds$$

$$+ \sum_{i=1}^{k} \int_{2\mu\tau}^{t} U(t, s)B_i(s)[x(s - \mu\tau_i) - x(s)]ds.$$

On the basis of the inequality (3) we have for $0 \leqslant s \leqslant 2\mu\tau$ the estimate

$$|x(s)| \leqslant \exp\Big[\Big(\sum_{i=0}^{k} K_i\Big) 2\mu\tau\Big] \|\varphi\|,$$

where φ is the initial function of the solution x, given in $[-\mu\tau, 0]$. This estimate is obviously also valid for $s \leqslant 0$. We have set

$$K_0 = \sup_t |A(t)|, \qquad K_i = \sup_t |B_i(t)|, \qquad (i = 1, ..., k).$$

It follows that for $0 \leqslant s \leqslant 2\mu\tau$ we have, in any case,

$$|x(s - \mu\tau_i) - x(s)| \leqslant 2 \exp\Big[\Big(\sum_{i=0}^{k} K_i\Big) 2\mu\tau\Big] \|\varphi\|.$$

For $s \geqslant 2\mu\tau$ we may write

$$x(s - \mu\tau_i) - x(s) = \int_s^{s-\mu\tau_i} \dot{x}(\sigma)d\sigma = \int_s^{s-\mu\tau_i} \Big[A(\sigma)x(\sigma) + \sum_{j=1}^{k} B_j(\sigma)x(\sigma - \mu\tau_j)\Big]d\sigma;$$

hence

$$|x(s - \mu\tau_i) - x(s)| \leqslant \mu\tau_i \sum_{j=0}^{k} K_j \sup_{s-2\mu\tau \leqslant \sigma \leqslant s} |x(\sigma)|.$$

We obtain

$$| x(t)| \leqslant Ke^{-\alpha t}\| \varphi \| + \sum_{i=1}^{k} \int_0^{2\mu\tau} Ke^{-\alpha(t-s)}K_i 2 \exp \Big[\Big(\sum_{i=0}^{k} K_i\Big) 2\mu\tau\Big] \| \varphi \| \, ds$$

$$+ \sum_{i=1}^{k} \int_{2\mu\tau}^{t} Ke^{-\alpha(t-s)}K_i\mu\tau_i \sum_{j=0}^{k} \sup_{s-2\mu\tau\leqslant\sigma\leqslant s} | x(\sigma)| \, ds$$

$$= Ke^{-\alpha t}\| \varphi \| + 4K \Big(\sum_{i=1}^{k} K_i\Big) \exp \Big[\Big(\sum_{i=0}^{k} K_i\Big) 2\mu\tau\Big] e^{-\alpha t} \frac{1}{\alpha} (e^{2\sigma\mu\tau} - 1)\| \varphi \|$$

$$+ K \sum_{i=1}^{k} \tau_i K_i \sum_{j=0}^{k} K_j\mu \int_{2\mu\tau}^{t} e^{-\alpha(t-s)} \sup_{s-2\mu\tau\leqslant\sigma\leqslant s} | x(\sigma)| \, ds.$$

We set

$$L = K\| \varphi \| \Big(1 + \frac{4}{\alpha} (e^{2\alpha\mu\tau} - 1)\Big) \Big(\sum_{i=1}^{k} K_i\Big) \exp \Big(2\mu\tau \sum_{i=0}^{k} K_i\Big),$$

$$M = K \sum_{i=1}^{k} \tau_i K_i \sum_{j=0}^{k} K_j\mu$$

We have the estimate

$$| x(t)| \leqslant Le^{-\alpha t} + M \int_{2\mu\tau}^{t} e^{-\alpha(t-s)} \sup_{s-2\mu\tau\leqslant\sigma\leqslant s} | x(\sigma)| \, ds.$$

Let

$$v(t) = e^{-\alpha t} \Big[L + M \int_{2\mu\tau}^{t} e^{\alpha s} \sup_{s-2\mu\tau \leqslant\sigma\leqslant s} | x(\sigma)| ds \Big].$$

We have

$$v'(t) = -\alpha e^{-\alpha t} \Big[L + M \int_{2\mu\tau}^{t} e^{\alpha s} \sup_{s-2\mu\tau\leqslant\sigma\leqslant s} | x(\sigma)| \, ds\Big] + e^{-\alpha t}Me^{\alpha t} \sup_{t-2\mu\tau\leqslant\sigma\leqslant t} | x(\sigma)|$$

$$= -\alpha v(t) + M \sup_{t-2\mu\tau\leqslant\sigma\leqslant t} | x(\sigma)|.$$

However,

$$| x(t)| \leqslant v(t);$$

hence

$$\sup_{t-2\mu\tau\leqslant\sigma\leqslant t} | x(\sigma)| \leqslant \sup_{t-2\mu\tau\leqslant\sigma\leqslant t} v(\sigma).$$

We obtain

$$v'(t) \leqslant -\alpha v(t) + M \sup_{k-2\mu\tau\leqslant\sigma\leqslant t} v(\sigma).$$

If $M < \alpha$, it follows, by virtue of the lemma, that there exist constants N and γ such that

$$v(t) \leqslant N e^{-\gamma(t-t_0)};$$

hence a similar inequality also occurs for $|x(t)|$. Consequently, the trivial solution of system (31′) is exponentially stable, provided that $M < \alpha$. This condition leads to

$$\mu < \frac{\alpha}{K \sum_{i=1}^{k} \tau_i K_i \sum_{j=0}^{k} K_j}.$$

4.6. The Stability of Some Control Systems with Time Lag

We shall show below the way in which, by using the V. M. Popov method, one may obtain conditions of asymptotic stability in the large for nonlinear systems with time lag, of the type which occur in the theory of automatic control systems.

Let the system

$$\frac{dx}{dt} = Ax(t) + Bx(t-\tau) + lf[\sigma(t-\tau)] \qquad [\sigma = (c, x)].$$

Here A, B are constant matrices, l a constant vector. We will assume that the equation

$$\det(A + e^{-\lambda\tau}B - \lambda E) = 0$$

has all roots in the semiplane $\operatorname{Re}\lambda \leqslant -\alpha < 0$. We will likewise assume that

$$h_1\sigma^2 \leqslant \sigma f(\sigma) \leqslant h_2\sigma^2 \qquad \text{with} \quad h_2 < k.$$

Let $x(t)$ be any solution of the system and $u(t)$ the solution of the system

$$\frac{du}{dt} = Au(t) + Bu(t-\tau) + l\psi(t-\tau),$$

where $\psi(t) = f[\sigma(t)]$ for $-\tau \leqslant t \leqslant 0$, $\psi(t) \equiv 0$ for $t > 0$, which verifies the same initial conditions as $x(t)$ in $[-\tau, 0]$. Let

$$f_T(t) = \begin{cases} 0 & \text{for} \quad -\tau \leqslant t < 0, \\ f[\sigma(t)] & \text{for} \quad 0 \leqslant t \leqslant T, \\ 0 & \text{for} \quad T < t. \end{cases}$$

We denote by $w(t)$ the solution of the nonhomogeneous linear system

$$\frac{dw}{dt} = Aw(t) + Bw(t-\tau) + lf_T(t-\tau),$$

which verifies zero initial conditions. We have

$$w(t) = x(t) - u(t) \qquad \text{for} \quad -\tau \leqslant t \leqslant T+\tau,$$

since the initial conditions are verified and the difference $x(t) - u(t)$ satisfies the same system as $w(t)$.

Let

$$\begin{aligned}\chi(T) &= \int_0^T \left[(c, w(t)) - \frac{1}{k} f_T(t) + q\left(c, \frac{dw}{dt}\right)\right] f_T(t)dt \\ &= \int_0^\infty \left[(c, w(t)) - \frac{1}{k} f_T(t) + q\left(c, \frac{dw}{dt}\right)\right] f_T(t)dt \\ &= \frac{1}{2\pi}\int_{-\infty}^{+\infty} \mathrm{Re}\left\{(c, \tilde{w}) - \frac{1}{k}\tilde{f}_T + q(c, i\omega\tilde{w})\right\}\tilde{f}_T^*\, d\omega.\end{aligned}$$

Since w verifies the homogeneous system for $t > T$, it follows that w and dw/dt decrease exponentially; hence that we can apply the Fourier transform theory. We have denoted by $\tilde{w}$ and $\tilde{f}_T$ the Fourier transforms of w and f_T, respectively. From the system of equations for w we obtain, by applying the Fourier transform,

$$i\omega\tilde{w} = A\tilde{w} + e^{-i\omega\tau}B\tilde{w} + l\tilde{f}_T e^{-i\omega\tau},$$

from which we deduce

$$\tilde{w} = -(A + e^{-i\omega\tau}B - i\omega E)^{-1} l e^{-i\omega\tau}\tilde{f}_T .$$

The inverse of the matrix $(A + e^{-i\omega\tau}B - i\omega E)^{-1}$ exists, since we have supposed that its spectrum is situated in the semiplane $\mathrm{Re}\, z \leqslant -\alpha < 0$.

We write $M = e^{-i\omega\tau}(A + e^{-i\omega\tau}B - i\omega E)^{-1}l$ and $\mathscr{G} = (c, M)$. We have $\tilde{w} = -M\tilde{f}_T$; hence

$$\begin{aligned}\chi(T) &= \frac{1}{2\pi}\int_{-\infty}^{\infty} \mathrm{Re}\left\{-(c, M)\tilde{f}_T - \frac{1}{k}\tilde{f}_T - q(c, M)i\omega\tilde{f}_T\right\}\tilde{f}_T^*\, d\omega \\ &= -\frac{1}{2\pi}\int_{-\infty}^{\infty} \mathrm{Re}\left\{\frac{1}{k} + (1 + i\omega q)\mathscr{G}\right\} |\tilde{f}_T|^2\, d\omega.\end{aligned}$$

Supposing that $(1/k) + \mathrm{Re}(1 + i\omega q)\mathscr{G} > 0$, we obtain $\chi(T) \leqslant 0$.

On the other hand,

$$\chi(T) = \int_0^T \left[(c,x(t)) - \frac{1}{k} f[\sigma(t)] + q\left(c, \frac{dx(t)}{dt}\right) - (c,u(t)) - q\left(c, \frac{du(t)}{dt}\right)\right] f[\sigma(t)]dt.$$

It follows that

$$\int_0^T \left\{\sigma(t) - \frac{1}{k} f[\sigma(t)] + q\frac{d\sigma(t)}{dt}\right\} f[\sigma(t)]dt \leqslant \int_0^T \left\{(c, u(t)) + q\left(c, \frac{du(t)}{dt}\right)\right\} f[\sigma(t)]dt.$$

However,

$$f(\sigma)\left(\sigma - \frac{1}{k} f(\sigma)\right) \geqslant \frac{k - h_2}{k} h_1 \sigma^2 = h_3 \sigma^2.$$

It follows that

$$h_3 \int_0^T \sigma^2(t)dt + q \int_{\sigma(0)}^{\sigma(T)} f(\sigma)d\sigma \leqslant \int_0^T \left\{(c, u(t)) + q\left(c, \frac{du(t)}{dt}\right)\right\} f[\sigma(t)]dt.$$

Writing $F(\sigma) = \int_0^\sigma f(\sigma)d\sigma$, we obtain

$$h_3 \int_0^T \sigma^2(t)dt + qF[\sigma(T)] \leqslant qF[\sigma(0)] + \int_0^T \left\{(c, u(t)) + q\left(c, \frac{du(t)}{dt}\right)\right\} f[\sigma(t)]dt.$$

We have

$$F[\sigma(T)] > \frac{h_1}{2} \sigma^2(T);$$

hence we can write the inequality

$$q\frac{h_1}{2} \sigma^2(T) + h_3 \int_0^T \sigma^2(t)dt \leqslant qF[\sigma(0)] + \int_0^T \left\{(c, u(t)) + q\left(c, \frac{du(t)}{dt}\right)\right\} f[\sigma(t)]dt.$$

If φ is the initial function of solution $x(t)$, we have

$$|u(t)| \leqslant \beta e^{-\alpha' t} \| \varphi \|, \qquad \left|\frac{du}{dt}\right| \leqslant \gamma e^{-\alpha' t} \| \varphi \|.$$

From $\sigma f(\sigma) \leqslant h_2 \sigma^2$ we obtain $|f(\sigma)| \leqslant h_2 |\sigma|$; hence

$$\left| \int_0^T \left\{(c, u(t)) + q\left(c, \frac{du(t)}{dt}\right)\right\} f[\sigma(t)]dt \right| \leqslant L_1 \sup_{0 \leqslant t \leqslant T} |\sigma(t)| \| \varphi \| \int_0^T e^{-\alpha' t} dt$$

Taking this into account, we finally obtain

$$\frac{qh_1}{2}\sigma^2(T) + h_3\int_0^T \sigma^2(t)dt \leqslant qF[\sigma(0)] + L_2\|\varphi\| \sup_{0\leqslant t\leqslant T} |\sigma(t)|.$$

From the inequality

$$\frac{qh_1}{2}\sigma^2(T) \leqslant qF[\sigma(0)] + L_2\|\varphi\| \sup_{0\leqslant t\leqslant T} |\sigma(t)|$$

we deduce, as in Chapter 2, that

$$|\sigma(t)| \leqslant a_1(\|\varphi\|),$$

and taking into account formula (19) we also deduce

$$|x(t)| \leqslant a_2(\|\varphi\|).$$

From here it follows that $| d\sigma/dt | \leqslant a_3(\|\varphi\|)$ and through the same arguments as in Chapter 2 it follows from $\int_0^T \sigma^2(t)dt \leqslant C$ that $\lim_{t\to\infty}\sigma(t) = 0$. Again taking formula (19) into account, we deduce that $\lim_{t\to\infty} x(t) = 0$, and the following theorem is thus proved:

Theorem 4.16. *If the equation*

$$\det(A + e^{-\lambda\tau}B - \lambda E) = 0$$

has its roots in the semiplane $\operatorname{Re}\lambda \leqslant -\alpha < 0$ *and if there exists a* $q > 0$ *such that*

$$\frac{1}{k} + \operatorname{Re}(1 + i\omega q)e^{-i\omega\tau}(c, (A + e^{-i\omega\tau}B - i\omega E)^{-1}l) > 0,$$

then, for any function f *with the property that there exists* h_1 *and* $h_2 < k$ *such that* $h_1\sigma^2 \leqslant \sigma f(\sigma) \leqslant h_2\sigma^2$, *the trivial solution of the system is asymptotically stable in the large.*

Let us emphasize some general aspects of the V. M. Popov method which will allow us to obtain other results in the theory of absolute stability of automatic systems with time lag.

The method of V. M. Popov enables us to obtain the stability condition for nonlinear integral equations of the form

$$\sigma(t) = z(t) + \int_0^t k(t-\alpha)f[\sigma(\alpha)]d\alpha.$$

Let us consider the case where $h_1\sigma^2 \leqslant \sigma f(\sigma) \leqslant h_2\sigma^2$, $h_2 < h$ and $| z(t)| + | dz(t)/dt | + | k(t)| + | dk(t)/dt | \leqslant Ae^{-\alpha t}$ for $t \geqslant 0$. Let

$$f_T(t) = \begin{cases} f[\sigma(t)] & \text{for } 0 \leqslant t \leqslant T, \\ 0 & \text{for } t > T, \end{cases}$$

$$\sigma_T(t) = \begin{cases} \sigma(t) & \text{for } 0 \leqslant t \leqslant T, \\ 0 & \text{for } t > T, \end{cases}$$

$$z_T(t) = \begin{cases} z(t) & \text{for } 0 \leqslant t \leqslant T, \\ -\int_0^T k(t-\alpha) f[\sigma(\alpha)] & \text{for } t > T. \end{cases}$$

We have

$$\chi(T) = \int_0^T \left\{ \sigma(t) - z(t) - \frac{1}{h} f[\sigma(t)] + q\left(\frac{d\sigma(t)}{dt} - \frac{dz(t)}{dt}\right)\right\} f[\sigma(t)]dt$$

$$= \int_0^\infty \left\{ \sigma_T - z_T - \frac{1}{h} f_T + q\left(\frac{d\sigma_T}{dt} - \frac{dz_T}{dt}\right)\right\} f_T\, dt$$

$$= \frac{1}{2\pi}\int_{-\infty}^{\infty} \operatorname{Re}\left\{\left[\tilde{\sigma}_T - \tilde{z}_T - \frac{1}{h}\tilde{f}_T + qi\omega(\tilde{\sigma}_T - \tilde{z}_T)\right\}\tilde{f}_T^*\right\} d\omega,$$

where $\sim$ denotes, as above, the respective Fourier transform. We have been using the fact that $\sigma_T(0) - z_T(0) = 0$; hence the Fourier transform of the derivative is obtained from $\tilde{\sigma}_T - \tilde{z}_T$ through multiplication by $i\omega$.

We have

$$\sigma_T(t) - z_T(t) = \int_0^t k(t-\tau) f_T(\tau) d\tau,$$

from which follows $\tilde{\sigma}_T - \tilde{z}_T = \tilde{k}\tilde{f}_T$. Then

$$\chi(T) = \frac{1}{2\pi}\int_{-\infty}^{\infty} \operatorname{Re}\left\{\left[\tilde{k}_T\tilde{f} - \frac{1}{h}\tilde{f}_T + i\omega q\tilde{k}\tilde{f}_T\right]\tilde{f}_T^*\right\} d\omega$$

$$= \frac{1}{2\pi}\int_{-\infty}^{\infty} \left[\operatorname{Re}(1 + i\omega q)\tilde{k} - \frac{1}{h}\right] |\tilde{f}_T|^2\, d\omega.$$

If the condition $\operatorname{Re}(1 + i\omega q)\tilde{k} - (1/h) \leqslant 0$ is fulfilled, then $\chi(T) \leqslant 0$. This means that

$$\int_0^T \left\{\sigma(t) - \frac{1}{h} f[\sigma(t)] + q\frac{d\sigma(t)}{dt}\right\} f[\sigma(t)]dt \leqslant \int_0^T \left[z(t) + q\frac{dz(t)}{dt}\right] f[\sigma(t)]dt.$$

From here the proof further continues as above and we obtain $| \sigma(t)| \leqslant M$, $\lim_{t\to\infty} \sigma(t) = 0$.

Let us now consider a system of the form

$$\dot{x}(t) = \int_{-\infty}^{0} x(t+s)d\eta(s) + bf[\sigma(t)] \qquad (\sigma = xc) \tag{33}$$

From formula (23′) it follows that

$$x(t) = x(0)X(t) + \int_{-\tau}^{0} x(s)d_s \int_{0}^{s+\tau} \eta(s-\alpha)X(t-\alpha)d\alpha + \int_{0}^{t} bf[\sigma(\alpha)]X(t-\alpha)d\alpha.$$

We have been using in this representation the fact that if η does not depend on t, the solution of the homogeneous linear system, which is zero for $t < \alpha$ and for $t = \alpha$ coincides with the unit matrix, solely depends on the difference $t - \alpha$. Consequently,

$$\sigma(t) = x(0)X(t)c + \int_{-\tau}^{0} x(s)d_s \int_{0}^{s+\tau} \eta(s-\alpha)X(t-\alpha)c\, d\alpha + \int_{0}^{t} f[\sigma(\alpha)]bX(t-\alpha)c\, d\alpha.$$

Let us write

$$bX(t)c = k(t),$$

$$x(0)X(t)c + \int_{-\tau}^{0} x(s)d_s \int_{0}^{s+\tau} \eta(s-\alpha)X(t-\alpha)c\, d\alpha = z(t).$$

We obtain

$$\sigma(t) = z(t) + \int_{0}^{t} k(t-\alpha)f[\sigma(\alpha)]d\alpha,$$

an integral equations of the considered form.

If the zero solution of the linear part is uniformly asymptotically stable, then $|X(t)| \leqslant l_0 e^{-\lambda_0 t}$, from where it follows that z and k fulfill the above conditions, and thus $|\sigma(t)| \leqslant M$, $\lim_{t\to\infty} \sigma(t) = 0$; in addition $M \to 0$ if the norm of the initial function approaches zero. From the formula which gives $x(t)$ and from the already known evaluation for $X(t)$ it follows that x has the same behavior. We thus have

Theorem 4.16′. *If the zero solution of the linear system is asymptotically stable and if there exists a $q > 0$ such that*

$$\operatorname{Re}(1 + i\omega q)\tilde{k} - \frac{1}{h} \leqslant 0 \qquad (\tilde{k} = b\tilde{X}c),$$

then the zero solution of system (33) is asymptotically stable in the large whichever be function f in the considered class.

In the same way, we can study the stability problem for systems of the form

$$\dot{x}(t) = \int_{-\infty}^{0} x(t+s)d\eta(s) + bf[\sigma(t-\tau)] \qquad (\sigma = xc) \tag{34}$$

The same computations as above yield

$$\sigma(t) = x(0)X(t)c + \int_{-\tau}^{0} x(s)d_s \int_{0}^{s+\tau} \eta(s-\alpha)X(t-\alpha)c\, d\alpha$$
$$+ \int_{0}^{t} bX(t-\alpha)cf[\sigma(\alpha-\tau)]d\alpha;$$

hence

$$\sigma(t) = z(t) + \int_{0}^{t} k(t-\alpha)f[\sigma(\alpha-\tau)]d\alpha.$$

Let

$$k_1(t) = \begin{cases} k(t-\tau) & \text{for } \ t \geqslant \tau, \\ 0 & \text{for } \ 0 \leqslant t < \tau. \end{cases}$$

We obtain

$$\sigma(t) = z(t) + \int_{-\tau}^{t-\tau} k(t-\tau-\beta)f[\sigma(\beta)]d\beta = z(t) + \int_{-\tau}^{t-\tau} k_1(t-\beta)f[\sigma(\beta)]d\beta$$
$$= z(t) + \int_{-\tau}^{0} k_1(t-\beta)f[\sigma(\beta)]d\beta + \int_{0}^{t-\tau} k_1(t-\beta)f[\sigma(\beta)]d\beta.$$

We denote

$$z_1(t) = z(t) + \int_{-\tau}^{0} k_1(t-\beta)f[\sigma(\beta)]d\beta$$

Taking into account that for $\beta > t - \tau$ we have $t - \beta < \tau$, we have $\sigma(t) = z_1(t) + \int_0^t k_1(t-\beta)f[\sigma(\beta)]d\beta$; hence we have again obtained an integral equation of the form considered.

Let us observe that we have

$$k_1 = \int_{0}^{\infty} e^{-i\omega t}k_1(t)dt = \int_{\tau}^{\infty} e^{-i\omega t}k(t-\tau)dt = e^{-i\omega\tau}\int_{0}^{\infty} e^{-i\omega t}k(t)dt = e^{-i\omega\tau}\tilde{k}.$$

We obtain

Theorem 4.16″. *If the zero solution of the linear system is asymptotically stable and if there exists a $q > 0$ such that*

$$\operatorname{Re}(1 + i\omega q)e^{-i\omega\tau}\tilde{k} - \frac{1}{h} \leqslant 0 \qquad (\tilde{k} = b\tilde{X}c),$$

then the zero solution of system (34) is asymptotically stable in the large for every function f of the considered class.

Investigating the first critical case, V. M. Popov has essentially considered an equation of the form

$$\sigma(t) = z(t) + \int_0^t k(t-\alpha)f[\sigma(\alpha)]d\alpha - \gamma\xi(t), \qquad \frac{d\xi(t)}{dt} = f[\sigma(t)] \qquad (\gamma > 0),$$

where z and k verify the same conditions as above and in addition $(d^2z/dt^2) \in L^1(0, \infty)$. Let

$$f_T(t) = \begin{cases} f[\sigma(t)] & \text{for } 0 \leqslant t \leqslant T, \\ 0 & \text{for } T < t. \end{cases}$$

$$w_T(t) = \begin{cases} \sigma(t) + \gamma\xi(t) - z(t) & \text{for } 0 \leqslant t \leqslant T, \\ \int_0^T k(t-\alpha)f[\sigma(\alpha)]d\alpha & \text{for } T < t. \end{cases}$$

Then

$$w_T(t) = \int_0^t k(t-\alpha)f_T(\alpha)d\alpha.$$

Let us consider the function

$$\begin{aligned}
\chi(T) &= \int_0^T \left\{w_T - \frac{1}{h}f_T + q\left(\frac{dw_T}{dt} - \gamma f_T\right)\right\} f_T\, dt \\
&= \int_0^\infty \left\{w_T - \frac{1}{h}f_T + q\left(\frac{dw_T}{dt} - \gamma f_T\right)\right\} f_T\, dt \\
&= \frac{1}{2\pi}\int_{-\infty}^{\infty} \operatorname{Re}\left\{\left[\tilde{w}_T - \frac{1}{h}\tilde{f}_T + i\omega q\tilde{w}_T - q\gamma\tilde{f}_T\right]\tilde{f}_T^*\right\} d\omega.
\end{aligned}$$

However, $\tilde{w}_T = \tilde{k}\tilde{f}_T$; hence

$$\chi(T) = \frac{1}{2\pi}\int_{-\infty}^{\infty}\left\{\operatorname{Re}(1 + i\omega q)\tilde{k} - \left(q\gamma + \frac{1}{h}\right)\right\} |\tilde{f}_T|^2\, d\omega.$$

From the condition,

$$\operatorname{Re}(1 + i\omega q)\tilde{k} - \left(q\gamma + \frac{1}{h}\right) \leqslant 0;$$

it follows that $\chi(T) \leqslant 0$. This means that

$$\int_0^T \left\{\sigma(t) + \gamma\xi(t) - z(t) - \frac{1}{h}f[\sigma(t)] + q\left(\frac{d\sigma}{dt} + \gamma\frac{d\xi}{dt} - \frac{dz}{dt} - \gamma f[\sigma(t)]\right\} f(\sigma(t))dt \leqslant 0;$$

hence

$$\int_0^T \left\{\sigma(t) - \frac{1}{h} f[\sigma(t)]\right\} f[\sigma(t)]dt + \gamma \int_0^T \xi(t) \frac{d\xi(t)}{dt} dt + q \int_0^T f[\sigma(t)]d\sigma(t)$$
$$\leqslant \int_0^T \left(z(t) + q \frac{dz(t)}{dt}\right) f[\sigma(t)]dt = \int_0^T \left(z + q \frac{dz}{dt}\right) d\xi$$
$$= \left(z(T) + q \frac{dz(T)}{dt}\right) \xi(T) - \left(z(0) + q \frac{dz(0)}{dt}\right) \xi(0) - \int_0^T \left(\frac{dz}{dt} + q \frac{d^2z}{dt^2}\right) \xi(t)dt.$$

From this we obtain

$$\int_0^T \left\{\sigma(t) - \frac{1}{h} f[\sigma(t)]\right\} f[\sigma(t)]dt + \frac{\gamma}{2} \xi^2(T) + q \int_0^{\sigma(T)} f(\sigma)d\sigma$$
$$\leqslant M_0 + M_1 \sup_{0 \leqslant t \leqslant T} |\xi(t)|.$$

Then

$$\frac{\gamma}{2} \xi^2(T) \leqslant M_0 + M_1 \sup_{0 \leqslant t \leqslant T} |\xi(t)|;$$

hence $|\xi(t)| \leqslant M_2$. Further,

$$\int_0^T \left\{\sigma(t) - \frac{1}{h} f[\sigma(t)]\right\} f[\sigma(t)]dt + q \int_0^{\sigma(T)} f(\sigma)d\sigma \leqslant M_4,$$

and if $\int_0^\infty f(\sigma)d\sigma = \infty$ we obtain $|\sigma(t)| \leqslant M_5$.

From

$$\frac{d\sigma}{dt} = \frac{dz}{dt} + \int_0^t \frac{dk(t-\alpha)}{dt} f[\sigma(\alpha)]d\alpha + k[0] f[\sigma(t)] - \gamma f[\sigma(t)]$$

we deduce that $|d\sigma/dt| \leqslant M_6$. Then, from the convergence of the integral $\int_0^\infty [\sigma - (1/h)f(\sigma)]f(\sigma)dt$ it follows that $\lim_{t\to\infty} \sigma(t) = 0$. If for z and k we have exponential estimates, it follows that

$$\lim_{t\to\infty} \left[z(t) + \int_0^t k(t-\alpha) f[\sigma(\alpha)]d\alpha\right] = 0,$$

hence that

$$\lim_{t\to\infty} \xi(t) = 0.$$

Let us now consider a system of the form

$$\dot{y}(t) = \int_{-\infty}^0 y(t+s)d\eta(s), \qquad \frac{d\xi(t)}{dt} = f[\sigma(t)], \qquad \sigma(t) = y(t)c - r\xi(t). \tag{35}$$

We have

$$y(t) = y(0)X(t) + \int_{-\tau}^{0} y(s)d_s \int_{0}^{s+\tau} \eta(s-\alpha)X(t-\alpha)d\alpha + \int_{0}^{t} b\xi(\alpha)X(t-\alpha)d\alpha;$$

hence

$$\sigma(t) = y(0)X(t)c + \int_{-\tau}^{0} y(s)d_s \int_{0}^{s+\tau} \eta(s-\alpha)X(t-\alpha)c\, d\alpha$$

$$+ \int_{0}^{t} \xi(\alpha)bX(t-\alpha)c\, d\alpha - r\xi(t).$$

Let $k_0(t) = bX(t)c$; for $t \geqslant 0$ this function is continuous and the estimate $|k_0(t)| \leqslant l_0 e^{-\lambda_0 t}$ shows that $\int_t^\infty k_0(\beta)d\beta < \infty$.

Let $k(t) = \int_t^\infty k_0(\beta)d\beta$; we have $|k(t)| \leqslant le^{-\lambda_0 t}$. Then

$$\int_0^t bX(t-\alpha)c\xi(\alpha)d\alpha = \int_0^t k_0(t-\alpha)\xi(\alpha)d\alpha = \int_0^t \xi(\alpha)\frac{d}{d\alpha}k(t-\alpha)d\alpha$$

$$= \xi(\alpha)k(t-\alpha)|_0^t - \int_0^t k(t-\alpha)\frac{d\xi(\alpha)}{d\alpha}\,d\alpha$$

$$= k(0)\xi(t) - k(t)\xi(0) - \int_0^t k(t-\alpha)f[\sigma(\alpha)]d\alpha$$

and

$$\sigma(t) = y(0)X(t)c + \int_{-\tau}^{0} y(s)d_s \int_{0}^{s+\tau} \eta(s-\alpha)X(t-\alpha)c\, d\alpha - k(t)\xi(0)$$

$$- \int_0^t k(t-\alpha)f[\sigma(\alpha)]d\alpha - [r-k(0)]\xi(t).$$

If we set

$$z(t) = y(0)X(t)c + \int_{-\tau}^{0} y(s)d_s \int_{0}^{s+\tau} \eta(s-\alpha)X(t-\alpha)c\, d\alpha - k(t)\xi(0),$$

$$\gamma = r - k(0),$$

we obtain

$$\sigma(t) = z(t) - \int_0^t k(t-\alpha)f[\sigma(\alpha)]d\alpha - \gamma\xi(t), \qquad \frac{d\xi(t)}{dt} = f[\sigma(t)].$$

If we require that $\gamma > 0$ and

$$\operatorname{Re}(1+i\omega q)\tilde{k} + \left(q\gamma + \frac{1}{h}\right) \geqslant 0,$$

we deduce that $|\xi(t)| \leqslant M_2$; the above formulas immediately yield estimates for $\sigma(t)$, $y(t)$, $\dot{y}(t)$, $\dot{\xi}(t)$, $\dot{\sigma}(t)$. Further we obtain

$$\lim_{t\to\infty} \sigma(t) = 0, \qquad \lim_{t\to\infty} \xi(t) = 0, \qquad \lim_{t\to\infty} y(t) = 0.$$

From $k' = -k_0$ we deduce $\tilde{k} = (-1/i\omega)(\tilde{k}_0 - k(0))$.

The stability condition becomes

$$\operatorname{Re}\left(q + \frac{1}{i\omega}\right)\tilde{k}_0 - qr - \frac{1}{h} \leqslant 0 \qquad (\tilde{k}_0 = b\tilde{X}c).$$

We have thus obtained

Theorem 4.16‴. *If the zero solution of the first approximation linear system is asymptotically stable and if there exists a $q \geqslant 0$ such that*

$$\operatorname{Re}\left(q + \frac{1}{i\omega}\right) b\tilde{X}c - qr - \frac{1}{h} \leqslant 0,$$

and if in addition $r > \int_0^\infty bX(t)c\,dt$, then the zero solution of system (35) is asymptotically stable in the large for every function f with $0 \leqslant \sigma f(\sigma) \leqslant h\sigma^2$.

In his investigation of the second critical case, V. M. Popov considered an equation of the form

$$\sigma(t) = z(t) + \int_0^t k(t-\gamma) f[\sigma(\gamma)]d\gamma - \alpha\xi(t) - \beta\eta(t), \qquad \frac{d\xi}{dt} = \eta, \qquad \frac{d\eta}{dt} = f(\sigma). \tag{36}$$

We have

$$\frac{d\sigma}{dt} = \frac{dz}{dt} + \int_0^t \frac{dk(t-\gamma)}{dt} f[\sigma(\gamma)]d\gamma + k(0)f[\sigma(t)] - \alpha\eta(t) - \beta f[\sigma(t)]$$
$$= \frac{dz}{dt} - \int_0^t k_1(t-\theta) f[\sigma(\theta)]d\theta + rf[\sigma(t)] - \alpha\eta(t),$$

where we have set $k_1(t) = -dk/dt$, $r = k(0) - \beta$. Let

$$f_T(t) = \begin{cases} f[\sigma(t)] & \text{for } 0 \leqslant t \leqslant T, \\ 0 & \text{for } T < t, \end{cases}$$

$$w_T(t) = \begin{cases} \dfrac{d\sigma}{dt} - \dfrac{dz}{dt} - rf[\sigma(t)] + \alpha\eta(t) & \text{for } 0 \leqslant t \leqslant T, \\ -\displaystyle\int_0^T k_1(t-\theta) f[\sigma(\theta)]d\theta & \text{for } T < t. \end{cases}$$

We obtain

$$w_T(t) = -\int_0^t k_1(t-\theta) f_T(\theta)d\theta, \qquad \tilde{w}_T = -\tilde{k}_1 \tilde{f}_T.$$

Let

$$\chi(T) = \int_0^T \left(\frac{d\sigma}{dt} + \alpha\eta - \frac{dz}{dt}\right) f[\sigma(t)]dt = \int_0^T [w_T(t) + rf_T(t)] f_T(t)dt$$

$$= \frac{1}{2\pi}\int_{-\infty}^{\infty} \operatorname{Re}(\tilde{w}_T + r\tilde{f}_T)\tilde{f}_T^* \, d\omega = \frac{1}{2\pi}\int_{-\infty}^{\infty} (r - \operatorname{Re} \tilde{k}_1)| \tilde{f}_T |^2 \, d\omega.$$

If $r - \operatorname{Re} \tilde{k}_1 \leqslant 0$, we deduce that $\chi(T) \leqslant 0$. This means that

$$\int_{\sigma(0)}^{\sigma(T)} f(\sigma)d\sigma + \frac{\alpha}{2}\eta^2(T) - \frac{\alpha}{2}\eta^2(0) \leqslant \int_0^T \frac{dz}{dt}\frac{d\eta}{dt}\, dt$$

$$= \frac{dz(T)}{dt}\eta(T) - \frac{dz(0)}{dt}\eta(0) - \int_0^T \frac{d^2z}{dt^2}\eta(t)dt;$$

hence

$$\int_0^{\sigma(T)} f(\sigma)d\sigma + \frac{\alpha}{2}\eta^2(T) \leqslant a_0(| \eta(0)|, | \sigma(0)|) + a_1(\| z \|) \sup_{0\leqslant t\leqslant T} | \eta(t)|.$$

If $\alpha > 0$, it follows from here that $| \eta(t) | \leqslant M_1$ and if $\int_0^\infty f(\sigma)d\sigma = \infty$, we also deduce that $| \sigma(t)| \leqslant M_2$, $| d\sigma/dt | \leqslant M_3$, $| d\xi/dt | \leqslant M_4$.

If $r - \operatorname{Re} \tilde{k}_1 < 0$ and $\lim_{|\omega|\to\infty} (r - \operatorname{Re} \tilde{k}_1) < 0$, then

$$\chi(T) < -\frac{\epsilon}{2\pi}\int_{-\infty}^{\infty} | \tilde{f}_T |^2 \, d\omega = -\epsilon_0 \int_0^T f^2[\sigma(t)]dt;$$

hence $\int_0^T f^2[\sigma(t)]dt < M$. It follows from this that $\lim_{t\to\infty} \sigma(t) = 0$, and by using V. M. Popov's lemma (section 2.3) we also deduce that $\lim_{t\to\infty} \xi(t) = \lim_{t\to\infty} \eta(t) = 0$.

Let us now consider a system of the form

$$\dot{y}(t) = \int_{-\infty}^0 y(t+s)d\eta(s) + b\xi(t), \quad \frac{d^2\xi}{dt^2} = f[\sigma(t)], \quad \sigma = yc + p\xi + r\frac{d\xi}{dt}. \tag{37}$$

We have

$$y(t) = y(0)X(t) + \int_{-\tau}^0 y(s)d_s \int_0^{s+\tau} \eta(s-\alpha)X(t-\alpha)d\alpha + \int_0^t b\xi(\alpha)X(t-\alpha)d\alpha;$$

hence

$$\sigma(t) = y(0)X(t)c + \int_{-\tau}^0 y(s)d_s \int_0^{s+\tau} \eta(s-\alpha)X(t-\alpha)c\, d\alpha$$

$$+ \int_0^t \xi(\alpha)bX(t-\alpha)c\, d\alpha + p\xi(t) + r\frac{d\xi}{dt}$$

Let

$$k_0(t) = bX(t)c, \qquad | k_0(t)| \leqslant l_0 e^{-\lambda_0 t},$$

$$k_1(t) = \int_t^{\infty} k_0(\alpha)d\alpha, \qquad k(t) = \int_t^{\infty} k_1(\alpha)d\alpha.$$

Then $| k_1(t)| \leqslant l_1 e^{-\lambda_0 t}$, $| k(t)| \leqslant l e^{-\lambda_0 t}$.

We have

$$\begin{aligned}\int_0^t \xi(\alpha)bX(t-\alpha)c\, d\alpha &= \int_0^t k_0(t-\alpha)\xi(\alpha)d\alpha \\ &= k_1(0)\xi(t) - k_1(t)\xi(0) - \int_0^t k_1(t-\alpha)\frac{d\xi(\alpha)}{dt}\, d\alpha \\ &= k_1(0)\xi(t) - k_1(t)\xi(0) - k(0)\frac{d\xi(t)}{dt} \\ &\qquad + k(t)\frac{d\xi(0)}{dt} + \int_0^t k(t-\alpha)\frac{d^2\xi(\alpha)}{d\alpha^2}\, d\alpha\end{aligned}$$

and

$$\begin{aligned}\sigma(t) = y(0)X(t)c &+ \int_{-\tau}^0 y(s)d_s \int_0^{s+\tau} \eta(s-\alpha)X(t-\alpha)c\, d\alpha - k_1(t)\xi(0) + k(t)\frac{d\xi(0)}{dt} \\ &+ \int_0^t k(t-\alpha)f[\sigma(\alpha)]d\alpha + [p + k_1(0)]\xi(t) + [r - k(0)]\frac{d\xi(t)}{dt}.\end{aligned}$$

We write

$$y(0)X(t)c + \int_{-\tau}^0 y(s)d_s \int_0^{s+\tau} \eta(s-\alpha)X(t-\alpha)c\, d\alpha - k_1(t)\xi(0) + k(t)\frac{d\xi(0)}{dt} = z(t)$$

$$p + k_1(0) = -\alpha, \qquad r - k(0) = -\beta, \qquad \frac{d\xi}{dt} = \eta,$$

and we obtain an equation of the form (36).

We have

$$\tilde{k}_1 = -\frac{1}{i\omega}\tilde{k}_0 + \frac{1}{i\omega}k_1(0), \qquad \mathrm{Re}\,\tilde{k}_1 = -\mathrm{Re}\,\frac{1}{i\omega}\tilde{k}_0\,,$$

and the condition $r - \mathrm{Re}\,\tilde{k}_1 < 0$ is $r + \mathrm{Re}\,(1/i\omega)\tilde{k}_0 < 0$. However,

$$\tilde{k}_0 = b\tilde{X}c;$$

hence the condition becomes

$$r + \mathrm{Re}\,\frac{1}{i\omega}\, b\tilde{X}c < 0.$$

We have thus

Theorem 4.16''''. *If the zero solution of the linear system is asymptotically stable and if*

$$p + \int_0^\infty bX(t)c\,dt < 0, \qquad r + \mathrm{Re}\,\frac{1}{i\omega}\,b\tilde{X}c \leqslant 0,$$

$$\sigma f(\sigma) \geqslant 0, \qquad \int_0^{\pm\infty} f(\sigma)d\sigma = \infty,$$

then the zero solution of system (37) *is uniformly stable. If, in addition,* $\sigma f(\sigma) > 0$ *for* $\sigma \neq 0$ *and*

$$r < 0, \qquad r + \mathrm{Re}\,\frac{1}{i\omega}\,b\tilde{X}c < 0$$

then the zero solution of system (37) *is asymptotically stable in the large.*

Let us finally show how by using the method of V. M. Popov we can study the absolute stability of systems of the form

$$\dot{x}(t) = Ax(t) + Bx(t-\tau) + b\xi(t) + c\xi(t-\tau),$$

$$\ddot{\xi}(t) + \alpha\dot{\xi}(t) + \beta\xi(t) = f[\sigma(t)],$$

$$\sigma = p^*x + \gamma_1\xi + \gamma_2\frac{d\xi}{dt},$$

$$0 < \sigma f(\sigma) \leqslant h\sigma^2, \qquad \int_0^{\pm\infty} f(\sigma)d\sigma = \infty,$$

under the hypothesis that the roots of the equation $\det(A + Be^{-\lambda\tau} - \lambda E) = 0$ are situated in the semiplane $\mathrm{Re}\,\lambda < 0$.

We have

$$x(t) = X(t)x(0) + \int_{-\tau}^0 X(t-\alpha-\tau)Bx(\alpha)d\alpha + \int_0^t X(t-\alpha)b\xi(\alpha)d\alpha$$
$$+ \int_0^t X(t-\alpha)c\xi(\alpha-\tau)d\alpha$$

and

$$\sigma(t) = p^*X(t)x(0) + \int_{-\tau}^0 p^*X(t-\alpha-\tau)Bx(\alpha)d\alpha + \int_0^t p^*X(t-\alpha)b\xi(\alpha)d\alpha$$
$$+ \int_0^t p^*X(t-\alpha)c\xi(\alpha-\tau)d\alpha + \gamma_1\xi + \gamma_2\eta, \qquad \frac{d\xi}{dt} = \eta.$$

Let

$$k_1(t) = p^*X(t)b, \qquad k_2(t) = p^*X(t)e,$$

$$z_1(t) = p^*X(t)x(0) + \int_{-\tau}^0 p^*X(t-\alpha-\tau)Bx(\alpha)d\alpha$$

Then

$$\sigma(t) = z_1(t) + \int_0^t k_1(t-\alpha)\xi(\alpha)d\alpha + \int_0^t k_2(t-\alpha)\xi(\alpha-\tau)d\alpha + \gamma_1\xi(t) + \gamma_2\eta(t).$$

Let

$$k_3(t) = \begin{cases} k_2(t-\tau) & \text{for } t \geqslant \tau, \\ 0 & \text{for } 0 < t < \tau. \end{cases}$$

We have

$$\begin{aligned}\sigma(t) &= z_1(t) + \int_0^t k_1(t-\alpha)\xi(\alpha)d\alpha + \int_{-\tau}^{t-\tau} k_2(t-\tau-\alpha)\xi(\alpha)d\alpha + \gamma_1\xi(t) + \gamma_2\eta(t) \\ &= z_1(t) + \int_{-\tau}^0 k_2(t-\tau-\alpha)\xi(\alpha)d\alpha + \int_0^t k_1(t-\alpha)\xi(\alpha)d\alpha \\ &\quad + \int_0^{t-\tau} k_2(t-\tau-\alpha)\xi(\alpha)d\alpha + \gamma_1\xi(t) + \gamma_2\eta(t) \\ &= z_1(t) + \int_{-\tau}^0 k_2(t-\tau-\alpha)\xi(\alpha)d\alpha + \int_0^t k_1(t-\alpha)\xi(\alpha)d\alpha \\ &\quad + \int_0^t k_3(t-\alpha)\xi(\alpha)d\alpha + \gamma_1\xi(t) + \gamma_2\eta(t).\end{aligned}$$

Let us set

$$z_2(t) = z_1(t) + \int_{-\tau}^0 k_2(t-\tau-\alpha)\xi(\alpha)d\alpha, \qquad k_4(t) = k_1(t) + k_3(t).$$

We obtain

$$\sigma(t) = z_2(t) + \int_0^t k_4(t-\alpha)\xi(\alpha)d\alpha + \gamma_1\xi(t) + \gamma_2\eta(t).$$

From $|X(t)| \leqslant le^{-\lambda_0 t}$ follows $|k_j(t)| \leqslant l_j e^{-\lambda_0 t}$, $|z_j(t)| \leqslant m_j e^{-\lambda_0 t}$. Let $k_5(t) = \int_t^\infty k_4(s)ds$, $k_6(t) = \int_t^\infty k_5(s)ds$. We have $|k_5(t)| \leqslant l_5 e^{-\lambda_0 t}$, $|k_6(t)| \leqslant l_6 e^{-\lambda_0 t}$. Integrating by parts we obtain

$$\begin{aligned}\int_0^t k_4(t-\alpha)\xi(\alpha)d\alpha &= k_5(0)\xi(t) - k_5(t)\xi(0) - k_6(0)\eta(t) + k_6(t)\eta(0) \\ &\quad + \int_0^t k_6(t-\alpha)\ddot{\xi}(\alpha)d\alpha.\end{aligned}$$

From here follows

$$\begin{aligned}\sigma(t) &= z_2(t) - k_5(t)\xi(0) + k_6(t)\eta(0) \\ &\quad + \int_0^t k_6(t-\gamma)f[\sigma(\gamma)]d\gamma - \beta\int_0^t k_6(t-\gamma)\xi(\gamma)d\gamma \\ &\quad - \alpha\int_0^t k_6(t-\gamma)\eta(\gamma)d\gamma + [\gamma_1 + k_5(0)]\xi(t) + [\gamma_2 - k_6(0)]\eta(t).\end{aligned}$$

Let us set

$$z_2(t) - k_5(t)\xi(0) + k_6(t)\eta(0) = z_3(t),$$

$$\gamma_1 + k_5(0) = \gamma_3, \qquad \gamma_2 - k_6(0) = \gamma_4.$$

We obtain

$$\sigma(t) = z_3(t) + \int_0^t k_6(t-\gamma)f[\sigma(\gamma)]d\gamma - \beta\int_0^t k_6(t-\gamma)\xi(\gamma)d\gamma$$

$$-\alpha\int_0^t k_6(t-\gamma)\eta(\gamma)d\gamma + \gamma_3\xi(t) + \gamma_4\eta(t).$$

If $\alpha = 0$, $\beta = 0$ this equation becomes

$$\sigma(t) = z_3(t) + \int_0^t k_6(t-\gamma)f[\sigma(\gamma)]d\gamma + \gamma_3\xi(t) + \gamma_4\eta(t),$$

and the conditions of absolute stability obtained by the method of V. M. Popov are

$$\gamma_3 < 0, \qquad \gamma_2 + \operatorname{Re}\tilde{k}_5 < 0, \qquad \lim_{|\omega|\to\infty}(\gamma_2 + \operatorname{Re}\tilde{k}_5) < 0.$$

Now let $\alpha > 0$, $\beta = 0$. Then $\dot{\eta}(t) + \alpha\eta(t) = f[\sigma(t)]$ and

$$\eta(t) = e^{-\alpha t}\eta(0) + \int_0^t e^{-\alpha(t-\gamma)}f[\sigma(\gamma)]d\gamma.$$

Let $\zeta(t) = \eta(t) + \alpha\xi(t)$; then $\xi(t) = (1/\alpha)\zeta(t) - (1/\alpha)\eta(t)$. The equation in σ becomes

$$\sigma(t) = z_3(t) + \int_0^t k_6(t-\gamma)f[\sigma(\gamma)]d\gamma - \alpha\int_0^t k_6(t-\gamma)\eta(\gamma)d\gamma$$

$$+\frac{\gamma_3}{\alpha}\zeta(t) + \left(\gamma_4 - \frac{\gamma_3}{\alpha}\right)\eta(t).$$

Taking into account the expression of the function $\eta(t)$ we obtain

$$\sigma(t) = z_3(t) + \int_0^t k_6(t-\gamma)f[\sigma(\gamma)]d\gamma$$

$$-\alpha\int_0^t k_6(t-\gamma)\left[e^{-\alpha\gamma}\eta(0) + \int_0^\gamma e^{-\alpha(\gamma-\delta)}f[\sigma(\delta)]d\delta\right]d\gamma$$

$$+\frac{\gamma_3}{\alpha}\zeta(t) + \left(\gamma_4 - \frac{\gamma_3}{\alpha}\right)e^{-\alpha t}\eta(0) + \left(\gamma_4 - \frac{\gamma_3}{\alpha}\right)\int_0^t e^{-\alpha(t-\gamma)}f[\sigma(\gamma)]d\gamma.$$

We have

$$\int_0^t k_6(t-\gamma)\left[\int_0^\gamma e^{-\alpha(\gamma-\delta)}f[\sigma(\delta)]d\delta\right]d\gamma = \int_0^t f[\sigma(\delta)]d\delta \int_\delta^t k_6(t-\gamma)e^{-\alpha(\gamma-\delta)}\,d\gamma$$

$$= \int_0^t f[\sigma(\delta)]d\delta \int_0^{t-\delta} k_6(t-\delta-\gamma)e^{-\alpha\gamma}\,d\gamma = \int_0^t k_7(t-\delta)f[\sigma(\delta)]d\delta,$$

where

$$k_7(t) = \int_0^t k_6(t-\gamma)e^{-\alpha\gamma}\,d\gamma.$$

Let us set

$$z_4(t) = z_3(t) - \alpha k_7(t)\eta(0) + \left(\gamma_4 - \frac{\gamma_3}{\alpha}\right)e^{-\alpha t}\eta(0),$$

$$k_8(t) = k_6(t) + \left(\gamma_4 - \frac{\gamma_3}{\alpha}\right)e^{-\alpha t} - \alpha k_7(t).$$

We obtain the equation

$$\sigma(t) = z_4(t) + \int_0^t k_8(t-\gamma)f[\sigma(\gamma)]d\gamma + \frac{\gamma_3}{\alpha}\zeta(t), \qquad \frac{d\zeta}{dt} = f(\sigma),$$

where $|z_4(t)| \leqslant m_4 e^{-\lambda_0 t}$, $|k_8(t)| \leqslant l_8 e^{-\lambda_1 t}$, $\lambda_1 = \min(\lambda_0, \alpha)$.

From this equation we obtain by the method of V. M. Popov the stability condition

$$\mathrm{Re}(1 + i\omega q)k_8 + q\frac{\gamma_0}{\alpha} - \frac{q}{h} \leqslant 0.$$

Now let $\alpha > 0$, $\beta > 0$. Then

$$\xi(t) = y_1(t)\xi(0) + y_2(t)\eta(0) + \int_0^t y_2(t-\gamma)f[\sigma(\gamma)]d\gamma,$$

$$\eta(t) = y_3(t)\xi(0) + y_4(t)\eta(0) + \int_0^t y_4(t-\gamma)f[\sigma(\gamma)]d\gamma,$$

where the y_j admit estimates of the form $|y_j(t)| \leqslant q_j e^{-\lambda_2 t}$.

For σ the equation becomes

$$\sigma(t) = z_3(t) + \int_0^t k_6(t-\gamma)f[\sigma(\gamma)]d\gamma - \beta\int_0^t k_6(t-\gamma)y_1(\gamma)d\gamma\xi(0)$$

$$-\beta\int_0^t k_6(t-\gamma)y_2(\gamma)d\gamma\eta(0) - \beta\int_0^t k_6(t-\gamma)\left[\int_0^\gamma y_2(\gamma-\delta)f[\sigma(\delta)]d\delta\right]d\gamma$$

$$-\alpha\int_0^t k_6(t-\gamma)y_3(\gamma)d\gamma\xi(0) - \alpha\int_0^t k_6(t-\gamma)y_4(\gamma)d\gamma\eta(0)$$

$$- \alpha \int_0^t k_6(t-\gamma) \left[\int_0^\gamma y_3(\gamma - \delta) f[\sigma(\delta)] d\delta \right] d\gamma + \gamma_3 y_1(t) \xi(0)$$

$$+ \gamma_3 y_2(t) \eta(0) + \int_0^t \gamma_3 y_2(t-\gamma) f[\sigma(\gamma)] d\gamma + \gamma_4 y_3(t) \xi(0)$$

$$+ \gamma_4 y_4(t) \eta(0) + \int_0^t \gamma_4 y_4(t-\gamma) f[\sigma(\gamma)] d\gamma.$$

We set

$$k_9(t) = \int_0^t k_6(t-\gamma) y_2(\gamma) d\gamma, \qquad k_{10}(t) = \int_0^t k_6(t-\gamma) y_4(\gamma) d\gamma,$$

$$k_{11}(t) = k_6(t) - \beta k_9(t) - \alpha k_{10}(t) + \gamma_3 y_2(t) + \gamma_4 y_4(t),$$

$$z_5(t) = z_3(t) - \beta \int_0^t k_6(t-\gamma) y_1(\gamma) d\gamma \xi(0) - \beta \int_0^t k_6(t-\gamma) y_2(\gamma) d\gamma \eta(0)$$

$$- \alpha \int_0^t k_6(t-\gamma) y_3(\gamma) d\gamma \xi(0) - \alpha \int_0^t k_6(t-\gamma) y_4(\gamma) d\gamma \eta(0)$$

$$+ \gamma_3 y_1(t) \xi(0) + \gamma_3 y_2(t) \eta(0) + \gamma_4 y_3(t) \xi(0) + \gamma_4 y_4(t) \eta(0).$$

We obtain the equation

$$\sigma(t) = z_5(t) + \int_0^t k_{11}(t-\gamma) f[\sigma(\gamma)] d\gamma.$$

From this equation we obtain from the method of V. M. Popov the stability condition

$$\operatorname{Re}(1 + i\omega q) \tilde{k}_{11} - \frac{1}{h} \leqslant 0.$$

Let us observe that $\tilde{y}_2 = 1/(-\omega^2 + i\omega\alpha + \beta)$, $\tilde{y}_4 = i\omega/(-\omega^2 + i\omega\alpha + \beta)$, $\tilde{k}_9 = \tilde{k}_6 \tilde{y}_2$, $\tilde{k}_{10} = \tilde{k}_6 \tilde{y}_4$.

In the same way we can also study the absolute stability of systems of the form

$$\dot{x}(t) = \int_{-\infty}^0 x(t+s) d\eta(s) + b\xi(t) + c\xi(t-\tau),$$

$$\ddot{\xi}(t) + \alpha\dot{\xi}(t) + \beta\xi(t) = f[\sigma(t)], \qquad \sigma = xp + \gamma_1 \xi + \gamma_2 \frac{d\xi}{dt},$$

and systems of the form

$$\dot{x}(t) = Ax(t) + Bx(t-\tau) + b\xi(t) + c\xi(t-\tau),$$

$$\ddot{\xi}(t) + \alpha_1 \dot{\xi}(t) + \alpha_2 \dot{\xi}(t-\tau) + \beta_1 \xi(t) + \beta_2 \xi(t-\tau) = f[\sigma(t)],$$

$$\sigma = p^* x + \gamma_1 \xi + \gamma_2 \frac{d\xi}{dt}.$$

For systems of this form we obtain

$$\sigma(t) = z_2(t) + k_5(0)\xi(t) - k_5(t)\xi(0) - k_6(0)\eta(t) + k_6(t)\eta(0)$$
$$+ \int_0^t k_6(t-\alpha)\ddot{\xi}(\alpha)d\alpha + \gamma_1\xi(t) + \gamma_2\eta(t),$$

and taking into account the equation for ξ,

$$\sigma(t) = z_2(t) - k_5(t)\xi(0) + k_6(t)\eta(0) - \alpha_1 \int_0^t k_6(t-\alpha)\eta(\alpha)d\alpha$$
$$-\alpha_2 \int_0^t k_6(t-\alpha)\eta(\alpha-\tau)d\alpha - \beta_1 \int_0^t k_6(t-\alpha)\xi(\alpha)d\alpha$$
$$-\beta_2 \int_0^t k_6(t-\alpha)\xi(\alpha-\tau)d\alpha + \gamma_3\xi(t) + \gamma_4\eta(t) + \int_0^t k_6(t-\alpha)f[\sigma(\alpha)]d\alpha.$$

Let

$$k_{12}(t) = \begin{cases} k_6(t-\tau) & \text{for } t \geqslant \tau, \\ 0 & \text{for } 0 \leqslant t < \tau. \end{cases}$$

Then

$$\int_0^t k_6(t-\alpha)\eta(\alpha-\tau)d\alpha = \int_{-\tau}^{t-\tau} k_6(t-\beta-\tau)\eta(\beta)d\beta$$
$$= \int_{-\tau}^{0} k_6(t-\beta-\tau)\eta(\beta)d\beta + \int_0^{t-\tau} k_6(t-\beta-\tau)\eta(\beta)d\beta$$
$$= \int_{-\tau}^{0} k_6(t-\beta-\tau)\eta(\beta)d\beta + \int_0^t k_{12}(t-\beta)\eta(\beta)d\beta,$$

and

$$\int_0^t k_6(t-\alpha)\xi(\alpha-\tau)d\alpha = \int_{-\tau}^{0} k_6(t-\beta-\tau)\xi(\beta)d\beta + \int_0^t k_{12}(t-\beta)\xi(\beta)d\beta.$$

We set

$$z_6(t) = z_2(t) - k_5(t)\xi(0) + k_6(t)\eta(0) - \alpha_2 \int_{-t}^{0} k_6(t-\beta-\tau)\eta(\beta)d\beta$$
$$- \beta_2 \int_{-\tau}^{0} k_6(t-\beta-\tau)\xi(\beta)d\beta,$$

$$k_{13}(t) = \alpha_1 k_6(t) + \alpha_2 k_{12}(t),$$
$$k_{14}(t) = \beta_1 k_6(t) + \beta_2 k_{12}(t),$$

and we obtain the equation

$$\sigma(t) = z_6(t) + \int_0^t k_6(t-\alpha)f[\sigma(\alpha)]d\alpha - \int_0^t k_{13}(t-\alpha)\eta(\alpha)d\alpha$$

$$- \int_0^t k_{14}(t-\alpha)\xi(\alpha)d\alpha + \gamma_3\xi(t) + \gamma_4\eta(t),$$

which is of the same form as the one considered above.

If we suppose that the roots of the equation

$$\lambda^2 + \alpha_1\lambda + \alpha_2\lambda e^{-\lambda\tau} + \beta_1 + \beta_2 e^{-\lambda\tau} = 0$$

are in the semiplane Re $\lambda < 0$, we obtain an equation of the form

$$\sigma(t) = z_7(t) + \int_0^t k_{15}(t-\alpha)f[\sigma(\alpha)]d\alpha,$$

which may be studied by the method of V. M. Popov.

4.7. Periodic Linear Systems with Time Lag

Let us consider linear systems of the form

$$\dot{x}(t) = \int_{-\infty}^0 x(t+s)d_s\eta(t, s)$$

under the hypothesis that the matrix $\eta(t, s)$ is periodic with respect to t of period $\omega > \tau$.

We define the operator U through the relation $U\varphi = x(\omega + s; \varphi)$, where $x(t, \varphi)$ is the solution of the system which coincides with φ on $[-\tau, 0]$. Then from the general formula (23) of representation of the solutions it follows that

$$U\varphi = \varphi(0)X(\omega + s, 0) + \int_{-\tau}^0 \varphi(\sigma)d_\sigma \int_0^{\sigma+\tau} \eta(\alpha, \sigma - \alpha)X(\omega + s, \alpha)d\alpha.$$

The operator U is compact: it maps every bounded set into a relative compact set. Indeed, from $\| \varphi \| \leqslant M$ we obtain $\| U\varphi \| \leqslant M'$ and from $\omega > \tau$ we obtain $\omega + s > 0$ for $s \in [-\tau, 0]$; hence $U\varphi$ is differentiable and

$$\frac{d}{ds} x(\omega + s; \varphi) = \int_{-\tau}^0 x(\omega + s + \sigma; \varphi)\, d_\sigma\eta(s, \sigma);$$

hence $|(d/ds)x(\omega + s; \varphi)| < M''$. The functions $\{U\varphi\}$ thus form a set of uniformly bounded and equally continuous functions, consequently, on the basis of the Arzela theorem, a relative compact set.

From the fact that the operator U is compact it follows that

(a) If $\sigma(U)$ is the spectrum of the operator U, the set $\sigma(U)$ is at most countable and is a compact set in the complex plane.

(b) $0 \in \sigma(U)$ and if $\lambda \in \sigma(U)$, $\lambda \neq 0$, then λ is an eigenvalue of the operator U, i.e., the equation $U\varphi = \lambda\varphi$ has a nonzero solution $\varphi \in \mathscr{X}$ (we denote by $\mathscr{X}$ the Banach space of the vector functions continuous in $[-\tau, 0]$).

(c) If $\sigma(U)$ is infinite, the point $z = 0$ is the only limit point of the spectrum.

(d) If $\lambda \neq 0$, $\lambda \in \sigma(U)$ there exist closed subspaces $K(\lambda)$, $E(\lambda)$, $\dim E < \infty$, such that $\mathscr{X} = K(\lambda) \oplus E(\lambda)$, $UK \subset K$, $UE \subset E$, and the restriction $U \mid K$ of the operator U to the space K is likewise a compact operator.

(e) $K(\lambda)$ is likewise a Banach space and $\sigma(U \mid K) = \sigma(U) - \{\lambda\}$.

Let us observe that if the condition $\omega > \tau$ is not fulfilled, then there exists an m such that $m\omega > \tau$; it is easy to see that if $V\varphi = x(k\omega + s; \varphi)$ then $V = U^k$ and V is compact. Then the operator U has all the above properties (see, for example, Riesz and Nagy, *Functional Analysis*).

Let us observe also that we could have considered the operator U_{t_0} defined by the formula $U_{t_0}\varphi = x(\omega + s; t_0, \varphi)$, $s \in [t_0 - \tau, t_0]$, for which all the above properties are maintained.

Definition. *The eigenvalues of the operator U are called the multipliers of the system.*

To justify this definition let us observe that if ρ is a multiplier there exists a solution of the system such that $x(t + \omega) = \rho x(t)$ and conversely. Indeed, let φ be an eigenvector corresponding to the eigenvalue ρ. We have $U\varphi = \rho\varphi$, hence $U_{t+\omega}\varphi = U_t U\varphi = \rho U_t\varphi$; hence $x(t + \omega + s; \varphi) = \rho x(t + s; \varphi)$, and for $s = 0$ we obtain $x(t + \omega; \varphi) = \rho x(t; \varphi)$.

We have denoted here by U_t the operator defined by $U_t\varphi = x(t + s; \varphi)$; it is easy to see that $U_{t+\omega} = U_t U_\omega$. Indeed,

$$U_{t+\omega}\varphi = x(t + \omega + s; \varphi) = x(t + s; x(\omega + s; \varphi)) = U_t U_\omega \varphi,$$

since the solutions $x(t + \omega + s; \varphi)$ and $x(t + s; x(\omega + s; \varphi))$ coincide for $t = 0$ (hence in $[-\tau, 0]$). The fact that $x(t + \omega; \varphi)$ is a solution of the system together with $x(t; \varphi)$ follows from the periodicity of the system.

Conversely, if $x(t+\omega;\varphi) = \rho x(t;\varphi)$, then for $s \in [-\tau, 0]$ we have $x(s+\omega;\varphi) = \rho\varphi$; hence $U\varphi = \rho\varphi$ and ρ is an eigenvalue of U.

Let ρ be a multiplier, $E(\rho)$ the corresponding invariant subspace formed by functions φ for which there exists n such that $(U - \rho I)^n\varphi = 0$ (where I is the identity operator). This subspace is of finite dimension and therefore a Jordan canonical basis, $\varphi_1^l, \varphi_2^l, \ldots, \varphi_{k(l)}^l$, can be chosen in it such that

$$U\varphi_1^l = \rho\varphi_1^l, \qquad U\varphi_2^l = \rho\varphi_2^l + \varphi_1^l, \ldots, U\varphi_{k(l)}^l = \rho\varphi_{k(l)}^l + \varphi_{k(l)-1}^l.$$

We have seen above that the solution corresponding to the initial function φ_1^l has the property $x(t+\omega;\varphi_1^l) = \rho x(t;\varphi_1^l)$.

The solutions corresponding to the other functions of the canonical basis have the property

$$x(t+\omega;\varphi_j^l) = \rho x(t;\varphi_j^l) + x(t;\varphi_{j-1}^l).$$

Indeed, $x(t+\omega;\varphi_j^l)$ and $\rho x(t;\varphi_j^l) + x(t;\varphi_{j-1}^l)$ are solutions of the system and these solutions coincide for $t \in [-\tau, 0]$.

If $\lambda = (1/\omega)\ln\rho$, we have $x(t;\varphi_1^l) = e^{\lambda t}u_1^l(t)$, where $u_1^l(t)$ is a periodic function of period ω. Let

$$x(t;\varphi_2^l) = e^{\lambda t}(c_1 t u_1^l + u_2^l); \quad \text{i.e.,} \quad u_2^l = e^{-\lambda t}x(t;\varphi_2^l) - c_1 t u_1^l.$$

We have

$$\begin{aligned} u_2^l(t+\omega) &= e^{-\lambda t}e^{-\Lambda\omega}x(t+\omega;\varphi_2^l) - c_1(t+\omega)u_1^l(t) \\ &= e^{-\lambda t}\frac{1}{\rho}[\rho x(t;\varphi_2^l) + x(t;\varphi_1^l)] - c_1 t u_1^l(t) - c_1\omega u_1^l(t) \\ &= e^{-\lambda t}x(t;\varphi_2^l) + \frac{1}{\rho}e^{-\lambda t}x(t;\varphi_1^l) - c_1 t u_1^l(t) - c_1\omega u_1^l(t) \\ &= u_2^l(t) + \left(\frac{1}{\rho} - c_1\omega\right)u_1(t). \end{aligned}$$

If we take $c_1 = 1/\rho\omega$ it follows that u_2^l will be a periodic function.

Analogously we show that

$$x(t;\varphi_j^l) = e^{\lambda t}(c_{j,1}^l t^{j-1} u_1^l + c_{j,2}^l t^{j-2} v_2^l + \cdots + c_{j,j-1}^l t v_{j-1}^l + u_j^l),$$

where $u_1^l, v_2^l, \ldots, u_{j-1}^l, u_j^l$ are periodic functions with period ω. We have thus obtained a Floquet-type family of solutions. This family of solutions could also be obtained in the following way (A. Stokes).

From dim $E(\rho) < \infty$ it follows that there exists a basis ψ_i in $E(\rho)$ and a matrix M such that if $\psi = (\psi_1, \ldots, \psi_r)$ we obtain $U\psi = \psi M$ [M is a matrix which represents the restriction to $E(\rho)$ of the operator U]. From the fact that in $E(\rho)$ the only eigenvalue of operator U is $\rho \neq 0$ it follows that M is nonsingular and admits ρ as a unique eigenvalue. Hence. $B = (1/\omega) \ln M$ exists. Let $p(t)$ be the vector defined by the relation $p(t) = x(t; \psi)e^{-Bt}$, where $x(t; \psi) = (x(t; \psi_1), \ldots, x(t; \psi_r))$. Then

$$\begin{aligned} p(t+\omega) &= x(t+\omega; \psi)e^{-B\omega}e^{-Bt} = x(t; x(\omega+s; \psi))e^{-B\omega}e^{-Bt} \\ &= x(t; U\psi)M^{-1}e^{-Bt} = x(t; \psi M)M^{-1}e^{-Bt} = x(t; \psi)MM^{-1}e^{-Bt} \\ &= x(t; \psi)e^{-Bt} = p(t). \end{aligned}$$

We obtain $x(t; \psi) = p(t)e^{Bt}$, where p is periodic. If $\varphi = \sum c_i\psi_i$ we will have $x(t; \varphi) = \sum c_i x(t; \psi_i) = x(t; \psi)c' = p(t)e^{Bt}c'$. We have thus obtained the structure of the solutions defined by the initial functions in $E(\rho)$.

Remark. Let $x(t; t_0, \varphi)$ be the solution of the system defined for $t \geqslant t_0 - \tau$, which in $[t_0 - \tau, t_0]$ coincides with φ. We denote by $U_{t,t_0}\varphi = x(t + s - t_0; t_0, \varphi)$, $s \in [t_0 - \tau, t_0]$. We have $U_{t_0,t_0}\varphi = \varphi$ and $x(t + \omega + s - t_0; t_0, \varphi) = U_{t,t_0}x(\omega + s; t_0, \varphi) = U_{t,t_0}U_{t_0+\omega,t_0}\varphi$; hence $U_{t+\omega,t_0} = U_{t,t_0}U_{t_0+\omega,t_0}$. The eigenvalues of $U_{t_0+\omega,t_0}$ coincide with the multipliers of the system. Let $n \geqslant 0$ such that $t_0 + n\omega \geqslant 0$, $\psi = x(u + n\omega; \varphi)$, $u \in [t_0 - \tau, t_0]$. Then $x(t; t_0, \psi) = x(t + n\omega; \varphi)$, since in both members we have solutions of the system and these coincide in $[t_0 - \tau, t_0]$. We have $U_{t_0+\omega,t_0}\psi = x(\omega + u; t_0, \psi) = x((n+1)\omega + u; \varphi)$.

Let ρ be a multiplier, φ a corresponding eigenvector. Then

$$\begin{aligned} x((n+1)\omega + u; \varphi) &= x((n+1)\omega + t_0 + s; \varphi) = U_{(n+1)\omega+t_0}\varphi \\ &= U_{t_0+n\omega}U\varphi = U_{t_0+n\omega}\rho\varphi = \rho U_{t_0+n\omega}\varphi = \rho x(n\omega + t_0 + s; \varphi) \\ &= \rho x(n\omega + u; \varphi) = \rho\psi; \end{aligned}$$

hence $U_{t_0+\omega,t_0}\psi = \rho\psi$ and ρ is an eigenvalue for $U_{t_0+\omega,t_0}$. Interchanging the roles of t_0 and 0 we deduce that the spectra of the operators $U_{t_0+\omega,t_0}$ and U coincide.

Let $\rho_1, \rho_2, \ldots, \rho_n \ldots$, be the multipliers of the system ordered in such a way that $|\rho_n| \geqslant |\rho_{n+1}|$. Let $A_n = \{\rho_1, \rho_2, \ldots, \rho_n\}$ and $R_n = \{\rho_{n+1}, \ldots\}$, where $|\rho_{n+1}| < \alpha < 1$. From the properties of the spectrum of a compact operator, it follows that there exists only a finite number of multipliers outside the circle $|z| \leqslant \alpha$.

To the decomposition $\sigma(U) = A_n \cup R_n \cup \{0\}$ corresponds a direct decomposition $\mathscr{X} = \mathscr{X}_n \oplus Y$, where $\mathscr{X}_n = E(\rho_1) \oplus E(\rho_2) \oplus \cdots \oplus E(\rho_n)$

and $\sigma(U \mid Y) = R_n \cup \{0\}$. If $\varphi \in \mathscr{X}$ we have $\varphi = \varphi_n + \psi$ and $x(t; \varphi) = x(t; \varphi_n) + x(t; \psi)$.

We have seen, however, that the solution $x(t; \varphi_n)$ is a linear combination of Floquet-type solutions. We will show that the solution $x(t; \psi)$ approaches zero as $e^{-\beta t}$, where $\beta = -(1/\omega) \ln \alpha$.

Let $t \geqslant t_0$ and N such that $N\omega \leqslant t - t_0 < (N+1)\omega$; hence $t = t_0 + N\omega + t'$, $0 \leqslant t' < \omega$. We have

$$U_{t,t_0} = U_{t_0+t'+N\omega,t_0} = U_{t_0+t',t_0} U^N_{t_0+\omega,t_0} \,.$$

However, $\| U_{t_0+t',t_0} \| \leqslant M_0$, where M_0 is a constant depending only on the function η. It follows from here that

$$\| U_{t,t_0} \| \leqslant M_0 \| U_{t_0+\omega,t_0} \|^N \qquad \text{and} \qquad | x(t; t_0, \varphi)| \leqslant M_0 \| U^N_{t_0+\omega,t_0} \| \| \varphi \|.$$

For every operator we have $\sup | \sigma(U)| = \lim_{n\to\infty} \| U^n \|^{1/n}$, and if the operator is compact, $\sup | \sigma(U)|$ is attained for an eigenvalue, since the single limit point of the spectrum is $z = 0$. For $\psi \in Y$ we have $| x(t, \psi)| \leqslant M_0 \|(U \mid Y)^N \| \cdot \| \psi \|$ and $\lim_{n\to\infty} \| (U \mid Y)^n \|^{1/n} < \alpha$; from here follows that for N large enough we have $\|(U \mid Y)^N \| \leqslant \alpha^N$ and $| x(t; \psi)| \leqslant M_0 \alpha^N \| \psi \|$. From $N > (1/\omega)t - 1$ follows $\alpha^N < (1/\alpha)\alpha^{(1/\omega)t}$; if $\beta = -(1/\omega) \ln \alpha$, we have $\alpha^{1/\omega} = e^{-\beta}$ and $| x(t; \psi)| \leqslant (M_0/\alpha) e^{-\beta t} \| \psi \|$.

We have thus shown that every solution of the system differs from a linear combination of Floquet solutions by a function which tends exponentially to zero (as $e^{-\beta t}$, with $\beta > 0$ arbitrarily large).

4.8. Periodic Linear Systems with Time Lag. Stability Theory

We have obtained above the relation

$$| x(t; t_0, \varphi)| \leqslant M_0 \| U^N_{t_0+\omega,t_0} \| \cdot \| \varphi \|,$$

where N is $[(t - t_0)/\omega]$. From this relation it follows that the stability properties of the system depend on the behavior of the sequence $\| U^N_{t_0+\omega,t_0} \|$.

If there exists an $M > 0$ such that for every natural N and every $t_0 \geqslant 0$ we have $\| U^N_{t_0+\omega,t_0} \| \leqslant M$, the zero solution of the system is uniformly stable. If there exists a $k > 0$ and $\epsilon > 0$ such that for every natural N and every $t_0 \geqslant 0$ we have $\| U^N_{t_0+\omega,t_0} \| \leqslant k(1 - \epsilon)^N$, then the zero solution of the system is uniformly asymptotically stable. For every operator U the values λ with the property that $| \lambda | \geqslant \| U \|$

do not belong to the spectrum; hence for every point of the spectrum we have $|\lambda| \leqslant \| U \|$; hence $|\lambda^N| \leqslant \| U^N \|$ (since if λ belongs to the spectrum of the operator U then λ^N belongs to the spectrum of U^N); from $\| U^N \| \leqslant M$ we obtain $|\lambda^N| \leqslant M$ for $N = 1, 2, ..., n$. This means, however, that $|\lambda| \leqslant 1$. Consequently from $\| U^N \| \leqslant M$ for every N it follows that $\sigma(U) \subset \{\lambda; |\lambda| \leqslant 1\}$.

Let $\sigma(U) = \sigma_1 \cup \sigma_2$, where $\sigma_1 \subset \{\lambda; |\lambda| < 1\}$ and $\sigma_2 \subset \{\lambda; |\lambda| = 1\}$. If U is compact, the sets σ_1 and σ_2 are separated and σ_2 is finite. The space $\mathscr{X}$ is decomposed in the direct sum $\mathscr{X} = \mathscr{X}_1 \oplus \mathscr{X}_2$ and corresponding to this decomposition the operator U is decomposed in the direct sum $U = U_1 \oplus U_2$, where $\sigma(U_1) = \sigma_1$, $\sigma(U_2) = \sigma_2$; from $U = U_1 \oplus U_2$ we obtain $U^N = U_1^N \oplus U_2^N$. If $\| U^N \| \leqslant M$ we obtain $\| U_2^N \| \leqslant M$; from the fact that $\lambda = 0$ does not belong to $\sigma(U_2)$, it follows that $\dim \mathscr{X}_2 < \infty$ and that a matrix corresponds to the operator U_2. From $\| U_2^N \| \leqslant M$ and from the fact that the eigenvalues of U_2 are situated on the circumference of the unit circle, it follows that the corresponding elementary divisors are simple. Thus, if U is compact and $\| U^N \| \leqslant M$ for every natural N, the spectrum $\sigma(U)$ is situated in the unit circle and simple elementary divisors correspond to the eigenvalues situated on the circumference.

Conversely, let U be compact and the spectrum $\sigma(U)$ situated in the unit circle, and let us suppose that to the eigenvalues situated on the circumference correspond simple elementary divisors. Then $U = U_1 \oplus U_2$, $\| U_2^N \| \leqslant M$, $\sigma(U_1) \subset \{\lambda; |\lambda| < 1\}$. From the fact that U is compact it follows that $\sup |\sigma(U_1)| < 1$ and $\lim_{n\to\infty} \| U_1^n \|^{1/n} = \alpha < 1$. It follows from here that for n sufficiently large we have $\| U_1^n \| < (1 - \epsilon)^n$; therefore for every natural N we will have $\| U_1^N \| < k(1 - \epsilon)^N$. It immediately follows from here that $\| U^N \| \leqslant M$.

Taking into account that the spectrum of the operator U does not depend on t_0, we can state the following theorem:

Theorem 4.17. *If the zero solution of the system is uniformly stable, the multipliers of the system are in $\{\lambda; |\lambda| \leqslant 1\}$, and to multipliers situated on the circumference correspond simple elementary divisors. If the zero solution is uniformly asymptotically stable, there exists an $\epsilon > 0$ such that the multipliers of the system are situated inside the circle $\{\lambda; |\lambda| \leqslant 1 - \epsilon\}$. Conversely, if the multipliers are situated in the circle $\{\lambda; |\lambda| < 1\}$ the zero solution of the system is uniformly asymptotically stable. If the multipliers of the system are inside the unit circle and to the multipliers situated on the circumference correspond simple elementary divisors, the zero solution is uniformly stable.*

Let us consider as an application of this theorem the case where

$\eta(t, s)$ does not depend on t. Then, setting $x(t+s, \varphi) = U(t)\varphi$, $U(t)$ defines a strongly continuous semi-group of operators. Indeed, we have $U(t+t_1)\varphi = x(t+t_1+s; \varphi) = x(t+s; x(t_1+s; \varphi))$, since both members contain solutions of the system and these solutions coincide for $t = 0$, namely, in $[t_1 - \tau, t_1]$.

However, this means that $U(t+t_1)\varphi = U(t)U(t_1)\varphi$; hence $U(t+t_1) = U(t)U(t_1)$. The strong continuity of this semigroup follows immediately from the general properties of the solutions. Let us observe that we also have $x(t+s; t_0, \varphi) = U(t-t_0)\varphi$.

Let $A = \lim_{r\to 0+} (1/r)[U(r) - I]$; then, as has been shown by N. N. Krasovski, we have $\sigma(A) = \{\lambda; \det(\int_{-\tau}^{0} e^{\lambda s}\, d\eta(s) - \lambda E) = 0\}$. From the general theory of semigroups it follows that $\sigma(U(t)) < \exp t\sigma(A) \cup 0$.

It follows from here that if $\sigma(A) \subset \{\lambda; \operatorname{Re}\lambda < 0\}$, then $\sigma(U(t))$ is situated for every t in $\{\lambda; |\lambda| < 1\}$. If we apply Theorem 4.17 for arbitrary ω, from $\sigma(A) \cup \{\lambda; \operatorname{Re}\lambda < 0\}$ follows the uniform asymptotic stability. This is the theorem of N. N. Krasovski.‡ The foregoing arguements, through which the result of N. N. Krasovski is deduced from Theorem 4.17, are due to A. Stokes.

Let us also show an immediate application of Theorem 4.17. We consider the system

$$\dot{x}(t) = \int_{-\infty}^{0} x(t+s)d_s\eta(t, s) + e^{\lambda t}g(t). \tag{38}$$

Let us see under which conditions this system admits solutions of the form $e^{\lambda t}h(t)$, where g and h are periodic functions of period ω. From the system we obtain

$$\lambda e^{\lambda t}h(t) + e^{\lambda t}\dot{h}(t) = \int_{-\infty}^{0} e^{\lambda(t+s)}h(t+s)d_s\eta(t, s) + e^{\lambda t}g(t),$$

from which we obtain

$$\dot{h}(t) = -\lambda h(t) + \int_{-\infty}^{0} h(t+s)e^{\lambda s}d_s\eta(t, s) + g(t),$$

which can also be written in the form

$$\dot{h}(t) = \int_{-\infty}^{0} h(t+s)d_s\eta_1(t, s) + g(t)$$

where η_1 has the same properties as η.

‡ We have already applied this result in Section 4.6.

As we will see in Section 4.9 this system admits a periodic solution of period ω, whichever be g periodic of period ω, if and only if the corresponding homogeneous system does not have periodic solutions of period ω, hence if the multipliers of this system are different from 1. These multipliers are, however, obtained from those of the system

$$\dot{x}(t) = \int_{-\infty}^{0} x(t+s)d_s\eta(t, s) \tag{39}$$

by multiplying through by $e^{-\lambda\omega}$. Indeed, let

$$x(t+\omega) = \rho x(t).$$

It follows that

$$e^{\lambda(t+\omega)}h(t+\omega) = \rho e^{\lambda t}h(t);$$

hence $e^{\lambda\omega}h(t+\omega) = \rho h(t)$, hence $h(t+\omega) = e^{-\lambda\omega}\rho h(t)$. Conversely, if $h(t+\omega) = \rho_1 h(t)$, we have

$$x(t+\omega) = e^{\lambda(t+\omega)}h(t+\omega) = e^{\lambda t}e^{\lambda\omega}\rho_1 h(t) - e^{\lambda\omega}\rho_1 x(t);$$

hence $\rho = e^{\lambda\omega}\rho_1$, $\rho_1 = e^{-\lambda\omega}\rho$.

Taking this into account, the condition that system (38) admits (whichever be g periodic of period ω) solutions of the form $e^{\lambda t}h$, with h periodic of period ω, is equivalent to the requirement that $e^{\lambda\omega}$ not be a multiplier of system (39).

Theorem 4.18. *If for every g periodic of period ω and for every λ with $|e^{\lambda\omega}| \geqslant 1$, system (38) admits a solution of the form $e^{\lambda t}h(t)$ with h periodic of period ω, the zero solution of system (39) is uniformly asymptotically stable.*

Indeed, if the condition of the statement is fulfilled, it follows from the above that the numbers $e^{\lambda\omega}$ with $|e^{\lambda\omega}| \geqslant 1$ are not multipliers of the system, hence that the multipliers are strictly inside the unit circle, which, in conformity with Theorem 4.17, implies uniform asymptotic stability.

Let us observe that Theorem 4.18 is of the same type as 4.15; the conclusions on the stability of the zero solution of system (39) are obtained from the information concerning the response to "excitations" of a certain form [from the information about the solutions of system (38)].

Now let us prove the following theorem.

Theorem 4.19. *Consider the system*

$$\dot{x}(t) = [A(t) + C(t)]x(t) + [B(t) + D(t)]x(t - \tau) \tag{40}$$

where A, B, C, D are periodic of period $\omega > \tau$. Suppose that the zero solution of the system

$$\dot{y}(t) = A(t)y(t) + B(t)y(t - \tau) \tag{41}$$

is uniformly asymptotically stable and

$$\int_0^\omega \{| C(t) | + | D(t) |\} \, dt$$

is sufficiently small. Then the zero solution of system (40) *is uniformly asymptotically stable.*

Proof. Let U be the operator corresponding to system (40) and V the operator corresponding to system (41). From the stability assumption it follows that the eigenvalues of V are in the circle $| z | \leqslant 1 - \epsilon$. We shall prove that

$$\| U - V \| \leqslant M \int_0^\omega \{| C(s) | + | D(s) |\} \, ds. \tag{42}$$

From here it will follow that if the condition in the statement is verified, the eigenvalues of U lie in a circle $| z | \leqslant 1 - (\epsilon/2)$, and the theorem will be proved.

To prove (42) let $z(t, \varphi) = x(t, \varphi) - y(t, \varphi)$. We have

$$\dot{z}(t) = A(t)z(t, \varphi) + B(t)z(t - \tau, \varphi) + C(t)x(t) + D(t)x(t - \tau, \varphi).$$

From here follows

$$z(t, \varphi) = \int_0^t Y(t, \alpha)[C(\alpha)x(\alpha) + D(\alpha)x(\alpha - \tau, \varphi) \, d\alpha$$

where $Y(t, s)$ is the solution of system (41), $Y(t, s) \equiv 0$ for $t < s$, $Y(s, s) = E$.

We deduce that

$$| U\varphi - V\varphi | = | z(\omega + s, \varphi) |$$

$$\leqslant M \int_0^{\omega+s} \{| C(\alpha) | \, | x(\alpha) | + | D(\alpha) | \, | x(\alpha - \tau, \varphi) |\} \, d\alpha.$$

But we have, for $\alpha \in [o, \omega]$,

$$| x(\alpha) | \leqslant K \| \varphi \|$$

hence

$$| U\varphi - V\varphi | \leqslant MK \int_0^{\omega+s} \{| C(\alpha) | + | D(\alpha) |\} d\alpha \| \varphi \|$$

and

$$\| U\varphi - V\varphi \| \leqslant MK \int_0^{\omega} \{| C(\alpha) | + | D(\alpha) |\} d\alpha \| \varphi \|.$$

The inequality (42) is established and the theorem is thus proved.

4.9. Periodic Solutions of Linear Periodic Systems with Retarded Argument

We shall now consider the problem of the existence of the periodic solutions of linear periodic nonhomogeneous systems. Let the system be

$$\dot{x}(t) = \int_{-\infty}^{0} x(t+s)d_s\eta(t, s) + f(t), \tag{43}$$

where η and f are periodic in t with period $\omega > \tau$.

Let $x(t; \varphi)$ be the solution of the system defined for $t \geqslant 0$ by the function φ given in $[-\tau, 0]$. From the fact that η and f are periodic, it follows that $x(t + \omega; \varphi)$ is likewise a solution of the system and this solution is defined for $t + \omega \geqslant \tau$; if in $[-\tau, 0]$ this solution coincides with φ, on the basis of the uniqueness theorem it follows that $x(t + \omega; \varphi) = x(t; \varphi)$ for all $t \geqslant -\tau$ and the solution is periodic. Thus the periodicity condition of the solution is written $x(\omega + s; \varphi) = \varphi(s)$ for $s \in [-\tau, 0]$. Let V be the operator defined by $V\varphi = x(\omega + s; \varphi)$; the function φ is an initial function for a periodic solution of the system if and only if $V\varphi = \varphi$, in other words, the periodic solutions of the system correspond to the fixed points of the operator V.

Let $z(t; \varphi)$ be the solution of the corresponding homogeneous system, defined for $t \geqslant 0$ by the initial function φ given in $[-\tau, 0]$. Then $x(t; \varphi) = z(t; \varphi) + \int_0^t f(\alpha)X(t, \alpha)d\alpha$.

If U is the operator defined by the relation $U\varphi = z(\omega + s; \varphi)$, we have

$$V\varphi = U\varphi + \int_0^{\omega+s} f(\alpha)X(\omega + s, \alpha)d\alpha.$$

The periodicity condition is

$$\varphi = U\varphi + \int_0^{\omega+s} f(\alpha)X(\omega + s, \alpha)d\alpha;$$

i.e.,

$$(I - U)\varphi = \int_0^{\omega+s} f(\alpha)X(\omega + s, \alpha)d\alpha,$$

where I is the identity operator.

The operator U is compact; hence $I = U$ has an inverse if and only if the equation $U\varphi = \varphi$ has no other solutions except $\varphi = 0$.

The equation $U\varphi = \varphi$ determines the initial functions of the periodic solutions of the homogeneous system. We have, therefore, the following theorem:

Theorem 4.20. *A necessary and sufficient condition in order that system* (43) *have a periodic solution of period* ω *for an arbitrary function* f *periodic of period* ω *is that the corresponding homogeneous system does not have periodic solutions of period* ω *different from the zero solution.*

We shall now prove a theorem characterizing the behavior of the solution of system (43), in the case where it does not admit periodic solutions.

Theorem 4.21. *If system* (43) *does not have periodic solutions, then all the solutions are unbounded.*

Proof. Let $\psi = \int_0^{\omega+s} f(\alpha)X(\omega + s, \alpha)d\alpha$. The initial functions of the periodic solutions of system (43) verify the relation $(I - U)\varphi = \psi$. If system (43) does not have periodic solutions, this equation does not have solutions; hence ψ does not belong to the space $(I - U)\mathscr{X}$. But the operator U is compact and thus $(I - U)\mathscr{X}$ is a closed subspace of $\mathscr{X}$. It follows from this that the distance from ψ to this subspace is not zero and thus there exists a linear functional y such that $y[\varphi] = 0$ for $\varphi \in (I - U)\mathscr{X}$ and $y[\psi] = 1$. For every $\varphi \in \mathscr{X}$ we have $y[(I - U)\varphi] = 0$; hence $y[\varphi - U\varphi] = y[\varphi] - y[U\varphi] = 0$ and $y[\varphi] = y[U\varphi]$. From $x(\omega + s; \varphi) = U\varphi + \psi$, we obtain

$$y[x(\omega + s; \varphi)] = y[U\varphi] + y[\psi] = y[\varphi] + 1.$$

We have the relation

$$x(t + n\omega; \varphi) = z(t; x(n\omega + s; \varphi)) + \int_0^t f(\alpha)X(t, \alpha)d\alpha.$$

Indeed, in the second member we have a solution of system (43), and this solution coincides in $[-\tau, 0]$ with $x(t + n\omega; \varphi)$. From this relation we deduce that

$$x[(n+1)\omega + s; \varphi] = Ux(n\omega + s; \varphi) + \psi.$$

From here, by induction, we obtain

$$y[x(n\omega + s; \varphi)] = y[\varphi] + n$$

Indeed, we have previously obtained this relation for $n = 1$. Further,

$$\begin{aligned} y[x((n+1)\omega + s; \varphi)] &= y[Ux(n\omega + s; \varphi) + \psi] \\ &= y[Ux(n\omega + s; \varphi)] + y[\psi] \\ &= y[x(n\omega + s; \varphi)] + y[\psi] = y[\varphi] + n + 1 \end{aligned}$$

and the relation is proved by induction. From this we deduce that the sequence $y[x(n\omega + s; \varphi)]$ is unbounded, which shows that the solution $x(t; \varphi)$ cannot be bounded. The theorem is thus proved.

Let us observe that this theorem shows that if system (43) admits at least one bounded solution, it also admits a periodic solution.

The homogeneous system corresponding to system (43) *can only have a finite number of linearly independent periodic solutions.*

Indeed, the corresponding initial functions are solutions of the equation $U\varphi = \varphi$ and from the fact that the operator U is compact it follows that this equation has only a finite number of independent solutions.

In the following section we shall study in detail the critical case in which the homogeneous system admits periodic solutions of period ω different from the zero solution. We shall present this study in detail for the simplest systems with time lag, the arguments being carried out for the general case in the same way.

4.10. The Critical Case for Linear Periodic Systems with Time Lag

We shall consider a system of the form

$$\dot{x}(t) = A(t)x(t) + B(t)x(t - \tau) + f(t), \tag{44}$$

where A, B, f are continuous and periodic of period $\omega > \tau$. The corresponding homogeneous system is

$$\dot{x}(t) = A(t)x(t) + B(t)x(t - \tau), \tag{45}$$

and the adjoint system is

$$\dot{y}(t) = -y(t)A(t) - y(t+\tau)B(t+\tau). \tag{46}$$

Theorem 4.22. *If system* (44) *has periodic solutions of period* ω, *then* $\int_0^\omega y(t)f(t)dt = 0$ *for all the periodic solutions* $y(t)$ *of period* ω *of the adjoint system* (46).

Proof. Let $x(t)$ be a solution of system (44) defined for $t \geqslant -\tau$ and $y(t)$ a solution of system (46) defined for $t \leqslant \omega + \tau$. For $0 \leqslant t \leqslant \omega$ we define the function (y, x) as in Section 4.3, through the formula

$$(y, x) = y(t)x(t) + \int_0^\tau y(t+\eta)B(t+\eta)x(t+\eta-\tau)d\eta.$$

Then

$$\frac{d}{dt}(y, x) = \frac{d}{dt}\left(y(t)x(t) + \int_t^{t+\tau} y(\xi)B(\xi)x(\xi-\tau)d\xi\right) = y(t)f(t). \tag{47}$$

If $x(t)$ and $y(t)$ are periodic of period ω we see at once that (y, x) is a periodic function of t. We obtain, by integrating relation (47),

$$0 = (y, x)(\omega) - (y, x)(0) = \int_0^\omega y(t)f(t)dt,$$

and the theorem is thus proved.

We shall prove now that system (46) has the same number of independent periodic solutions as system (45) and that the condition of the preceding theorem is sufficient in order that system (44) have periodic solutions. To do this we will need a series of preliminary results which will lead to results interesting in themselves.

Let $y(t, \psi)$ be the solution of system (46) defined for $t \leqslant \omega + \tau$ by the function ψ given in $[\omega, \omega + \tau]$. It follows from the periodicity of the system that $y(t-\omega; \psi)$ will likewise be a solution; this solution is defined in $t - \omega \leqslant \omega + \tau$, hence for $t \leqslant 2\omega + \tau$. If $y(t-\omega; \psi)$ coincides with ψ in $[\omega, \omega+\tau]$, then from the uniqueness theorem it follows that $y(t-\omega; \psi) = y(t; \psi)$ and the solution will be periodic. Taking into account formula (20), the periodicity condition is

$$\psi(t) = \psi(\omega)X(\omega, t-\omega) + \int_\omega^{\omega+\tau} \psi(\xi)B(\xi)X(\xi-\tau, t-\omega)d\xi \quad (t \in [\omega, \omega+\tau])$$

We write $\tilde{\varphi}(s) = \psi(s + \omega + \tau)$, $s \in [-\tau, 0]$. Then

$$\tilde{\varphi}(s) = \tilde{\varphi}(-\tau)X(\omega, s+\tau) + \int_\omega^{\omega+\tau} \tilde{\varphi}(\xi-\omega-\tau)B(\xi)X(\xi-\tau, s+\tau)d\xi;$$

i.e.,

$$\tilde{\varphi}(s) = \tilde{\varphi}(-\tau)X(\omega, s + \tau) + \int_{-\tau}^{0} \tilde{\varphi}(\eta)B(\eta + \tau)X(\eta + \omega, s + \tau)d\eta. \quad (48)$$

We shall prove that this equation has the same number of linearly independent solutions as the equation $\varphi - U\varphi = 0$ and that the equation $\varphi - U\varphi = \phi$ has a solution if and only if

$$\tilde{\varphi}(-\tau)\phi(0) + \int_{-\tau}^{0} \tilde{\varphi}(\eta)B(\eta + \tau)\phi(\eta)d\eta = 0 \quad (49)$$

for all the solutions of $\tilde{\varphi}$ of equation (48).

For the matrix functions ψ, φ defined in $[-\tau, 0]$ for which multiplication is possible, we define the operation

$$\langle\psi, \varphi\rangle = \psi(-\tau)\varphi(0) + \int_{-\tau}^{0} \psi(\xi)B(\xi + \tau)\varphi(\xi)d\xi.$$

We have the fundamental property

$$\langle\langle L(\sigma), M(\alpha, \sigma)\rangle, N(\alpha)\rangle = \langle L(\sigma), \langle M(\alpha, \sigma), N(\alpha)\rangle\rangle \quad (50)$$

Let $K(\alpha) = \langle L(\sigma), M(\alpha, \sigma)\rangle$; we have

$$\langle K(\alpha), N(\alpha)\rangle = K(-\tau)N(0) + \int_{-\tau}^{0} K(\xi)B(\xi + \tau)N(\xi)d\xi,$$

$$K(\alpha) = L(-\tau)M(\alpha, 0) + \int_{-\tau}^{0} L(\xi)B(\xi + \tau)M(\alpha, \xi)d\xi;$$

hence

$$\langle K(\alpha), N(\alpha)\rangle = \left[L(-\tau)M(-\tau, 0) + \int_{-\tau}^{0} L(\xi)B(\xi + \tau)M(-\tau, \xi)d\xi\right] N(0)$$

$$+ \int_{-\tau}^{0} \left[L(-\tau)M(\xi, 0) + \int_{-\tau}^{0} L(\eta)B(\eta + \tau)M(\xi, \eta)d\eta\right] B(\xi + \tau)N(\xi)d\xi$$

$$= L(-\tau)M(-\tau, 0)N(0) + \int_{-\tau}^{0} L(\xi)B(\xi + \tau)M(-\tau, \xi)N(0)d\xi$$

$$+ L(-\tau) \int_{-\tau}^{0} M(\xi, 0)B(\xi + \tau)N(\xi)d\xi$$

$$+ \int_{-\tau}^{0} \left[\int_{-\tau}^{0} L(\eta)B(\eta + \tau)M(\xi, \eta)d\eta\right] B(\xi + \tau)N(\xi)d\xi$$

$$= L(-\tau)\left[M(-\tau, 0)N(0) + \int_{-\tau}^{0} M(\xi, 0)B(\xi + \tau)N(\xi)d\xi\right]$$
$$+ \int_{-\tau}^{0} L(\eta)B(\eta + \tau)M(-\tau, \eta)N(0)d\eta$$
$$+ \int_{-\tau}^{0} L(\eta)B(\eta + \tau)\left[\int_{-\tau}^{0} M(\xi, \eta)B(\xi + \tau)N(\xi)d\xi\right] d\eta$$

$$= L(-\tau)\left[M(-\tau, 0)N(0) + \int_{-\tau}^{0} M(\xi, 0)B(\xi + \tau)N(\xi)d\xi\right]$$
$$+ \int_{-\tau}^{0} L(\eta)B(\eta + \tau)\left[M(-\tau, \eta)N(0) + \int_{-\tau}^{0} M(\xi, \eta)B(\xi + \tau)N(\xi)d\xi\right] d\eta$$

$$= \langle L(\sigma), \langle M(\alpha, \sigma), N(\alpha)\rangle\rangle.$$

The relation in (50) is thus proved.

With this notation the operator U is written

$$U\varphi = \langle X(\omega + s, \eta + \tau), \varphi(\eta)\rangle.$$

Let us consider the operator $\tilde{U}$ defined by $\tilde{U}\tilde{\varphi} = \langle\tilde{\varphi}(\eta), X(\omega + \eta, s + \tau)\rangle$. Let $\tilde{V}$ be the operator defined by $\tilde{V}\psi = y(\sigma - \omega; \psi)$, $\sigma \in [\omega, \omega + \tau]$, ψ continuous in $[\omega, \omega + \tau]$. If ρ is an eigenvalue of $\tilde{V}$ we will say that $1/\rho$ is a multiplier of the adjoint system. This definition is justified by the fact that if ρ is an eigenvalue of $\tilde{V}$, system (46) admits a solution with the property $y(t + \omega; \psi) = (1/\rho)y(t; \psi)$, and conversely. Indeed, if $\tilde{V}\psi = \rho\psi$, then $y(t - \omega; \psi) = \rho y(t; \psi)$, since both members of the equality are solutions of systems (46) and these solutions coincide in $[\omega, \omega + \tau]$; conversely, if this relation holds for $t \in [\omega, \omega + \tau]$, it yields $\tilde{V}\psi = \rho\psi$. The relation obtained can also be represented in the form $y(t + \omega; \psi) = (1/\rho)y(t; \psi)$. We have

$$\tilde{V}\psi = \psi(\omega)X(\omega, \sigma - \omega) + \int_{\omega}^{\omega+\tau} \psi(\xi)B(\xi)X(\xi - \tau, \sigma - \omega)d\xi \quad (\sigma \in [\omega, \omega + \tau]).$$

If ρ is an eigenvalue of $\tilde{V}$, there exists a nonzero solution of the equation

$$\rho\psi(\sigma) = \psi(\omega)X(\omega, \sigma - \omega) + \int_{\omega}^{\omega+\tau} \psi(\xi)B(\xi)X(\xi - \tau, \sigma - \omega)d\xi \quad (\sigma \in [\omega, \omega + \tau]).$$

This equation is written, setting $\tilde{\varphi}(s) = \psi(s + \omega + \tau)$, $s \in [-\tau, 0]$,

$$\rho\tilde{\varphi}(s) = \tilde{\varphi}(-\tau)X(\omega, s + \tau) + \int_{\omega}^{\omega+\tau} \tilde{\varphi}(\xi - \omega - \tau)B(\xi)X(\xi - \tau, s + \tau)d\xi$$

or

$$\rho\tilde{\varphi}(s) = \tilde{\varphi}(-\tau)X(\omega, s+\tau) + \int_{-\tau}^{0} \tilde{\varphi}(\eta)B(\eta+\tau)X(\eta+\omega, s+\tau)d\eta$$
$$= \tilde{U}\tilde{\varphi}.$$

Consequently, the eigenvalues of the operators $\tilde{V}$ and $\tilde{U}$ coincide and, in addition, if ψ is an eigenfunction for $\tilde{V}$, then $\tilde{\varphi}(s) = \psi(s+\omega+\tau)$ is an eigenfunction for $\tilde{U}$.

In the following lines we shall prove that the eigenvalues of the operators U and $\tilde{U}$ coincide and that for each eigenvalue ρ both operators have the same number of linearly independent eigenfunctions. Thus for $\rho = 1$ the assertion relative to periodic solutions will follow, since equation (48) is just $\tilde{\varphi} - U\tilde{\varphi} = 0$.

Let us observe that we have the relation

$$\langle \tilde{U}\tilde{\varphi}, \varphi \rangle = \langle \tilde{\varphi}, U\varphi \rangle,$$

which is valid for every pair of functions $\tilde{\varphi}$, φ continuous in $[-\tau, 0]$ ($\tilde{\varphi}$ is a row vector and φ is a column vector). Indeed, we have

$$\langle \tilde{U}\tilde{\varphi}, \varphi \rangle = \langle\langle \tilde{\varphi}(\eta), X(\omega+\eta, s+\tau)\rangle, \varphi(s)\rangle$$
$$= \langle \tilde{\varphi}(\eta), \langle X(\omega+\eta, s+\tau), \varphi(s)\rangle\rangle = \langle \tilde{\varphi}, U\varphi \rangle.$$

Let us now consider an equation of the form

$$\varphi(s) - \lambda\langle K_1(s, \alpha), \varphi(\alpha)\rangle = \chi(s).$$

We seek the solution under the form $\varphi(s) = \sum_{i=0}^{\infty} \lambda^i \varphi_i(s)$. Substituting in the equation and identifying the coefficients of the powers of λ, we obtain

$$\varphi_0(s) = \chi(s), \qquad \varphi_i(s) = \langle K_1(s, \alpha), \varphi_{i-1}(\alpha)\rangle.$$

From here we obtain $|\varphi_i(s)| \leq M^i \sup |\chi(s)|$, $M = \sup |K_1|$.

The series converges uniformly and absolutely for $|\lambda| M < 1$, hence for $|\lambda| < 1/M$. We have

$$\varphi_1(s) = \langle K_1(s, \alpha), \chi(\alpha)\rangle.$$

We verify by induction the formula

$$\varphi_l(s) = \langle K_l(s, \alpha), \chi(\alpha)\rangle,$$

where

$$K_l(s, \eta) = \langle K_1(s, \alpha), K_{l-1}(\alpha, \eta)\rangle.$$

Indeed, we have

$$\varphi_{l+1}(s) = \langle K_1(s, \alpha), \varphi_l(\alpha)\rangle = \langle K_1(s, \alpha), \langle K_l(\alpha, \eta), \chi(\eta)\rangle\rangle$$
$$= \langle\langle K_1(s, \alpha), K_l(\alpha, \eta)\rangle, \chi(\eta)\rangle = \langle K_{l+1}(s, \eta), \chi(\eta)\rangle.$$

Setting

$$\Gamma(s, \eta) = \sum_1^\infty \lambda^l K_l(s, \eta)$$

it follows that the solution of the equation is written, for $|\lambda| < 1/M$,

$$\varphi(s) = \chi(s) + \Sigma\lambda^l\langle K_l(s, \alpha), \chi(\alpha)\rangle$$
$$= \chi(s) + \langle\Sigma\lambda^l K_l(s, \alpha), \chi(\alpha)\rangle$$
$$= \chi(s) + \langle\Gamma(s, \alpha), \chi(\alpha)\rangle.$$

Now consider the equation

$$\tilde\varphi(s) - \lambda\langle\tilde\varphi(\alpha), K_1(\alpha, s)\rangle = \tilde\chi(s).$$

We again seek a solution, in the form

$$\tilde\varphi(s) = \sum_{i=0}^\infty \lambda^i \tilde\varphi_i(s),$$

and we obtain $\tilde\varphi_0(s) = \tilde\chi(s)$, $\tilde\varphi_i(s) = \langle\tilde\varphi_{i-1}(\alpha), K_1(\alpha, s)\rangle$.

As above, the series will be uniformly and absolutely convergent for $|\lambda| < 1/M$. By induction, we obtain

$$\tilde\varphi_l(s) = \langle\tilde\chi(\alpha), \tilde K_l(\alpha, s)\rangle, \qquad \tilde K_l(\eta, s) = \langle\tilde K_{l-1}(\eta, \alpha), K_1(\alpha, s)\rangle.$$

We finally obtain the solution in the form

$$\tilde\varphi(s) = \tilde\chi(s) + \langle\tilde\chi(\alpha), \tilde\Gamma(\alpha, s)\rangle,$$

where

$$\tilde\Gamma(\alpha, s) = \sum_{l=1}^\infty \lambda^l \tilde K_l(\eta, s).$$

We prove the relation

$$\tilde K_l(\eta, s) = K_l(\eta, s).$$

We have

$$K_2(\eta, s) = \langle K_1(\eta, \alpha), K_1(\alpha, s)\rangle = \tilde K_2(\eta, s).$$

We suppose that the equality holds for $j \leqslant l$. We have

$$K_l(\eta, s) = \langle K_1(\eta, \alpha), K_{l-1}(\alpha, s)\rangle = \tilde{K}_l(\eta, s) = \langle \tilde{K}_{l-1}(\eta, \alpha), K_1(\alpha, s)\rangle$$
$$= \langle K_{l-1}(\eta, \alpha), K_1(\alpha, s)\rangle;$$

hence

$$K_{l+1}(\eta, s) = \langle K_1(\eta, \alpha), K_l(\alpha, s)\rangle = \langle K_1(\eta, \alpha), \langle K_{l-1}(\alpha, \beta), K_1(\beta, s)\rangle\rangle$$
$$= \langle\langle K_1(\eta, \alpha), K_{l-1}(\alpha, \beta)\rangle, K_1(\beta, s)\rangle = \langle K_l(\eta, \beta), K_1(\beta, s)\rangle$$
$$= \langle \tilde{K}_l(\eta, \beta), K_1(\beta, s)\rangle = \tilde{K}_{l+1}(\eta, s).$$

Thus we obtain $\tilde{\Gamma}(\eta, s) = \Gamma(\eta, s)$.

Since $X(\omega + s, \eta + \tau)$ is uniformly continuous in $[-\tau, 0] \times [-\tau, 0]$, we may write $X(\omega + s, \eta + \tau) = \sum_k a_k(s)b_k(\eta) + K_1(s, \eta)$, where the $a_k(s)$ are column vectors and the $b_k(\eta)$ row vectors, $\{a_k\}$ and $\{b_k\}$ are linearly independent, and $| K_1 |$ can be taken arbitrarily small.

The equation $\rho\varphi - U\varphi = F$ is written

$$\rho\varphi(s) - \langle X(\omega + s, \eta + \tau), \varphi(\eta)\rangle = F(s);$$

hence

$$\rho\varphi(s) - \left\langle \sum_k a_k(s)b_k(\eta) + K_1(s, \eta), \varphi(\eta)\right\rangle = F(s);$$

i.e.,

$$\rho\varphi(s) - \sum_k a_k(s)\langle b_k(\eta), \varphi(\eta)\rangle - \langle K_1(s, \eta), \varphi(\eta)\rangle = F(s);$$

hence

$$\rho\varphi(s) - \langle K_1(s, \eta), \varphi(\eta)\rangle = \sum_k a_k(s)\langle b_k(\eta), \varphi(\eta)\rangle + F(s).$$

Setting

$$\frac{1}{\rho}\sum_k a_k(s)\langle b_k(\eta), \varphi(\eta)\rangle + \frac{1}{\rho}F(s) = \chi(s),$$

we obtain

$$\varphi(s) - \frac{1}{\rho}\langle K_1(s, \eta), \varphi(\eta)\rangle = \chi(s).$$

If $1/| \rho | < 1/M$ and $\sup | K_1 | < | \rho |$, we deduce

$$\varphi(s) = \chi(s) + \langle \Gamma(s, \alpha), \chi(\alpha)\rangle.$$

Thus we obtain for $\chi(s)$ the equation

$$\rho\chi(s) = \sum_k a_k(s)\langle b_k(\eta), \chi(\eta) + \langle \Gamma(\eta, \alpha), \chi(\alpha)\rangle\rangle + F(s),$$

which can also be written

$$\rho\chi(s) = \sum_k a_k(s)(\langle b_k(\eta), \chi(\eta)\rangle + \langle b_k(\eta), \langle \Gamma(\eta, \alpha), \chi(\alpha)\rangle\rangle) + F(s)$$

$$= \sum_k a_k(s)(\langle b_k(\eta), \chi(\eta)\rangle + \langle\langle b_k(\eta), \Gamma(\eta, \alpha)\rangle, \chi(\alpha)\rangle) + F(s)$$

$$= \sum_k a_k(s)\langle b_k(\alpha) + \langle b_k(\eta), \Gamma(\eta, \alpha)\rangle, \chi(\alpha)\rangle + F(s);$$

hence

$$\rho\chi(s) = \sum_k a_k(s)\langle \bar{b}_k(\alpha), \chi(\alpha)\rangle + F(s),$$

where

$$\bar{b}_k(\alpha) = b_k(\alpha) + \langle b_k(\eta), \Gamma(\eta, \alpha)\rangle.$$

It follows from this that

$$\rho\chi(s) - F(s) = \sum_k \lambda_k a_k(s);$$

hence

$$\sum_k \lambda_k a_k(s) = \sum_k a_k(s)\langle \bar{b}_k(\alpha), \frac{1}{\rho} F(\alpha) + \frac{1}{\rho} \sum_j \lambda_j a_j(\alpha)\rangle.$$

Taking into account that the vectors a_k are linearly independent, we deduce that

$$\rho\lambda_k = \sum_j \gamma_{kj}\lambda_j + f_k ,$$

where

$$\gamma_{kj} = \langle \bar{b}_k(\alpha), a_j(\alpha)\rangle, \qquad f_k = \langle \bar{b}_k(\alpha), F(\alpha)\rangle.$$

The system for λ_k has solution if and only $\sum f_k\mu_k = 0$ for all the solutions of the system

$$\rho\mu_k = \sum_j \gamma_{jk}\mu_j . \tag{51}$$

On the other hand, the equation $\rho\tilde{\varphi} - \tilde{U}\tilde{\varphi} = 0$ is written

$$\rho\tilde{\varphi}(s) = \langle \tilde{\varphi}(\alpha), \sum_k a_k(\alpha) b_k(s) + K_1(\alpha, s)\rangle;$$

hence

$$\rho\tilde{\varphi}(s) - \langle \tilde{\varphi}(\alpha), K_1(\alpha, s)\rangle = \sum_k \langle \tilde{\varphi}(\alpha), a_k(\alpha)\rangle b_k(s).$$

Setting

$$\tilde{\chi}(s) = \frac{1}{\rho} \sum_k \langle \tilde{\varphi}(\alpha), a_k(\alpha) \rangle b_k(s),$$

we have

$$\tilde{\varphi}(s) - \frac{1}{\rho} \langle \tilde{\varphi}(\alpha), K_1(\alpha, s) \rangle = \tilde{\chi}(s),$$

which for $\sup | K_1 | < | \rho |$ yields

$$\tilde{\varphi}(s) = \tilde{\chi}(s) + \langle \tilde{\chi}(\alpha), \Gamma(\alpha, s) \rangle.$$

From this we obtain for $\chi(s)$ the equation

$$\rho \tilde{\chi}(s) = \sum_k \langle \tilde{\chi}(\alpha) + \langle \tilde{\chi}(\eta), \Gamma(\eta, \alpha) \rangle, a_k(\alpha) \rangle b_k(s),$$

which can also be written

$$\rho \tilde{\chi}(s) = \sum_k \langle \tilde{\chi}(\eta), \bar{a}_k(\eta) \rangle b_k(s),$$

where

$$\bar{a}_k(\eta) = a_k(\eta) + \langle \Gamma(\eta, \alpha), a_k(\alpha) \rangle.$$

The solution of this equation will be of the form

$$\rho \tilde{\chi}(s) = \sum_k \mu_k b_k(s);$$

hence

$$\sum_k \mu_k b_k(s) = \sum_k \left\langle \frac{1}{\rho} \sum_j \mu_j b_j(\eta), \bar{a}_k(\eta) \right\rangle b_k(s),$$

from which, taking into account that the vectors b_k are linearly independent, we deduce that

$$\rho \mu_k = \sum_j \tilde{\gamma}_{jk} \mu_j, \qquad \gamma_{jk} = \langle b_j(\eta), \bar{a}_k(\eta) \rangle. \tag{52}$$

Let us obtain the equality $\tilde{\gamma}_{jk} = \gamma_{jk}$. We have

$$\begin{aligned}
\tilde{\gamma}_{jk} &= \langle b_j(\eta), a_k(\eta) + \langle \Gamma(\eta, \alpha), a_k(\alpha) \rangle \rangle \\
&= \langle b_j(\eta), a_k(\eta) \rangle + \langle b_j(\eta), \langle \Gamma(\eta, \alpha), a_k(\alpha) \rangle \rangle \\
&= \langle b_j(\eta), a_k(\eta) \rangle + \langle \langle b_j(\eta), \Gamma(\eta, \alpha) \rangle, a_k(\alpha) \rangle \\
&= \langle b_j(\alpha) + \langle b_j(\eta), \Gamma(\eta, \alpha) \rangle, a_k(\alpha) \rangle \\
&= \langle \bar{b}_j(\alpha), a_k(\alpha) \rangle = \gamma_{jk}.
\end{aligned}$$

It follows that systems (51) and (52) coincide.

The systems

$$\rho\lambda_k = \sum_j \gamma_{kj}\lambda_j \tag{53}$$

and (51) have the same number of linearly independent solutions. To a solution of system (53) corresponds $\chi(s) = (1/\rho) \Sigma_k \lambda_k a_k(s)$, and to this corresponds the solution $\varphi(s) = \chi(s) + \langle \Gamma(s, \alpha), \chi(\alpha)\rangle$ for the equation $\rho\varphi - U\varphi = 0$, linearly independent solutions corresponding to the linearly independent solutions of system (53). Likewise, a solution of the equation $\rho\tilde{\varphi} - \tilde{U}\tilde{\varphi} = 0$ will correspond to a solution of system (52), which coincides with (51), linearly independent solutions corresponding to linearly independent solutions.

It follows from here that the equations $\rho\varphi - U\varphi = 0$ and $\rho\tilde{\varphi} - \tilde{U}\tilde{\varphi} = 0$ have the same number of independent solutions, which implies in particular the fact that U and $\tilde{U}$ have the same eigenvalues, hence that if ρ is a multiplier of the system, then $1/\rho$ is a multiplier of the adjoint system.

The condition $\sum f_k\mu_k = 0$, necessary and sufficient in order that equation $\rho\varphi - U\varphi = F$ has solutions, is explicitly written

$$\sum \mu_k \langle b_k(\alpha) + \langle b_k(\eta), \Gamma(\eta, \alpha)\rangle, F(\alpha)\rangle = 0.$$

If $\{\mu_k\}$ is a solution of system (51), it is also a solution of system (52), $\Sigma\, \mu_k b_k(s) = \rho\tilde{\chi}(s)$ and the condition becomes

$$\rho\langle\tilde{\chi}(\alpha), F(\alpha)\rangle + \rho\langle\langle\tilde{\chi}(\eta), \Gamma(\eta, \alpha)\rangle, F(\alpha)\rangle = 0.$$

However, $\tilde{\chi}(\alpha) + \langle\tilde{\chi}(\eta), \Gamma(\eta, \alpha)\rangle = \tilde{\varphi}(\alpha)$, and we obtain the condition $\langle\tilde{\varphi}(\alpha), f(\alpha)\rangle = 0$.

We have thus shown that a necessary and sufficient condition in order that the equation $\rho\varphi - U\varphi = F$ have solutions is that $\langle\tilde{\varphi}(\alpha), F(\alpha)\rangle = 0$ for all solutions $\tilde{\varphi}$ of the equation $\rho\tilde{\varphi} - \tilde{U}\tilde{\varphi} = 0$.

If we consider the case where $\rho = 1, F(s) = \int_0^{\omega+s} X(\omega + s, \alpha)f(\alpha)d\alpha$, by taking $\tilde{\varphi}(s) = \psi(s + \tau + \omega)$ the condition $\langle\tilde{\varphi}(\alpha), F(\alpha)\rangle = 0$ becomes

$$\psi(\omega) \int_0^{\omega} X(\omega, \alpha)f(\alpha)d\alpha + \int_{-\tau}^{0} \psi(\eta + \tau + \omega)B(\eta + \tau)$$

$$\times \left[\int_0^{\omega+\eta} X(\omega + \eta, \alpha)f(\alpha)d\alpha\right] d\eta = 0.$$

We interchange the order of integration in the last integral and we obtain

$$\psi(\omega)\int_0^{\omega} X(\omega,\alpha)f(\alpha)d\alpha + \int_0^{\omega-\tau}\Big[\int_{-\tau}^{0}\psi(\eta+\tau+\omega)B(\eta+\tau)X(\omega+\eta,\alpha)d\eta\Big]f(\alpha)d\alpha$$
$$+\int_{\omega-\tau}^{\omega}\Big[\int_{\alpha-\omega}^{0}\psi(\eta+\tau+\omega)B(\eta+\tau)X(\omega+\eta,\alpha)d\eta\Big]f(\alpha)d\alpha = 0.$$

However, for $\eta < \alpha - \omega$ we have $\alpha > \omega + \eta$; hence $X(\omega+\eta,\alpha)\equiv 0$. Thus in the last integral we can substitute $-\tau$ for $\alpha - \omega$. The condition is written

$$\psi(\omega)\int_0^{\omega} X(\omega,\alpha)f(\alpha)d\alpha$$
$$+\int_0^{\omega}\Big[\int_{-\tau}^{0}\psi(\eta+\tau+\omega)B(\eta+\tau)X(\omega+\eta,\alpha)d\eta\Big]f(\alpha)d\alpha = 0;$$

namely,

$$\int_0^{\omega}\Big[\psi(\omega)X(\omega,\alpha)+\int_{\omega}^{\omega+\tau}\psi(\xi)B(\xi)X(\xi-\tau,\alpha)d\xi\Big]f(\alpha)d\alpha = 0;$$

hence $\int_0^{\omega} y(\alpha)f(\alpha)d\alpha = 0$, where y is the solution of system (46) which in $[\omega, \omega+\tau]$ coincides with ψ.

We have thus proved the following theorem:

Theorem 4.23. *Systems (45) and (46) have the same number of linearly independent periodic solutions of period $\omega > \tau$. If*

$$\int_0^{\omega} y(\alpha)f(\alpha)d\alpha = 0$$

for all independent periodic solutions of period ω of system (46), then system (47) has periodic solutions of period ω.

4.11. Almost-Periodic Solutions for Linear Systems

We again consider system (44), under the hypothesis that f is an almost-periodic vector of the form

$$f(t) = \sum_{k=1}^{N} e^{i\nu_k t}f_k(t), \tag{54}$$

where the f_k are periodic functions of period ω and ν_k are such that $\nu_j - \nu_k \not\equiv \pm 2n\pi/\omega (\mathrm{mod}\ 2\pi)$. This last condition can always be fulfilled if f has the form (54).

We will assume that system (45) has its multipliers situated on the unit circle and we will formulate necessary and sufficient conditions in order that system (44) admits almost-periodic solutions.

Let us first observe that if system (44) admits almost-periodic solutions, then

$$\lim_{T\to\infty} \frac{1}{T} \int_0^T y(t)f(t)dt = 0 \tag{55}$$

for all almost-periodic solutions $y(t)$ of the adjoint system (46). Indeed. from relation (47) we deduce that $y(t)f(t)$ has a primitive $(y(t), x(t))$ which is bounded together with $x(t)$ and $y(t)$. If $x(t)$ and $y(t)$ are almost periodic it follows that $y(t)f(t)$ has an almost-periodic primitive and in this case its mean value is zero. Thus our assertion is proved.

System (45) and (46) with periodic coefficients have almost-periodic solutions if and only if they admit multipliers situated on the unit circle, and the number of the linearly independent almost-periodic solutions coincides with the number of the linearly independent eigenvectors corresponding to the multipliers situated on the unit circle. Taking into account the results proved in Section 4.10, we deduce that systems (45) and (46) have the same number of almost-periodic linearly independent solutions.

Let us now consider the system

$$\dot{x}(t) = A(t)x(t) + B(t)x(t-\tau) + e^{i\nu_k t}f_k(t) \tag{56}$$

and seek conditions which assure the existence of a solution of the form $e^{i\nu_k t}h(t)$, where $h(t)$ is periodic of period ω. By putting $x(t) = e^{i\nu_k t}h(t)$ we obtain

$$\dot{h}(t) = (A(t) - i\nu_k E)h(t) + B(t)e^{-i\nu_k \tau}h(t-\tau) + f_k(t). \tag{57}$$

This system admits periodic solutions if and only if

$$\int_0^\omega l_j(t)f_k(t)dt = 0$$

for all the periodic solutions of period ω of the adjoint system

$$\dot{l}(t) = -l(t)(A(t) - i\nu_k E) - l(t+\tau)B(t+\tau)e^{-i\nu_k \tau}. \tag{58}$$

Let us observe that if $l_j(t)$ is a periodic solution of system (58), then $y_j(t) = e^{-i\nu_k t}l_j(t)$ is an almost-periodic solution of system (46) corresponding to the multiplier $e^{-i\nu_k \omega}$.

Indeed,

$$\begin{aligned}\dot{y}_j(t) &= -i\nu_k e^{-i\nu_k t} l_j(t) + e^{-i\nu_k t}\dot{l}_j(t)\\ &= -i\nu_k e^{-i\nu_k t} l_j(t) - e^{-i\nu_k t} l_j(t)(A(t) - i\nu_k E)\\ &\quad -e^{i\nu_k t} l_j(t+\tau)B(t+\tau)e^{-i\nu_k \tau}\\ &= -y_j(t)A(t) - y_j(t+\tau)B(t+\tau).\end{aligned}$$

If $e^{i\nu_k\omega}$ is not a multiplier of system (45), then $e^{-i\nu_k\omega}$ is not a multiplier of system (46); hence system (58) does not have periodic solutions and system (57) has a periodic solution. Thus (56) has an almost-periodic solution of the form $e^{i\nu_k t}h_k(t)$. If $e^{i\nu_k\omega}$ is a multiplier of system (45), then system (46) has almost-periodic solutions of the form $y_{jk}(t) = e^{-i\nu_k t}l_j(t)$ and

$$\begin{aligned}\lim_{T\to\infty}\frac{1}{T}\int_0^T & y_{jk}(t)[f(t) - e^{i\nu_k t}f_k(t)]dt\\ &= \lim_{T\to\infty}\frac{1}{T}\int_0^T e^{-i\nu_k t}l_j(t)\sum_{\substack{\alpha=1\\ \alpha\neq k}}^{N} e^{i\nu_\alpha t}f_\alpha(t)dt\\ &= \sum_{\substack{\alpha=1\\ \alpha\neq k}}^{N}\lim_{T\to\infty}\frac{1}{T}\int_0^T e^{i(\nu_\alpha-\nu_k)t}f_\alpha(t)l_j(t)dt = 0.\end{aligned}$$

If condition (55) is fulfilled, it follows that

$$\lim_{T\to\infty}\frac{1}{T}\int_0^T y_{jk}(t)e^{i\nu_k t}f_k(t)dt = 0;$$

hence

$$\lim_{T\to\infty}\frac{1}{T}\int_0^T e^{-i\nu_k t}l_j(t)e^{i\nu_k t}f_k(t)dt = 0;$$

namely,

$$\int_0^\omega l_j(t)f_k(t)dt = 0.$$

However, then system (57) admits a periodic solution; hence system (56) admits an almost-periodic solution of the form $e^{i\nu_k t}h_k(t)$. By repeating the same reasoning for $k = 1, 2, \ldots, N$, we obtain an almost-periodic solution of system (44) of the form $\sum_{k=1}^{N} e^{i\nu_k t}h_k(t)$.

We have thus obtained the following theorem:

Theorem 4.24. *System* (44) *with* f *of form* (54) *admits an almost-periodic solution if and only if condition* (55) *is satisfied for all the almost-periodic solutions of system* (46).

The same conclusions are valid for linear systems with time lag of a general form.

4.12. Systems with a Small Parameter with Time Lag

We begin the study of nonlinear systems with the problem of the determination of periodic solutions of systems with a small parameter. We consider a system of the form

$$\frac{dx(t)}{dt} = f[t, x(t+s), \mu], \tag{59}$$

where f is periodic of period $\omega > \tau$ and has the properties stated in Section 4.1.

Theorem 4.25. *If system* (59) *admits for* $\mu = 0$ *a periodic solution* $x_0(t)$, *of period* ω, *such that the corresponding variational system does not admit periodic solutions of period* ω *different from the trivial solution, then there exists* $\mu_0 > 0$ *such that for* $|\mu| < \mu_0$ *system* (59) *admits a unique periodic solution* $x(t, \mu)$ *of period* ω, *with the property that* $\lim_{\mu \to 0} x(t, \mu) = x_0(t)$.

Proof. Since the components of f are differentiable, we may write

$$f[t, x(t+s), 0] - f[t, x_0(t+s), 0] = A[t, x(t+s) - x_0(t+s)] + o(\| x - x_0 \|),$$

where

$$A(t, \varphi) = \int_{-\tau}^{0} \varphi(s) d_s \eta(t, s).$$

The variational system corresponding to the solution $x_0(t)$ is the linear system

$$\dot{y}(t) = \int_{-\tau}^{0} y(t+s) d_s \eta(t, s). \tag{60}$$

In Section 4.1. we proved relation (8), from which it follows in particular that

$$\| x(\omega + s; \varphi, 0) - x(\omega + s; \varphi_0, 0) - y(\omega + s; \varphi - \varphi_0) \| = o(\| \varphi - \varphi_0 \|),$$

where we have denoted by $x(t; \varphi, \mu)$ the solution of system (59) which for $t \in [-\tau, 0]$ coincides with φ, and by $y(t, \varphi)$ the solution of system (60) which for $t \in [-\tau, 0]$ coincides with φ. Owing to the periodicity of system (59), $x(t + \omega; \varphi, \mu)$ is likewise a solution, and if $x(\omega + s; \varphi, \mu) =$

$\varphi(s)$ for $s \in [-\tau, 0]$, this solution is periodic (and conversely). Let $F[\varphi, \mu] = x(\omega + s; \varphi, \mu) - \varphi$. If φ_0 is the initial function of the periodic solution $x_0(t)$, we have $F[\varphi_0, 0] = 0$. It follows from relation (8) that for every μ, $F[\varphi, \mu]$ is differentiable; indeed,

$$F[\varphi_2, \mu] - F[\varphi_1, \mu] = x(\omega + s; \varphi_2, \mu) - \varphi_2 - x(\omega + s; \varphi_1, \mu) + \varphi_1$$

and, because of relation (8),

$$\begin{aligned} &\| F[\varphi_2, \mu] - F[\varphi_1, \mu] - I(\varphi_2 - \varphi_1) - U_\mu(\varphi_2 - \varphi_1)\| \\ &\quad = \| x(\omega + s; \varphi_2, \mu) - x(\omega + s; \varphi_1, \mu) - y(\omega + s; \varphi_2 - \varphi_1, \mu)\| \\ &\quad = o(\| \varphi_2 - \varphi_1 \|), \end{aligned}$$

where $y(t; \varphi, \mu)$ is the solution of the variational system corresponding to the solution $x(t; \varphi_1, \mu)$. It follows that the derivative of $F[\varphi, \mu]$ is $I - U_\mu$, where $U_\mu \varphi = y(\omega + s; \varphi, \mu)$.

In particular, the derivative at the point $[\varphi_0, 0]$ is $I - U_0$, where $U_0\varphi = y(\omega + s; \varphi)$ [we recall that $y(t; \varphi)$ is the solution of system (60), the variational system corresponding to the solution $x_0(t)$]. The operator U_0 is completely continuous (compact), as we have shown it in Section 7.4. Since by virtue of the hypothesis, the system (60) does not admit periodic solutions of period ω different from the trivial one, the equation $\varphi - U_0\varphi = 0$ has no solutions different from the trivial solution. However, it follows then from the general properties of the completely continuous operators that $I - U_0$ has an inverse. Since $F[\varphi, \mu]$ is differentiable, $F[\varphi_0, 0] = 0$, and the derivative has an inverse at the point $[\varphi_0, 0]$, it follows, on the basis of the implicit function theorem in Banach spaces, that there exists a $\mu_0 > 0$ such that for $|\mu| < \mu_0$ the equation $F[\varphi, \mu] = 0$ admits a solution $[\varphi_\mu, \mu]$ with the property that $\lim_{\mu \to 0} \varphi_\mu = \varphi_0$. From $F[\varphi_\mu, \mu] \equiv 0$, it follows that the solution $x(t; \varphi_\mu, \mu)$ is periodic; in addition, $\lim_{\mu \to 0} x(t; \varphi_\mu, \mu) = x(t; \varphi_0, 0) = x_0(t)$. The theorem is thus proved.

Application. We consider the system

$$\frac{dx(t)}{dt} = \int_{-\infty}^{0} x(t + s) d_s\eta(t, s) + f(t) + g[t, x(t + s,) \mu], \tag{61}$$

where η has the same properties as in Section 4.7, for fixed t the components of g are functionals defined in the space of vector functions continuous in $[-\tau, 0]$ and these functionals are periodic in t with period ω. We suppose as previously that $\omega > \tau$. We assume that the linear system

$$\frac{dy(t)}{dt} = \int_{-\infty}^{0} y(t + s) d_s\eta(t, s) \tag{62}$$

does not have periodic solutions of period ω different from the trivial one. Then system (61) admits for $\mu = 0$ a unique periodic solution $x_0(t)$ of period ω.

The corresponding variational system is precisely system (62). The conditions of Theorem 4.25 are verified. System (61) admits a periodic solution $x(t, \mu)$ unique, of period ω, with the property that $\lim_{\mu\to 0} x(t, \mu) = x_0(t)$.

Let us suppose now that system (62) admits periodic solution of period ω. As we have seen in Section 4.9, there exists a finite number of such solutions which are linearly independent; we will denote them $p_1, p_2, \ldots, p_k$. The adjoint system admits the same finite number of independent periodic solutions $q_1, q_2, \ldots, q_k$.

System (61) admits for $\mu = 0$ periodic solutions of period ω if and only if $\int_0^\omega f(t)q_j(t)dt = 0$ for $j = 1, 2, \ldots, k$. The periodic solutions of system (61) for $\mu = 0$ are given by the formula

$$x(t) = x(0)X(t, 0) + \int_{-\tau}^{0} x(s)d_s \int_0^{s+\tau} \eta(\alpha, s - \alpha)X(t, \alpha)d\alpha + \int_0^t f(\alpha)X(t, \alpha)d\alpha;$$

the initial functions $x(s)$, $s \in [-\tau, 0]$ are given by the system

$$x(s) = x(0)X(\omega + s, 0) + \int_{-\tau}^{0} x(\beta)d_\beta \int_{-\tau}^{\beta} \eta(\alpha + \tau, \beta - \alpha - \tau)X(\omega + s, \alpha + \tau)d\alpha$$
$$+ \int_0^{\omega+s} f(\alpha)X(\omega + s, \alpha)d\alpha.$$

(see Section 4.10). As we have already seen in Section 4.10, the solutions of this system are of the form

$$x(s) = \chi(s) + \langle \chi(\alpha), \Gamma(\alpha, s)\rangle,$$

$$\chi(s) = \int_0^{\omega+s} f(\alpha)X(\omega + s, \alpha)d\alpha + \sum_j \lambda_j b_j(s),$$

where Γ and $b_k(s)$ depend on system (62) and λ_j verifies the system

$$\lambda_i = \sum_j \gamma_{ij}\lambda_j + f_i\,.$$

If $\int_0^\omega f(t)q_j(t)dt = 0, j = 1, \ldots, k,$ the system in λ_i admits solutions. Simple results from linear algebra show that there exists one solution and only one which verifies an estimate of the form $|\lambda_i| \leqslant K_1 \max_j |f_j|$, where K_1 depends on γ_{ij}, hence on system (62). Taking into account the expression for f_j we obtain an estimate of the form $|\lambda_i| \leqslant$

$K_2 \sup |f|$, where K_2 depends only on system (62). It follows from here that there exists a unique $\chi(s)$ admitting an estimate of the form $|\chi(s)| \leqslant K_3 \sup |f|$, where K_3 depends only on system (62). We finally deduce that there exists a unique periodic solution of system (61), for $\mu = 0$, which admits an estimate of the form $|x(t)| \leqslant K \sup |f|$, where K depends only on system (62).

Denoting this solution by $p(t)$, the periodic solutions of period ω of system (61) for $\mu = 0$ will be of the form $p(t) + \Sigma_{j=1}^{k} p_j(t)$.

Theorem 4.26. *Let*

$$P_j(\alpha_1, \alpha_2, ..., \alpha_k, \mu) = \int_0^{\omega} g\left[t, p(t+s) + \sum_{j=1}^{k} \alpha_i p_i(t+s), \mu\right] q_j(t)dt.$$

If $\alpha_1^0, \alpha_2^0, ..., \alpha_k^0$ *verify the relations*

$$P_j(\alpha_1^0, \alpha_2^0, ..., \alpha_k^0, 0) = 0, \qquad \frac{\partial(P_1, P_2, ..., P_k)}{\partial(\alpha_1, \alpha_2, ..., \alpha_k)} \neq 0 \quad \text{for} \quad \alpha_j = \alpha_j^0, \mu - 0,$$

then there exists a $\mu_0 > 0$ *such that for* $|\mu| < \mu_0$ *system* (61) *admits a periodic solution* $x(t, \mu)$, *of period* ω, *with the property*

$$\lim_{\mu \to 0} x(t, \mu) = p(t) + \sum_{j=1}^{k} \alpha_j^0 p_j(t).$$

We suppose that g is differentiable in a neighborhood of the point $p(t+s) + \Sigma_{i=1}^{k} \alpha_i^0 p_i(t+s)$.

Proof. On the basis of the implicit-function theorem, there exist functions $\alpha_j^0(\mu)$ with $\alpha_j^0(0) = \alpha_j^0$, such that

$$P_j[\alpha_1^0(\mu), ..., \alpha_k^0(\mu), \mu] \equiv 0.$$

Taking into account the way in which the P_j are defined, it follows that the system

$$\frac{dx(t)}{dt} = \int_{-\infty}^{0} x(t+s)d_s\eta(t, s) + g\left[t, p(t+s) + \sum_{i=1}^{k} \alpha_i^0(\mu)p_i(t+s), \mu\right]$$

admits periodic solutions of period ω. Let $x_1^*(t)$ be the periodic solution of this system chosen such that

$$|x_1^*| < K \sup \left| g\left[t, p(t+s) + \sum_{i=1}^{k} \alpha_i^0(\mu)p_i(t+s), \mu\right]\right|.$$

We put

$$x_1(t) = p(t) + \sum_{j=1}^{k} \alpha_j^1 p_j(t) + \mu x_1^*(t).$$

The function $x_1(t)$ is a periodic solution, of period ω, of the system

$$\frac{dx(t)}{dt} = \int_{-\infty}^{0} x(t+s)d_s\eta(t,s) + f(t) + \mu g\left[t, p(t+s) + \sum_{j=1}^{k} \alpha_j^0(\mu)p_j(t+s), \mu\right].$$

We consider the system

$$\frac{dx(t)}{dt} = \int_{-\infty}^{0} x(t+s)d_s\eta(t,s) + g[t, x_1(t+s), \mu]. \tag{63}$$

The condition that this system admits a periodic solution of period ω is written

$$\int_0^{\omega} g\left[t, p(t+s) + \sum_{i=1}^{k} \alpha_i^1 p_i(t+s) + \mu x_1^*(t+s), \mu\right] q_j(t)dt = 0 \quad (j = 1, 2, ..., k).$$

These conditions are verified for $\mu = 0$, $\alpha_i^1 = \alpha_i^0$, and in addition the Jacobian with respect to $\alpha_1^1, ..., \alpha_k^1$ is nonzero in this point; hence, on the basis of the implicit function theorem, we may find functions $\alpha_i^1(\mu)$ with $\alpha_i^1(0) = \alpha_i^0$ such that the conditions be verified.

We suppose α_i^1 so chosen and $x_1(t)$ correspondingly defined. Let $x_2^*(t)$ be the periodic solution, of period ω, of system (63) which admits the estimate

$$x_2^*(t)| < K \sup | g[t, x_1(t+s), \mu]|.$$

We put

$$x_2(t) = p(t) + \sum_{j=1}^{k} \alpha_j^2 p_j(t) + \mu x_2^*(t)$$

and choose $\alpha_j^2(\mu)$ such that the procedure be continued. We thus obtain a sequence $\alpha_j^i(\mu)$ with $\alpha_j^i(0) = \alpha_j^0$ and a sequence of periodic functions

$$x_i(t) = p(t) + \sum_{j=1}^{k} \alpha_j^i(\mu)p_j(t) + \mu x_i^*(t)$$

which verify the relations

$$\dot{x}_i(t) = \int_{-\infty}^{0} x_i(t+s)d_s\eta(t,s) + f(t) + \mu g[t, x_{i-1}(t+s), \mu],$$

$$| x_i^*(t)| \leqslant K \sup | g[t, x_{i-1}(t+s), \mu]|.$$

It is easy to verify that for $|\mu|$ small enough, the functions $x_i(t)$ so defined do not leave the neighborhood of point $p(t+s) + \sum_{i=1}^{k} \alpha_i^0 p_i(t+s)$ where g is differentiable.

If we prove that the sequence $x_i(t)$ converges uniformly, it will follow that its limit is a periodic solution, of period ω, of system (61), with the stated properties. We have

$$x_{i+1}(t) - x_i(t) = \sum_j [\alpha_j^{i+1}(\mu) - \alpha_j^i(\mu)]p_j(t) + \mu[x_{i+1}^*(t) - x_i^*(t)].$$

Taking into account the way in which the solutions $x_i^*(t)$ have been chosen, it follows that

$$\begin{aligned} |x_{i+1}^*(t) - x_i^*(t)| &\leqslant K \sup |g[t, x_i(t+s), \mu] - g[t, x_{i-1}(t+s), \mu]| \\ &\leqslant KL\| x_i(t+s) - x_{i-1}(t+s)\| \leqslant KL \sup |x_i(t) - x_{i-1}(t)|. \end{aligned}$$

Let us denote $a_i = \sup |x_{i+1}(t) - x_i(t)|$, $b_i = \max_j \sup |a_j^{i+1}(\mu) - a_j^i(\mu)|$, $L_1 = \sup \sum_{j=1}^{k} |p_i(t)|$. We obtain

$$a_i \leqslant L_1 b_i + |\mu| KLa_{i-1}.$$

We consider the functions

$$\begin{aligned} R_j^l(\beta_1, ..., \beta_k, \mu, \lambda) \equiv \int_0^\omega g[t, p(t+s) + \sum_i \beta_i p_i(t+s) + \mu x_{l-1}^*(t+s) \\ + \lambda[x_l^*(t+s) - x_{l-1}^*(t+s)], \mu] q_j(t) dt. \end{aligned}$$

Let $\beta_i^l(\mu, \lambda)$ be defined by the relations $R_j^l(\beta_1, ..., \beta_k, \mu, \lambda) = 0$ and by the conditions $\beta_i^l(0, 0) = \alpha_j^0$ (on the basis of the theorem of implicit functions). It is obvious that $\beta_i^l(\mu, 0) = \alpha_j^{l-1}(\mu)$, $\beta_i^l(\mu, \mu) = \alpha_i^l(\mu)$; hence

$$\alpha_i^l(\mu) - \alpha_i^{l-1}(\mu) = \beta_i^l(\mu, \mu) - \beta_i^l(\mu, 0) = \frac{\partial}{\partial \lambda} \beta_i^l(\mu, \theta\mu)\mu.$$

From this will follow an estimate of the form

$$|\alpha_i^l(\mu) - \alpha_i^{l-1}(\mu)| \leqslant |\mu| L_2 \sup |x_l^* - x_{l-1}^*| \leqslant |\mu| L_2 KLa_{l-1}$$

since

$$\frac{\partial}{\partial \lambda} \beta_i^l = - \frac{\partial(R_1^l, R_2^l, ..., R_k^l)/\partial(\beta_1, ..., \lambda, \beta_{i+1}, ..., \beta_k)}{\partial(R_1^l, R_2^l, ..., R_k^l)/\partial(\beta_1, ..., \beta_i, ..., \beta_k)},$$

$$\frac{\partial R_j^l}{\partial \lambda} = \mathscr{L}[x_l^*(t+s) - x_{l-1}^*(t+s)],$$

where $\mathscr{L}$ is a linear operator.

We deduce that $b_{l-1} \leqslant |\mu| LL_2K\, a_{l-1}$ and thus that

$$a_i \leqslant L_1 |\mu| LL_2Ka_i + |\mu| KLa_{i-1}, \qquad a_i \leqslant \frac{|\mu| L_3}{1 + |\mu| L_4} a_{i-1}.$$

Taking this estimate into account, we obtain for $|\mu|$ small enough the convergence of the series $\Sigma\, a_i$, hence the uniform convergence of the sequence $x_i(t)$. The theorem is thus proved.

4.13. Systems with Retarded Argument Containing a Small Parameter

In this section we shall give up the investigation within the general framework of systems with time lag and consider only systems with time lag of the form

$$\frac{dx(t)}{dt} = f[t, x(t), x(t-\tau), \mu]. \tag{64}$$

Here x and f are column vectors; f is periodic in t of period $\omega > \tau$.

Let us suppose that the generating system obtained for $\mu = 0$ admits a family of periodic solutions of period ω. Let $x_0(t, h)$ be this family. The variational system

$$\frac{dy(t)}{dt} = f'_u[t, x_0(t, h_0), x_0(t-\tau, h_0), 0]y(t)$$
$$+ f'_v[t, x_0(t, h_0), x_0(t-\tau, h_0), 0]y(t-\tau) \tag{65}$$

admits the periodic solutions $\partial x_0(t, h)/\partial h$. Indeed, from

$$\frac{dx_0(t, h)}{dt} = f[t, x_0(t, h), x_0(t-\tau, h), 0]$$

we obtain

$$\frac{d}{dt}\frac{\partial}{\partial h} x_0(t, h) = f'_u[t, x_0(t, h), x_0(t-\tau, h), 0) \frac{\partial x_0(t, h)}{\partial h}$$
$$+ f'_v[t, x_0(t, h), x_0(t-\tau, h), 0] \frac{\partial x_0(t-\tau, h)}{\partial h}.$$

Hence the columns of the matrix $\partial x_0(t, h)/\partial h$ represent solutions of the variational system considered. *We suppose that the variational system* (65) *does not admit, for any h_0 in a certain domain, periodic solutions of period ω independent of these.*

Let $q_1(t, h_0), ..., q_k(t, h_0)$ be the independent periodic solutions of the adjoint system of system (65). If system (64) admits a periodic solution of period ω of the form

$$x(t, \mu) = x_0(t, h_0) + \mu x_1(t, \mu),$$

then

$$\int_0^{\omega} q_j(t, h_0) f'_u[t, x_0(t, h_0), x_0(t-\tau, h_0), 0]dt = 0 \qquad (j = 1, ..., k). \tag{66}$$

We have

$$\begin{aligned}\frac{d}{dt} x(t, \mu) &= \frac{d}{dt} x_0(t, h_0) + \mu \frac{d}{dt} x_1(t, \mu)\\ &= f[t, x_0(t, h_0) + \mu x_1(t, \mu), x_0(t-\tau, h_0) + \mu x_1(t-\tau, \mu), \mu]\\ &= f[t, x_0(t, h_0), x_0(t-\tau, h_0), 0] + \mu f'_u[t, x_0(t, h_0), x_0(t-\tau, h_0), 0] x_1(t, 0)\\ &\quad + \mu f'_v[t, x_0(t, h_0), x_0(t-\tau, h_0), 0] x_1(t-\tau, 0)\\ &\quad + \mu f'_\mu[t, x_0(t, h_0), x_0(t-\tau, h_0), 0] + O(\mu^2).\end{aligned}$$

We obtain

$$\begin{aligned}\frac{d}{dt} x_1(t, 0) - f'_u[t, x_0(t, h_0), x_0(t-\tau, h_0), 0] x_1(t, 0)&\\ + f'_v[t, x_0(t, h_0), x_0(t-\tau, h_0), 0] x_1(t-\tau, 0)&\\ + f'_\mu[t, x_0(t, h_0), x_0(t-\tau, h_0), 0]&\end{aligned}$$

Since $x_1(t, 0)$ is periodic of period ω we obtain, on the basis of Theorem 4.23, the equalities (66).

Theorem 4.27. *Let*

$$P_j(h) \equiv \int_0^{\omega} q_j(t, h) f'_\mu[t, x_0(t, h), x_0(t-\tau, h), 0]dt.$$

If h_0 verifies the relations

$$P_j(h_0) = 0, \qquad \det \frac{\partial}{h_l} \int_0^{\omega} q_j(t, h_0) f'_\mu[t, x_0(t, h), x_0(t-\tau, h), 0]dt \neq 0$$

for $h = h_0$, and f is analytic, then system (64) admits a periodic solution $x(t, \mu)$ such that

$$\lim_{\mu \to 0} x(t, \mu) = x_0(t, h_0).$$

Proof. We represent system (64) in the form

$$\frac{dx(t)}{dt} = f_0[t, x(t), x(t-\tau)] + \mu f_1[t, x(t), x(t-\tau)] + \mu^2 f_2[t, x(t), x(t-\tau)] + \cdots,$$

where, obviously,

$$f_0(t, u, v) = f(t, u, v, 0), \qquad f_1(t, u, v) = f'_\mu(t, u, v, 0).$$

We seek the periodic solution in the form

$$x(t, \mu) = x_0(t) + \mu x_1(t) + \mu^2 x_2(t) + \cdots.$$

By substituting the system we obtain

$$\frac{dx_0(t)}{dt} = f_0[t, x_0(t), x_0(t-\tau)],$$

$$\frac{dx_1(t)}{dt} = f'_{0u}[t, x_0(t), x_0(t-\tau)]x_1(t) + f'_{0v}[t, x_0(t), x_0(t-\tau)]x_1(t-\tau) + f_1[t, x_0(t), x_0(t-\tau)],$$

$$\frac{dx_2(t)}{dt} = f'_{0u}[t, x_0(t), x_0(t-\tau)]x_2(t) + f'_{0v}[t, x_0(t), x_0(t-\tau)]x_2(t-\tau) + f'_{1u}[t, x_0(t), x_0(t-\tau)]x_1(t) + f'_{1v}[t, x_0(t), x_0(t-\tau)]x_1(t-\tau) + f_2[t, x_0(t), x_0(t-\tau)],$$

and so on.

We choose $x_0(t) = x_0(t, h_0)$. Since $P_j(h_0) = 0, j = 1, \ldots, k,$ there exists periodic solutions of the system which determine $x_1(t)$. These solutions are of the form

$$p^1(t) + \sum_{j=1}^{k} \alpha_j^1 p_j(t), \qquad p_j(t) = \frac{\partial x_0(t, h_0)}{\partial h_j}.$$

In order that the system which determines $x_2(t)$ admits periodic solutions it is necessary and sufficient that

$$\int_0^\omega q_j(t, h_0) \Big\{ f'_{1u}[t, x_0(t), x_0(t-\tau)] \Big[p^1(t) + \sum_{l=1}^{k} \alpha_l^1 p_l(t)\Big] + f'_{1v} \Big[p^1(t-\tau) + \sum_{l=1}^{k} \alpha_l^1 p_l(t-\tau)\Big] + f_2 \Big\} \, dt = 0.$$

These conditions represent a system of linear equations in α_l' whose matrix has the elements A_{jl} given by

$$A_{jl} = \int_0^\omega q_j(t, h_0) \left\{ f_{1u}'[t, x_0(t), x_0(t-\tau)] \frac{\partial x_0(t, h_0)}{\partial h_l} + f_{1v}' \frac{\partial x_0(t-\tau, h_0)}{\partial h_l} \right\} dt$$

$$= \frac{\partial}{\partial h_l} \int_0^\omega q_j(t, h_0) f_\mu'[t, x_0(t, h_0), x_0(t-\tau, h_0), 0] dt.$$

According to the hypotheses in the statement, $\det A_{jl} \neq 0$; hence we may choose, uniquely, the constants α_j^l such that the system which determines $x_2(t)$ admits periodic solutions. Continuing the computations, we successively and uniquely determine the functions $x_2(t)$, $x_3(t)$, ...

From the analyticity hypotheses will follow estimates of the form

$$|f_j| \leqslant K_1 L^j, \qquad |f_{ju}'| + |f_{jv}'| \leqslant K_2 L^j.$$

We have

$$|p^1(t)| \leqslant K_0 K_1 L, \qquad \sum |p_j(t)| \leqslant K_3, \qquad |\alpha_i^1| \leqslant K_4 K_1 L^2;$$

hence

$$|x_1(t)| \leqslant K_1 L (K_0 + K_3 K_4 L).$$

Further,

$$|p^2(t)| \leqslant K_0 [K_2 L K_1 L (K_0 + K_3 K_4 L) + K_1 L^2]$$
$$= K_0 K_1 L^2 [1 + K_2 (K_0 + K_3 K_4 L)],$$
$$|\alpha_l^2| \leqslant K_4 \{K_2 L^2 K_1 L (K_0 + K_3 K_4 L) + K_1 L^3\}$$
$$= K_1 K_4 L^3 [1 + K_2 + K_3 K_4 L)];$$

hence

$$|x_2(t)| \leqslant K_1 L^2 \{K_0 [1 + K_2 (K_0 + K_3 K_4 L) + K_3 K_4 L [1 + K_2 (K_0 + K_3 K_4 L)]\}$$
$$= K_1 L^2 (K_0 + K_3 K_4 L) [1 + K_2 (K_0 + K_3 K_4 L)].$$

In general,

$$|p^j(t)| \leqslant K_0 \{K_2 L \sup |x_{j-1}| + K_2 L^2 \sup |x_{j-2}| + \cdots + K_2 L^{j-1} \sup |x_1| + K_1 L^j\},$$

$$|\alpha_j^l| \leqslant K_4 \{K_2 L^2 \sup |x_{j-1}| + \cdots + K_2 L^j \sup |x_1| + K_1 L^{j+1}\};$$

hence

$$| x_j(t)| \leqslant K_2L(K_0 + K_3K_4L) \sup| x_{j-1} | + \cdots$$
$$+ K_2L^{j-1}(K_0 + K_3K_4L) \sup| x_1 | + K_1L^j(K_0 + K_3K_4L).$$

Let us suppose that

$$| x_{j-1}(t)| \leqslant K_1L^{j-1}(K_0 + K_3K_4L)[1 + K_2(K_0 + K_3K_4L)]^{j-2}.$$

We have

$$\begin{aligned}
| x_j(t)| &\leqslant K_2L(K_0 + K_3K_4L)K_1L^{j-1}(K_0 + K_3K_4L)[1 + K_2(K_0 + K_3K_4L)]^{j-2} \\
&\quad + K_2L^2(K_0 + K_3K_4L)K_1L^{j-2}(K_0 + K_3K_4L)[1 + K_2(K_0 + K_3L_4L)^{j-3}] + \cdots \\
&\quad + K_2L^{j-1}(K_0 + K_3K_4L)K_1L(K_0 + K_3K_4L) + K_1L^j(K_0 + K_3K_4L) \\
&= K_1L^j(K_0 + K_3K_4L)\{1 + K_2(K_0 + K_3K_4L) + \cdots \\
&\quad + K_2(K_0 + K_3K_4L)[1 + K_2(K_0 + K_3K_4L)]^{j-3} \\
&\quad + K_2(K_0 + K_3K_4L)[1 + K_2(K_0 + K_3K_4L)]^{j-2}\} \\
&= K_1L^j(K_0 + K_3K_4L)[1 + K_2(K_0 + K_3K_4L)] \\
&\quad \times \{1 + \cdots + K_2(K_0 + K_3K_4L)[1 + K_2(K_0 + K_3K_4L)]^{j-4} \\
&\quad + K_2(K_0 + K_3K_4L)[1 + K_2(K_0 + K_3K_4L)]^{j-3} \\
&= K_1L^j(K_0 + K_3K_4L)[1 + K_2(K_0 + K_3K_4L)]^{j-1}.
\end{aligned}$$

We finally obtain an inequality of the form $|x_j(t)| \leqslant K_5K_6^{j-1}$, which shows that the series is convergent for $| \mu |$ sufficiently small. With this the proof is complete.

We consider now the case of autonomous systems of the form

$$\frac{dx(t)}{dt} = f[x(t), x(t-\tau), \mu]. \tag{67}$$

We suppose that for $\mu = 0$ system (67) admits a periodic solution $p(t)$ with period $\omega_0 > \tau$. Let

$$A(t) = f'_u[p(t), p(t-\tau), 0], \qquad B(t) = f'_v[p(t), p(t-\tau), 0].$$

The system

$$\frac{dz(t)}{dt} = A(t)z(t) + B(t)z(t-\tau) \tag{68}$$

is the variational system corresponding to the solution $p(t)$; it has periodic coefficients of period ω_0 and admits in any case the solutions $z_0(t) = dp(t)/dt$. Indeed, from

$$\frac{dp(t)}{dt} = f[p(t), p(t-\tau), 0]$$

we obtain

$$\frac{d}{dt}\frac{dp}{dt} = f'_u[p(t), p(t-\tau), 0]\frac{dp(t)}{dt} + f'_v[p(t), p(t-\tau), 0]\frac{dp(t-\tau)}{dt}.$$

Lemma. *Let us suppose that system* (68) *does not admit solutions of the form* $z_1(t) + tz_0(t)$, *where* $z_1(t)$ *is periodic of period* ω_0. *Then*

$$\int_0^{\omega_0} q(t)G(t)dt \neq 0,$$

where $q(t)$ *is a periodic solution of the adjoint system of system* (68) *and*

$$\begin{aligned} G(t) &= f[p(t), p(t-\tau), 0] + \tau B(t)f[p(t-\tau), p(t-2\tau), 0] \\ &= z_0(t) + \tau B(t)z_0(t-\tau). \end{aligned}$$

Conversely, if

$$\int_0^{\omega_0} q(t)G(t)dt \neq 0$$

for a periodic solution of the adjoint system, then system (68) *does not admit solutions of the considered form.*

Proof. Let us suppose that

$$\int_0^{\omega_0} q(t)G(t)dt = 0$$

for all periodic solutions of the adjoint system of system (68). Let $z(t)$ be a solution of system (68) and $z_1(t) = z(t) - tz_0(t)$. We have

$$\begin{aligned} \frac{dz_1(t)}{dt} &= \frac{dz(t)}{dt} - z_0(t) - t\frac{dz_0(t)}{dt} \\ &= A(t)z(t) + B(t)z(t-\tau) - z_0(t) - tA(t)z_0(t) - tB(t)z_0(t-\tau) \\ &= A(t)[z(t) - tz_0(t)] + B(t)[z(t-\tau) - (t-\tau)z_0(t-\tau)] \\ &\quad - z_0(t) - \tau B(t)z_0(t-\tau) \\ &= A(t)z_1(t) + B(t)z_1(t-\tau) - G(t). \end{aligned}$$

Since

$$\int_0^{\omega_0} q(t)G(t)dt = 0$$

for all periodic solutions of period ω_0 of the adjoint system of system (68), on the basis of Theorem 4.23 there exists a solution $z_1(t)$ periodic of period ω_0, hence a solution $z(t)$ of system (68) of the form $z_1(t) + tz_0(t)$, which we have excluded. We see likewise that if system (68) admits solutions of this form, the integral would be zero for all the periodic solutions of period ω_0 of the adjoint system of system (68). The lemma is thus proved.

Theorem 4.28. *If system* (68) *does not admit periodic solutions of period* ω_0 *independent of* $z_0(t)$, *nor solutions of the form* $z_1(t) + tz_0(t)$, *with* $z_1(t)$ *periodic of period* ω_0, *then for* $|\mu|$ *sufficiently small system* (67) *admits a periodic solution* $x(t, \mu)$ *of period* $\omega(\mu)$ *such that*

$$\lim_{\mu\to 0} \omega(\mu) = \omega_0, \qquad \lim_{\mu\to 0} x(t, \mu) = p(t).$$

Proof. Let $\omega(\mu) = \omega_0(1 + \mu\alpha(\mu))$, $t = s[1 + \mu\alpha(\mu)]$, $y(s, \mu) = x[s(1 + \mu\alpha), \mu]$. We have

$$\begin{aligned}\frac{d}{ds} y(s, \mu) &= \frac{d}{dt} x[s(1 + \mu\alpha), \mu](1 + \mu\alpha)\\ &= (1 + \mu\alpha)f(x[s(1 + \mu\alpha), \mu], x[s(1 + \mu\alpha) - \tau, \mu], \mu)\\ &= (1 + \mu\alpha)f[y(s, \mu), y(s - \theta(\mu), \mu), \mu], \qquad \theta(\mu) = \frac{\tau}{1 + \mu\alpha(\mu)}.\end{aligned}$$

If x is periodic of period $\omega(\mu)$, y will be periodic of period ω_0 and conversely. We have

$$\frac{d}{ds} y(s, \mu) = f[y(s, \mu), y(s - \theta, \mu), \mu] + \mu\alpha f[y(s, \mu), y(s - \theta, \mu), \mu]. \quad (69)$$

We put $y(s, \mu) = p(s) + \mu z(s, \mu)$. We obtain

$$\begin{aligned}\frac{d}{ds} p(s) + \mu \frac{d}{ds} z(s, \mu) &= f[p(s) + \mu z(s, \mu), p(s - \theta) + \mu z(s - \theta, \mu), \mu]\\ &\quad + \mu\alpha f[p(s) + \mu z(s, \mu), p(s - \theta) + \mu z(s - \theta, \mu), \mu]\\ &= f[p(s), p(s - \theta), 0] + \mu f_u'[p(s), p(s - \theta), 0]z(s, \mu)\\ &\quad + \mu f_v'[p(s), p(s - \theta), 0]z(s - \theta, \mu) + \mu f_\mu'[p(s), p(s - \theta), 0]\\ &\quad + \mu\alpha f[p(s), p(s - \theta), 0] + \mu O(\mu)\end{aligned}$$

$$
\begin{aligned}
&= f[p(s), p(s-\tau), 0] + \mu f'_u[p(s), p(s-\tau), 0]z(s, \mu) \\
&\quad + \mu f'_v[p(s), p(s-\tau), 0]z(s-\theta, \mu) \\
&\quad + \mu f'_\mu[p(s), p(s-\tau), 0] + \mu\alpha f[p(s), p(s-\tau), 0] \\
&\quad + f[p(s), p(s-\theta), 0] - f[p(s), p(s-\tau), 0] + \mu O(\mu).
\end{aligned}
$$

We have

$$
\begin{aligned}
&f[p(s), p(s-\theta), 0] - f[p(s), p(s-\tau), 0] \\
&\quad = f'_v[p(s), p(s-\tau), 0][p(s-\theta) - p(s-\tau)] + O(\mu^2) \\
&\quad = f'_v[p(s), p(s-\tau), 0]\dot{p}(s-\tau)(\tau-\theta) + O(\mu^2) \\
&\quad = \frac{\mu\alpha\tau}{1+\mu\alpha} f'_v[p(s), p(s-\tau), 0] f[p(s-\tau), p(s-2\tau), 0] + O(\mu^2).
\end{aligned}
$$

We obtain

$$
\begin{aligned}
\frac{dz(s, \mu)}{ds} &= A(s)z(s, \mu) + B(s)z(s-\theta, \mu) + F(s) \\
&\quad + \alpha(\mu)G(s) + \mu H(s, z(s, \mu), z(s-\theta, \mu), \mu), \qquad (70)
\end{aligned}
$$

where we have set

$$
F(s) = f'_\mu[p(s), p(s-\tau), 0].
$$

We consider the system

$$
\dot{z}(s) = A(s)z(s) + B(s)z(s-\tau) + F(s) + \alpha_0 G(s). \qquad (71)
$$

The condition that this system has a periodic solution of period ω_0 is that

$$
\int_0^{\omega_0} q(s)[F(s) + \alpha_0 G(s)]ds = 0.
$$

According to the hypothesis in the statement and by virtue of the lemma, it follows that

$$
\int_0^{\omega_0} q(s)G(s)ds \neq 0.
$$

This condition allows the unique determination of α_0. Let α_0 be so determined and $z_0(s)$ be the periodic solution of system (71) which admits the estimate

$$
|z_0(s)| \leqslant K(\sup|F| + \alpha_0 |\sup|G|).
$$

We form the system

$$\dot{z}(s) = A(s)z(s) + B(s)z(s-\tau) + F(s) + \alpha_1(\mu)G(s) + B(s)[z_0(s-\theta_0) - z_0(s-\tau)] + \mu H_0[s, z_0(s), z_0(s-\theta_0), \mu] \quad (72)$$

where $\theta_0 = \tau/(1+\mu\alpha_0)$ and H_0 is what H becomes when α is replaced by α_0. System (72) admits a periodic solution of period ω_0 if and only if

$$\int_0^{\omega_0} q(s)\{F(s) + \alpha_1 G(s) + B(s)[z_0(s-\theta_0) - z_0(s-\tau)] + \mu H_0[s, z_0(s), z_0(s-\theta_0), \mu]\}ds = 0.$$

Since

$$\int_0^{\omega_0} q(s)G(s)ds \neq 0,$$

this equation allows the unique determination of $\alpha_1(\mu)$ such that $\lim_{\mu\to 0}\alpha_1(\mu) = \alpha_0$. We suppose $\alpha_1(\mu)$ so determined and let $z_1(s, \mu)$ be the corresponding periodic solution uniquely chosen as above. We form the system

$$\dot{z}(s) = A(s)z(s) + B(s)z(s-\tau) + F(s) + \alpha_2(\mu)G(s) + B(s)[z_1(s-\theta_1, \mu) - z_1(s-\tau, \mu)] + \mu H_1[s, z_1(s, \mu), z_1(s-\theta_1, \mu), \mu],$$

where $\theta_1 = \tau/(1+\mu\alpha_1)$ and H_1 is what H becomes when α is replaced by α_1.

As above, from the condition that this system admits a periodic solution of period ω_0, $\alpha_2(\mu)$ is determined and then the periodic solution $z_2(s, \mu)$ is chosen. In general, we consider the system

$$\dot{z}(s) = A(s)z(s) + B(s)z(s-\tau) + F(s) + \alpha_n(\mu)G(s) + B(s)[z_{n-1}(s-\theta_{n-1}, \mu) - z_{n-1}(s-\tau, \mu)] + \mu H_{n-1}[s, z_{n-1}(s, \mu), z_{n-1}(s-\theta_{n-1}, \mu), \mu],$$

where $\theta_{n-1} = \tau/(1+\mu\alpha_{n-1})$ and H_{n-1} is what H becomes when α is replaced by α_{n-1}. The condition that this system admits a periodic solution allows the determination of $\alpha_n(\mu)$, and then we choose the periodic solution $z_n(s, \mu)$. If we prove that the sequences $\alpha_n(\mu)$ and $z_n(s, \mu)$ converge uniformly for $|\mu| \leqslant \mu_0$ and if

$$\alpha(\mu) = \lim_{n\to\infty}\alpha_n(\mu), \qquad z(s, \mu) = \lim_{n\to\infty} z_n(s, \mu), \qquad \theta(\mu) = \lim_{n\to\infty}\theta_n(\mu),$$

then $z(s, \mu)$ verifies system (70). The computations performed show that $y(s, \mu) = p(s) + \mu z(s, \mu)$ is a periodic solution of period ω_0 of system (69) and $x(t, \mu)$, obtained from $y(s, \mu)$ by putting $s = t/(1 + \mu\alpha)$, will be a periodic solution of period $\omega(\mu) = \omega_0(1 + \mu\alpha)$ of system (67) which for $\mu \to 0$ tends to $p(t)$. In this way, to prove the theorem, it remains to prove the convergence of the successive approximations. We have

$$\frac{d}{ds}[z_{n+1}(s, \mu) - z_n(s, \mu)] = A(s)[z_{n+1}(s, \mu) - z_n(s, \mu)]$$
$$+ B(s)[z_{n+1}(s - \tau, \mu) - z_n(s - \tau, \mu)] + [\alpha_{n+1}(\mu) - \alpha_n(\mu)]G(s)$$
$$+ B(s)[z_n(s - \theta_n, \mu) - z_{n-1}(s - \theta_{n-1}, \mu)]$$
$$+ B(s)[z_{n-1}(s - \tau, \mu) - z_n(s - \tau, \mu)] + \mu H_n - \mu H_{n-1}.$$

Let

$$b_n = \sup| z_{n+1}(s, \mu) - z_n(s, \mu)|,$$
$$a_n = \sup| \alpha_{n+1}(\mu) - \alpha_n(\mu)|.$$

It follows then that

$$b_n \leqslant M_0 a_n + | \mu | M_1 b_{n-1} + | \mu | M_2 b_{n-1} + | \mu | M_3 a_{n-1},$$

hence

$$b_n \leqslant M_0 a_n + | \mu | M(b_{n-1} + a_{n-1}).$$

Further, from

$$\int_0^{\omega_0} q(s)\{F(s) + \alpha_{n+1}G(s) + B(s)[z_n(s - \theta_n, \mu) - z_n(s - \tau, \mu)] + \mu H_n\}ds = 0,$$

$$\int_0^{\omega_0} q(s)\{F(s) + \alpha_n G(s) + B(s)[z_{n-1}(s - \theta_{n-1}, \mu) - z_{n-1}(s - \tau, \mu)] + \mu H_{n-1}\}ds = 0,$$

we obtain

$$(\alpha_{n+1} - \alpha_n) \int_0^{\omega_0} q(s)G(s)ds = \int_0^{\omega_0} q(s)B(s)[z_n(s - \theta_n, \mu) - z_{n-1}(s - \theta_{n-1}, \mu)$$
$$- z_n(s - \tau, \mu) + z_{n-1}(s - \tau, \mu)]ds + \mu \int_0^{\omega_0} q(s)[H_n - H_{n-1}]ds.$$

From here we obtain

$$a_n \leqslant M_4 | \mu | b_{n-1} + M_5 | \mu | b_{n-1} + M_6 | \mu | a_{n-1};$$

hence

$$a_n \leqslant |\mu| M(b_{n-1} + a_{n-1}).$$

Finally we obtain

$$b_n + a_n \leqslant |\mu| M'(b_{n-1} + a_{n-1}),$$

which shows that if $|\mu|$ is small enough, uniform convergence is achieved.

The estimations performed have supposed previous estimates of the successive approximations in order to assure that these approximations do not leave a certain domain, with respect to which the constants M apearing in these estimates are calculated. These previous estimates are immediately obtained by induction. The theorem is thus proved.

Continuing the study of systems of the form (67) we will suppose that for $\mu = 0$ the system admits a family of periodic solutions $p(t, c_1, ..., c_k)$ of period $\omega_0(c_1, c_2, ..., c_k) > \tau$. We will make the hypothesis that $\omega_0(c_1, c_2, ..., c_k)$ admits continuous partial derivatives. Where there is no danger of confusion, we will write c instead of $(c_1, c_2, ..., c_k)$.

Let

$$A(t, c) = f'_u[p(t, c), p(t-\tau, c), 0], \; B(t, c) = f'_v[p(t, c), p(t-\tau, c), 0].$$

We consider the system

$$\frac{dz(t)}{dt} = A(t, c)z(t) + B(t, c)z(t-\tau). \tag{73}$$

We have

$$\frac{d}{dt} p(t, c) = f[p(t, c), p(t-\tau, c), 0],$$

$$\frac{d}{dt}\frac{d}{dt} p(t, c) = f'_u[p(t, c), p(t-\tau, c), 0]\frac{dp(t, c)}{dt}$$
$$+ f'_v[p(t, c), p(t-\tau, c), 0]\frac{dp(t-\tau, c)}{dt}$$
$$= A(t, c)\frac{d}{dt}p(t, c) + B(t, c)\frac{d}{dt}p(t-\tau, c);$$

hence $(d/dt)p(t, c)$ is a solution of system (73) and this solution is periodic of period $\omega_0(c)$.

Similarly,

$$\frac{d}{dt}\frac{\partial p}{\partial c_i} = \frac{\partial}{\partial c_i}\frac{dp}{dt} = \frac{\partial}{\partial c_i} f[p(t, c), p(t-\tau, c), 0]$$
$$= A(t, c)\frac{\partial p(t, c)}{\partial c_i} + B(t, c)\frac{\partial p(t-\tau, c)}{\partial c_i};$$

hence the $\partial p/\partial c_1$ are solutions of system (73). If $\omega_0(c)$ is not constant, these solutions are not periodic.

In what follows we shall consider the case where $\omega_0(c)$ *is not constant.* Let c^* be a fixed value of c. We consider the function

$$p\left[\frac{\omega_0(c)}{\omega_0(c^*)}t, c\right]$$

which is periodic of period $\omega_0(c^*)$. Its derivatives with respect to c_i in point c^* will be periodic functions of period $\omega_0(c^*)$. We will denote these derivatives by $\varphi_i(t, c^*)$.

We have

$$\varphi_i(t, c^*) = \frac{\partial p\left[\dfrac{\omega_0(c^*)}{\omega_0(c^*)}t, c^*\right]}{\partial c_i} + \frac{1}{\omega(c^*)}\frac{dp\left[\dfrac{\omega_0(c^*)}{\omega_0(c^*)}t, c^*\right]}{dt}\frac{\partial \omega_0(c^*)}{\partial c_i}t;$$

hence

$$\frac{\partial p(t, c^*)}{dc_i} = \varphi_i(t, c^*) - \frac{t}{\omega_0(c^*)}\frac{\partial \omega_0(c^*)}{\partial c_i}\frac{dp(t, c^*)}{dt}.$$

We consider the function

$$z(t) = t\frac{dp(t, c^*)}{dt} = tf[p(t, c^*), p(t-\tau, c^*), 0].$$

We have

$$\frac{dz}{dt} = f[p(t, c^*), p(t-\tau, c^*), 0] + tA(t, c^*)\frac{dp(t, c^*)}{dt} + tB(t, c^*)\frac{dp(t-\tau, c^*)}{dt};$$

hence

$$\frac{dz}{dt} = A(t, c^*)z(t) + B(t, c^*)z(t-\tau) + f[p(t, c^*), p(t-\tau, c^*), 0] + \tau B(t, c^*)f[p(t-\tau, c^*), p(t-2\tau, c^*), 0].$$

Setting

$$G(t, c^*) = f[p(t, c^*), p(t-\tau, c^*), 0] + \tau B(t, c^*)f[p(t-\tau, c^*), p(t-2\tau, c^*), 0]$$

we obtain

$$\frac{dz}{dt} = A(t, c^*)z(t) + B(t, c^*)z(t-\tau) + G(t, c^*). \tag{74}$$

We suppose that for the index i, $\partial\omega_0(c^*)/\partial c_i \neq 0$. Then

$$\frac{\omega_0(c^*)}{\partial\omega_0(c^*)/\partial c_i}\varphi_i(t, c^*) = z(t) + \frac{\partial p(t, c^*)}{\partial c_i}\frac{\omega_0(c^*)}{\partial\omega_0(c^*)/\partial c_i}.$$

However,

$$\frac{\partial p(t, c^*)}{\partial c_i} \frac{\omega_0(c^*)}{\partial \omega_0(c^*)/\partial c_i}$$

is a solution of system (73), with $c = c^*$, and z verifies system (74); it follows that

$$\frac{\omega_0(c^*)}{\partial \omega_0(c^*)/\partial c_i} \varphi_i(t, c^*)$$

verifies system (74).

Since $\varphi_i(t, c^*)$ is periodic of period $\omega_0(c^*)$, it follows that the system (74) admits periodic solutions of period $\omega_0(c^*)$. On the other hand,

$$\frac{\partial p(t, c)}{\partial c_1} = \varphi_1(t, c) - \frac{t}{\omega_0(c)} \frac{\partial \omega_0(c)}{\partial c_1} \frac{d}{dt} p(t, c),$$

$$\frac{\partial p(t, c)}{\partial c_j} = \varphi_j(t, c) - \frac{t}{\omega_0(c)} \frac{\partial \omega_0(c)}{\partial c_j} \frac{d}{dt} p(t, c).$$

It follows that

$$\frac{\partial \omega_0(c)}{\partial c_j} \frac{\partial p(t, c)}{\partial c_1} - \frac{\partial \omega_0(c)}{\partial c_1} \frac{\partial p(t, c)}{\partial c_j} = \frac{\partial \omega_0(c)}{\partial c_j} \varphi_1(t, c) - \frac{\partial \omega_0(c)}{\partial c_1} \varphi_j(t, c),$$

and since $\varphi_j(t, c)$ are periodic of period $\omega_0(c)$, the function in the first member is periodic of period $\omega_0(c)$. It follows that for all c system (73) admits at least the periodic solutions of period $\omega_0(c)$,

$$\frac{d}{dt} p(t, c), \frac{\partial \omega_0}{\partial c_j} \frac{\partial p(t, c)}{\partial c_1} - \frac{\partial \omega_0}{\partial c_1} \frac{\partial p(t, c)}{\partial c_j} \qquad (j = 2, 3, ..., k).$$

The system adjoint to system (73) will likewise admit k periodic solutions of period $\omega_0(c)$, which we will denote by $\psi_j(t, c), j = 1, 2, ..., k$.

Since system (74) admits periodic solutions of period $\omega_0(c^*)$, it follows, on the basis of Theorem 4.23, that

$$\int_0^{\omega_0(c^*)} \psi_j(s, c^*) G(s, c^*) ds = 0 \qquad (j = 1, 2, ..., k).$$

Theorem 4.29. *If for* $|\mu| < \mu_0$ *system* (67) *admits a periodic solution* $x(t, c^*, \mu)$ *of period* $\omega(c^*, \mu)$ *such that*

$$\lim_{\mu \to 0} x(t, c^*, \mu) = p(t, c^*), \qquad \lim_{\mu \to 0} \omega(c^*, \mu) = \omega_0(c^*),$$

then

$$P_j(c^*) = 0,$$

where

$$P_j(c) \equiv \int_0^{\omega_0(c)} \psi_j(t, c) f'_\mu[p(t, c), p(t - \tau, c), 0]dt, \qquad (j = 1, 2, ..., k).$$

Proof. Let $\omega(c^*, \mu) = \omega_0(c^*)[1 + \mu\alpha(c^*, \mu)]$. We perform the change of variable $t = s[1 + \mu\alpha(c^*, \mu)]$. We set

$$y(s, c^*, \mu) = x[s(1 + \mu\alpha), c^*, \mu].$$

We have

$$\frac{d}{ds} y(s, c^*, \mu) = (1 + \mu\alpha) f[y(s, c^*, \mu), y(s - \theta(c^*, \mu), c^*, \mu)],$$

where

$$\theta(c^*, \mu) = \frac{\tau}{1 + \mu\alpha(c^*, \mu)}.$$

We put

$$y(s, c^*, \mu) = p(s, c^*) + \mu z(s, c^*, \mu).$$

We obtain

$$\begin{aligned}
&\frac{dp(s, c^*)}{ds} + \mu \frac{d}{ds} z(s, c^*, \mu) \\
&= (1 + \mu\alpha) f[p(s, c^*) + \mu z(s, c^*, \mu), p(s - \theta, c^*) + \mu z(s - \theta, c^*, \mu), \mu] \\
&= (1 + \mu\alpha) f[p(s, c^*), p(s - \tau, c^*), 0] \\
&\quad + (1 + \mu\alpha)\{ f[p(s, c^*) + \mu z(s, c^*, \mu), p(s - \theta, c^*) + \mu z(s - \theta, c^*, \mu), \mu] \\
&\quad - f[p(s, c^*), p(s - \tau, c^*), 0]\} \\
&= (1 + \mu\alpha) f[p(s, c^*), p(s - \tau, c^*), 0] \\
&\quad + (1 + \mu\alpha)\{A(s, c^*)\mu z(s, c^*, \mu) \\
&\quad + B(s, c^*)[\mu z(s - \theta, c^*, \mu) + p(s - \theta, c^*) - p(s - \tau, c^*)] \\
&\quad + \mu f'_\mu[p(s, c^*), p(s - \tau, c^*), 0] + O(\mu^2)\} \\
&= (1 + \mu\alpha) f[p(s, c^*), p(s - \tau, c^*), 0] + \mu(1 + \mu\alpha) A(s, c^*) z(s, c^*, \mu) \\
&\quad + \mu(1 + \mu\alpha) B(s, c^*) z(s - \theta, c^*, \mu) + (1 + \mu\alpha) \frac{\mu\alpha\tau}{1 + \mu\alpha} B(s, c^*) \frac{d}{dt} p(s - \tau, c^*) \\
&\quad + \mu f'_\mu[p(s, c^*), p(s - \tau, c^*), 0] + O(\mu^2).
\end{aligned}$$

From here we obtain

$$\begin{aligned}
\frac{d}{ds} z(s, c^*, \mu) = {} & A(s, c^*) z(s, c^*, \mu) + B(s, c^*) z(s - \theta, c^*, \mu) \\
& + f'_\mu[p(s, c^*), p(s - \tau, c^*), 0] + \alpha f[p(s, c^*), p(s - \tau, c^*), 0] \\
& + \alpha\tau B(s, c^*) f[p(s - \tau, c^*), p(s - 2\tau, c^*), 0] + O(\mu).
\end{aligned}$$

Setting

$$F(s, c^*) = f'_\mu[p(s, c^*), p(s - \tau, c^*), 0]$$

we have

$$\frac{d}{ds} z(s, c^*, \mu) = A(s, c^*)z(s, c^*, \mu) + B(s, c^*)z(s - \tau, c^*, \mu) + F(s, c^*)$$
$$+ \alpha G(s, c^*) + \mu H[s, z(s, c^*, \mu), z(s - \theta, c^*, \mu), \mu]. \quad (75)$$

If $x(t, \mu)$ is of period $\omega(c^*, \mu)$, then $y(s, c^*, \mu)$ is periodic of period $\omega_0(c^*)$; hence $z(s, c^*, \mu)$ is periodic of period $\omega_0(c^*)$. Since system (75) admits periodic solutions of period $\omega_0(c^*)$, it follows, on the basis of Theorem 4.23, that

$$\int_0^{\omega_0(c^*)} \psi_j(s, c^*)\{F(s, c^*) + \alpha G(s, c^*) + \mu H\} ds = 0.$$

We have seen, however, that

$$\int_0^{\omega_0(c^*)} \psi_j(s, c^*)G(s, c^*) ds = 0;$$

hence

$$\int_0^{\omega_0(c^*)} \psi_j(s, c^*)\{F(s, c^*) + \mu H\} ds = 0.$$

Since this relation is verified for all μ with $|\mu| < \mu_0$, it follows that

$$\int_0^{\omega_0(c^*)} \psi_j(s, c^*)F(s, c^*) ds = 0;$$

hence $P_j(c^*) = 0$, and the theorem is thus proved.

To obtain certain sufficient conditions of existence of the periodic solutions, we use a method given by S. N. Šimanov. Let $z_1, z_2, \ldots, z_k$ be the periodic solutions of period $\omega_0(c^*)$ of system (73) for $c = c^*$. *We will suppose that system* (73) *does not admit periodic solutions of period* $\omega_0(c^*)$ *independent of these nor solutions of the form* $z_0(t) + t \sum_{j=1}^{k} \gamma_j z_j(t, c^*)$ *where* z_0 *is periodic of period* $\omega_0(c^*)$.‡ This last hypothesis is equivalent to the fact that

$$\det \int_0^{\omega_0(c^*)} \psi_j(s, c^*)[z_i(s, c^*) + \tau B(s, c^*)z_i(s - \tau, c^*)] ds \neq 0.$$

‡ Observe that this condition is not fulfilled in the case considered above when $\omega_0(c)$ is not a constant.

Indeed, the function $z(t) = t \sum_j \gamma_j z_j$ verifies the system

$$\frac{dz(t)}{dt} = A(t, c^*)z(t) + B(t, c^*)z(t - \tau) + \sum_j \gamma_j[z_j(t, c^*) + \tau B(t, c^*)z_j(t - \tau, c^*)]. \tag{76}$$

If the determinant is zero, γ_i may be chosen such that

$$\sum_i \int_0^{\omega_0 c(*)} \psi_j(s, c^*)[z_i(s, c^*) + \tau B(s, c^*)z_i(s - \tau, c^*)]ds\, \gamma_i = 0;$$

hence system (76) admits a solution $z_0(t)$ periodic of period $\omega_0(c^*)$. Then $z_0(t) - t \sum_j \gamma_j z_j$ would be a solution of system (73). Conversely, if there exists a solution of this form of system (73), the function $z_0(t)$ verifies system (76); if system (76) has a periodic solution, there exists γ_j for which the system of linear equations has solutions; hence the determinant is zero.

Let us now consider the auxiliary system

$$\begin{aligned}\frac{dz(s)}{ds} = {} & A(s, c^*)z(s) + B(s, c^*)z(s - \tau) + B(s, c^*)[z(s - \theta) - z(s - \tau)] \\ & + F(s, c^*) + \alpha(c^*, \mu)G(s, c^*) + \mu H[s, z(s), z(s - \theta), \mu] \\ & + \sum_{j=1}^{k} W_j[z_j(s, c^*) + \tau B(s, c^*)z_j(s - \tau, c^*)].\end{aligned} \tag{77}$$

We prove that a procedure of successive approximations can be considered which allows the simultaneous determination of the constants W_j and of a periodic solution $z(s, M_1, ..., M_k, \alpha, \mu)$ of system (77) corresponding to a solution $\sum M_j z_j$ of system (73). If $M_j(\mu)$ and $\alpha_j(\mu)$ can be chosen such that for the corresponding solution we have $W_j = 0, j = 1, ..., k$, this solution verifies system (75) and leads to a periodic solution of period $\omega(c^*, \mu)$ of system (67). We choose

$$z^0 = M_1 z_1 + \cdots + M_k z_k, \qquad W_j^0 = 0$$

and consider the system

$$\begin{aligned}\frac{dz(s)}{ds} = {} & A(s, c^*)z(s) + B(s, c^*)z(s - \tau) + B(s, c^*)[z^0(s - \theta) - z^0(s - \tau)] \\ & + F(s, c^*) + \alpha(c^*, \mu)G(s, c^*) \\ & + \mu H[s, z^0(s), z^0(s - \theta), \mu] + \sum_j W_j \chi_j(s, c^*),\end{aligned}$$

where we have set

$$\chi_j(s, c^*) = z_j(s, c^*) + \tau B(s, c^*) z_j(s - \tau, c^*).$$

This system admits periodic solutions of period $\omega_0(c^*)$ if and only if

$$\int_0^{\omega_0(c^*)} \psi_j(s, c^*)\{B(s, c^*)[z^0(s - \theta) - z^0(s - \tau)] + F(s, c^*) + \mu H + \sum W_i \chi_i\} ds = 0.$$

Since

$$\det \int_0^{\omega_0(c^*)} \psi_j \chi_i \, ds \neq 0,$$

these conditions permit the unique determination of constants W_i^1 and then of the periodic solution

$$z^1(s) = M_1 z_1 \cdots M_k z_k + z^{1*}(s).$$

The procedure continues; we form the system

$$\begin{aligned}\frac{dz(s)}{ds} = {} & A(s, c^*) z(s) + B(s, c^*) z(s - \tau) \\ & + B(s, c^*)[z^{n-1}(s - \theta) - z^{n-1}(s - \tau)] + F(s, c^*) + \alpha(c^*, \mu) G(s, c^*) \\ & + \mu H[s, z^{n-1}(s), z^{n-1}(s - \theta), \mu] + \sum W_i \chi_i \, .\end{aligned}$$

W_i^n is determined such that this system admits periodic solutions of period $\omega_0(c^*)$ and we chose the periodic solution

$$z^n(s) = M_1 z_1 \cdots M_k z_k + z^{n*}(s),$$

the solution $z^{n*}(s)$ being determined such that

$$| z^{n*}(s)| < LK,$$

where L depends on the homogeneous system (73) and K is the upper bound of the free term. The constants W_i^n depend on μ and it is obvious that the $W_i^n(0)$ are given by the system

$$\int_0^{\omega_0(c^*)} \psi_j(s, c^*) F(s, c^*) ds + \sum_i W_i \int_0^{\omega_0(c^*)} \psi_j \chi_i \, ds = 0.$$

If we suppose that the condition $P_j(c^*) = 0, j = 1, \ldots, k$ is satisfied, we obtain $W_i^n(0) = 0$ for all n, We shall further write $W_i^n(\mu) = \mu \overline{W}_i^n(\mu)$

and $z^{n*}(s) = z^*(s) + z^{n**}(s)$, where $z^*(s)$ is the periodic solution of the system

$$\frac{dz(s)}{ds} = A(s, c^*)z(s) + B(s, c^*)z(s-\tau) + F(s, c^*) + \alpha(c^*, \mu)G(s, c^*) \quad (78)$$

chosen such that

$$|z^*(s)| \leqslant L \sup\{|F(s, c^*)| + |\alpha(c^*, \mu)|\,|G(s, c^*)|\}.$$

We have

$$z^n(s) = \sum_j M_j z_j + z^*(s) + \mu z^{n**}(s).$$

The function $\mu z^{n**}(s)$ verifies the system

$$\frac{dz(s)}{ds} = A(s, c^*)z(s) + B(s, c^*)z(s-\tau) + B(s, c^*)[z_{n-1}(s-\theta) - z_{n-1}(s-\tau)] + \mu H_{n-1} + \mu \sum \overline{W}_j^n \chi_j,$$

where we have written H_{n-1} for what H becomes when z is replaced by z^{n-1}. Let $u_n = z^{(n+1)**}(s) - z^{n**}(s)$. We have

$$\mu \frac{du_n}{ds} = A(s, c^*)\mu u_n(s) + B(s, c^*)\mu u_n(s-\tau) + B(s, c^*)[z^n(s-\theta) - z^{n-1}(s-\theta)] - B(s, c^*)[z^n(s-\tau) - z^{n-1}(s-\tau)] + \mu(H_n - H_{n-1}) + \mu \sum_j (\overline{W}_j^{(n+1)} - \overline{W}_j^{(n)})\chi_j.$$

However,

$$z^n(s-\theta) - z^{n-1}(s-\theta) = \mu z^{n**}(s-\theta) - \mu z^{n-1**}(s-\theta) = \mu u_{n-1}(s-\theta).$$

We obtain

$$\mu \frac{du_n}{ds} = \mu A(s, c^*)u_n(s) + \mu B(s, c^*)u_n(s-\tau) + \mu B(s, c^*)u_{n-1}(s-\theta) - \mu B(s, c^*)u_{n-1}(s-\tau) + \mu(H_n - H_{n-1}) + \mu \sum_j (\overline{W}_j^{(n+1)} - \overline{W}_j^n)\chi_j.$$

Hence

$$\frac{du_n}{ds} = A(s, c^*)u_n(s) + B(s, c^*)u_n(s-\tau) + B(s, c^*)[u_{n-1}(s-\theta) - u_{n-1}(s-\tau) + H_n - H_{n-1} + \sum_j [\overline{W}_j^{n-1} - \overline{W}_j^n]\chi_j.$$

Let $b_n = \sup | u_n(s)|$. We have

$$H_n = H[s, z^n(s), z^{n-1}(s-\theta), \mu], \qquad H_{n-1} = H[s, z^{n-1}(s), z^{n-1}(s-\theta), \mu].$$

Hence

$$| H_n - H_{n-1} | \leqslant L_1 | z^n(s) - z^{n-1}(s)| + L_2 | z^n(s-\theta) - z^{n-1}(s-\theta)|$$
$$= | \mu | L_1 | u_{n-1}(s)| + | \mu | L_2 | u_{n-1}(s-\theta)| \leqslant | \mu | L b_{n-1} .$$

Further,

$$u_{n-1}(s-\theta) - u_{n-1}(s-\tau) = \int_{s-\tau}^{s-\theta} \dot{u}_{n-1}(t)dt$$
$$= \int_{s-\tau}^{s-\theta} \{A(t, c^*)u_{n-1}(t) + B(t, c^*)u_{n-1}(t-\tau)$$
$$+ B(t, c^*)[u_{n-2}(t-\theta) - u_{n-2}(t-\tau)]$$
$$+ (H_{n-1} - H_{n-2}) + \sum_j (\overline{W}_j^n - \overline{W}_j^{n-1})\chi_j\}dt.$$

Hence

$$| u_{n-1}(s-\theta) - u_{n-1}(s-\tau)| \leqslant | \mu | | \alpha\theta | (L_3 b_{n-1} + L_4 b_{n-2} + | \mu | L_5 b_{n-2} + | \mu | L_6 \beta_{n-1}),$$

where we have set

$$| \mu | \beta_n = \sup_j | \overline{W}_j^{n+1} - \overline{W}_j^n |.$$

We obtain

$$| u_n | \leqslant | \mu | L_7(b_{n-1} + b_{n-2} + | \mu | \beta_{n-1} + \beta_n)$$

and thus

$$b_n \leqslant | \mu | L_7(b_{n-1} + b_{n-2} + | \mu | \beta_{n-1} + \beta_n).$$

The constants $\mu \overline{W}_i^n$ are given by the system

$$\int_0^{\omega_0(c^*)} \psi_j(s, c^*)\{B(s, c^*)[z^{n-1}(s-\theta) - z^{n-1}(s-\tau)] + H_{n-1}\}ds$$
$$+ \mu \sum_i \int_0^{\omega_0(c^*)} \psi_j \chi_i \, ds \overline{W}_i^n = 0.$$

Setting $\overline{W}_i^{n+1} - \overline{W}_i^n = v_i^n$ we obtain

$$\mu \int_0^{\omega_0(c^*)} \psi_j \chi_i \, ds \, v_i^n + \int_0^{\omega_0(c^*)} \psi_j(s, c^*)B(s, c^*)[z^n(s-\theta) - z^{n-1}(s-\theta)$$
$$- z^n(s-\tau) + z^{n-1}(s-\tau)]ds + \mu \int_0^{\omega_0(c^*)} \psi_j(s, c^*)[H_n - H_{n-1}]ds = 0;$$

hence

$$\sum_i \int_0^{\omega_0(c^*)} \psi_j \chi_i \, ds \, v_i^n + \int_0^{\omega_0(c^*)} \psi_j(s, c^*) B(s, c^*)[u_{n-1}(s-\theta) - u_{n-1}(s-\tau)] ds$$

$$+ \int_0^{\omega_0(c^*)} \psi_i(s, c^*)[H_n - H_{n-1}] ds = 0.$$

From here follows

$$|\mu| \beta_n \leqslant L_8(|\mu| L_9(b_{n-1} + b_{n-2} + |\mu| \beta_{n-1}) + |\mu| L_{10} b_{n-1});$$

hence

$$\beta_n \leqslant L_{11}(b_{n-1} + b_{n-2}) + L_{12} |\mu| \beta_{n-1} .$$

The estimates obtained for b_n and β_n allow us to deduce for $|\mu|$ small enough the uniform convergence of the successive approximations. Passing at the limit in the relations which give $\overline{W}_i^n$ it follows that $\overline{W}_i$ verifies the relations

$$\int_0^{\omega_0(c^*)} \psi_j(s, c^*) \left\{ B(s, c^*) \frac{1}{\mu} [z(s-\theta) - z(s-\tau)] + H \right\} ds$$

$$+ \sum_i \int_0^{\omega_0(c^*)} \psi_j \chi_i \, ds \, \overline{W}_i = 0.$$

The condition that $\overline{W}_i$ is zero is written

$$\int_0^{\omega_0(c^*)} \psi_j(s, c^*) \left\{ B(s, c^*) \frac{1}{\mu} [z(s-\theta) - z(s-\tau)] + H \right\} ds = 0.$$

However,

$$z(s-\theta) - z(s-\tau) = \sum_i M_i[z_i(s-\theta, c^*) - z_i(s-\tau, c^*)]$$

$$+ z^*(s-\theta) - z^*(s-\tau) + \mu[z^{**}(s-\theta) - z^{**}(s-\tau)].$$

We obtain the condition

$$\int_0^{\omega_0(c^*)} \psi_j(s, c^*) \frac{1}{\mu} B(s, c^*) \left\{ \sum_i M_i[z_i(s-\theta, c^*) - z_i(s-\tau, c^*)] \right.$$

$$\left. + z^*(s-\theta) - z^*(s-\tau) \right\} ds$$

$$+ \int_0^{\omega_0(c^*)} \psi_j(s, c^*) \left\{ B(s, c^*)[z^{**}(s-\theta) - z^{**}(s-\tau)] + H \right\} ds = 0. \quad (79)$$

For $\mu \to 0$ this condition becomes

$$\int_0^{\omega_0(c^*)} \psi_j(s, c^*)\alpha(c^*, 0)\tau B(s, c^*) \left[\sum_i M_i \dot{z}_i(s - \tau, c^*) + \dot{z}^*(s - \tau)\right] ds$$
$$+ \int_0^{\omega_0(c^*)} \psi_j(s, c^*)H \, ds = 0,$$

where

$$H = H\left[s, \sum_i M_i z_i(s, c^*) + z^*(s), \sum_i M_i z_i(s - \tau, c^*) + z^*(s - \tau), 0\right],$$

and z^* is the periodic solution of system (78) in which $\alpha(c^*, \mu)$ is replaced by $\alpha(c^*, 0)$.

These conditions allow the determination of the constants $M_i(0)$ and $\alpha(c^*, 0)$, one of the constants $M_i(0)$ being taken zero. Once $M_i(0)$ and $\alpha(c^*, 0)$ are thus chosen, the conditions (79) permit the determination, on the basis of the implicit-function theorem (if the corresponding Jacobian is different from zero), of functions $M_i(\mu)$ and $\alpha(c^*, \mu)$ such that $\overline{W}_i(\mu) \equiv 0$. Then we obtain the solution

$$z(s, \mu) = \sum M_i(\mu) z_i(s, c^*) + z^*(s) + \mu z^{**}(s)$$

of system (75).

Putting

$$y(s, \mu) = p(s, c^*) + \mu z(s, \mu),$$

we have

$$x(t, \mu) = y\left[\frac{t}{1 + \mu\alpha}, \mu\right],$$

and we obtain a periodic solution of system (67) with the required properties.

4.14. Almost-Periodic Solutions for Quasi-Linear Systems with Time Lag

For quasi-linear systems with a small parameter we shall indicate a new method for proving the existence of periodic solutions. For the problem of periodic solutions this method leads to weaker results than those previously obtained, but its advantage consists in the fact that it can also be applied in the proof of the existence of almost-periodic solutions. The essential role is played by the following

Lemma. *We consider the system*

$$\frac{dx(t)}{dt} = \int_{-\infty}^{0} x(t+s)d_s\eta(t,s) + f(t), \tag{80}$$

where η has the properties discussed in Section 4.3 *and f is bounded for $t \geqslant 0$. If the trivial solution of the corresponding homogeneous system is uniformly asymptotically stable, then all the solutions of system* (80) *are bounded for* $t \geqslant 0$.

Proof. On the basis of Theorem 4.4′ there exists a functional $V[t, \varphi]$ defined for every $t \geqslant 0$ on the space of functions φ continuous in $[-\tau, 0]$ with the following properties:

1. $\| \varphi \|^2 \leqslant V[t, \varphi] < K_1 \| \varphi \|^2$,
2. $| V[t, \varphi_1] - V[t, \varphi_2] | \leqslant K_1(\| \varphi_1 \| + \| \varphi_2 \|) \| \varphi_1 - \varphi_2 \|$,
3. $\limsup_{h \to 0+} \dfrac{V[t+h, y(t+h+s; t_0, \varphi)] - V[t, y(t+s; t_0, \varphi)]}{h}$
$\leqslant - \| y(t+s; t_0, \varphi) \|^2$,

where $y(t; t_0, \varphi)$ is the solution of the homogeneous system which in $[t_0 - \tau, t_0]$ coincides with φ.

Taking into account formula (28′) we obtain the estimate

$$\| x(t+h+s; t, x(t+s; t_0, \varphi)) \| \leqslant L_1 \| x(t+s; t_0, \varphi) \| + hL_2M, \quad M = \sup |f(t)|$$

and

$$\| x(t+h+s; t, x(t+s; t_0, \varphi)) - y(t+h+s; t, x(t+s; t_0, \varphi)) \| \leqslant hL_2M.$$

It follows that

$$| V[t+h, x(t+h+s; t, x(t+s; t_0, \varphi))] - V[t+h, y(t+h+s; t, x(t+s; t_0, \varphi))] |$$
$$\leqslant K_1(2L_1 \| x(t+s; t_0, \varphi) \| + hL_2M) hL_2M;$$

hence

$$\limsup_{h \to 0+} \frac{V[t+h, x(t+h+s; t_0, \varphi)] - V[t, x(t+s; t_0, \varphi)]}{h}$$
$$\leqslant - \| x(t+s; t_0, \varphi) \|^2 + LM \| x(t+s; t_0, \varphi) \|.$$

Now let $x(t; 0, \varphi)$ be any solution for which the initial function verifies the relation $V[0, \varphi] < K_1L^2M^2$. We prove that for every $t \geqslant 0$ we have

$$V[t, x(t+s; 0, \varphi)] \leqslant K_1L^2M^2.$$

If this would not occur, there would exist a $t_1 > 0$ such that

$$V[t_1, x(t_1 + s; 0, \varphi)] > K_1 L^2 M^2$$

and thus there would exist $0 < t_2 < t_1$ such that

$$V[t_2, x(t_2 + s; 0, \varphi)] = K_1 L^2 M^2$$

and

$$V[t, x(t + s; 0, \varphi)] > K_1 L^2 M^2$$

for $t_2 < t \leqslant t_1$. From here follows

$$V[t_2 + h, x(t_2 + h + s; t_2, x(t_2 + s; 0, \varphi))] > V[t_2, x(t_2 + s; 0, \varphi)];$$

hence

$$\limsup_{h \to 0+} \frac{V[t_2 + h, x(t_2 + h + s; t_2, x(t_2 + s; 0, \varphi))] - V[t_2, x(t_2 + s; 0, \varphi)]}{h} \geqslant 0.$$

On the other hand,

$$\begin{aligned} \limsup_{h \to 0+} & \frac{V[t_2 + h, x(t_2 + h + s; 0, \varphi)] - V[t_2, x(t_2 + s; 0, \varphi)]}{h} \\ & \leqslant - \| x(t_2 + s; 0, \varphi)\|^2 + LM \| x(t_2 + s; 0, \varphi)\| \\ & = \| x(t_2 + s; 0, \varphi)\| (- \| x(t_2 + s; 0, \varphi)\| + LM). \end{aligned}$$

From

$$V[t_2, x(t_2 + s; 0, \varphi)] = K_1 L^2 M^2$$

and

$$V[t, \varphi] < K_1 \| \varphi \|^2$$

follows

$$K_1 L^2 M^2 < K_1 \| x(t_2 + s; 0, \varphi)\|^2;$$

hence

$$\| x(t_2 + s; 0, \varphi)\|^2 > L^2 M^2$$

or

$$\| x(t_2 + s; 0, \varphi)\| > LM.$$

We obtain

$$\limsup_{h \to 0+} \frac{V[t_2 + h, x(t_2 + h + s; 0, \varphi)] - V[t_2, x(t_2 + s; 0, \varphi)]}{h} < 0.$$

We have reached a contradiction; hence

$$V[t, x(t + s; 0, \varphi)] \leqslant K_1 L^2 M^2$$

for all $t \geqslant 0$. However, $V[t, \varphi] \geqslant \| \varphi \|^2$; hence

$$\| x(t+s; 0, \varphi)\| \leqslant \sqrt{K_1} LM = KM.$$

The lemma is thus proved.

The lemma asserts that if the trivial solution of a linear system is uniformly asymptotically stable, then the system satisfies the Perron condition. From here it follows as in the proof of Theorem 4.15 that $| X(t, t_0)| \leqslant M/(t - t_0)$. Using this fact we can now prove that there exists an $\alpha > 0$ such that $| X(t, t_0)| < Le^{-\alpha(t-t_0)}$.

Indeed, for $t \geqslant t_0 + (k+1)(T+\tau)$ we have

$$X(t, t_0) = X(t, t_0 + k(T+\tau) + \tau)X(t_0 + k(T+\tau) + \tau, t_0)$$
$$+ \int_{t_0+k(T+\tau)}^{t_0+k(T+\tau)+\tau} X(t, \alpha+\tau)B(\alpha+\tau)X(\alpha, t_0)d\alpha.$$

(To avoid technical complications we prove our assertion only for the simplest system with retarded argument.)

This formula allows us to obtain by induction the estimate

$$| X(t, t_0)| \leqslant \frac{M^k(1+\tau B)^{k-1}}{(T-\tau)^k}, \qquad (B = \sup| B(t)|,\ t_0 + k(T+\tau) \leqslant t).$$

We have then for $t \geqslant t_0 + (k+1)(T+\tau)$

$$|X(t, t_0)| \leqslant \frac{M}{T}\frac{M^k(1+\tau B)^{k-1}}{(T-\tau)^k} + \tau B \frac{M}{T-\tau}\frac{M^k(1+\tau B)^{k-1}}{(T-\tau)^k} < \frac{M^{k+1}(1+\tau B)^k}{(T-\tau)^{k+1}}.$$

For $k = 1$ the estimate is obvious.

We may choose $T = eM(1+\tau B) + \tau$ and obtain

$$| X(t, t_0)| < \frac{1}{e^k} \quad \text{for} \quad t \geqslant t_0 + k(T+\tau).$$

If $t \geqslant t_0$, we can define k such that

$$t_0 + k(T+\tau) \leqslant t < t_0 + (k+1)(T+\tau).$$

Then $-k < -[1/(T+\tau)](t - t_0) + 1$ and

$$| X(t, t_0)| < ee^{-\alpha(t-t_0)}.$$

This conclusion is not trivial; we have supposed uniform asymptotic stability with respect to the solutions defined *by continuous initial functions*, and we have obtained the above evaluation for a solution $X(t, t_0)$, which is defined by the initial conditions $X(t_0, t_0) = E$, $X(t, t_0) \equiv 0$ for $t < t_0$.

We have already used this conclusion in Section 4.6 for the estimation of $X(t)$.

Theorem 4.30. *In system* (80) *let the functions* η *and* f *be almost periodic in* t (η *almost periodic in* t, *uniformly with respect to* s). *If the trivial solution of the corresponding homogeneous system is uniformly asymptotically stable, then system* (80) *admits an almost-periodic solution. This solution is obviously unique and verifies an inequality of the form* $|x_0(t)| \leqslant KM$, *where* K *depends only on the homogeneous system, and* $M = \sup |f|$.

Proof. According to the preceding lemma, the solutions of system (80) are bounded; let $u(t)$ be such a solution. We write

$$\begin{aligned}\frac{d}{dt}[u(t+\theta) - u(t)] &= \int_{-\infty}^{0} u(t+\theta+s)d_s\eta(t+\theta, s) + f(t+\theta) \\ &\quad - \int_{-\infty}^{0} u(t+s)d_s\eta(t, s) - f(t) \\ &= \int_{-\infty}^{0} [u(t+\theta+s) - u(t+s)]d_s\eta(t, s) \\ &\quad + \int_{-\infty}^{0} u(t+\theta+s)d_s[\eta(t+\theta, s) - \eta(t, s)] + f(t+\theta) - f(t).\end{aligned}$$

Let $y(t)$ be the solution of the homogeneous system which in $[-\tau, 0]$ coincides with $u(t+\theta) - u(t)$; we set $v(t) = u(t+\theta) - u(t) - y(t)$. We have $v(t) \equiv 0$ in $[-\tau, 0]$ and

$$\begin{aligned}\frac{dv(t)}{dt} &= \int_{-\infty}^{0} v(t+s)d_s\eta(t, s) + \int_{-\infty}^{0} u(t+\theta+s)d_s[\eta(t+\theta, s) - \eta(t, s)] \\ &\quad + f(t+\theta) - f(t).\end{aligned}$$

On the basis of the formula for integration by parts,

$$\begin{aligned}\int_{-\tau}^{0} u(t+\theta+s)d_s[\eta(t+\theta, s) - \eta(t, s)] &= u(t+\theta)[\eta(t+\theta, 0) - \eta(t, 0)] \\ &\quad - u(t+\theta-\tau)[\eta(t+\theta, -\tau) - \eta(t, -\tau)] \\ &\quad - \int_{-\tau}^{0} \left(\frac{d}{dt} u(t+\theta+s)\right)[\eta(t+\theta, s) - \eta(t, s)]ds.\end{aligned}$$

Let $M_1 = \sup |u(t)|$, $M_2 = \sup |du(t)/dt|$. It follows that

$$\left|\int_{-\tau}^{0} u(t+\theta+s)d_s[\eta(t+\theta, s) - \eta(t, s)]\right| \leqslant M_1(|\eta(t+\theta, 0) - \eta(t, 0)|$$
$$+ |\eta(t+\theta, -\tau) - \eta(t, -\tau)|) + M_2\tau\sup_{s,t}|\eta(t+\theta, s) - \eta(t, s)|.$$

Let $M_0 = \max\{2M_1, \tau M_2, 1\}$ and θ be a common $\epsilon/4KM_0$ almost-period of function η and f; i.e.,

$$|\eta(t+\theta, s) - \eta(t, s)| < \frac{\epsilon}{4KM_0}, \qquad |f(t+\theta) - f(t)| < \frac{\epsilon}{4KM_0}.$$

By virtue of the lemma it follows that

$$|v(t)| \leqslant K\{M_1 \sup(|\eta(t+\theta, 0) - \eta(t, 0)| + |\eta(t+\theta, -\tau) - \eta(t, -\tau)|)$$
$$+ M_2\tau \sup|\eta(t+\theta, s) - \eta(t, s)| + \sup|f(t+\theta) - f(t)|\};$$

hence

$$|v(t)| \leqslant K\left(2M_1\frac{\epsilon}{4KM_0} + M_2\tau\frac{\epsilon}{4KM_0} + \frac{\epsilon}{4KM_0}\right) < \frac{3\epsilon}{4}.$$

Consequently,

$$|u(t+\theta) - u(t) - y(t)| < \frac{3\epsilon}{4} \qquad \text{for} \quad t \geqslant -\tau.$$

On the basis of the hypothesis made with regard to the homogeneous system, there exists a $T(\epsilon)$ with the property that $t > T$ implies $|y(t)| < \epsilon/4$. From here, for $t > T$, we deduce that

$$|u(t+\theta) - u(t)| < \epsilon.$$

It follows that for every $\epsilon > 0$ there exist quantities $l(\epsilon)$ and $T(\epsilon)$ with the property that in every interval of length l there exists a θ such that $|u(t+\theta) - u(t)| < \epsilon$ if $t > T$. This means that the solution $u(t)$ is asymptotically almost periodic.

Then $u(t) = x_0(t) + \omega(t)$, where $x_0(t)$ is an almost-periodic function and $\lim_{t\to\infty} \omega(t) = 0$. We have

$$\frac{dx_0(t)}{dt} + \frac{d\omega(t)}{dt} = \int_{-\infty}^{0} x_0(t+s)d_s\eta(t, s) + f(t) + \int_{-\infty}^{0} \omega(t+s)d_s\eta(t, s).$$

Since $\omega(t)$ tends to zero when $t \to \infty$, it follows that

$$\lim \int_{-\infty}^{0} \omega(t+s)d_s\eta(t, s) = 0$$

$$\left[\left|\int_{-\infty}^{0} \omega(t+s)d_s\eta(t, s)\right| \leqslant \sup|\omega(t+s)| \bigvee_{s=-\tau}^{0} \eta(t, s)\right].$$

We deduce that

$$\frac{dx_0(t)}{dt} = \int_{-\infty}^{0} x_0(t+s)d_s\eta(t,s) + f(t),$$

and the existence of the almost-periodic solution is proved.

From $|u(t)| \leqslant KM$ we obtain $|x_0(t)| \leqslant KM + |\omega(t)|$. Let $\epsilon > 0$; from $\lim_{t\to\infty} \omega(t) = 0$ it follows that there exists a $T > 0$ such that for $t > T$ we have $|\omega(t)| < \epsilon/2$; hence $|x_0(t)| \leqslant KM + (\epsilon/2)$ for $t > T$. Let t be arbitrary; there exists an $\epsilon/2$ almost-period θ such that $t + \theta > T$. Then

$$|x_0(t+\theta)| \leqslant KM + \frac{\epsilon}{2} \quad \text{and} \quad |x_0(t+\theta) - x_0(t)| < \frac{\epsilon}{2};$$

hence

$$|x_0(t)| \leqslant KM + \epsilon.$$

Since ϵ is arbitrary, we deduce

$$|x_0(t)| \leqslant KM.$$

The theorem is completely proved.

Theorem 4.31. *We consider the system*

$$\frac{dx(t)}{dt} = \int_{-\infty}^{0} x(t+s)d_s\eta(t,s) + f(t) + \mu g[t, x(t+s), \mu], \tag{81}$$

where η and f are as in the preceding theorem, and g verifies a Lipschitz-type condition in the neighborhood of the almost-periodic solution $x_0(t)$ of the generating system obtained for $\mu = 0$.

If the trivial solution of the system

$$\frac{dy(t)}{dt} = \int_{-\infty}^{0} y(t+s)d_s\eta(t,s)$$

is uniformly asymptotically stable, there exists a $\mu_0 > 0$ such that for $|\mu| < \mu_0$ system (81) admits an almost-periodic solution $x(t,\mu)$ with the property $\lim_{\mu\to\infty} x(t,\mu) = x_0(t)$. This solution is uniformly asymptotically stable.

Proof. The existence of the almost-periodic solution $x_0(t)$ of the system for $\mu = 0$ follows from Theorem 4.30. Let

$$z(t) = x(t) - x_0(t).$$

We obtain

$$\frac{dz(t)}{dt} = \int_{-\infty}^{0} z(t+s)d_s\eta(t,s) + \mu Z[t, z(t+s), \mu].$$

Let $z_1(t)$ be the almost-periodic solution of the system

$$\frac{dz(t)}{dt} = \int_{-\infty}^{0} z(t+s)d_s\eta(t,s) + \mu Z(t,0,0)$$

and $z_k(t)$ the almost-periodic solution of the system

$$\frac{dz(t)}{dt} = \int_{-\infty}^{0} z(t+s)d_s\eta(t,s) + \mu Z[t, z_{k-1}(t+s), \mu].$$

These solutions exist and are uniquely determined according to Theorem 4.30. Denoting

$$v_k(t) = z_k(t) - z_{k-1}(t),$$

we deduce

$$\frac{dv_k(t)}{dt} = \int_{-\infty}^{0} v_k(t+s)d_s\eta(t,s) + \mu\{Z[t, z_{k-1}(t+s), \mu] - Z[t, z_{k-2}(t+s), \mu]\};$$

hence, taking Theorem 4.30 into account we obtain the evaluation

$$| v_k(t)| \leqslant |\mu| KL \sup| z_{k-1}(t) - z_{k-2}(t)| = |\mu| KL \sup| v_{k-1}(t)|.$$

From here follows, for $|\mu|$ sufficiently small, the uniform convergence of the sequence of successive approximations. The limit of this sequence is an almost-periodic function $z(t,\mu)$ with $\lim_{\mu\to 0} z(t,\mu) = 0$. By putting $x(t,\mu) = x_0(t) + z(t,\mu)$ we obtain the almost-periodic solution of system (81). The stability of the solution follows by applying Theorem 4.6 concerning stability by the first approximation. The theorem is thus proved.

In the particular case where η, f, g are periodic in t with period ω, a particular case of Theorem 4.25 (the application) is obtained.

The above method can be applied to systems of the form

$$\frac{dx(t)}{dt} = X_0[t, x(t), x(t-\tau)] + \mu X_1[t, x(t), x(t-\tau), \mu],$$

where X_0 and X_1 are almost periodic in t, uniformly with respect to the other variables. We suppose that the generating system obtained for $\mu = 0$ admits an almost-periodic solution $x_0(t)$ with the property that the corresponding variational system has the trivial solution uniformly asymptotically stable. Then the system admits for $|\mu|$ small enough an almost-periodic solution, which for $\mu \to 0$ tends to the trivial solution. Putting $z(t) = x(t) - x_0(t)$ we obtain a system of the form

$$\frac{dz(t)}{dt} = A(t)z(t) + B(t)z(t-\tau) + Z_0[t, z(t), z(t-\tau)] + \mu Z_1[t, z(t), z(t-\tau), \mu]$$

for which the successive approximations are constructed according to the scheme

$$\begin{aligned} z_0(t) &= 0, \\ \frac{dz_k}{dt} &= A(t)z_k(t) + B(t)z_k(t) + Z_0[t, z_{k-1}(t), z_{k-1}(t-\tau)] \\ &\quad + \mu Z_1[t, z_{k-1}(t), z_{k-1}(t-\tau), \mu], \end{aligned}$$

where $z_k(t)$ is almost periodic.

4.15. The Averaging Method for Systems with Retarded Argument

In this section we shall present some results of the extension of the averaging method to systems with retarded argument.

Theorem 4.32. *We consider the system*

$$\frac{dx(t)}{dt} = \epsilon X[t, x(t), x(t-\tau)]. \tag{82}$$

We suppose that $X(t, x, y)$ is bounded for $t \in (0, \infty)$, $x \in D$, $y \in D$,

$$\lim_{T\to\infty} \frac{1}{T} \int_0^T X(t, x, y)dt = X_0(x, y) \qquad (x \in D, y \in D),$$

and, in addition, that for every $\eta > 0$ there exists a $\delta(\eta) > 0$ such that

$$|x' - x''| < \delta(\eta), \; |y' - y''| < \delta(\eta)$$

implies

$$|X(t, x', y') - X(t, x'', y'')| < \eta, \qquad |X_0(x', y') - X_0(x'', y'')| < \eta.$$

We also suppose that the system

$$\frac{dy(t)}{dt} = X_0[y(t), y(t)] \tag{83}$$

admits a unique solution verifying the condition $y(0) = x_0$. *If* $x(t, \epsilon)$ *is an arbitrary solution of system* (82) *with* $x(0, \epsilon) = x_0$, *and* $y(t, \epsilon)$ *is the solution of system* (83) *with* $y(0, \epsilon) = x_0$, *then for every* $T > 0$ *and* $\eta > 0$ *there exists an* $\epsilon_0 > 0$ *such that for* $0 < \epsilon < \epsilon_0$ *we have*

$$| x(t, \epsilon) - y(t, \epsilon)| < \eta \qquad (t \in [0, T/\epsilon]).$$

To prove this theorem we shall first state some lemmas.

Lemma 1. *If*

$$\lim_{T\to\infty} \frac{1}{T} \int_0^T X(t, x, y)dt = X_0(x, y) \qquad \textit{for every} \quad x \in D, y \in D,$$

then for every pair of piecewise constant functions $\tilde{x}(t), \tilde{y}(t)$, *we have the relation*

$$\lim_{\epsilon\to 0} \int_0^{t_1} X\left[\frac{t}{\epsilon}, \tilde{x}(t), \tilde{y}(t)\right] dt = \int_0^{t_1} X_0[\tilde{x}(t), \tilde{y}(t)]dt.$$

Proof. We have

$$\lim_{\epsilon\to 0} \int_0^{t_1} X\left(\frac{t}{\epsilon}, x, y\right) dt = \lim_{\epsilon\to 0} \epsilon \int_0^{t_1/\epsilon} X(u, x, y)du = t_1 \lim_{\epsilon\to 0} \frac{\epsilon}{t_1} \int_0^{t_1/\epsilon} X(u, x, y)du$$
$$= t_1 X_0(x, y) = \int_0^{t_1} X_0(x, y)dt_1 .$$

From here follows

$$\lim_{\epsilon\to 0} \int_{\tau_1}^{\tau_2} X\left(\frac{t}{\epsilon}, x, y\right) dt = \int_{\tau_1}^{\tau_2} X_0(x, y)dt$$

and

$$\lim_{\epsilon\to 0} \sum_i \int_{\tau_{i-1}}^{\tau_i} X\left(\frac{t}{\epsilon}, x_i, y_i\right) dt = \sum_i \int_{\tau_{i-1}}^{\tau_i} X_0(x_i, y_i)dt.$$

With this, the lemma is proved.

Lemma 2. *If* $X(t, x, y)$ *is bounded for* $t \in [0, \infty)$, $x \in D$, $y \in D$, *and* x_n *is the solution of the system*

$$\frac{dx(t)}{dt} = \epsilon_n X[t, x(t), x(t - \tau)],$$

then from $\lim_{n\to\infty} \epsilon_n = 0$ *and* $\lim_{n\to\infty} x_n(t/\epsilon_n) = y(t)$ *follows*

$$\lim_{n\to\infty} x_n\left(\frac{t}{\epsilon_n} - \tau\right) = y(t).$$

[*We suppose that for all t we have* $x_n(t) \in D$].

Proof. We have, for $u \geqslant \tau$,

$$x_n(u-\tau) = x_n(u) - \int_{u-\tau}^{u} \dot{x}_n(t)dt = x_n(u) - \int_{u-\tau}^{u} \epsilon_n X[t, x_n(t), x_n(t-\tau)]dt.$$

From here

$$x_n\left(\frac{t}{\epsilon_n}-\tau\right) = x_n\left(\frac{t}{\epsilon_n}\right) - \int_{(t/\epsilon_n)-\tau}^{t/\epsilon_n} \epsilon_n X[s, x_n(s), x_n(s-\tau)]ds \qquad (t \geqslant \tau\epsilon_n).$$

Let $|X(t, x, y)| < M$ for $t \in [0, \infty)$, $x \in D$, $y \in D$. We have

$$x_n\left(\frac{t}{\epsilon_n}-\tau\right) - y(t) = x_n\left(\frac{t}{\epsilon_n}\right) - y(t) - \epsilon_n \int_{(t/\epsilon_n)-\tau}^{t/\epsilon_n} X[s, x_n(s), x_n(s-\tau)]ds.$$

Hence

$$\left| x_n\left(\frac{t}{\epsilon_n}-\tau\right) - y(t)\right| \leqslant \left| x_n\left(\frac{t}{\epsilon_n}\right) - y(t)\right| + \epsilon_n\tau M, \qquad (t \geqslant \tau\epsilon_n).$$

For every $t > 0$ and $\eta > 0$ we choose $N(\eta, t)$ such that if $n > N(\eta, t)$ we have

$$\epsilon_n < \min\left\{\frac{t}{\tau}, \frac{\eta}{2\tau M}\right\}, \qquad \left| x_n\left(\frac{t}{\epsilon_n}\right) - y(t)\right| < \frac{\eta}{2}.$$

Then

$$\left| x_n\left(\frac{t}{\epsilon_n}-\tau\right) - y(t)\right| < \eta \qquad \text{for} \quad n > N(\eta, t),$$

and the lemma is proved.

Lemma 3. *If* $\lim_{n\to\infty} \epsilon_n = 0$ *and* $\lim_{n\to\infty} x_n(t/\epsilon_n) = y(t)$ *uniformly with respect to t in* $[0, T]$, *then*

$$\lim_{n\to\infty} \int_0^{t_1} X\left[\frac{t_1}{\epsilon_n}, x_n\left(\frac{t_1}{\epsilon_n}\right), x_n\left(\frac{t_1}{\epsilon_n}-\tau\right)\right] dt_1 = \int_0^{t_1} X_0[y(t), y(t)]dt.$$

Proof. We have

$$\left| \int_0^{t_1} X\left[\frac{t_1}{\epsilon_n}, x_n\left(\frac{t_1}{\epsilon_n}\right), x_n\left(\frac{t_1}{\epsilon_n}-\tau\right)\right] dt_1 - \int_0^{t_1} X_0[y(t), y(t)]dt \right|$$
$$\leqslant \left| \int_0^{\epsilon_n\tau} X\left[\frac{t_1}{\epsilon_n}, x_n\left(\frac{t_1}{\epsilon_n}\right), x_n\left(\frac{t_1}{\epsilon_n}-\tau\right)\right] dt_1 - \int_0^{\epsilon_n\tau} X_0[y(t_1), y(t_1)]dt_1 \right|$$
$$+ \left| \int_{\epsilon_n\tau}^{t_1} X\left[\frac{t_1}{\epsilon_n}, x_n\left(\frac{t_1}{\epsilon_n}\right), x_n\left(\frac{t_1}{\epsilon_n}-\tau\right)\right] dt_1 - \int_{\epsilon_n\tau}^{t_1} X_0[y(t_1), y(t_1)]dt_1 \right|.$$

However,

$$\left| \int_0^{\epsilon_n \tau} X \, dt_1 - \int_0^{\epsilon_n \tau} X_0 \, dt_1 \right| \leqslant 2M\epsilon_n \tau.$$

Let $\delta(\eta)$ be such that for $| x' - x''| < \delta$, $| y' - y''| < \delta$ we have

$$| X(t, x', y') - X(t, x'', y'')| < \frac{\eta}{12T}, \qquad | X_0(x', y') - X_0(x'', y'')| < \frac{\eta}{12T}.$$

Let $\tilde{y}(t)$ be a piecewise constant function such that

$$| y(t) - \tilde{y}(t)| < \delta(\eta) \qquad \text{for} \quad t \in [0, T].$$

We choose $N(\eta)$ such that for $n > N(\eta)$ we have $\epsilon_n < \eta/16M\tau$,

$$\left| x_n\left(\frac{t}{\epsilon_n}\right) - y(t)\right| < \delta(\eta), \quad \left| x_n\left(\frac{t}{\epsilon_n} - \tau\right) - y(t)\right| < \delta(\eta) \quad (\text{for } \epsilon_n \tau \leqslant t \leqslant T).$$

For this it suffices to take $N(\eta)$ such that if $n > N(\eta)$ we have

$$\epsilon_n < \min\left\{\frac{\eta}{16M\tau}, \frac{\delta(\eta)}{2M\tau}\right\}, \qquad \left| x_n\left(\frac{t}{\epsilon_n}\right) - y(t)\right| < \frac{1}{2}\delta(\eta).$$

In addition, $N(\eta)$ will be chosen such that for $n > N(\eta)$ we also have

$$\left| \int_{\tau\epsilon_n}^{t_1} X\left[\frac{t_1}{\epsilon_n}, \tilde{y}(t_1), \tilde{y}(t_1)\right] dt_1 - \int_{\tau\epsilon_n}^{t_1} X_0[\tilde{y}(t_1), \tilde{y}(t_1)]dt_1 \right| < \frac{\eta}{4}$$

for $\eta/2M \leqslant t_1 \leqslant T$. Then

$$\left| X\left[\frac{t_1}{\epsilon_n}, x_n\left(\frac{t_1}{\epsilon_n}\right), x_n\left(\frac{t_1}{\epsilon_n} - \tau\right)\right] - X\left[\frac{t_1}{\epsilon_n}, y(t_1), y(t_1)\right]\right| < \frac{\eta}{12T}$$

$$\text{for} \quad \tau\epsilon_n \leqslant t_1 \leqslant T,$$

$$\left| X\left[\frac{t_1}{\epsilon_n}, y(t_1), y(t_1)\right] - X\left[\frac{t_1}{\epsilon_n}, \tilde{y}(t_1), \tilde{y}(t_1)\right]\right| < \frac{\eta}{12T},$$

$$| X_0[y(t_1), y(t_1)] - X_0[\tilde{y}(t_1), \tilde{y}(t_1)]| < \frac{\eta}{12T}.$$

Consequently,

$$\left| \int_{\tau\epsilon_n}^{t_1} X\left[\frac{t_1}{\epsilon_n}, x_n\left(\frac{t_1}{\epsilon_n}\right), x_n\left(\frac{t_1}{\epsilon_n} - \tau\right)\right] dt_1 - \int_{\tau\epsilon_n}^{t_1} X_0[y(t_1), y(t_1)]dt_1 \right|$$

$$\leqslant \left| \int_{\tau\epsilon_n}^{t_1} X\left[\frac{t_1}{\epsilon_n}, x_n\left(\frac{t_1}{\epsilon_n}\right), x_n\left(\frac{t_1}{\epsilon_n} - \tau\right)\right] dt_1 - \int_{\tau\epsilon_n}^{t_1} X\left[\frac{t_1}{\epsilon_n}, y(t_1), y(t_1)\right] dt_1 \right|$$

$$+\left|\int_{\tau\epsilon_n}^{t_1} X\left[\frac{t_1}{\epsilon_n}, y(t_1), y(t_1)\right] dt_1 - \int_{\tau\epsilon_n}^{t_1} X\left[\frac{t_1}{\epsilon_n}, \tilde{y}(t_1), \tilde{y}(t_1)\right] dt_1\right|$$

$$+\left|\int_{\tau\epsilon_n}^{t_1} X\left[\frac{t_1}{\epsilon_n}, \tilde{y}(t_1), \tilde{y}(t_1)\right] dt_1 - \int_{\tau\epsilon_n}^{t_1} X_0[\tilde{y}(t_1), \tilde{y}(t_1)]dt_1\right|$$

$$+\left|\int_{\tau\epsilon_n}^{t_1} X_0[\tilde{y}(t_1), \tilde{y}(t_1)]dt_1 - \int_{\tau\epsilon_n}^{t_1} X_0[y(t_1), y(t_1)]dt_1\right|$$

$$< \frac{\eta}{12} + \frac{\eta}{12} + \frac{\eta}{4} + \frac{\eta}{12} = \frac{\eta}{2}; \qquad \left|\int_0^{\epsilon_n\tau} X\, dt_1 - \int_0^{\epsilon_n\tau} X_0\, dt_1\right| < \frac{\eta}{2}.$$

We finally have for $n > N(\eta)$,

$$\left|\int_0^{t_1} X\left[\frac{t_1}{\epsilon_n}, x_n\left(\frac{t_1}{\epsilon_n}\right), x_n\left(\frac{t_1}{\epsilon_n} - \tau\right)\right] dt_1 - \int_0^{t_1} X_0[y(t_1), y(t_1)]dt_1\right| < \eta,$$

and the lemma is proved.

Let us observe that we have performed all the estimates for $t_1 \geqslant \eta/2M$ since for $0 < t_1 < \eta/2M$ we have

$$\left|\int_0^{t_1} X\, dt_1 - \int_0^{t_1} X_0\, dt_1\right| < \eta \qquad \text{for all} \quad n.$$

Proof of Theorem 4.32. We have

$$x(t, \epsilon) = x_0 + \epsilon \int_0^t X[u, x(u), x(u - \tau)]du.$$

For $t = t_1/\epsilon$ we obtain

$$x\left(\frac{t_1}{\epsilon}, \epsilon\right) = x_0 + \epsilon \int_0^{t_1/\epsilon} X[u, x(u), x(u - \tau)]du.$$

We perform in the integral the change of variable $v = \epsilon u$. Then

$$x\left(\frac{t_1}{\epsilon}, \epsilon\right) = x_0 + \int_0^{t_1} X\left[\frac{v}{\epsilon}, x\left(\frac{v}{\epsilon}\right), x\left(\frac{v}{\epsilon} - \tau\right)\right] d\tau.$$

From the fact that $|X| < M$, it follows that for $0 \leqslant t_1 \leqslant T$ the family $\{x(t_1/\epsilon, \epsilon)\}$ is uniformly bounded and has uniformly bounded derivatives, hence is equally continuous. Thus the family $\{x(t_1/\epsilon, \epsilon)\}$ is compact and for every sequence $\{\epsilon_n\}$ with $\lim_{n\to\infty} \epsilon_n = 0$ we can find a subsequence $\{\epsilon_{n_k}\}$ such that $\lim_{k\to\infty} x_{n_k}(t_1/\epsilon_{n_k}, \epsilon_{n_k}) = y(t_1)$, the convergence being uniform in $[0, T]$. Then $y(0) = x_0$ and from

$$x_{n_k}\left(\frac{t_1}{\epsilon_{n_k}}, \epsilon_{n_k}\right) = x_0 + \int_0^{t_1} X\left[\frac{v}{\epsilon_{n_k}}, x_{n_k}\left(\frac{v}{\epsilon_{n_k}}, \epsilon_{n_k}\right), x_{n_k}\left(\frac{v}{\epsilon_{n_k}} - \tau, \epsilon_{n_k}\right)\right] dv$$

we obtain, on the basis of Lemma 3,

$$y(t_1) = x_0 + \int_0^{t_1} X_0[y(v), y(v)]dv.$$

It follows from here that $y(t_1)$ is a solution of the system

$$\dot{y}(t) = X_0[y(t), y(t)].$$

Since this solution is by hypothesis unique, we deduce that for every sequence $\epsilon_n \to 0$ there exists a subsequence $\epsilon_{n_k} \to 0$ such that

$$\lim_{k\to\infty} x_{n_k}\left(\frac{t_1}{\epsilon_{n_k}}, \epsilon_{n_k}\right) = y(t_1).$$

This means, however, that $\lim_{\epsilon\to 0} x(t_1/\epsilon, \epsilon) = y(t_1)$; therefore for every $\eta > 0$ there exists $\epsilon_0 > 0$ such that if $0 < \epsilon < \epsilon_0$, then $| x(t_1/\epsilon, \epsilon) - y(t_1)| < \eta$ for $t_1 \in [0, T]$. Let $t = t_1/\epsilon$. We have $| x(t, \epsilon) - y(\epsilon t)| < \eta$.

We set $y(\epsilon t) = y(t, \epsilon)$. It follows that $(d/dt)\, y(t, \epsilon) = (d/dt)\, y(\epsilon t) = \epsilon(d/dt_1)y(\epsilon t) = \epsilon X_0[y(\epsilon t), y(\epsilon t)] = \epsilon X_0[y(t, \epsilon), y(t, \epsilon)]$; hence $y(t, \epsilon)$ is the solution of system (83) and $y(0, \epsilon) = y(0) = x_0$. The theorem is thus proved.

Theorem 4.33. *We consider the system*

$$\frac{dz(t)}{dt} = \epsilon Z[t, z(t), z(t-\tau), \epsilon], \tag{84}$$

where $Z(t, u, v, \epsilon)$ has continuous partial derivatives of the first order and $Z(t + T, u, v, \epsilon) = Z(t, u, v, \epsilon)$. Let

$$Z_0(u, v, \epsilon) = \frac{1}{T}\int_0^T Z(t, u, v, \epsilon)dt$$

and ζ^0 be a solution of $Z_0(u, u, 0) = 0$. If the eigenvalues of the matrix

$$\frac{\partial Z_0(\zeta^0, \zeta^0, 0)}{\partial u} + \frac{\partial Z_0(\zeta^0, \zeta^0, 0)}{\partial v}$$

have negative real parts, there exists an $\epsilon_0 > 0$ such that for $0 < \epsilon < \epsilon_0$ system (84) admits a periodic solution of period T which for $\epsilon \to 0$ tends to ζ^0.

The proof of this theorem will likewise be preceded by some lemmas.

Lemma 4. *Let H_1 and H_2 be quadratic matrices of the nth order. We suppose that the eigenvalues of matrix $H_1 + H_2$ have negative real* *parts. Then there exists a* $\gamma_0 > 0$ *and* $\epsilon_0 > 0$ *such that if* $0 < \epsilon < \epsilon_0$, *the roots of the equation*

$$\det(\epsilon H_1 + \epsilon H_2 e^{-r\tau} - Er) = 0,$$

where E is the unit matrix, verify the inequality

$$\operatorname{Re} r \leqslant -\epsilon\gamma_0 .$$

Proof. We put $r = \epsilon s$. The equation takes the form

$$\det(\epsilon H_1 + \epsilon H_2 e^{-\epsilon s\tau} - E\epsilon s) = 0$$

or

$$\det(H_1 + H_2 e^{-\epsilon s\tau} - Es) = 0.$$

However,

$$H_1 + H_2 e^{-\epsilon s\tau} - Es = H_1 + H_2 - Es + H_2(e^{-\epsilon s\tau} - 1).$$

If follows from here that

$$\det(H_1 + H_2 e^{-\epsilon s\tau} - Es) = \det(H_1 + H_2 - Es) + (e^{-\epsilon s\tau} - 1)f(s, \epsilon)$$
$$= g(s) + (e^{-\epsilon s\tau} - 1)f(s, \epsilon).$$

The equation $g(s) = 0$ has roots with negative real parts; hence there exists a $\gamma_0 > 0$ such that in the half-plane $\operatorname{Re} z \geqslant -\gamma_0$ roots of the equation $g(s) = 0$ do not exist. We consider the contour which contains the portion of the line $\operatorname{Re} z = -\gamma_0$ for which $| Im\, z | \leqslant R$ and the arc of circle of radius R situated in the half-plane $\operatorname{Re} z > 0$. Since in the interior of this contour $g(s)$ is regular and does not have zeros, the variation of the argument on the contour is zero. Then, for ϵ small enough, the variation on this contour of the arguments of function $g(s) + (e^{-\epsilon s\tau} - 1)f(s, \epsilon)$ will likewise be equal to zero. It follows from here that there exists an ϵ_0 such that if $\epsilon < \epsilon_0$, the given equation does not have roots inside the considered contour. Let us show that if R is large enough, the equation cannot have roots in the half-plane $\operatorname{Re} z > -\gamma_0$ outside this contour. If s is a root of the equation, there exists a vector c such that

$$(H_1 + H_2 e^{-\epsilon s\tau})c = sc;$$

however,

$$| e^{-\epsilon s\tau} | \leqslant e^{\epsilon\gamma_0\tau}, \qquad | s | \| c \| = \|(H_1 + H_2 e^{-\epsilon s\tau})c \|$$
$$\leqslant \| H_1 + H_2 e^{-\epsilon s\tau} \| \| c \| \leqslant (\| H_1 \| + \| H_2 \| e^{\epsilon\gamma_0\tau}) \| c \| \leqslant M \| c \|;$$

hence $| s | \leqslant M$. With this the lemma is proved, since if

$$\operatorname{Re} s < -\gamma_0$$

we obtain

$$\operatorname{Re} r < -\epsilon\gamma_0 .$$

Lemma 5. *If the characteristic numbers of matrix $H_1 + H_2$ have negative real parts, there exists a functional V with the following properties:*

1. $V[\varphi]$ is defined on the space of the functions continuous in $[-\tau, 0]$.
2. $\| \varphi \|^2 \leqslant V[\varphi] \leqslant K^2(1 + (1/2\epsilon\gamma_0)) \| \varphi \|^2$.
3. $| V[\varphi_1] - V[\varphi_2]| \leqslant L_0(1 + (1/\epsilon\gamma_0))\|(\| \varphi_1 \| + \| \varphi_2 \|) \| \varphi_1 - \varphi_2 \|$.
4. *The set of functions for which $V[\varphi] \leqslant C$ is closed and convex.*
5. $\limsup_{h\to 0+} \dfrac{V[z(t + h + s; t, \varphi)] - V[\varphi]}{h} \leqslant -\tfrac{1}{2}\| \varphi \|^2 \qquad$ for $\epsilon < \epsilon_0$,

$\| \varphi \| \leqslant \delta_0(\epsilon_0)$, *where $z(t; t_0, \varphi)$ is the solution of the system*

$$\dot{z}(t) = \epsilon[E + A(t, z(t), z(t-\tau), \epsilon)]\{H_1 z(t) + H_2 z(t-\tau) + B[z(t), z(t-\tau)]\},$$

where

$$| A(t, u, v, \epsilon)| < M_1\epsilon^\alpha, \qquad (t \geqslant 0 \quad \text{for} \quad | u | + | v | \leqslant M_0),$$
$$| B(u, v)| < M_2\{| u | + | v |\}^{1+\beta} \qquad (\beta > 0 \quad \text{for} \quad | u | + | v | \leqslant M_0).$$

Proof. We consider the system

$$\dot{y}(t) = \epsilon\{H_1 y(t) + H_2 y(t-\tau)\}. \tag{85}$$

If the characteristic numbers of matrix $H_1 + H_2$ have negative real parts, it follows from Lemma 4 that the roots of the equation $\det(\epsilon H_1 + \epsilon H_2 e^{-r\tau} - Er) = 0$ verify the inequality $\operatorname{Re} r \leqslant -\epsilon\gamma_1$ for $0 < \epsilon < \epsilon_0$. However, in this case, as we know it, the trivial solution of the system is uniformly asymptotically stable and we have for every solution the inequality

$$| y(t; t_0, \varphi)| \leqslant K e^{-\epsilon\gamma_0(t-t_0)} \| \varphi \|$$

for $t \geqslant t_0$, $\gamma_0 < \gamma_1$ arbitrary.

Let

$$V[\varphi] = \int_0^\infty \| y(t+s; \varphi)\|^2 \, dt + \sup_{\sigma \geqslant 0} \| y(\sigma + s; \varphi)\|^2.$$

We have denoted by $y(t; \varphi)$ the solution of system (85) which for $-\tau \leqslant t \leqslant 0$ coincides with $\varphi(t)$; in our formulas $s \in [-\tau, 0]$, and

$$\| y(t+s; \varphi)\| = \sup_{-\tau \leqslant s \leqslant 0} | y(t+s; \varphi)|.$$

Since the integral is positive and $y(s; \varphi) = \varphi$, it follows that $V[\varphi] \geqslant \| \varphi \|^2$. On the other hand,

$$\| y(t+s; \varphi)\| \leqslant K e^{-\epsilon\gamma_0 t} \| \varphi \|;$$

hence

$$V[\varphi] \leqslant K^2 \| \varphi \|^2 \int_0^\infty e^{-2\epsilon\gamma_0 t} \, dt + K^2 \| \varphi \|^2 = K^2 \left(1 + \frac{1}{2\epsilon\gamma_0}\right) \| \varphi \|^2.$$

Let

$$\delta_0 > 0 \qquad \text{and} \qquad T(\eta) = \frac{1}{\epsilon\gamma_0} \ln \frac{K\delta_0}{\eta};$$

if $\| \varphi \| < \delta$, $t > T(\eta)$, we have $| y(t, \varphi)| < \eta$; hence if

$$\| \varphi \| < \delta_0 \qquad \text{and} \qquad \sigma > \frac{1}{\epsilon\gamma_0} \ln \frac{2K\delta_0}{\| \varphi \|},$$

we have

$$\| y(\sigma + s; \varphi)\|^2 < \frac{\| \varphi \|^2}{4}$$

and

$$\sup_{\sigma \geqslant 0} \| y(\sigma + s; \varphi)\|^2 = \sup_{0 \leqslant \sigma \leqslant \frac{1}{\epsilon\gamma_0} \frac{2K\delta_0}{\| \varphi \|}} \| y(\sigma + s; \varphi)\|^2 = \| y(\sigma^1 + s; \varphi)\|^2,$$

since $\| y(\sigma + s; \varphi)\|^2$ is a continuous function of σ.

Further,

$$\begin{aligned} &\Big| \| y(\sigma + s; \varphi_1)\|^2 - \| y(\sigma + s; \varphi_2)\|^2 \Big| \\ &\quad = (\| y(\sigma + s; \varphi_1)\| + \| y(\sigma + s; \varphi_2)\|) \Big| \| y(\sigma + s; \varphi_1)\| - \| y(\sigma + s; \varphi_2)\| \Big| \\ &\quad \leqslant (\| y(\sigma + s; \varphi_1)\| + \| y(\sigma + s; \varphi_2)\|) \| y(\sigma + s; \varphi_1 - \varphi_2)\| \\ &\quad \leqslant 2K e^{\epsilon\gamma_0\tau} (\| \varphi_1 \| + \| \varphi_2 \|) K e^{\epsilon\gamma_0\tau} \| \varphi_1 - \varphi_2 \| \\ &\quad < L_0 (\| \varphi_1 \| + \| \varphi_2 \|) \| \varphi_1 - \varphi_2 \|. \end{aligned}$$

It follows from here that

$$\sup_{\sigma \geqslant 0} \| y(\sigma + s; \varphi_1)\|^2 = \| y(\sigma^1 + s; \varphi_1)\|^2 \leqslant \| y(\sigma^1 + s; \varphi_2)\|^2$$

$$+ L_0(\| \varphi_1 \| + \| \varphi_2 \|)\| \varphi_1 - \varphi_2 \| \leqslant \sup_{\sigma \geqslant 0} \| y(\sigma + s; \varphi_2)\|^2$$

$$+ L_0(\| \varphi_1 \| + \| \varphi_2 \|)\| \varphi_1 - \varphi_2 \|.$$

Finally,

$$| \sup_{\sigma \geqslant 0} \| y(\sigma + s; \varphi_2)\|^2 - \sup_{\sigma \geqslant 0} \| y(\sigma + s; \varphi_1)\|^2 | \leqslant L_0(\| \varphi_1 \| + \| \varphi_2 \|)\| \varphi_1 - \varphi_2 \|,$$

$$\begin{aligned} | V[\varphi_1] - V[\varphi_2]| &\leqslant \int_0^\infty \Big| \| y(t + s; \varphi_1)\|^2 - \| y(t + s; \varphi_2)\|^2 \Big| \, dt \\ &\quad + L_0(\| \varphi_1 \| + \| \varphi_2 \|)\| \varphi_1 - \varphi_2 \| \\ &\leqslant L_0(\| \varphi_1 \| + \| \varphi_2 \|) \int_0^\infty e^{-\epsilon\gamma_0 t} \, dt \| \varphi_1 - \varphi_2 \| \\ &\quad + L_0(\| \varphi_1 \| + \| \varphi_2 \|)\| \varphi_1 - \varphi_2 \|; \end{aligned}$$

hence

$$| V[\varphi_1] - V[\varphi_2]| \leqslant L_0 \left[1 + \frac{1}{\epsilon\gamma_0} \right] (\| \varphi_1 \| + \| \varphi_2 \|)\| \varphi_1 - \varphi_2 \|.$$

We have shown that the functional $V[\varphi]$ verifies a Lipschitz condition; hence $V[\varphi]$ is continuous and therefore the set $V[\varphi] \leqslant C$ is closed. Let us verify that it is convex.

Let $V[\varphi_1] \leqslant C$, $V[\varphi_2] \leqslant C$. We have

$$\begin{aligned} V[\lambda\varphi_1 + (1 - \lambda)\varphi_2] &= \int_0^\infty \| y(t + s; \lambda\varphi_1 + (1 - \lambda)\varphi_2)\|^2 \, dt \\ &\quad + \sup_{\sigma \geqslant 0} \| y(\sigma + s; \lambda\varphi_1 + (1 - \lambda)\varphi_2)\|^2, \end{aligned}$$

$$y(t + s; \lambda\varphi_1 + (1 - \lambda)\varphi_2) = \lambda y(t + s; \varphi_1) + (1 - \lambda) y(t + s; \varphi_2),$$

$$\| y(t + s; \lambda\varphi_1 + (1 - \lambda)\varphi_2)\| \leqslant \lambda \| y(t + s; \varphi_1]\| + (1 - \lambda)\| y(t + s; \varphi_2)\|,$$

$$\begin{aligned} &\| y(t + s; \lambda\varphi_1 + (1 - \lambda)\varphi_2)\|^2 \\ &\quad \leqslant \lambda^2 \| y(t + s; \varphi_1)\|^2 + 2\lambda(1 - \lambda)\| y(t + s; \varphi_1)\| \, \| y(t + s; \varphi_2)\| \\ &\qquad + (1 - \lambda)^2 \| y(t + s; \varphi_2)\|^2 \\ &\quad \leqslant \lambda^2 \| y(t + s; \varphi_1)\|^2 + \lambda(1 - \lambda)[\| y(t + s; \varphi_1)\|^2 + \| y(t + s; \varphi_2)\|^2] \\ &\qquad + (1 - \lambda)^2 \| y(t + s; \varphi_2)\|^2 \\ &\quad = \lambda \| y(t + s; \varphi_1)\|^2 + (1 - \lambda)\| y(t + s; \varphi_2)\|^2; \end{aligned}$$

hence

$$\begin{aligned}&\sup_{t\geqslant 0}\| y(t+s; \lambda\varphi_1+(1-\lambda)\varphi_2)\|^2\\&\qquad\leqslant \lambda\sup_{t\geqslant 0}\| y(t+s;\varphi_1)\|^2+(1-\lambda)\sup_{t\geqslant 0}\| y(t+s;\varphi_2)\|^2.\end{aligned}$$

From here we obtain

$$\begin{aligned}V[\lambda\varphi_1+(1-\lambda)\varphi_2] &\leqslant \lambda\int_0^\infty \| y(t+s;\varphi_1)\|^2\,dt+(1-\lambda)\int_0^\infty \| y(t+s;\varphi_2)\|^2\,dt\\&\quad+\lambda\sup_{t\geqslant 0}\| y(t+s;\varphi_1)\|^2+(1-\lambda)\sup_{t\geqslant 0}\| y(t+s;\varphi_2)\|^2\\&=\lambda V[\varphi_1]+(1-\lambda)V[\varphi_2]\leqslant C;\end{aligned}$$

hence $V[\varphi]\leqslant C$ is convex.

It remains to prove the last assertion of the lemma. We have

$$\begin{aligned}&V[y(t+s;t_0,\varphi)]\\&\quad=\int_0^\infty \| y(u+s;y(t+s;t_0,\varphi))\|^2\,du+\sup_{\sigma\geqslant 0}\| y(\sigma+s;y(t+s;t_0,\varphi))\|^2\\&\quad=\int_0^\infty \| y(t+u+s;t,y(t+s;t_0,\varphi))\|^2\,du\\&\quad\quad+\sup_{\sigma\geqslant 0}\| y(t+\sigma+s;t,y(t+s;t_0,\varphi))\|^2\\&\quad=\int_0^\infty \| y(t+u+s;t_0,\varphi)\|^2\,du+\sup_{\sigma\geqslant 0}\| y(t+\sigma+s;t_0,\varphi)\|^2\\&\quad=\int_t^\infty \| y(u+s;t_0,\varphi)\|^2\,du+\sup_{\sigma\geqslant t}\| y(\sigma+s;t_0,\varphi)\|^2.\end{aligned}$$

From the fact that $\sup_{\sigma\geqslant t}\| y(\sigma+s;t_0,\varphi)\|^2$ is a monotone-decreasing function, it follows that

$$\limsup_{h\to 0+}\frac{V[y(t+h+s;t_0,\varphi)]-V[y(t+s;t_0,\varphi)]}{h}\leqslant -\| y(t+s;t_0,\varphi)\|^2.$$

Consider the system

$$\begin{aligned}\dot z(t)&=\epsilon\{H_1z(t)+H_2z(t-\tau)\}+A[t,z(t),z(t-\tau)]\{H_1z(t)+H_2z(t-\tau)\}\\&\quad+\epsilon\{E+A[t,z(t),z(t-\tau)]\}B[z(t),z(t-\tau)].\end{aligned}$$

We have

$$z(u;t,\varphi)=\varphi(t)+\int_t^u \epsilon[E+A][H_1z(v;t,\varphi)+H_2\varphi(v-\tau)+B]dv;$$

hence

$$| z(u; t, \varphi)| \leqslant \| \varphi \| + \epsilon M \int_t^{t+h} | z(v; t, \varphi)| \, dv + \epsilon Mh \| \varphi \| + \epsilon L \int_t^{t+h} | B | \, dv.$$

The function

$$B^*(v) = | B[z(v; t, \varphi), \varphi(v - \tau)]|$$

is continuous; hence

$$\int_t^{t+h} B^*(v) dv = hB^*(t) + \eta h,$$

where

$$\lim_{h\to 0} \eta = 0, \qquad B^*(t) = | B[\varphi(t), \varphi(t - \tau)]| \leqslant 2M_2 \| \varphi \|^{1+\beta}.$$

We finally obtain for $t \leqslant u \leqslant t + h$;

$$| z(u; t, \varphi)| \leqslant \{\| \varphi \| + \epsilon h(M \| \varphi \| + 2M_2 L \| \varphi \|^{1+\beta} + L\eta)\} e^{\epsilon Mh},$$

from which

$$\| z(t + h + s; t, \varphi)\| \leqslant \{\| \varphi \| + \epsilon h(M \| \varphi \| + 2M_2 L \| \varphi \|^{1+\beta} + L\eta)\} e^{\epsilon Mh}.$$

The same computations yield

$$\| y(t + h + s; t, \varphi)\| < \{\| \varphi \| + \epsilon hM \| \varphi \|\} e^{\epsilon Mh}.$$

Further,

$$\begin{aligned} | z(u; t, \varphi) - y(u; t, \varphi)| &\leqslant \epsilon M \int_t^{t+h} | z(v; t, \varphi) - y(v; t, \varphi)| \, dv \\ &+ 2MM_1 h \epsilon^{1+\alpha} \{\| \varphi \| + \epsilon h(M \| \varphi \| + 2M_2 L \| \varphi \|^{1+\beta} + L\eta)\} e^{\epsilon Mh} \\ &+ 2\epsilon LM_2 h \| \varphi \|^{1+\beta} + L\epsilon\eta h. \end{aligned}$$

From here, for $t \leqslant u \leqslant t + h$,

$$\begin{aligned} &| x(u; t, \varphi) - y(u; t, \varphi)| \\ &\leqslant \epsilon h\{2MM_1 \epsilon^{\alpha} [\| \varphi \| + \epsilon h(M \| \varphi \| + 2M_2 L \| \varphi \|^{1+\beta} + L\eta)] e^{\epsilon Mh} \\ &\quad + 2LM_2 \| \varphi \|^{1+\beta} + L\eta\} e^{\epsilon Mh}; \end{aligned}$$

hence

$$\begin{aligned} &\| z(t + h + s; t, \varphi) - y(t + h + s; t, \varphi)\| \\ &= \sup_{-\tau \leqslant s \leqslant 0} | z(t + h + s; t, \varphi) - y(t + h + s; t, \varphi)| \\ &= \sup_{-h \leqslant s \leqslant 0} | z(t + h + s; t, \varphi) - y(t + h + s; t, \varphi)| \\ &\leqslant \epsilon h\{2MM_1 \epsilon^{\alpha} [\| \varphi \| + \epsilon h(M \| \varphi \| + 2M_2 L \| \varphi \|^{1+\beta} + L\eta)] e^{\epsilon Mh} \\ &\quad + 2LM_2 \| \varphi \|^{1+\beta} + L\eta\} e^{\epsilon Mh}. \end{aligned}$$

From this we obtain

$$\begin{aligned}&| V[z(t+h+s; t, \varphi)] - V[y(t+h+s; t, \varphi)]| \\ &\leqslant L_0\left(1+\frac{1}{\epsilon\gamma_0}\right)[2\|\varphi\| + \epsilon h(\ )]e^{\epsilon Mh}\epsilon h\{2MM_1\epsilon^\alpha[\|\varphi\| + \epsilon h(\ )]e^{\epsilon Mh} \\ &\quad + 2LM_2\|\varphi\|^{1+\beta} + L\eta\}e^{\epsilon Mh}.\end{aligned}$$

Hence

$$\begin{aligned}&\limsup_{h\to 0+} \frac{| V[z(t+h+s; t, \varphi)] - V[y(t+h+s; t, \varphi)]|}{h} \\ &\leqslant L_0\left[\epsilon + \frac{1}{\gamma_0}\right] 2\|\varphi\|[2MM_1\epsilon^\alpha\|\varphi\| + 2LM_2\|\varphi\|^{1+\beta}].\end{aligned}$$

Further, we obtain

$$\begin{aligned}&\limsup_{h\to 0+} \frac{V[z(t+h+s; t, \varphi)] - V[\varphi]}{h} \\ &\leqslant \limsup_{h\to 0+} \frac{V[z(t+h+s; t, \varphi)] - V[y(t+h+s; t, \varphi)]}{h} \\ &\quad + \limsup_{h\to 0+} \frac{V[y(t+h+s; t, \varphi)] - V[\varphi]}{h} \\ &\leqslant 4L_0\left(\epsilon + \frac{1}{\gamma_0}\right)[MM_1\epsilon^\alpha\|\varphi\|^2 + LM_2\|\varphi\|^{2+\beta}] - \|\varphi\|^2 \\ &= -\|\varphi\|^2\left[1 - 4L_0\left(\epsilon + \frac{1}{\gamma_0}\right)MM_1\epsilon^\alpha - 4LM_2L_0\left(\epsilon + \frac{1}{\gamma_0}\right)\|\varphi\|^\beta\right].\end{aligned}$$

For $\epsilon < \epsilon_0$ we have

$$4L_0\left(\epsilon + \frac{1}{\gamma_0}\right)M\epsilon^\alpha < \tfrac{1}{4},$$

and for $\|\varphi\| < \delta_0$ we have

$$4LM_2L_0\left(\epsilon + \frac{1}{\gamma_0}\right)\|\varphi\|^\beta < \tfrac{1}{4};$$

hence

$$\limsup_{h\to 0+} \frac{V[z(t+h+s; t, \varphi)] - V[\varphi]}{h} \leqslant -\tfrac{1}{2}\|\varphi\|^2.$$

The lemma is thus proved.

Lemma 6. *We consider the system*

$$\begin{aligned}\dot{x}(t) = \epsilon\{&E[A(t, x(t), x(t-\tau), \epsilon)][H_1x(t) + H_2x(t-\tau) + B(x(t), x(t-\tau))] \\ &+ C(t, x(t), x(t-\tau), \epsilon)\}\end{aligned}$$

where H_1, H_2, B are as in the preceding lemma, $A(t, u, v, \epsilon)$ and $C(t, u, v, \epsilon)$ are periodic with respect to t of period T, and

$$| A(t, u, v, \epsilon)| < M_1\epsilon^{\alpha}, \qquad | C(t, u, v, \epsilon)| < M_3\epsilon^{1-\alpha}, \qquad \alpha < \tfrac{1}{2}.$$

Then the system admits for $\epsilon > 0$ sufficiently small a periodic solution of period T which for $\epsilon \to 0$ tends to zero.

Proof. We have

$$x(u; t, \varphi) = \varphi(t) + \epsilon \int_t^u \{[E + A][H_1 x(v; t, \varphi) + H_2\varphi(v - \tau) + B] + C\}dv$$

$$z(u; t, \varphi) = \varphi(t) + \epsilon \int_t^u [E + A][H_1 z(v; t, \varphi) + H_2\varphi(v - \tau) + B]dv$$

$$| x(u; t, \varphi) - z(u; t, \varphi)| \leqslant \epsilon M_4 \int_t^u | x(v; t, \varphi) - z(v; t, \varphi)| \, dv$$
$$+ \epsilon^{\alpha+1}h\| \varphi \| + 2M_2L\| \varphi \|^{1+\beta}\epsilon h + L\eta\epsilon h + \epsilon h M_3\epsilon^{1-\alpha};$$

hence

$$| x(u; t, \varphi) - z(u; t, \varphi)| \leqslant \epsilon h[M_3\epsilon^{1-\alpha} + M\epsilon^{\alpha}\| \varphi \| + 2M_2L\| \varphi \|^{1+\beta}]e^{\epsilon h M_4}$$

and

$$\| x(t + h + s; t, \varphi) - z(t + h + s; t, \varphi)\|$$
$$\leqslant \epsilon h[M_3\epsilon^{1-\alpha} + M\epsilon^{\alpha}\| \varphi \| + 2M_2L\| \varphi \|^{1+\beta}]e^{\epsilon h M_4},$$

$$\| x(t + h + s; t, \varphi)\|$$
$$\leqslant \| z(t + h + s; t, \varphi)\| + \epsilon h e^{\epsilon h M_4}[M_3\epsilon^{1-\alpha} + M\epsilon^{\alpha}\| \varphi \| + 2M_2L\| \varphi \|^{1+\beta}]$$
$$\leqslant \{\| \varphi \| + \epsilon h(M\| \varphi \| + 2M_2L\| \varphi \|^{1+\beta} + L\eta)\}e^{\epsilon M h}$$
$$+ \epsilon h[M_3\epsilon^{1-\alpha} + M\epsilon^{\alpha}\| \varphi \| + 2M_2L\| \varphi \|^{1+\beta}]e^{\epsilon h M_4}$$
$$\leqslant \{\| \varphi \| + \epsilon h(\quad)\}e^{\epsilon M_5 h}.$$

From here follows

$$| V[x(t + h + s; t, \varphi)] - V[z(t + h + s; t, \varphi)]|$$
$$\leqslant L_0\left(1 + \frac{1}{\epsilon\gamma_0}\right)\{2\| \varphi \| + 2\epsilon h(\quad)\}$$
$$\times e^{\epsilon h(M_5+M_4)}h\epsilon[M_3\epsilon^{1-\alpha} + M\epsilon^{\alpha}\| \varphi \| + 2M_2L\| \varphi \|^{1+\beta}];$$

hence

$$\limsup_{h\to 0+} \frac{V[x(t + h + s; t, \varphi)] - V[z(t + h + s; t, \varphi)]}{h}$$
$$\leqslant 2L_0\left(\epsilon + \frac{1}{\gamma_0}\right) M_6\| \varphi \|[\epsilon^{1-\alpha} + \epsilon^{\alpha}\| \varphi \| + \| \varphi \|^{1+\beta}].$$

We finally obtain

$$\limsup_{h\to 0+} \frac{V[x(t+h+s;t,\varphi)] - V[\varphi]}{h}$$

$$\leqslant 2L_0\left(\epsilon + \frac{1}{\gamma_0}\right) M_6 \|\varphi\| [\epsilon^{1-\alpha} + \epsilon^{\alpha}\|\varphi\| + \|\varphi\|^{1+\beta}] - \tfrac{1}{2}\|\varphi\|^2$$

$$= \|\varphi\| [M_7 \epsilon^{1-\alpha} + M_7 \epsilon^{\alpha}\|\varphi\| + M_7\|\varphi\|^{1+\beta} - \tfrac{1}{2}\|\varphi\|].$$

For $0 < \epsilon < \epsilon_0$, $\|\varphi\| < \delta_0$, we have

$$M_7 \epsilon^{\alpha}\|\varphi\| + M_7\|\varphi\|^{1+\beta} < \tfrac{1}{4}\|\varphi\|;$$

hence

$$\limsup_{h\to 0+} \frac{V[x(t+h+s;t,\varphi)] - V[\varphi]}{h} \leqslant \|\varphi\| [M_7 \epsilon^{1-\alpha} - \tfrac{1}{4}\|\varphi\|].$$

Now let $C = \delta_0^2$, $V[\varphi] \leqslant C$. We have $V[x(t+s;\varphi)] \leqslant C$ for $t = 0$. If there exist a t_1 in $(0, T)$ such that $V[x(t_1+s;\varphi)] > C$ there exists a t_2 satisfying $0 \leqslant t_2 < T$ such that $V[x(t_2+s;\varphi)] = C$ and $V[x(t_2+h+s;\varphi)] > C$ for $0 < h < \delta$; hence

$$\limsup_{h\to 0+} \frac{V[x(t_2+h+s;\varphi)] - V[x(t_2+s;\varphi)]}{h} \geqslant 0.$$

However,

$$\limsup_{h\to 0+} \frac{V[x(t_2+h+s;\varphi)] - V[x(t_2+s;\varphi)]}{h}$$

$$= \limsup_{h\to 0+} \frac{V[x(t_2+h+s;t_2, x(t_2+s;\varphi))] - V[x(t_2+s;\varphi)]}{h}$$

$$\leqslant \|x(t_2+s;\varphi)\| [M_7 \epsilon^{1-\alpha} - \tfrac{1}{4}\|x(t_2+s;\varphi)\|].$$

From $V[x(t_2+s;\varphi)] = C$ we obtain

$$C \leqslant K^2\left(1 + \frac{1}{2\epsilon\gamma_0}\right)\|x(t_2+s;\varphi)\|^2$$

and

$$\|x(t_2+s;\varphi)\|^2 \leqslant C = \delta_0^2;$$

hence

$$\|x(t_2+s;\varphi)\| \leqslant \delta_0$$

and

$$\| x(t_2 + s; \varphi)\| \geqslant \frac{\sqrt{C}}{K\sqrt{1 + (1/2\epsilon\gamma_0)}},$$

$$-\tfrac{1}{4}\| x(t_2 + s; \varphi)\| \leqslant -\frac{1}{4K}\frac{\sqrt{2C\gamma_0}}{\sqrt{1 + 2\epsilon\gamma_0}}\sqrt{\epsilon}.$$

From this we obtain

$$\limsup_{h\to 0+} \frac{V[x(t_2 + h + s; t_2, x(t_2 + s; \varphi))] - V[x(t_2 + s; \varphi)]}{h}$$

$$\leqslant \| x(t_2 + s; \varphi)\| [M_7\epsilon^{1-\alpha} - M_8\sqrt{\epsilon}\,].$$

However, $\alpha < \frac{1}{2}$, $1 - \alpha > \frac{1}{2}$; hence for $\epsilon > 0$ small enough we have $M_7\epsilon^{1-\alpha} - M_8\sqrt{\epsilon} < 0$ and this leads us to a contradiction. Consequently, $V[x(t + s; \varphi)] \leqslant C$ for all $t \in [0, T]$ and $V[x(T + s; \varphi)] \leqslant C$.

We have thus shown that the closed, bounded, and convex set $V[\varphi] \leqslant C$ is mapped into itself by the completely continuous operator $U[\varphi] = x(T + s; \varphi)$. It follows from this that there exists a fixed point of this operator; to this fixed point corresponds a periodic solution of the system, of period T. Our computations show that we can take $C = O(\epsilon^{\alpha'})$, $\alpha' < 1 - 2\alpha$, from which it follows that the periodic solution obtained tends to zero when $\epsilon \to 0$.

Proof of Theorem 4.33. We perform in system (84) the change $z = \zeta_0 + b$. We obtain the system

$$\dot{b}(t) = \epsilon B(t, b(t), b(t - \tau), \epsilon),$$

where B has the same regularity properties as Z and is periodic in t of period T. Let

$$B_0(u, v, \epsilon) = \frac{1}{T}\int_0^T B(t, u, v, \epsilon)dt.$$

Obviously,

$$B_0(0, 0, 0) = 0.$$

We let

$$B^*(t, u, v, \epsilon) = B(t, u, v, \epsilon) - B_0(u, v, \epsilon).$$

We have

$$\frac{1}{T}\int_0^T B^*(t, u, v, \epsilon)dt = 0.$$

Let

$$B_\eta^*(t, u, v, \epsilon) = \int_{-\infty}^t e^{-\eta(t-s)}B^*(s, u, v, \epsilon)ds.$$

We have

$$B_\eta^*(t, u, v, \epsilon) = \int_0^\infty e^{-\eta\sigma} B^*(t-\sigma; u, v, \epsilon) d\sigma$$

$$= \sum_{n=0}^{\infty} e^{-n\eta T} \int_{nT}^{(n+1)T} B^*(t-\sigma, u, v, \epsilon) e^{-\eta(\sigma-nT)}\, d\sigma$$

$$= \sum_{n=0}^{\infty} e^{-n\eta T} \int_0^T e^{-\eta\sigma} B^*(t-\sigma; u, v, \epsilon) d\sigma$$

$$= \frac{1}{1-e^{-\eta T}} \int_0^T e^{-\eta s} B^*(t-s; u, v, \epsilon) ds.$$

Let

$$B^{**}(\sigma; u, v, \epsilon) = \int_0^\sigma B^*(\xi; u, v, \epsilon) d\xi.$$

We have further

$$B_\eta^*(t; u, v, \epsilon) = \frac{1}{1-e^{-\eta T}} \int_0^T e^{-\eta s} B^*(t-s; u, v, \epsilon) ds$$

$$= \frac{-1}{1-e^{-\eta T}} \int_t^{t-T} e^{-\eta t} e^{\eta\sigma} B^*(\sigma; u, v, \epsilon) d\sigma$$

$$= \frac{e^{-\eta t}}{1-e^{-\eta T}} \int_{t-T}^{t} e^{\eta\sigma} B^*(\sigma; u, v, \epsilon) d\sigma = \frac{e^{-\eta t}}{1-e^{-\eta T}} \int_{t-T}^{t} e^{\eta\sigma}\, dB^{**}$$

$$= \frac{e^{-\eta t}}{1-e^{-\eta T}} [e^{\eta\sigma} B^{**}] \Big|_{t-T}^{t} - \frac{\eta e^{-\eta t}}{1-e^{-\eta T}} \int_{t-T}^{t} e^{\eta\sigma} B^{**}(\sigma; u, v, \epsilon) d\sigma$$

$$= \frac{e^{-\eta t}}{1-e^{-\eta T}} [e^{\eta t} B^{**}(t, u, v, \epsilon) - e^{\eta t} e^{\eta T} B^{**}(t, u, v, \epsilon)]$$

$$- \frac{\eta e^{-\eta t}}{1-e^{-\eta T}} \int_0^T e^{\eta(t-s)} B^{**}(t-s; u, v, \epsilon) ds$$

$$= B^{**}(t, u, v, \epsilon) - \frac{\eta}{1-e^{-\eta T}} \int_0^T e^{-\eta s} B^{**}(t-s; u, v, \epsilon) ds.$$

However, B^* has the mean value zero, hence B^{**} is a periodic function; hence B^{**} is bounded. It follows that

$$| B_\eta^*(t, u, v, \epsilon)| \leqslant M + M \frac{\eta}{1-e^{-\eta T}} \int_0^T e^{-\eta s}\, ds = 2M.$$

Let us observe that

$$\frac{\partial}{\partial t} B_\eta^*(t, u, v, \epsilon) = - \int_{-\infty}^{t} \eta e^{-\eta(t-s)} B^*(s, u, v, \epsilon) ds + B^*(t, u, v, \epsilon)$$

$$= - \eta B_\eta^*(t, u, v, \epsilon) + B^*(t, u, v, \epsilon).$$

Further,

$$\frac{\partial}{\partial u} B_\eta^*(t, u, v, \epsilon) = \int_{-\infty}^{t} e^{-\eta(t-s)} \frac{\partial}{\partial u} B^*(s, u, v, \epsilon) ds,$$

$$\frac{\partial}{\partial u} B^*(s, u, v, \epsilon) = \frac{\partial}{\partial u} B(s, u, v, \epsilon) - \frac{\partial}{\partial u} B_0(u, v, \epsilon).$$

However,

$$\frac{\partial}{\partial u} B_0(u, v, \epsilon) = \frac{1}{T} \int_0^T \frac{\partial}{\partial u} B(t, u, v, \epsilon) dt;$$

hence

$$\frac{1}{T} \int_0^T \frac{\partial}{\partial u} B^*(s, u, v, \epsilon) ds = 0.$$

It follows from here that the matrix $(\partial/\partial u)B^*(t, u, v, \epsilon)$ has the mean value zero, hence that all the computations we have carried out for the vector $B^*(t, u, v, \epsilon)$ can be repeated. We finally obtain

$$\left| \frac{\partial}{\partial u} B_\eta^*(t, u, v, \epsilon) \right| < M_1$$

and, analogously,

$$\left| \frac{\partial}{\partial v} B_\eta^*(t, u, v, \epsilon) \right| < M_2 .$$

Let us now perform in the system the change of variables

$$\dot{b}(t) = h(t) + \epsilon B_\eta^*(t, h(t), h(t), \epsilon).$$

We obtain

$$\dot{h}(t) + \epsilon \frac{\partial B_\eta^*(t, h(t), h(t), \epsilon)}{\partial t} + \epsilon \frac{\partial B_\eta^*(t, h(t), h(t), \epsilon)}{\partial u} \dot{h}(t)$$

$$+ \epsilon \frac{\partial B_\eta^*(t, h(t), h(t), \epsilon)}{\partial v} \dot{h}(t)$$

$$= \epsilon B[t, h(t) + \epsilon B_\eta^* , h(t - \tau) + \epsilon B_\eta^* , \epsilon]$$

$$= \epsilon B_0[h(t) + \epsilon B_\eta^* , h(t - \tau) + \epsilon B_\eta^* , \epsilon]$$

$$+ \epsilon B^*[t, h(t) + \epsilon B_\eta^* , h(t - \tau) + \epsilon B_\eta^* , \epsilon],$$

$$B_0[h(t) + \epsilon B_\eta^* , h(t - \tau) + \epsilon B_\eta^* , \epsilon] = B_0[h(t), h(t - \tau), \epsilon] + O(\epsilon)$$

$$= H_1 h(t) + H_2 h(t - \tau) + B_1[h(t), h(t - \tau)] + O(\epsilon),$$

where

$$H_1 = \frac{\partial}{\partial u} B_0(0, 0, 0), \qquad H_2 = \frac{\partial}{\partial v} B_0(0, 0, 0).$$

From

$$B_0(u, v, \epsilon) = \frac{1}{T}\int_0^T B(t, u, v, \epsilon)dt$$
$$= \frac{1}{T}\int_0^T Z(t, \zeta^0 + u, \zeta^0 + v, \epsilon)dt = Z_0(\zeta^0 + u, \zeta^0 + v, \epsilon)$$

we obtain

$$H_1 = \frac{\partial}{\partial u} Z_0(\zeta^0, \zeta^0, 0), \qquad H_2 = \frac{\partial}{\partial v} Z_0(\zeta^0, \zeta^0, 0).$$

Further,

$$B^*[t, h(t) + \epsilon B^*_\eta, h(t-\tau) + \epsilon B^*_\eta, \epsilon]$$
$$= B^*[t, h(t) + \epsilon B^*_\eta, h(t) + \epsilon B^*_\eta, \epsilon] + O(\epsilon) = B^*[t, h(t), h(t), \epsilon] + O(\epsilon).$$

We have

$$\left(E + \epsilon \frac{\partial B^*_\eta}{\partial u} + \epsilon \frac{\partial B^*_\eta}{\partial v}\right) \dot{h}(t) = \epsilon H_1 h(t) + \epsilon H_2 h(t-\tau) + \epsilon B_1[h(t), h(t-\tau)]$$
$$+ \epsilon B^*[t, h(t), h(t), \epsilon] - \epsilon \frac{\partial}{\partial t} B^*_\eta[t, h(t), h(t), \epsilon] + \epsilon O(\epsilon).$$

However,

$$\left[E + \epsilon \frac{\partial B^*_\eta}{\partial u} + \epsilon \frac{\partial B^*_\eta}{\partial v}\right]^{-1} = E + O(\epsilon)$$

and

$$B^*[t, h(t), h(t), \epsilon] - \frac{\partial}{\partial t} B^*_\eta[t, h(t), h(t), \epsilon] = \eta B^*_\eta[t, h(t), h(t), \epsilon].$$

Let $\eta = \epsilon$. We finally obtain the system

$$\dot{h}(t) = \epsilon\{[E + O(\epsilon)][H_1 h(t) + H_2 h(t-\tau) + B_1(h(t), h(t-\tau))] + O(\epsilon)\}.$$

This system verifies the conditions of Lemma 6; hence for $\epsilon > 0$ small enough it has a periodic solution $h(t)$ of period T which for $\epsilon \to 0$ approaches zero. However $B^*_\epsilon(t, u, v, \epsilon)$ is a periodic function of period T; hence we obtain a solution $b(t)$ periodic of period T which for $\epsilon \to 0$ approaches zero. This means, however, that system (84) has a periodic solution $z(t)$ of period T which for $\epsilon \to 0$ tends to ζ^0. The theorem is thus proved.

Let us point out a consequence of this theorem. We consider the system

$$\dot{x}(t) = X_0(t, x) + \epsilon X_1[t, x(t), x(t-\tau), \epsilon], \tag{86}$$

where X_0 and X_1 are periodic with respect to t of period T. We suppose that the general solution of the system

$$\dot{x}(t) = X_0(t, x)$$

is periodic of period T. Let $x_0(t, h)$ be this solution.

We perform the change of variables $x = x_0(t, z)$. We obtain

$$\frac{\partial x_0(t, z)}{\partial t} + \frac{\partial x_0}{\partial z}\frac{dz}{dt} = X_0[t, x_0(t, z)] + \epsilon X_1[t, x_0(t, z(t)), x_0(t - \tau, z(t - \tau))].$$

However,

$$\frac{\partial x_0(t, z)}{\partial t} = X_0[t, x_0(t, z)];$$

$x_0(t, h)$ is the general solution, hence the matrix $\partial x_0/\partial z$ has an inverse. From this we obtain

$$\dot{z}(t) = \epsilon \left[\frac{\partial x_0(t, z(t))}{\partial z}\right]^{-1} X_1[t, x_0(t, z(t)), x_0(t - \tau, z(t - \tau)), \epsilon].$$

If we apply Theorem 4.33, we obtain the following result: Let ζ^0 be a solution of the system

$$Z_0(\zeta^0, \zeta^0, 0) = \frac{1}{T}\int_0^T \left(\frac{\partial x_0(t, \zeta^0)}{\partial z}\right)^{-1} X_1[t, x_0(t, \zeta^0), x_0(t, \zeta^0), 0]dt = 0$$

such that the matrix $[\partial Z_0(\zeta^0, \zeta^0, 0)/\partial u] + [\partial Z_0(\zeta^0, \zeta^0, 0)/\partial v]$ has all eigenvalues with negative real parts; then system (86) has a periodic solution of period T which for $\epsilon \to 0$ tends to the solution $x_0(t, \zeta^0)$ of the generating system. Let us observe that in the case where X_0 and X_1 are analytic, this result follows from Theorem 4.27.

Theorem 4.34. *We consider system (86) and suppose that X_0 and X_1 are almost periodic in t, uniformly with respect to the other variables, and that they have partial derivatives continuous up to the second order inclusively. We suppose that the system*

$$\dot{x} = X_0(t, x)$$

has the general solution $x_0(t, h)$ almost periodic in t, uniformly with respect to h. Let

$$Z(t, u, v, \epsilon) = \left[\frac{\partial x_0(t, u)}{\partial u}\right]^{-1} X_1[t, x_0(t, u), x_0(t - \tau, v), \epsilon].$$

We write

$$Z_0(u, v, \epsilon) = \lim_{T\to\infty} \frac{1}{T}\int_0^T Z(t, u, v, \epsilon)dt.$$

Let ζ^0 be the solution of the equation $Z_0(u, u, 0) = 0$. If the eigenvalues of the matrix $(\partial/\partial u)Z_0(\zeta^0, \zeta^0, 0) + (\partial/\partial v)Z_0(\zeta^0, \zeta^0, 0)$ have negative real parts, then there exists an $\epsilon_0 > 0$ such that for $0 < \epsilon \leqslant \epsilon_0$ system (86) admits a unique almost-periodic solution $x(t, \epsilon)$ with the property

$$\lim_{\epsilon \to 0} x(t, \epsilon) = x_0(t, \zeta^0).$$

Proof. After the change of variables $x = x_0(t, z)$ we obtain the system

$$\dot{z}(t) = \epsilon Z(t, z(t), z(t-\tau), \epsilon),$$

and after the new change of variables $z = \zeta^0 + b$ we obtain

$$\frac{db(t)}{dt} = \epsilon B[t, b(t), b(t-\tau), \epsilon].$$

We write

$$B_0(u, v, \epsilon) = \lim_{T\to\infty} \frac{1}{T} \int_0^T B(t, u, v, \epsilon)dt,$$

$$B^*(t, u, v, \epsilon) = B(t, u, v, \epsilon) - B_0(u, b, v, \epsilon).$$

We have

$$B_0(0, 0, 0) = 0, \qquad \lim_{T\to\infty} \frac{1}{T} \int_0^T B^*(t, u, v, \epsilon)dt = 0.$$

Let

$$B_\epsilon^*(t, u, v, \epsilon) = \int_{-\infty}^t e^{-\epsilon(t-s)} B^*(s, u, v, \epsilon)ds.$$

Then B_ϵ^* is an almost-periodic function of t, and on the basis of a lemma of N. N. Bogoliubov (Chapter 3) we have

$$|B_\epsilon^*| \leqslant \frac{\zeta(\epsilon)}{\epsilon}.$$

where $\lim_{\epsilon\to 0} \zeta(\epsilon) = 0$.

We perform the new change of variables

$$b(t) = h(t) + \epsilon B_\epsilon^*(t, h(t), h(t), \epsilon).$$

We obtain

$$\dot{h}(t) + \epsilon \frac{\partial B_\epsilon^*}{dt} + \epsilon \frac{\partial B_\epsilon^*}{\partial u} \dot{h}(t) + \epsilon \frac{\partial B_\epsilon^*}{\partial v} \dot{h}(t) = \epsilon B_0 + \epsilon B^*.$$

However,

$$\begin{aligned} &B_0[h(t) + \epsilon B_\epsilon^*(t, h(t), h(t), \epsilon), h(t-\tau) + \epsilon B_\epsilon^*(t-\tau, h(t-\tau), h(t-\tau), \epsilon), \epsilon] \\ &\quad = B_0[h(t), h(t-\tau), \epsilon] + O(\zeta(\epsilon)) \\ &\quad = H_1 h(t) + H_2 h(t-\tau) + B_1(h(t), h(t-\tau)] + O(\zeta(\epsilon)) + O(\epsilon), \end{aligned}$$

where

$$H_1 = \frac{\partial Z_0}{\partial u}(\zeta^0, \zeta^0, 0), \qquad H_2 = \frac{\partial Z_0}{\partial v}(\zeta^0, \zeta^0, 0),$$

$$| B_1(u, v)| \leqslant B(| u | + | v |)^2,$$

$$| B_1(u_1, v_1) - B_1(u_2, v_2)| \leqslant \beta(| u_1 | + | v_1 | + | u_2 | + | v_2 |)(| u_1 - u_2 | + | v_1 - v_2 |).$$

Further,

$$B^*[t, h(t) + \epsilon B_\epsilon^*(t, h(t), h(t), \epsilon), h(t-\tau) + \epsilon B_\epsilon^*(t-\tau, h(t-\tau), h(t-\tau), \epsilon), \epsilon]$$
$$= B^*[t, h(t) + \epsilon B_\epsilon^*(t, h(t), h(t), \epsilon), h(t) + \epsilon B_\epsilon^*(t, h(t), h(t), \epsilon), \epsilon]$$
$$+ O(\epsilon) + O(\zeta(\epsilon)) = B^*[t, h(t), h(t), \epsilon] + O(\epsilon) + O(\zeta(\epsilon)).$$

From

$$\frac{\partial}{\partial t} B_\epsilon^*(t, u, v, \epsilon) = B^*(t, u, v, \epsilon) - \epsilon B_\epsilon^*(t, u, v, \epsilon)$$

it follows that

$$\frac{\partial}{\partial t} B^*[t, h(t), h(t), \epsilon] = B^*[t, h(t), h(t), \epsilon] - \epsilon B_\epsilon^*[t, h(t), h(t), \epsilon];$$

hence

$$B^*[t, h(t), h(t), \epsilon] - \frac{\partial}{\partial t} B_\epsilon^*[t, h(t), h(t), \epsilon] = O(\zeta(\epsilon)).$$

Further, from

$$\epsilon\left(\left|\frac{\partial B_\epsilon^*}{\partial u}\right| + \left|\frac{\partial B_\epsilon^*}{\partial v}\right|\right) < \zeta_1(\epsilon)$$

we deduce

$$\left[E + \epsilon\frac{\partial B_\epsilon^*}{\partial u} + \epsilon\frac{\partial B_\epsilon^*}{\partial v}\right]^{-1} = E + O(\zeta_2(\epsilon)),$$

where $\lim_{\epsilon\to 0} \zeta_2(\epsilon) = 0$.

We finally obtain

$$\dot{h}(t) = \epsilon H_1 h(t) + \epsilon H_2 h(t-\tau) + \epsilon B_1[h(t), h(t-\tau)] + \epsilon\Gamma[t, h(t), h(t-\tau), \epsilon];$$

here $H_1 = \partial Z_0(\zeta^0, \zeta^0, 0)/\partial u$, $H_2 = \partial Z_0(\zeta^0, \zeta^0, 0)/\partial v$, B_1 verifies the inequalities written above, and $| \Gamma(t, u, v, \epsilon)| < \gamma(\epsilon)$ with $\lim_{\epsilon\to 0} \gamma(\epsilon) = 0$; Γ is almost periodic in t, uniformly with respect to the other variables. We prove that for $0 < \epsilon < \epsilon_0$, this system admits a unique almost-periodic solution, which for $\epsilon \to 0$ tends to zero.

We deduce from the fact that the eigenvalues of the matrix $H_1 + H_2$ have negative real parts, on the basis of Lemmas 4 and 5, that there exists a functional $V[\varphi]$ with the following properties:

1. $\frac{1}{\epsilon}\|\varphi\|^2 \leqslant V[\varphi] \leqslant \frac{K_1}{\epsilon}\|\varphi\|^2,$

2. $|V[\varphi_1] - V[\varphi_2]| \leqslant \frac{L_0}{\epsilon}(\|\varphi_1\| + \|\varphi_2\|)\|\varphi_1 - \varphi_2\|,$

3. $$\limsup_{h\to 0+} \frac{V[y(t+h+s; t_0, \varphi)] - V[y(t+s; t_0, \varphi)]}{h} \leqslant -\|y(t+s; t_0, \varphi)\|^2,$$

where $y(t; t_0, \varphi)$ is the solution of system (85).

From here, as in the proof of Theorem 4.30, we deduce that for every almost-periodic $f(t)$ the system

$$\dot{x}(t) = \epsilon H_1 x(t) + \epsilon H_2 x(t-\tau) + f(t)$$

admits a unique almost-periodic solution $x_0(t)$ for which we have the estimate

$$|x_0(t)| < \frac{L}{\epsilon}\sup|f|.$$

Let $h_0(t)$ be the almost-periodic solution of the system

$$\dot{h}(t) = \epsilon H_1 h(t) + \epsilon H_2 h(t-\tau) + \epsilon\Gamma(t, 0, 0, \epsilon).$$

We have

$$|h_0(t)| \leqslant \frac{L}{\epsilon}\epsilon\gamma(\epsilon) = L\gamma(\epsilon).$$

Further, let $h_k(t)$ be the almost-periodic solution of the system

$$\dot{h}(t) = \epsilon H_1 h(t) + \epsilon H_2 h(t-\tau) - B_1[h_{k-1}(t), h_{k-1}(t-\tau)] + \epsilon\Gamma[t, h_{k-1}(t), h_{k-1}(t-\tau), \epsilon].$$

We suppose, by induction, that

$$|h_{k-1}(t)| \leqslant 2L\gamma(\epsilon).$$

Then

$$|B_1[h_{k-1}(t), h_{k-1}(t-\tau)]| \leqslant 16\beta L^2\gamma^2(\epsilon);$$

hence

$$|h_k(t)| < \frac{L}{\epsilon}\epsilon[16\beta L^2\gamma^2(\epsilon) + \gamma(\epsilon)] = L[16\beta L^2\gamma^2(\epsilon) + \gamma(\epsilon)].$$

If $\gamma(\epsilon) < 1/16\beta L^2$, we deduce $| h_k(t)| \leqslant 2L\gamma(\epsilon)$ and the estimate is proved. Let $l_k(t) = h_k(t) - h_{k-1}(t)$. We have

$$\begin{aligned} \dot{l}_{k+1}(t) = {} & \epsilon H_1 l_{k+1}(t) + \epsilon H_2 l_{k+1}(t-\tau) \\ & + \epsilon B_1[h_k(t), h_k(t-\tau)] - \epsilon B_1[h_{k-1}(t), h_{k-1}(t-\tau)] \\ & + \epsilon \Gamma[t, h_k(t), h_k(t-\tau), \epsilon] - \epsilon \Gamma[t, h_{k-1}(t), h_{k-1}(t-\tau), \epsilon]. \end{aligned}$$

According to the hypotheses,

$$| \epsilon B_1[h_k(t), h_k(t-\tau)] - \epsilon B_1[h_{k-1}(t), h_{k-1}(t-\tau)]| \leqslant 16\epsilon\beta\gamma L(\epsilon) \sup | l_k |.$$

From here follows

$$| l_{k+1}(t)| \leqslant \frac{L}{\epsilon} \epsilon[16\beta L\gamma(\epsilon) \sup | l_k | + 2\gamma(\epsilon)].$$

We have $| l_0 | = h_0 | \leqslant L\gamma(\epsilon)$; we suppose that $| l_k | \leqslant 3L\gamma(\epsilon)$. It follows that $| l_{k+1}(t)| \leqslant L[48\beta L^2\gamma^2(\epsilon) + 2\gamma(\epsilon)]$; if $\gamma(\epsilon) < 1/48\beta^2$ we deduce that $| l_{k+1}(t)| \leqslant 3L\gamma(\epsilon)$, and the estimate is established.

From this follows the uniform convergence of the successive approximations, hence the existence of the almost-periodic solution of the system in h. Taking into account the change of variables performed, we deduce the existence of an almost-periodic solution of system (86) with all the required properties. The theorem is thus proved.

4.16. Other Theorems Relative to Periodic and Almost-Periodic Solutions of Systems with Time Lag

We shall now give some theorems relative to periodic and almost-periodic solutions of systems with time lag.

Theorem 4.35. *We consider the general system* (59). *If for* $\mu = 0$ *the system admits a periodic solution* $x_0(t)$, *of period* $\omega > \tau$, *uniformly asymptotically stable, then for* $| \mu |$ *sufficiently small, system* (59) *admits a periodic solution* $x(t, \mu)$ *with the property*

$$\lim_{\mu \to 0} x(t, \mu) = x_0(t).$$

Proof. Let U_ω^μ be the operator defined by the relation

$$U_\omega^\mu \varphi = x(t+s; \varphi, \mu),$$

where $x(t; \varphi, \mu)$ is the solution of system (59) which in $[-\tau, 0]$ coincides with φ. We will prove with the help of a theorem of F. Browder that U

has a fixed point. We do not restrict the generality by taking $x_0(t) \equiv 0$, since we obtain this condition through a simple change of variables which preserves the properties of the system. The uniform asymptotic stability signifies the existence of a number $\delta_0 > 0$ and of two functions $\delta(\epsilon)$ and $T(\epsilon)$ such that if $\| \varphi \| < \delta(\epsilon)$, then $| x(t; \varphi, 0)| < \epsilon$ for $t \geqslant -\tau$ and if $\| \varphi \| < \delta_0$, $t > T(\epsilon)$, then $| x(t; \varphi, 0) | < \epsilon$. Let $\delta_1 = \delta(\frac{1}{2}h)$, $0 < \eta < \min\{\delta_0, \delta(\frac{1}{2}\delta_1)\}$, $T = T[\frac{1}{2}\delta(\frac{1}{2}\eta)]$, m the smallest natural number for which $m\omega > T + \tau$.

Let S be the sphere $\| \varphi \| < \delta_1$. Then $| x(t; \varphi, 0)| < \frac{1}{2}h$ for $\varphi \in S$ and $t \geqslant -\tau$. If $| \mu |$ is small enough, we obtain $| x(t, \varphi, \mu)| < h$ for $\varphi \in S$, $-\tau \leqslant t \leqslant m\omega$. It follows from here that for $\varphi \in S$ we have $\| U^\mu_\omega \varphi \| < h$, and also taking into account system (59) it follows that the operator U^μ_ω is compact in S. From the estimate obtained it also follows that the solutions with $\varphi \in S$ are defined for $-\tau < t \leqslant m\omega$, hence the operator is defined for all $\varphi \in S$. Let S_1 be the sphere $\| \varphi \| < \eta$ and S_0 the sphere $\| \varphi \| \leqslant \frac{3}{4}\delta(\frac{1}{2}\eta)$. For $\| \varphi \| < \eta, t \geqslant -\tau$ we have $| x(t; \varphi, 0)| < \frac{1}{2}\delta_1$, since $\eta < \delta(\frac{1}{2}\delta_1)$; for $| \mu |$ small enough we obtain $| x(t; \varphi, \mu)| < \delta_1$ for $-\tau \leqslant t \leqslant m\omega$. From here we deduce $[U^\mu_\omega]^j(S_1) \subset S$ for $0 \leqslant j \leqslant m$, since $[U^\mu_\omega]^j(\varphi) = x(j\omega + s; \varphi, \mu)$. From $\| \varphi \| \leqslant \frac{3}{4}\delta(\frac{1}{2}\eta)$, $t \geqslant -\tau$ we obtain $| x(t; \varphi, 0)| < \frac{1}{2}\eta$, hence for $| \mu |$ small enough we obtain $| x(t; \varphi, \mu)| < \eta$ if $\| \varphi \| \leqslant \frac{3}{4}\delta(\frac{1}{2}\eta)$, $-\tau \leqslant t \leqslant m\omega$ and thus $[U^\mu_\omega]^j(S_0) \subset S_1$ for $0 \leqslant j \leqslant m$. It follows from $\eta < \delta_0$ that for $\varphi \in S_1$, $t > T$ we have $| x(t, \varphi, 0)| < \frac{1}{2}\delta(\frac{1}{2}\eta)$; hence for $| \mu |$ small enough $| x(t; \varphi, \mu)| \leqslant \frac{3}{4}\delta(\frac{1}{2}\eta)$ if $\varphi \in S_1$, $m\omega - \tau \leqslant t \leqslant m\omega$, i.e., $[U^\mu_\omega]^m(S_1) \subset S_0$. The conditions of the theorem of F. Browder are thus fulfilled; the operator U^μ_ω has a fixed point, hence system (59) has a periodic solution with the property in the statement.

Definition. *A solution $x_0(t)$ of the general system (2) is called stable (T) if there exists $\delta > 0$ such that $\sup_{t-\tau \leqslant s \leqslant t} | x(s) - x_0(s)| < \delta$ implies $\lim_{t\to\infty} \sup_{t-\tau \leqslant s \leqslant t} | x(s) - x_0(s)| = 0$, whichever be the solution $x(t)$ of the system.*

Theorem 4.36. *If f is periodic in t with period ω and if system (2) admits a bounded solution, stable (T), then it admits a periodic solution of period $k\omega$.*

Proof. Let $x_0(t)$ be the bounded and stable (T) solution. We consider the family of functions $\varphi_n(s) = x_0(s + n\omega)$, $s \in [-\tau, 0]$. We have $| \varphi_n(s)| < M$, and for n large enough we also obtain $| \dot\varphi_n(s)| < L(M)$; hence the set $\{\varphi_n(s)\}$ is compact. It follows from this that there exist two numbers n_1 and n_2 such that $\max_{-\tau \leqslant s \leqslant 0} | \varphi_{n_1}(s) - \varphi_{n_2}(s)| < \delta$. Let $n_2 > n_1$, $k = n_2 - n_1$.

We consider the solution $x_0(t + k\omega)$; we have

$$\max_{n_1\omega-\tau\leqslant t\leqslant n_1\omega} | x_0(t + k\omega) - x_0(t)| = \max_{-\tau\leqslant s\leqslant 0} | x_0(s + n_1\omega + k\omega) - x_0(s + n_1\omega)|$$
$$= \max_{-\tau\leqslant s\leqslant 0} | x_0(s + n_2\omega) - x_0(s + n_1\omega)|$$
$$= \max_{-\tau\leqslant s\leqslant 0} | \varphi_{n_2}(s) - \varphi_{n_1}(s)| < \delta.$$

Since the solution $x_0(t)$ is stable (T), it follows that

$$\lim_{t\to\infty} \max_{t-\tau\leqslant s\leqslant t} | x_0(s + k\omega) - x_0(s)| = 0.$$

From the fact that the set $\{\varphi_n(s)\}$ is compact, it follows that there exists a limit point φ^*; let $\varphi^*(s) = \lim_{j\to\infty} \varphi_{n_j}$ and $x^*(t) = x(t; 0, \varphi^*(s))$. Then

$$x^*(t) = \lim_{j\to\infty} x_0(t + n_j\omega)$$

since

$$x_0(t + n_j\omega) = x(t; 0, x_0(s + n_j\omega)) = x(t; 0, \varphi_{n_j}(s)).$$

For $t = s + k\omega$ we obtain

$$\lim_{j\to\infty} x_0(s + k\omega + n_j\omega) = x^*(s + k\omega);$$

hence

$$\lim_{j\to\infty} \varphi_{n_j+k}(s) = x^*(s + k\omega).$$

But from

$$\lim_{t\to\infty} \max_{t-\tau\leqslant s\leqslant t} | x_0(s + k\omega) - x_0(s)| = 0$$

we obtain

$$\lim_{j\to\infty} \max_{-\tau\leqslant s\leqslant 0} | \varphi_{n_j+k}(s) - \varphi_{n_j}(s)| = 0.$$

From

$$| \varphi_{n_j+k}(s) - \varphi^*(s)| \leqslant | \varphi_{n_j+k}(s) - \varphi_{n_j}(s)| + | \varphi_{n_j}(s) - \varphi^*(s)|$$

we obtain

$$\lim_{j\to\infty} \varphi_{n_j+k}(s) = \varphi^*(s),$$

and this means that

$$x^*(s + k\omega) = \varphi^*(s);$$

hence the solution $x^*(t)$ is periodic of period $k\omega$.

We prove the following proposition in the same way: *If system* (2) *admits a bounded solution* $x_0(t)$ *such that*

$$\lim_{t\to\infty} [x_0(t + \omega) - x_0(t)] = 0,$$

then it admits a periodic solution of period ω.

Proof. The set $\{\varphi_n(s)\}$ is compact; let

$$\varphi^*(s) = \lim_{j\to\infty} \varphi_{n_j}(s).$$

From

$$\lim_{j\to\infty} [x_0(s + n_j\omega + \omega) - x_0(s + n_j\omega)] = 0$$

it follows that

$$\varphi^*(s) = \lim_{j\to\infty} \varphi_{n_j+k}(s).$$

From here on, the proof continues as above with $k = 1$:

$$x(t; 0, \varphi^*(s)) = \lim_{j\to\infty} x(t; 0, \varphi_{n_j}) = \lim_{j\to\infty} x(t; 0, \varphi_{n_j+k}).$$

However,

$$x(t; 0, \varphi_{n_j}) = x_0(t + n_j\omega);$$

hence

$$x(t; 0, \varphi^*) = \lim_{j\to\infty} x_0(t + n_j\omega) = \lim_{j\to\infty} x_0(t + \omega + n_j\omega).$$

From here, for $t = s + \omega$, we obtain

$$x(s + \omega; 0, \varphi^*) = \lim_{j\to\infty} x_0(s + \omega + n_j\omega) = x(s; 0, \varphi^*) = \varphi^*(s),$$

which shows that the solution $x(t; 0, \varphi^*)$ is periodic of period ω.

Theorem 4.37. *If* f *is periodic in* t, *every bounded and uniformly stable solution of system* (2) *is asymptotically almost periodic.*

To prove this theorem some preparatory facts are necessary.

Definition. *Let* U *be a continuous mapping of a metric space in itself. The mapping* U *is called asymptotically almost-periodic in point* p, *if for every* $\epsilon > 0$ *there exist positive integers* l *and* N *such that within any* $l + 1$ *positive consecutive integers there exists at least one integer* τ *for which* $\rho(U^n p, U^{n+\tau} p) < \epsilon$ *if* $n \geq N$.

Lemma. *If from every sequence of points* $\{U^{n+h_m}p\}(m = 1, 2, \ldots)$ *we can extract a subsequence uniformly convergent with respect to n, then U is asymptotically almost-periodic in point p.*

Proof. We suppose that U is not asymptotically almost-periodic in p; then there exists an $\epsilon_0 > 0$ such that for every couple l, N there exists an interval of positive numbers $L_{l,N}$ of length l such that for every $\tau \in L_{l,N}$ we have $\rho(U^n p, U^{n+\tau}p) \geqslant \epsilon$ for at least one $n \geqslant N$. Let $L_1' = L_{1,1}$ and $h_1 \in L_1'$; we choose an integer h_2 such that $h_2 - h_1$ be in $L_2' = L_{2,2}$. We further choose an interval $L_3' = L_{\nu_3,\nu_3}$ such that $\nu_3 > 2(h_2 - h_1)$; we may find an integer h_3 such that $h_3 - h_1$ and $h_3 - h_2$ be in L_3'. In general we choose $L_{m+1}' = L_{\nu_{m+1},\nu_{m+1}}$ such that $\nu_{m+1} > \max_{1<\lambda\leqslant m} 2(h_\lambda - h_1)$, $\nu_{m+1} > \nu_m$; it suffices, for example, to take as $h_{m+1} - h_1$ one of the integers in the immediate neighborhood of the center of L_{m+1}'. We consider the sequence

$$U^{n+h_1}p,\ U^{n+h_2}p,\ \ldots,\ U^{n+h_m}p,\ \ldots;$$

according to the hypotheses, from this sequence we can extract a subsequence

$$U^{n+k_1}p,\ U^{n+k_2}p,\ \ldots,\ U^{n+k_m}p,\ \ldots,$$

uniformly convergent with respect to n; we may hence find R such that

$$\rho(U^{n+k_{r+s}}p, U^{n+k_r}p) < \epsilon_0 \qquad \text{for} \quad r \geqslant R,\ s = 1, 2, \ldots,$$

whichever be n. Replacing n by $n - k_r$, it follows that for $r \geqslant R$, $s = 1, 2, 3, \ldots$, and $n > k_r$ there occurs the relation

$$\rho(U^{n+k_{r+s}-k_r}p, U^n p) < \epsilon_0 .$$

Setting $k_{r+s} - k_r = \tau_s$, we have

$$\rho(U^{n+\tau_s}p, U^n p) < \epsilon_0 \qquad \text{for} \quad n > k_r;$$

τ_s is situated in the interval $L_{m_{r+s}}'$ corresponding to k_{r+s}. We leave r fixed, with $r \geqslant R$, and choose s large enough that $\nu_{m_{r+s}} > k_r$. We denote $N = \nu_{m_{r+s}}$. We have $\rho(U^{n+\tau}p, U^n p) < \epsilon_0$ for $n > N$ and $\tau \in L_{N,N}$, which is in contradiction with the way in which the intervals $L_{l,N}$ have been chosen. The lemma is thus proved.

Proof of Theorem 4.37. Let $x_0(t)$ be a bounded solution, uniformly stable, of system (2), $\varphi_0(s) = x_0(s)$, $s \in [-\tau, 0]$. There exists $\delta(\epsilon)$ such that from $\| x_0(t_0 + s) - \psi(u)\| < \delta$ it follows that $| x(t; t_0, \psi) - x_0(t)| < \epsilon$

for $t \geqslant t_0$. For $t_0 = n\omega$ we deduce that $\| x_0(n\omega + s) - \psi(u)\| < \delta$ implies $| x(t; n\omega, \psi) - x_0(t)| < \epsilon$ for $t \geqslant n\omega$; hence

$$| x(t + n\omega; n\omega, \psi) - x_0(t + n\omega)| < \epsilon \qquad \text{for} \quad t \geqslant 0.$$

However, $x(t + n\omega; n\omega, \psi) = x(t, 0, \psi^*)$, where $\psi^*(s) = \psi(n\omega + s)$, $s \in [-\tau, 0]$, since in both members we have solutions of system (2) (because of the hypothesis that f is periodic), and both solutions coincide for $t \in [-\tau, 0]$. Consequently, from

$$\| x_0(n\omega + s) - \psi^*(s)\| < \delta$$

we obtain

$$| x(t; 0, \psi^*) - x_0(t + n\omega)| < \epsilon.$$

We consider the operator $U\varphi = x(s + \omega; 0, \varphi)$. We have

$$x(t; 0, U\varphi) = x(t; 0, x(s + \omega; 0, \varphi)) = x(t + \omega; 0, \varphi)$$

and in general

$$x(t; 0, U^n\varphi) = x(t + n\omega; 0, \varphi), \qquad x(s + n\omega; 0, \varphi) = U^n\varphi.$$

From

$$| x(t; 0, \psi^*) - x_0(t + n\omega)| < \epsilon$$

we obtain

$$\| x(s + k\omega; 0, \psi^*) - x_0(s + (n + k)\omega)\| < \epsilon.$$

This means that from

$$\| U^n\varphi_0 - \psi^* | < \delta$$

we obtain

$$\| U^k\psi^* - U^{n+k}\varphi_0 \| < \epsilon \qquad (k > \tau/\omega).$$

Let $h_1, h_2, \ldots$ be a sequence of natural numbers, $\lim_{n\to\infty} h_m = \infty$. The set $\{U^{h_k}\varphi_0\}$ is compact due to the fact that the solution $x_0(t)$ has been assumed bounded. Let k_m be a subsequence such that

$$\lim_{m\to\infty} U^{k_m}\varphi_0 = \varphi_0^* .$$

We have

$$\| U^{l+k_m}\varphi_0 - U^l\varphi_0^* \| = \| U^l U^{k_m}\varphi_0 - U^l\varphi_0^* \|.$$

For m large enough we have

$$\| U^{k_m}\varphi_0 - \varphi_0^* \| < \delta;$$

hence

$$\| U^{l+k_m}\varphi_0 - U^l\varphi_0^* \| < \epsilon$$

for $l > \tau/\omega$. This means that

$$\lim_{m\to\infty} U^{l+k_m}\varphi_0 = U^l\varphi_0^*$$

uniformly with respect to l, for $l > \tau/\omega$. From here, by virtue of the lemma, it follows that U is asymptotically almost-periodic in point φ_0. It remains to deduce that the solution $x_0(t)$ is asymptotically almost-periodic. For every $\eta > 0$ there exist l and N such that among the $(l + 1)$ consecutive integers we may find an integer m such that

$$\| U^n\varphi_0 - U^{n+m}\varphi_0 \| < \eta,$$

if $n \geqslant N$; it follows that

$$\| x_0(s + n\omega) - x_0(s + (n + m)\omega)\| < \eta.$$

Let t be sufficiently large, $t = t' + k\omega$, $0 \leqslant t' < \omega$; we have

$$\begin{aligned} x(t + s; 0, \varphi_0) &= x(t' + k\omega + s; 0, \varphi_0) \\ &= x(t' + s; 0, x(k\omega + s; 0, \varphi_0)) = x(t' + s; 0, U^k\varphi_0). \end{aligned}$$

Let $\epsilon > 0$; there exists an $\eta > 0$ such that from $\| \varphi - \psi \| < \eta$ it follows that

$$\| x(t + s; 0, \varphi) - x(t + s; 0, \psi)\| < \epsilon \quad \text{for} \quad 0 \leqslant t \leqslant \omega.$$

Let $k > N(\eta)$; then $\| x(t + s; 0, \varphi_0) - x(t + s + m\omega; 0, \varphi_0)\| = \| x(t' + s; 0, U^k\varphi_0) - x(t' + s; 0, U^{k+m}\varphi_0)\| < \epsilon$, since

$$\| U^k\varphi_0 - U^{k+m}\varphi_0 \| < \eta.$$

Consequently,

$$| x_0(t) - x_0(t + m\omega)| < \epsilon$$

for $t > (N + 1)\omega$. The set $m\omega$ is relatively dense; hence $x_0(t)$ is asymptotically almost-periodic.

4.17. Singular Perturbation for Systems with Time Lag

The results from Section 3.11 relative to singular perturbations of nonautonomous systems are extended, without essential modifications of the proof, to systems with time lag of the form

$$\frac{dx(t)}{dt} = f[t, x(t), x(t-\tau), y(t), y(t-\tau), \epsilon],$$
$$\epsilon \frac{dy(t)}{dt} = g[t, x(t), y(t), \epsilon], \tag{87}$$

where f and g are, with respect to t, periodic or almost periodic, respectively (in the periodic case, the period will be assumed to be $\omega > \tau$, as usual).

For $\epsilon = 0$ we obtain the system

$$\frac{dx(t)}{dt} = f[t, x(t), x(t-\tau), y(t), y(t-\tau), 0],$$
$$g[t, x(t), y(t), 0] \equiv 0. \tag{88}$$

We suppose that this system admits a solution $[u(t), v(t)]$, periodic or almost periodic, respectively. We denote

$$U(t) = (g'_y[t, u(t), v(t), 0])^{-1} g'_x[t, u(t), v(t), 0],$$

$$A_1(t) = f'_x - f'_y U(t), \qquad B_1(t) = f'_{x_\tau} - f'_{y_\tau} U(t-\tau), \qquad A_2(t) = f'_y,$$

$$B_2(t) = f'_{y_\tau}, \qquad Q(t) = g'_y$$

where the partial derivatives are taken in the point

$$[t, u(t), u(t-\tau), v(t), v(t-\tau), 0].$$

Theorem 4.38. *If system* (88) *admits a periodic or an almost-periodic solution $u(t)$, $v(t)$, respectively, such that $(Q + Q^*)/2 \leqslant -\mu E$, and if the trivial solution of the system*

$$\frac{d\xi}{dt} = A_1(t)\xi(t) + B_1(t)\xi(t-\tau) \tag{89}$$

is uniformly asymptotically stable, system (87) *admits a unique periodic or an almost-periodic solution, respectively,* $x(t, \epsilon), y(t, \epsilon)$, *such that*

$$x(t, \epsilon) = u(t) + \epsilon\xi^*(t, \epsilon), \qquad y(t, \epsilon) = v(t) + \epsilon\eta^*(t, \epsilon) - \epsilon U(t)\xi^*(t, \epsilon).$$

Theorem 4.39. *We suppose that system* (88) *admits a family of periodic solutions of period* $\omega > \tau$, $[u(t, c), v(t, c)]$ *and that for the solution corresponding to the value* $c = c_0$ *we have* $(Q + Q^*)/2 \leqslant -\mu E$.

If system (87) *admits a periodic solution of period* ω *of the form*

$$x(t, \epsilon) = u(t, c_0) + \epsilon\xi^*(t, \epsilon),$$

$$y(t, \epsilon) = v(t, c_0) + \epsilon\eta^*(t, \epsilon) - \epsilon U(t)\xi^*(t, \epsilon),$$

then

$$\int_0^\omega q_j(t, c_0)\{A_2(t, c_0)\eta^{**}(t, c_0) + B_2(t, c_0)\eta^{**}(t - \tau, c_0) + f'_\epsilon\}dt = 0$$

for all the independent periodic solutions $q_j(t, c_0)$ *of period* ω *of the adjoint system of system* (89).

The function $\eta^{**}(t, c_0)$ *is given by the formula*

$$\eta^{**}(t, c_0) = -Q^{-1}(t, c_0)\left[g'_\epsilon - \frac{dv(t, c_0)}{dt}\right].$$

The problem of singular perturbations in autonomous systems with time lag can be treated in the same way.

We consider a system of the form

$$\begin{aligned} \frac{dx}{dt} &= f[x(t), x(t - \tau), y(t), y(t - \tau), \epsilon], \\ \epsilon\frac{dy}{dt} &= g[x(t), y(t), \epsilon]. \end{aligned} \qquad (90)$$

For $\epsilon = 0$ we obtain the system

$$\frac{dx}{dt} = f[x(t), x(t - \tau), y(t), y(t - \tau), 0], \qquad g[x(t), y(t), 0] = 0.$$

Let us suppose that the system obtained for $\epsilon = 0$ *has a periodic solution* $u(t), v(t)$ *of period* $\omega_0 > \tau$. *Let, as above,* $Q(t) = g'_u[u(t), v(t), 0]$. *We will suppose that*

$$\tfrac{1}{2}[Q(t) + Q^*(t)] \leqslant -\mu E.$$

We denote, as above,

$$U(t) = (g'_u[u(t), v(t), 0])^{-1} g'_x[u(t), v(t), 0].$$

We form the variational system (89). This system has a periodic solution $p(t) = du/dt$ of period ω_0. Indeed, from

$$\frac{du}{dt} = f[u(t), u(t-\tau), v(t), v(t-\tau), 0]$$

we obtain

$$\frac{dp}{dt} = f'_x p(t) + f'_{x_\tau} p(t-\tau) + f'_y \frac{dv(t)}{dt} + f'_{y_\tau} \frac{dv(t-\tau)}{dt}.$$

From $g[u(t), v(t), 0] \equiv 0$ we obtain

$$g'_x[u(t), v(t), 0] \frac{du(t)}{dt} + g'_y[u(t), v(t), 0] \frac{dv(t)}{dt} = 0,$$

from which we obtain

$$\frac{dv}{dt} = -U(t) \frac{du}{dt} = -U(t)p(t).$$

Consequently,

$$\begin{aligned} \frac{dp}{dt} &= [f'_x - f'_y U(t)]p(t) + [f'_{x_\tau} - f'_{y_\tau} U(t-\tau)]p(t-\tau) \\ &= A_1(t)p(t) + B_1(t)p(t-\tau). \end{aligned}$$

Let us suppose that the variational system has neither periodic solutions independent of $p(t)$ nor solutions of the form $p_1(t] + tp(t)$, with p_1 periodic of period ω_0.

From here, as in Section 4.14, it follows that $\int_0^{\omega_0} q(s)G(s)ds \neq 0$, where $q(s)$ is the periodic solution of period ω_0 of the system adjoint to the variational system, and

$$\begin{aligned} G(t) &= f[u(t), u(t-\tau), v(t), v(t-\tau), 0] \\ &\quad + \tau B_1(t) f[u(t-\tau), u(t-2\tau), v(t-\tau), v(t-2\tau), 0]; \end{aligned}$$

we will prove under these conditions that system (90) *admits a periodic solution of the period* $\omega_0(1+\epsilon\alpha)$, *which for* $\epsilon \to 0$ *tends to* $u(t)$, $v(t)$.

We perform in system (90) the change of variables $t = s[1+\epsilon\alpha(\epsilon)]$ and denote $\tilde{x}(s,\epsilon) = x[s(1+\epsilon\alpha),\epsilon]$, $\tilde{y}(s,\epsilon) = y[s(1+\epsilon\alpha),\epsilon]$. We obtain the system

$$\frac{d\tilde{x}}{ds} = (1+\epsilon\alpha)f[\tilde{x}(s,\epsilon), \tilde{x}(s-\theta,\epsilon), \tilde{y}(s,\epsilon), \tilde{y}(s-\theta.\ \epsilon),\epsilon],$$

$$\epsilon\frac{d\tilde{y}}{ds} = (1+\epsilon\alpha)g[\tilde{x}(s,\epsilon), \tilde{y}(s,\epsilon),\epsilon],$$

$$\theta = \frac{\tau}{1+\epsilon\alpha}.$$

Further, let

$$\tilde{x} = u(s) + \epsilon\xi(s),$$
$$\tilde{y} = v(s) + \epsilon\eta(s) - \epsilon U(s)\xi(s).$$

We obtain

$$\epsilon\frac{d\xi}{ds} = \epsilon f_x'\xi(s) + f_{x_\tau}'[\epsilon\xi(s-\theta) + u(s-\theta) - u(s-\tau)] + \epsilon f_y'[\eta(s) - U(s)\xi(s)]$$
$$+ f_{y_\tau}'[\epsilon\eta(s-\theta) + v(s-\theta) - v(s-\tau) - \epsilon U(s-\theta)\xi(s-\theta)] + \epsilon f_\epsilon'$$
$$+ O(\epsilon^2) + \epsilon\alpha f[u(s), u(s-\tau), v(s), v(s-\tau), 0] + O(\epsilon^2),$$

$$\epsilon\frac{d\eta}{ds} = g_x'[u(s), v(s), 0]\xi(s) + g_y'[u(s), v(s), 0][\eta(s) - U(s)\xi(s)] - \frac{dv}{ds} + g_\epsilon' + O(\epsilon).$$

Taking into account that

$$u(s-\theta) - u(s-\tau) = \dot{u}(s-\tau)(s-\theta-s+\tau) + O((\tau-\theta)^2)$$
$$= \epsilon\alpha\tau f[u(s-\tau), u(s-2\tau), v(s-\tau), v(s-2\tau), 0] + O(\epsilon^2),$$
$$v(s-\theta) - v(s-\tau) = \dot{v}(s-\tau)\epsilon\alpha\tau + O(\epsilon^2) = -\epsilon\alpha\tau U(s-\tau)\dot{u}(s-\tau) + O(\epsilon^2)$$
$$= -\epsilon\alpha\tau U(s-\tau)f[u(s-\tau), u(s-2\tau), v(s-\tau), v(s-2\tau), 0] + O(\epsilon^2),$$

we obtain

$$\frac{d\xi(s)}{ds} = A_1(s)\xi(s) + B_1(s)\xi(s-\theta) + A_2(s)\eta(s) + B_2(s)\eta(s-\theta)$$
$$+ F(s) + \alpha G(s) + \epsilon H_1,$$
$$\epsilon\frac{d\eta}{ds} = Q(s)\eta(s) + g_\epsilon' - \frac{dv}{ds} + \epsilon H_2,$$

where

$$F(s) = f'_\epsilon[u(s), u(s-\tau), v(s), v(s-\tau), 0].$$

We construct for the system thus obtained a periodic solution of period ω_0. Let $\eta_0(s)$ be the periodic solution of the system

$$\epsilon \frac{d\eta}{ds} = Q(s)\eta + g'_\epsilon - \frac{dv}{ds}.$$

We have $\eta_0(s) = -Q^{-1}(s)(g'_\epsilon - (dv/ds) + O(\epsilon)$. We form the system

$$\frac{d\xi}{ds} = A_1(s)\xi(s) + B_1(s)\xi(s-\tau) + A_2(s)\eta_0(s) + B_2(s)\eta_0(s-\tau) + F(s) + \alpha_0 G(s).$$

The condition that this system admits a periodic solution is that

$$\int_0^{\omega_0} q(s)[A_2(s)\eta_0(s) + B_2(s)\eta_0(s-\tau) + F(s) + \alpha_0 G(s)]ds = 0,$$

and the condition $\int_0^\omega q(s)G(s)ds \neq 0$ allows us to determine α_0 from this equation. For this α_0 we obtain a periodic solution $\xi_0(s)$ such that

$$|\xi_0(s)| \leqslant K \sup |A_2(s)\eta_0(s) + B_2(s)\eta_0(s-\tau) + F + \alpha_0 G|.$$

In general we construct the successive approximations in the following way. We will define $\eta_n(s)$ as a periodic solution of the system

$$\epsilon \frac{d\eta}{ds} = Q(s)\eta + g'_\epsilon - \frac{dv}{ds} + \epsilon H_2^{(n-1)},$$

where $H_2^{(n-1)}$ is H_2 in which α has been substituted by α_{n-1}, ξ by ξ_{n-1}, and η by η_{n-1}. Then we form the system

$$\frac{d\xi}{ds} = A_1(s)\xi(s) + B_1(s)\xi(s-\tau) + A_2(s)\eta_n(s) + B_2(s)\eta_n(s-\theta_{n-1})$$
$$+ F(s) + \alpha_n G(s) + B_1(s)[\xi_{n-1}(s-\theta_{n-1}) - \xi_{n-1}(s-\tau)] + \epsilon H_1^{(n-1)},$$

where $H_1^{(n-1)}$ is defined in the same way as $H_2^{(n-1)}$, and

$$\theta_{n-1} = \frac{\tau}{1+\epsilon\alpha_{n-1}}.$$

We choose α_n from the condition that there exists a periodic solution; then we take the periodic solution which verifies the estimate

$$|\xi_n| \leqslant K \sup |A_2(s)\eta_n(s) + B_2(s)\eta_n(s-\theta_{n-1}) + F(s) + \alpha_n G(s)$$
$$+ B_1(s)(\xi_{n-1}(s-\theta_{n-1}) - \xi_{n-1}(s-\tau)) + \epsilon H_1^{(n-1)}|.$$

From the construction of the successive approximations we see that if $\xi_n \to \xi$, $\eta_n \to \eta$; then ξ, η will be a periodic solution of period ω_0, which leads to a periodic solution

$$x(t, \epsilon) = u\left(\frac{t}{1+\epsilon\alpha}\right) + \epsilon\xi\left(\frac{t}{1+\epsilon\alpha}, \epsilon\right),$$

$$y(t, \epsilon) = v\left(\frac{t}{1+\epsilon\alpha}\right) + \epsilon\eta\left(\frac{t}{1+\epsilon\alpha}, \epsilon\right) - \epsilon U\left(\frac{t}{1+\epsilon\alpha}\right)\xi\left(\frac{t}{1+\epsilon\alpha}, \epsilon\right)$$

of the initial system.

The convergence of the successive approximations is proved in the same way as in Section 4.13.

Let us indicate another case of singularly perturbed systems. Let a system of the form

$$\epsilon\dot{x}(t) = \epsilon X_0(t, x(t)) + X_1(t, x(t), x(t-\epsilon\tau), \epsilon), \tag{91}$$

where X_0 and X_1 are periodic or almost periodic in t, uniformly with respect to the other variables, respectively.

We suppose that the system

$$\dot{x} = X_0(t, x)$$

has the general solution $x_0(t, h)$ periodic or almost periodic in t, respectively, of period ω. After the change of variables $x = x_0(t, z)$ we obtain a system of the form

$$\epsilon\dot{z}(t) = Z(t, z(t), z(t-\epsilon\tau), \epsilon), \tag{92}$$

where Z is periodic of period ω, or almost periodic with respect to t uniformly with respect to the other variables, respectively, and has the same regularity properties as X_0 and X_1.

We will suppose in what follows that Z admits continuous partial derivatives of the second order. Let $v(t)$ be a periodic or almost periodic solution, respectively, with continuous derivative, of the system $Z(t, v, v, 0) = 0$. We will give the condition under which system (92) has a periodic or almost-periodic solution, respectively, $z(t, \epsilon)$, with the property that $\lim_{\epsilon\to 0}[z(t, \epsilon) - v(t)] = 0$. To this solution will correspond a periodic or almost-periodic solution respectively, of system (91) of the form $x_0(t, z(t, \epsilon))$, such that

$$\lim_{\epsilon\to 0}[x_0(t, z(t, \epsilon)) - x_0(t, v(t))] = 0.$$

Let $\eta = z - v$. We deduce that

$$\epsilon\dot{\eta}(t) = A(t)\eta(t) + B(t)\eta(t - \epsilon\tau) + \epsilon f(t) + G(t, \eta(t), \eta(t - \epsilon\tau), \epsilon),$$

where $G = O(|\eta|^2 + \epsilon^2)$ and A, B, f, G are periodic of period ω or almost periodic, respectively.

A periodic or almost-periodic solution, respectively, is constructed for this system by the usual procedure of succesive approximations. To do this we will first prove that under certain conditions a linear system of the form

$$\epsilon\dot{\eta}(t) = A(t)\eta(t) + B(t)\eta(t - \epsilon\tau) + \epsilon f(t)$$

has a unique, periodic or almost-periodic solution, respectively, which admits the estimate

$$|\eta| \leqslant \epsilon K_1 M \qquad (M = \sup|f|).$$

The successive approximations η_n will be then constructed as being the periodic or almost-periodic solutions, respectively, of the system

$$\epsilon\dot{\eta}(t) = A(t)\eta(t) + B(t)\eta(t - \epsilon\tau) + \epsilon f(t) + G(t, \eta_{n-1}(t), \eta_{n-1}(t - \epsilon\tau), \epsilon).$$

The convergence of the process is proved in the usual way.

It remains then to state the facts relative to the linear system. To do this we will extend the lemmas of Flatto and Levinson to systems with time lag.

Lemma 1. *We consider the system with constant coefficients*

$$\dot{x}(t) = Ax(t) + Bx(t - \tau)$$

and suppose that the characteristic equation

$$\det(A + Be^{-\lambda\tau} - \lambda E) = 0$$

has its roots in the semiplane $\operatorname{Re}\lambda \leqslant -\mu < 0$, *and* $|A| \leqslant M$, $|B| \leqslant M$. *Then, for every* $\sigma \in (0, \mu)$ *there exists* $K(\mu, \sigma, M)$ *such that* $|X(t)| \leqslant K(\mu, \sigma, M)e^{-\sigma t}$, *where* $X(t)$ *is a matrix of solution of the system, with* $X(0) = E$, $X(t) \equiv 0$ *for* $-\tau \leqslant t < 0$.

Proof. The essential fact in this lemma is that the number K depends on M, μ, and σ and is independent of the other properties of the matrices A and B. The fact that from $\operatorname{Re}\lambda \leqslant -\mu$ we obtain such an evaluation for the solution is well known, and we will make use of it in the proof. The proof that K only depends on M will be made according to the Flatto and Levinson schema, by contradiction.

If the affirmation of the lemma is not true, then for every K there exists A and B with $|A| \leqslant M$, $|B| \leqslant M$, and there exists $t \geqslant 0$ such that $|X(t)| \geqslant Ke^{-\sigma t}$; consequently, there would exist a sequence A_n, B_n, t_n with $|A_n| \leqslant M$, $|B_n| \leqslant M$, $t_n \geqslant 0$, $|X_n(t_n)| \geqslant ne^{-\sigma t_n}$, i.e., $e^{\sigma t_n}|X_n(t_n)| \geqslant n$. From $|A_n| \leqslant M$ it follows that there exist convergent subsequences A_{n_k}, B_{n_k}. Let $A_0 = \lim_{k\to\infty} A_{n_k}$, $B_0 = \lim_{k\to\infty} B_{n_k}$. The roots of the equation $\det(A_0 + B_0e^{-\lambda\tau} - \lambda E)$ will be likewise situated in the semiplane $\operatorname{Re}\lambda \leqslant -\mu$; hence, if X_0 is a matrix of solutions of the system

$$\dot{x}(t) = A_0x(t) + B_0x(t - \tau),$$

with $X_0(s, s) = E$, $X_0(t, s) \equiv 0$ for $s - \tau \leqslant t < s$, we have

$$|X_0(t, s)| \leqslant K_0e^{-\sigma_1(t-s)}, \quad \sigma < \sigma_1 < \mu.$$

Let A_n, B_n be such that $|A_n - A_0| < (\sigma_1 - \sigma)/K(1 + e^{\sigma_1\tau})$, $|B_n - B_0| < (\sigma_1 - \sigma)/K_0(1 + e^{\sigma_1\tau})$; we consider the system

$$\dot{x}(t) = A_nx(t) + B_nx(t - \tau),$$

which we represent in the form

$$\dot{x}(t) = A_0x(t) + B_0x(t - \tau) + (A_n - A_0)x(t) + (B_n - B_0)x(t - \tau).$$

It follows that we can write

$$X_n(t) = X_0(t, 0) + \int_0^t X_0(t, \alpha)[(A_n - A_0)X_n(\alpha) + (B_n - B_0)X_n(\alpha - \tau)]d\alpha,$$

from which follows

$$e^{\sigma_1 t}|X_n(t)| \leqslant K_0 + \int_0^t \{K_0|A_n - A_0|e^{\sigma_1\alpha}|X_n(\alpha)| + K_0|B_n - B_0|e^{\sigma_1\tau}e^{\sigma_1(\alpha-\tau)}|X_n(\alpha - \tau)|\}d\alpha.$$

Denoting $u(t) = e^{\sigma_1 t}|X_n(t)|$ and taking into account the estimates for $|A_n - A_0|$ and $|B_n - B_0|$ we obtain

$$u(t) \leqslant K_0 + \frac{\sigma_1 - \sigma}{1 + e^{\sigma_1\tau}} \int_0^t \{u(\alpha) + e^{\sigma_1\tau} \sup_{\alpha-\tau\leqslant\beta\leqslant\alpha} u(\beta)\}d\alpha.$$

It follows from here as in Section 4.5 that $u(t) \leqslant y(t)$, where $y(t)$ verifies the integral equation

$$y(t) = K_0 + \frac{\sigma_1 - \sigma}{1 + e^{\sigma_1 \tau}} \int_0^t \{y(\alpha) + e^{\sigma_1 \tau} \sup_{\alpha - \tau \leqslant \beta \leqslant \alpha} y(\beta)\} d\alpha.$$

We seek $y(t)$ under the form $y(t) = K_0 e^{\gamma t}$. We obtain

$$e^{\gamma t} = 1 + \frac{\sigma_1 - \sigma}{1 + e^{\sigma_1 \tau}} (1 + e^{\sigma_1 \tau}) \frac{1}{\gamma} (e^{\gamma t} - 1),$$

a relation verified for $\gamma = \sigma_1 - \sigma$. It follows that $u(t) \leqslant K_0 e^{(\sigma_1 - \sigma)t}$; namely $e^{\sigma_1 t} | X_n(t)| \leqslant K_0 e^{(\sigma_1 - \sigma)t}$ for every $t \geqslant 0$. This means that $e^{\sigma t} |X_n(t)| \leqslant K_0$ for every $t \geqslant 0$, which contradicts the inequality $e^{\sigma t_n} | X_n(t_n)| \geqslant n$. The lemma is thus proved.

Taking into account also the fact that A and B are constant, it follows that $X(t, s) = X(t - s)$, and hence we have the bound $| X(t, s)| \leqslant K(\mu, \sigma, M) e^{-\sigma(t-s)}$.

Lemma 2. *We consider the system*

$$\epsilon \dot{x}(t) = A(t)x(t) + B(t)x(t - \epsilon\tau),$$

where $A(t)$, $B(t)$ are uniformly continuous for $t \geqslant 0$. We suppose that for every t the roots of the equation

$$\det(A + Be^{-\lambda\tau} - \lambda E) = 0$$

are situated in the semiplane $\operatorname{Re} \lambda \leqslant -2\mu$. *Then there exists a K such that $| X(t, s)| \leqslant K e^{-(\mu/\epsilon)(t-s)}$ for $t \geqslant s$.*

Proof. Let $0 \leqslant t_0$. We consider the system

$$\epsilon \dot{x}(t) = A(t_0)x(t) + B(t_0)x(t - \epsilon\tau).$$

The characteristic equation of this system is

$$\det\left(\frac{1}{\epsilon} A(t_0) + \frac{1}{\epsilon} B(t_0) e^{-\epsilon\lambda\tau} - \lambda E\right) = 0$$

or

$$\det(A(t_0) + B(t_0)e^{-\epsilon\lambda\tau} - \epsilon\lambda E) = 0.$$

According to the hypotheses, we have $\operatorname{Re} \epsilon\lambda \leqslant -2\mu$; hence $\operatorname{Re} \lambda \leqslant -2\mu/\epsilon$.

Let $M \geqslant \sup | A(t)|$, $M \geqslant \sup | B(t)|$. On the basis of the first lemma we deduce that

$$| X_{t_0}(t, s)| \leqslant K(M)e^{-(3\mu/2\epsilon)(t-s)}.$$

The given system is written

$$\epsilon\dot{x}(t) = A(t_0)x(t) + B(t_0)x(t - \epsilon\tau) + (A(t) - A(t_0))x(t) + (B(t) - B(t_0))x(t - \epsilon\tau).$$

On the basis of the variation-of-constants formula we have

$$X(t, s) = X_{t_0}(t, s) + \int_s^t X_{t_0}(s, \alpha) \left\{ \frac{1}{\epsilon} (A(\alpha) - A(t_0))X(\alpha, s) + \frac{1}{\epsilon} (B(\alpha) - B(t_0))X(\alpha - \epsilon\tau, s) \right\} d\alpha;$$

hence

$$| X(t, s) | \leqslant Ke^{-(3\mu/2\epsilon)(t-s)} + K \int_s^t e^{-(3\mu/2\epsilon)(t-\alpha)} \left\{ \frac{1}{\epsilon} | A(\alpha) - A(t_0) | | X(\alpha, s) | + \frac{1}{\epsilon} | B(\alpha) - B(t_0) | | X(\alpha - \epsilon\tau, s) | \right\} d\alpha.$$

Since all the estimations performed are valid for every t_0, it follows that they remain valid in particular for $t_0 = t$. It follows that

$$| X(t, s)| \leqslant Ke^{-(3\mu/2\epsilon)(t-s)} + \frac{K}{\epsilon} \int_s^t e^{-(3\mu/2\epsilon)(t-\alpha)} (| A(\alpha) - A(t)| | X(\alpha, s)| + | B(\alpha) - B(t)| | X(\alpha - \epsilon\tau, s)|)d\alpha.$$

Let $u(t, s) = e^{(\mu/\epsilon)(t-s)}| X(t, s)|$. We have

$$u(t, s) \leqslant Ke^{-(\mu/2\epsilon)(t-s)} + \frac{K}{\epsilon} \int_s^t e^{-(\mu/2\epsilon)(t-\alpha)}(| A(\alpha) - A(t)|e^{(\mu/\epsilon)(\alpha-s)}| X(\alpha, s)| + | B(\alpha) - B(t)|e^{\mu\tau}e^{(\mu/\epsilon)(\alpha-\epsilon\tau-s)}| X(\alpha - \epsilon\tau, s)|)d\alpha;$$

hence

$$u(t, s) \leqslant K + \frac{K}{\epsilon} \int_s^t e^{-(\mu/2\epsilon)(t-\alpha)}(| A(\alpha) - A(t)|u(\alpha, s) + e^{\mu\tau}| B(\alpha) - B(t)|u(\alpha - \epsilon\tau, s))d\alpha.$$

Let $M = \sup_{a \leqslant s \leqslant t \leqslant b} |u(t, s)|$. It follows that

$$M \leqslant K + \frac{KM}{\epsilon} \sup \int_s^t e^{-(\mu/2\epsilon)(t-\alpha)}(| A(\alpha) - A(t)| + e^{\mu\tau}| B(\alpha) - B(t)|)d\alpha.$$

However,

$$\int_s^t e^{-(\mu/2\epsilon)(t-\alpha)}(| A(\alpha) - A(t)| + e^{\mu\tau}| B(\alpha) - B(t)|)d\alpha$$

$$= \int_s^{t-\sqrt{\epsilon}} e^{-(\mu/2\epsilon)(t-\alpha)}(| A(\alpha) - A(t)| + e^{\mu\tau}| B(\alpha) - B(t)|)d\alpha$$

$$+ \int_{t-\sqrt{\epsilon}}^t e^{-(\mu/2\epsilon)(t-\alpha)}(| A(\alpha) - A(t)| + e^{\mu\tau}| B(\alpha) - B(t)|)d\alpha$$

$$\leqslant 2L(1 + e^{\mu\tau})e^{-(\mu/2\epsilon)t} \frac{2\epsilon}{\mu} e^{(\mu/2\epsilon)(t-\sqrt{\epsilon})} + \omega(\epsilon) \frac{2\epsilon}{\mu}$$

$$= \epsilon\omega_1(\epsilon), \qquad \lim_{\epsilon \to 0} \omega_1(\epsilon) = 0,$$

since for $t - \sqrt{\epsilon} \leqslant \alpha \leqslant t$ we have $| A(\alpha) - A(t)| + e^{\mu\tau}| B(\alpha) - B(t)| < \omega(\epsilon)$, owing to the uniform continuity of matrices $A(t)$ and $B(t)$. We obtain

$$M \leqslant K + \frac{KM}{\epsilon} \epsilon\omega_1(\epsilon) = K + KM\omega_1(\epsilon);$$

hence if ϵ is sufficiently small in order that $\omega_1(\epsilon) < 1/2K$ we have $M \leqslant 2K$; hence $| X(t, s)| \leqslant 2Ke^{-(\mu/\epsilon)(t-s)}$. The evaluation obtained does not depend on a and b; hence it is valid for every t, s. The lemma is thus proved.

Let us consider the nonhomogeneous system

$$\epsilon\dot{x}(t) = A(t)x(t) + B(t)x(t - \epsilon\tau) + \epsilon f(t).$$

The bounds obtained in Lemma 2 show that under the conditions of these lemmas the trivial solution of the homogeneous system is uniformly asymptotically stable; hence if A, B, f are periodic or almost periodic, respectively, the system admits a unique periodic or almost-periodic solution, respectively. In order to obtain an estimation for this solution, we will observe that every solution of the nonhomogeneous system is written on the basis of the "variation of constants" formula in the form

$$x(t, \varphi) = X(t, 0)\varphi(0) + \int_{-\epsilon\tau}^0 X(t, \alpha + \epsilon\tau)B(\alpha + \epsilon\tau)\varphi(\alpha)d\alpha + \int_0^t X(t, \alpha)f(\alpha)\, d\alpha.$$

We obtain the relation

$$| x(t, \varphi) | \leqslant K\| \varphi \| e^{-(\mu/\epsilon)t} + LK\| \varphi \| \int_{-\epsilon\tau}^{0} e^{-(\mu/\epsilon)(t-\alpha-\epsilon\tau)}\, d\alpha + KM \int_{0}^{t} e^{-(\mu/\epsilon)(t-\alpha)} d\alpha;$$

hence

$$| x(t, \varphi)| \leqslant K\| \varphi \| e^{-(\mu/\epsilon)t} + \frac{LK\| \varphi \|\epsilon}{\mu} e^{\mu\tau} e^{-(\mu/\epsilon)t} + KM \frac{\epsilon}{\mu}.$$

Observing that the first members tend to zero when $t \to \infty$, we deduce for the periodic or almost-periodic solution, respectively, the bound

$$| x(t)| \leqslant \epsilon K_1 M \qquad (M = \sup | f |).$$

This is all that we need to assure the convergence of the successive approximation process.

4.18. Invariant Periodic Surfaces in a Class of Systems with Time Lag

We will consider a system with time lag of the form

$$\begin{aligned} \dot{\theta}(t) &= \Theta(t, \theta(t), y(t), y(t-\tau)), \\ \dot{y}(t) &= Y(t, \theta(t), y(t), y(t-\tau)), \end{aligned} \tag{93}$$

where $\Theta(t, u, v_1, v_2)$, $Y(t, u, v_1, v_2)$ are periodic in t with period T and in u with period ω.

A solution of the system will be determined for $t \geqslant t_0$ by the value θ_0 of θ for $t = t_0$ and by the function ψ given in $t_0 - \tau, t_0$, representing the initial function for y. We will denote this solution by $\theta(t; t_0, \theta_0, \psi)$, $y(t; t_0, \theta_0, \psi)$. When we will take $t_0 = 0$ we will omit it.

Lemma 1. *We have the relations*

$$\begin{aligned} \theta(t; t_0, \theta_0 + \omega, \psi) &= \theta(t; t_0, \theta, \psi) + \omega, \\ y(t; t_0, \theta_0 + \omega, \psi) &= y(t; t_0, \theta_0, \psi). \end{aligned} \tag{94}$$

Proof. The periodicity of system (93) with respect to θ ensures that $\theta(t; t_0, \theta_0, \psi) + \omega$, $y(t, t_0, \theta_0, \psi)$ is also a solution together with $\theta(t; t_0, \theta_0, \psi)$, $y(t; t_0, \theta_0, \psi)$. For $t = t_0$ this solution yields for θ the value $\theta_0 + \omega$, and in $[t_0 - \tau, t_0]$ it yields for y the function ψ; hence it coincides with the solution $\theta(t; t_0, \theta_0 + \omega, \psi), y(t; t_0, \theta_0 + \omega, \psi)$. The lemma is thus proved.

The periodicity of system (1) with respect to t ensures that $\theta(t + T; t_0, \theta_0, \psi), y(t + T; t_0, \theta_0, \psi)$ is also a solution together with $\theta(t; t_0, \theta_0, \psi), y(t, t_0, \theta_0, \psi)$. For $t = t_0$ this solution yield for θ the value $\theta(t_0 + T; t_0, \theta_0, \psi)$ and in $[t_0 - \tau, t_0]$ it yields for y function $y(T + s; t_0, \theta_0, \psi)$. We obtain the relations

$$\begin{aligned} \theta(t + T; t_0, \theta_0, \psi) &= \theta(t; t_0, \theta(T + t_0; t_0, \theta_0, \psi), y(T + s; t_0, \theta_0, \psi)), \\ y(t + T; t_0, \theta_0, \psi) &= y(t; t_0, \theta(T + t_0; t_0, \theta_0, \psi), y(T + s; t_0, \theta_0, \psi)). \end{aligned} \tag{95}$$

Let C be the space of the vector $(n - 1)$-dimensional functions continuous in $[-\tau, 0]$, B the space of the periodic functions, of period ω, continuous, with values in C, with the usual norms.

For $\alpha \in B$ and $t \geqslant 0$ we will consider the function $\rho_t^\alpha : R \rightarrow R$ defined by $\rho_t^\alpha(\sigma) = \theta(t; \sigma, \alpha(\sigma))$. Let us suppose that for fixed t, α *the function* ρ_t^α *has an inverse*; we will denote by σ_t^α the inverse. For each natural N we define the mapping $T_N : B \rightarrow B$ by

$$[(T_N\alpha)(\rho)](s) = y(NT + s; \sigma_{NT}^\alpha(\rho), \alpha[\sigma_{NT}^\alpha(\rho)]).$$

The fact that $T_N\alpha$ is a continuous function follows from the continuity of the function σ_{NT}^α and from the general theorems of continuity of the solution with respect to the initial conditions. It remains to show that $T_N\alpha$ is a periodic function; this will follow from the lemmas we are now going to prove.

Lemma 2. *We have*

$$T_{N+1}\alpha = T_N(T_1\alpha) \qquad (\textit{for all } N);$$

hence

$$T_N\alpha = T_1^N\alpha.$$

Proof. We have, from (95),

$$\begin{aligned} \theta((N + 1)T; \sigma_0, \alpha(\sigma_0)) &= \theta(NT; \theta(T; \sigma_0, \alpha(\sigma_0)), y(T + u; \sigma_0, \alpha(\sigma_0))), \\ y((N + 1)T + s; \sigma_0, \alpha(\sigma_0)) &= y(NT + s; \theta(T; \sigma_0, \alpha(\sigma_0)), y(T + u; \sigma_0, \alpha(\sigma_0))). \end{aligned} \tag{96}$$

Let us put $\theta(T; \sigma_0, \alpha(\sigma_0)) = \rho_1$. We obtain $\sigma_0 = \sigma_T^\alpha(\rho_1)$; hence we may write

$$y(T + u; \sigma_0, \alpha(\sigma_0)) = y(T + u; \sigma_T^\alpha(\rho_1), \alpha[\sigma_T^\alpha(\rho_1)]) = [(T_1\alpha)(\rho_1)](u).$$

Let $\beta = T_1\alpha$. From the first equation (96) follows

$$\theta((N+1)T;\sigma_0,\alpha(\sigma_0)) = \theta(NT;\rho_1,\beta(\rho_1)) = \rho^{\beta}_{NT}(\rho_1)$$

or $\rho^{\alpha}_{(N+1)T}(\sigma_0) = \rho^{\beta}_{NT}(\rho_1)$. By taking $\sigma_0 = \sigma^{\alpha}_{(N+1)T}(\rho)$ we obtain

$$\rho^{\alpha}_{(N+1)T}[\sigma^{\alpha}_{(N+1)T}(\rho)] = \rho^{\beta}_{NT}(\rho_1);$$

hence $\rho = \rho^{\beta}_{NT}(\rho_1)$ or $\rho_1 = \sigma^{\beta}_{NT}(\rho)$.

Using the second equation (96) we further deduce that

$$\begin{aligned}[(T_{N+1}\alpha)(\rho)](s) &= y((N+1)T+s;\sigma^{\alpha}_{(N+1)T}(\rho),\alpha[\sigma^{\alpha}_{(N+1)T}(\rho)])\\ &= y(NT+s;\rho_1,\beta(\rho_1)) = y(NT+s;\sigma^{\beta}_{NT}(\rho),\beta[\sigma^{\beta}_{NT}(\rho)])\\ &= [(T_N\beta)(\rho)](s);\end{aligned}$$

hence $T_{N+1}\alpha = T_N\beta = T_N(T_1\alpha)$, and the lemma is thus proved.

Consequence. If there exists a natural N for which T_N admits a *unique* fixed point α_0, then α_0 is also a fixed point for T_1. Indeed, $T_NT_1\alpha_0 = T_1T_N\alpha_0 = T_1\alpha_0$; hence $T_1\alpha_0$ is likewise a fixed point of T_N; from the uniqueness of the fixed point it follows that $\alpha_0 = T_1\alpha_0$.

Lemma 3. $T_1\alpha$ is periodic together with α; hence for every N the function $T_N\alpha$ is periodic.

Proof. We have

$$\rho^{\alpha}_t(\sigma) = \theta(t;\sigma,\alpha(\sigma));$$

hence

$$\begin{aligned}\rho^{\alpha}_t(\sigma+\omega) &= \theta(t;\sigma+\omega,\alpha(\sigma+\omega)) = \theta(t;\sigma+\omega,\alpha(\sigma))\\ &= \theta(t;\sigma,\alpha(\sigma))+\omega = \rho^{\alpha}_t(\sigma)+\omega.\end{aligned}$$

From $\rho^{\alpha}_t(\sigma+\omega) = \rho^{\alpha}_t(\sigma)+\omega$ we obtain $\rho^{\alpha}_t[\sigma^{\alpha}_t(\rho)+\omega] = \rho^{\alpha}_t[\sigma^{\alpha}_t(\rho)]+\omega = \rho+\omega$; hence $\sigma^{\alpha}_t(\rho)+\omega = \sigma^{\alpha}_t(\rho+\omega)$. Further,

$$\begin{aligned}[(T_1\alpha)(\rho+\omega)](s) &= y(T+s;\sigma^{\alpha}_T(\rho+\omega),\alpha[\sigma^{\alpha}_T(\rho+\omega)])\\ &= y(T+s;\sigma^{\alpha}_T(\rho)+\omega,\alpha[\sigma^{\alpha}_T(\rho)+\omega])\\ &= y(T+s;\sigma^{\alpha}_T(\rho)+\omega,\alpha[\sigma^{\alpha}_T(\rho)])\\ &= y(T+s;\sigma^{\alpha}_T(\rho),\alpha[\sigma^{\alpha}_T(\rho)]) = [(T_1\alpha)(\rho)](s),\end{aligned}$$

and the lemma is thus proved.

We define the function $S : R^+ \times R \to C$ by the relation

$$S(t, \rho) = y(t + s; \sigma_t^\alpha(\rho), \alpha[\sigma_t^\alpha(\rho)]).$$

We have

Lemma 4. $S(0, \rho) = \alpha(\rho)$.

Proof. Indeed,

$$S(0, \rho) = y(s; \sigma_0^\alpha(\rho), \alpha[\sigma_0^\alpha(\rho)]) = y(s; \rho, \alpha(\rho)) = \alpha(\rho),$$

since $\rho_0^\alpha(\sigma) = \theta(0; \sigma, \alpha(\sigma)) = \sigma$; hence $\sigma_0^\alpha(\rho) = \rho$.

Lemma 5. *If* $\psi = \alpha(\theta_0)$, *then* $S(t, \theta(t; \theta_0, \psi)) = y(t + s; \theta_0, \psi)$.

Proof. Indeed,

$$\begin{aligned} S(t, \theta(t; \theta_0, \psi)) &= y(t + s; \sigma_t^\alpha(\theta(t; \theta_0, \psi)), \alpha[\sigma_t^\alpha(\theta(t; \theta_0, \psi))]) \\ &= y(t + s; \sigma_t^\alpha(\theta(t; \theta_0, \alpha(\theta_0))), \alpha[\sigma_t^\alpha(\theta(t; \theta_0, \alpha(\theta_0)))]) \\ &= y(t + s; \sigma_t^\alpha(\rho_t^\alpha(\theta_0)), \alpha[\sigma_t^\alpha(\rho_t^\alpha(\theta_0))]) \\ &= y(t + s; \theta_0, \alpha(\theta_0)) = y(t + s; \theta_0, \psi). \end{aligned}$$

Lemma 6. *We have*

$$S(t, \rho + \omega) = S(t, \rho).$$

Proof. Indeed,

$$\begin{aligned} S(t, \rho + \omega) &= y(t + s; \sigma_t^\alpha(\rho + \omega), \alpha[\sigma_t^\alpha(\rho + \omega)]) \\ &= y(t + s; \sigma_t^\alpha(\rho) + \omega, \alpha[\sigma_t^\alpha(\rho) + \omega]) \\ &= y(t + s; \sigma_t^\alpha(\rho) + \omega, \alpha[\sigma_t^\alpha(\rho)]) = y(t + s; \sigma_t^\alpha(\rho), \alpha[\sigma_t^\alpha(\rho)]) \\ &= S(t, \rho). \end{aligned}$$

Lemma 7. *If* α *is a fixed point of the mapping* T_1, *then*

$$S(t + T, \rho) = S(t, \rho).$$

Proof. If α is a fixed point for T_1, we have

$$[\alpha(\rho)](s) = y(T + s; \sigma_T^\alpha(\rho), \alpha[\sigma_T^\alpha(\rho)]).$$

We deduce

$$[\alpha(\rho_T^\alpha(\sigma))](s) = y(T + s; \sigma_T^\alpha(\rho_T^\alpha(\sigma)), \alpha[\sigma_T^\alpha(\rho_T^\alpha(\sigma))]) = y(T + s; \sigma, \alpha(\sigma)).$$

On the other hand, from the relations (95),

$$\theta(t + T; \sigma, \psi) = \theta(t; \theta(T; \sigma, \psi), y(T + u; \sigma, \psi)).$$

If $\psi = \alpha(\sigma)$ we have $\theta(T; \sigma, \psi) = \theta(T; \sigma, \alpha(\sigma)) = \rho_T^\alpha(\sigma)$ and $y(T + u; \sigma, \psi) = y(T + u; \sigma, \alpha(\sigma)) = [\alpha(\rho_T^\alpha(\sigma))](u)$; hence

$$\theta(t + T; \sigma, \alpha(\sigma)) = \theta(t; \rho_T^\alpha(\sigma), \alpha[\rho_T^\alpha(\sigma)]).$$

The relation obtained is written $\rho_{t+T}^\alpha(\sigma) = \rho_t^\alpha[\rho_T^\alpha(\sigma)]$. For $\sigma = \sigma_{t+T}^\alpha(\rho_0)$ we obtain $\rho_0 = \rho_t^\alpha[\rho_T^\alpha(\sigma_{t+T}^\alpha(\rho_0))]$ or $\sigma_t^\alpha(\rho_0) = \rho_T^\alpha(\sigma_{t+T}^\alpha(\rho_0))$; hence $\sigma_{t+T}^\alpha(\rho_0) = \sigma_T^\alpha[\sigma_t^\alpha(\rho_0)]$. From this follows

$$\begin{aligned} S(t + T, \rho) &= y(t + T + s; \sigma_{t+T}^\alpha(\rho), \alpha[\sigma_{t+T}^\alpha(\rho)]) \\ &= y(t + s; \theta(T; \sigma_{t+T}^\alpha(\rho), \alpha[\sigma_{t+T}^\alpha(\rho)]), y(T + u; \sigma_{t+T}^\alpha(\rho), \alpha[\sigma_{t+T}^\alpha(\rho)])) \\ &= y(t + s; \rho_T^\alpha(\sigma_{t+T}^\alpha(\rho)), \alpha[\rho_T^\alpha(\sigma_{t+T}^\alpha(\rho))]) \\ &= y(t + s; \sigma_t^\alpha(\rho), \alpha[\sigma_t^\alpha(\rho)]) = S(t, \rho). \end{aligned}$$

Definition. A function $S : R^+ \times R \to C$ defines a periodic invariant surface of system (93) if

1. $S(t + T; \rho) = S(t, \rho)$, $S(t, \rho + \omega) = S(t, \rho)$.
2. If $\psi = S(0, \theta_0)$, then $y(t + s; \theta_0, \psi) = S(t, \theta(t; \theta_0, \psi))$.

From Lemmas 4, 5, 6, and 7 it follows that if ρ_t^α has an inverse and if there exists an N such that T_N admits a unique fixed point, then system (93) admits an invariant periodic surface.

Theorem 4.40. *We consider the system*

$$\begin{aligned} \dot\theta(t) &= \Theta_0(t, \theta(t), y(t), y(t - \tau)) + \epsilon\Theta_1(t, \theta(t), y(t), y(t - \tau), \epsilon), \\ \dot y(t) &= Y_0(t, \theta(t), y(t), y(t - \tau)) + \epsilon Y_1(t, \theta(t), y(t), y(t - \tau), \epsilon). \end{aligned} \tag{97}$$

We suppose that

1. $\Theta_0(t, u, 0, 0) \equiv 1$, $Y_0(t, u, 0, 0) \equiv 0$,
2. *The zero solution of the system*

$$\dot z(t) = \frac{\partial Y_0}{\partial v_1}(t, t + \sigma, 0, 0)z(t) + \frac{\partial Y_0}{\partial v_2}(t, t + \sigma, 0, 0)z(t - \tau) \tag{98}$$

is uniformly asymptotically stable, for every $0 \leqslant \sigma \leqslant \omega$, uniformly with respect to σ. Then system (97) admits an invariant periodic surface.

Proof. Let us prove that if α verifies the conditions

$$\| \alpha \| \leqslant K | \epsilon |, \qquad \| \alpha(\sigma_1) - \alpha(\sigma_2) \| \leqslant L | \epsilon | \, | \sigma_1 - \sigma_2 |,$$

then ρ_t^α has an inverse for $0 \leqslant t \leqslant NT$.

To do this we will observe that under the given conditions the function ρ_t^α is monotone-increasing if $| \epsilon |$ is small enough. Indeed, from the general theory of the systems with time lag it follows that

$$\theta(t; \sigma_1, \alpha(\sigma_1), \epsilon) - \theta(t; \sigma_2, \alpha(\sigma_2), \epsilon) = \lambda(t) + o(| \sigma_1 - \sigma_2 | + | \alpha_1 - \alpha_2 |)$$
$$[\alpha_1 = \alpha(\sigma_1), \alpha_2 = \alpha(\sigma_2)],$$

where $\lambda(t)$ is the first component of the solution of the variational system

$$\dot{\lambda}(t) = \frac{\partial \Theta}{\partial u}(t, \theta(t; \sigma_2, \alpha(\sigma_2), \epsilon), y(t; \sigma_2, \alpha(\sigma_2), \epsilon), y(t - \tau; \sigma_2, \alpha(\sigma_2), \epsilon), \epsilon)\lambda(t)$$
$$+ \frac{\partial \Theta}{\partial v_1}(t, \ldots)z(t) + \frac{\partial \Theta}{\partial v_2}(t, \ldots)z(t - \tau), \qquad (99)$$
$$\dot{z}(t) = \frac{\partial Y}{\partial u}(t, \ldots)\lambda(t) + \frac{\partial Y}{\partial v_1}(t, \ldots)z(t) + \frac{\partial Y}{\partial v_2}(t, \ldots)z(t - \tau),$$

which verifies the initial conditions $\sigma_1 - \sigma_2$, $\alpha(\sigma_1) - \alpha(\sigma_2)$. We have set Θ, Y for $\Theta_0 + \epsilon\Theta_1$, $Y_0 + \epsilon Y_1$. We will have $\lambda(t) = \mu(t, \epsilon)(\sigma_1 - \sigma_2) + U(t, \epsilon)(\alpha(\sigma_1) - \alpha(\sigma_2))$.

From the general theorems of continuity with respect to the parameters it follows that $\mu(t, \epsilon)$ and $U(t, \epsilon)$ will be of the form $\mu(t) + O(\epsilon)$, $U(t) + O(\epsilon)$, where $\mu(t)$ and $U(t)$ are defined by the linear system

$$\dot{\lambda}(t) = \frac{\partial \Theta_0}{\partial u}(t, \theta(t; \sigma_2, 0, 0), y(t; \sigma_2, 0, 0), y(t - \tau; \sigma_2, 0, 0))\lambda(t)$$
$$+ \frac{\partial \Theta_0}{\partial v_1}(t, \ldots)z(t) + \frac{\partial \Theta_0}{\partial v_2}(t, \ldots)z(t - \tau),$$
$$\dot{z}(t) = \frac{\partial Y_0}{\partial u}(t, \ldots)\lambda(t) + \frac{\partial Y_0}{\partial v_1}(t, \ldots)z(t) + \frac{\partial Y_0}{\partial v_2}(t, \ldots)z(t - \tau).$$

But

$$\theta(t; \sigma_2, 0, 0) = t + \sigma_2, \qquad y(t; \sigma_2, 0, 0) \equiv 0,$$
$$\frac{\partial \Theta_0}{\partial u}(t, t + \sigma_2, 0, 0) \equiv 0, \qquad \frac{\partial Y_0}{\partial u}(t, t + \sigma_2, 0, 0) \equiv 0;$$

hence $\mu(t)$ and $U(t)$ are defined by the system

$$\dot{\lambda}(t) = \frac{\partial \Theta_0}{\partial v_1}(t, t+\sigma_2, 0, 0)z(t) + \frac{\partial \Theta_0}{\partial v_2}(t, t+\sigma_2, 0, 0)z(t-\tau),$$
$$\dot{z}(t) = \frac{\partial Y_0}{\partial v_1}(t, t+\sigma_2, 0, 0)z(t) + \frac{\partial Y_0}{\partial v_2}(t, t+\sigma_2, 0, 0)z(t-\tau). \tag{100}$$

From this system it follows that $\mu(t) \equiv 1$ and that $U(t)$ is bounded, which allows us to write

$$\begin{aligned}
&\theta(t; \sigma_1, \alpha(\sigma_1), \epsilon) - \theta(t; \sigma_2, \alpha(\sigma_2), \epsilon)\\
&\quad = [1 + O(\epsilon)](\sigma_1 - \sigma_2) + [U(t) + O(\epsilon)][\alpha(\sigma_1) - \alpha(\sigma_2)]\\
&\qquad + o(|\sigma_1 - \sigma_2| + |\alpha(\sigma_1) - \alpha(\sigma_2)|)\\
&\quad > \tfrac{1}{2}(\sigma_1 - \sigma_2) - ML|\epsilon|(\sigma_1 - \sigma_2) + o(\sigma_1 - \sigma_2) > 0
\end{aligned}$$

if $\sigma_1 - \sigma_2 > 0$, which proves that ρ_t^α is monotone, hence possesses an inverse (the continuity follows from the general theorems of continuity with respect to the initial conditions). Since ρ_t^α has an inverse for $0 \leqslant t \leqslant NT$, it follows that $T_k\alpha$ is defined for $1 \leqslant k \leqslant N$.

We shall now show that for N sufficiently large, $|\epsilon|$ sufficiently small, and K, L conveniently chosen, the set

$$\|\alpha\| \leqslant K|\epsilon|, \qquad \|\alpha(\sigma_1) - \alpha(\sigma_2)\| < L|\epsilon||\sigma_1 - \sigma_2|$$

is mapped into itself by the mapping T_N. Let $\beta = T_N\alpha$. We have

$$\begin{aligned}
|\beta(\rho)| &= |y(NT + s; \sigma_{NT}^\alpha(\rho), \alpha[\sigma_{NT}^\alpha(\rho)], \epsilon) - y(NT + s; \sigma_{NT}^\alpha(\rho), 0, 0)|\\
&\leqslant |y(NT + s; \sigma_{NT}^\alpha(\rho), \alpha[\sigma_{NT}^\alpha(\rho)], \epsilon) - y(NT + s; \sigma_{NT}^\alpha(\rho), 0, \epsilon)|\\
&\quad + |y(NT + s; \sigma_{NT}^\alpha(\rho), 0, \epsilon) - y(NT + s; \sigma_{NT}^\alpha(\rho), 0, 0)|\\
&\leqslant |z(NT + s) + o(|\alpha|)| + K_1|\epsilon|,
\end{aligned}$$

where K_1 does not depend on K and $z(t)$ is the second component of the solution of the variational system (99) (corresponding to the solution $\theta(t; \sigma_{NT}^\alpha(\rho), 0, \epsilon)$, $y(t; \sigma_{NT}^\alpha(\rho), 0, \epsilon)$, which verifies the initial conditions $0, \alpha[\sigma_{NT}^\alpha(\rho)]$).

We see as above that $z(t) = V(t, \epsilon)\alpha[\sigma_{NT}^\alpha(\rho)]$, where $V(t, \epsilon) = V(t) + O(|\epsilon|)$ and $V(t)$ is the operator attached to system (100). From the hypothesis made with regard to system (98) it follows that for N sufficiently large we will have $\|V(NT)\| \leqslant \frac{1}{2}$; hence

$$|z(NT + s)| < (\tfrac{1}{2} + O(|\epsilon|))K|\epsilon|$$

and

$$|\beta(\rho)| \leqslant (\tfrac{1}{2} + O(|\epsilon|))K|\epsilon| + K_1|\epsilon| + o(|\epsilon|),$$

which shows that for K conveniently chosen we will have $|\beta(\rho)| \leqslant K|\epsilon|$.

Further, as above,

$$\begin{aligned}
|\beta(\rho_1) - \beta(\rho_2)| &= |y(NT + s; \sigma_{NT}^{\alpha}(\rho_1), \alpha[\sigma_{NT}^{\alpha}(\rho_1)], \epsilon) \\
&\qquad - y(NT + s; \sigma_{NT}^{\alpha}(\rho_2), \alpha[\sigma_{NT}^{\alpha}(\rho_2)], \epsilon)| \\
&\leqslant |\mu_1(t, \epsilon)[\sigma_{NT}^{\alpha}(\rho_1) - \sigma_{NT}^{\alpha}(\rho_2)]| \\
&\quad + |V(NT, \epsilon)(\alpha[\sigma_{NT}^{\alpha}(\rho_1) - \alpha[\sigma_{NT}(\rho_2)])| \\
&\quad + o(|\sigma_{NT}^{\alpha}(\rho_1) - \sigma_{NT}^{\alpha}(\rho_2)| + \|\alpha[\sigma_{NT}^{\alpha}(\rho_1)] - \alpha[\sigma_{NT}^{\alpha}(\rho_2)]\|) \\
&\leqslant (|\mu_1(t)| + K_2|\epsilon|)|\sigma_{NT}^{\alpha}(\rho_1) - \sigma_{NT}^{\alpha}(\rho_2)| \\
&\quad + [\tfrac{1}{2} + O(|\epsilon|)]\|\alpha[\sigma_{NT}^{\alpha}(\rho_1)] - \alpha[\sigma_{NT}^{\alpha}(\rho_2)]\| \\
&\quad + o(|\sigma_{NT}^{\alpha}(\rho_1) - \sigma_{NT}^{\alpha}(\rho_2)| + \|\alpha[\sigma_{NT}^{\alpha}(\rho_1)] - \alpha[\sigma_{NT}^{\alpha}(\rho_2)]\|) \\
&\leqslant \{K_2|\epsilon| + (\tfrac{1}{2} + O(|\epsilon|))L|\epsilon|\}|\sigma_{NT}^{\alpha}(\rho_1) - \sigma_{NT}^{\alpha}(\rho_2)| \\
&\quad + o(|\sigma_{NT}^{\alpha}(\rho_1) - \sigma_{NT}^{\alpha}(\rho_2)|)
\end{aligned}$$

because $\mu_1(t) \equiv 0$, since the component z of the solution of system (100) does not depend on the initial conditions for component λ.

From

$$\begin{aligned}
\rho_1 - \rho_2 &= \theta(NT; \sigma_{NT}^{\alpha}(\rho_1), \alpha[\sigma_{NT}^{\alpha}(\rho_1)], \epsilon) - \theta(NT; \sigma_{NT}^{\alpha}(\rho_2), \alpha[\sigma_{NT}^{\alpha}(\rho_2)], \epsilon) \\
&= (1 + O(\epsilon))[\sigma_{NT}^{\alpha}(\rho_1) - \sigma_{NT}^{\alpha}(\rho_2)] \\
&\quad + [U(t) + O(\epsilon)](\alpha[\sigma_{NT}^{\alpha}(\rho_1)] - \alpha[\sigma_{NT}^{\alpha}(\rho_2)]) \\
&\quad + o(|\sigma_{NT}^{\alpha}(\rho_1) - \sigma_{NT}^{\alpha}(\rho_2)|)
\end{aligned}$$

it follows that

$$|\sigma_{NT}^{\alpha}(\rho_1) - \sigma_{NT}^{\alpha}(\rho_2)| < (1 + O(|\epsilon|))|\rho_1 - \rho_2|;$$

hence

$$|\beta(\rho_1) - \beta(\rho_2)| \leqslant \{K_2|\epsilon| + (\tfrac{1}{2} + O(|\epsilon|))L|\epsilon|\}(1 + O(|\epsilon|))|\rho_1 - \rho_2|.$$

Therefore, for L conveniently chosen and $|\epsilon|$ sufficiently small we have

$$|\beta(\rho_1) - \beta(\rho_2)| \leqslant L|\epsilon||\rho_1 - \rho_2|.$$

It remains to prove that T_N is a contraction. It will follow then that T_N admits a unique fixed point and hence that the system has an invariant periodic surface.

Let $\beta_1 = T_N\alpha_1$, $\beta_2 = T_N\alpha_2$. We have

$$|\beta_1 - \beta_2| = |y(NT + s; \sigma_{NT}^{\alpha_1}(\rho), \alpha_1[\sigma_{NT}^{\alpha_1}(\rho)], \epsilon) - y(NT + s; \sigma_{NT}^{\alpha_2}(\rho), \alpha_2[\sigma_{NT}^{\alpha_2}(\rho)], \epsilon)|$$

$$\leqslant K_2|\epsilon|\,|\sigma_{NT}^{\alpha_1}(\rho) - \sigma_{NT}^{\alpha_2}(\rho)| + (\tfrac{1}{2} + O(|\epsilon|))|\alpha_1[\sigma_{NT}^{\alpha_1}(\rho)] - \alpha_1[\sigma_{NT}^{\alpha_2}(\rho)]|$$

$$+ (\tfrac{1}{2} + O(|\epsilon|))\|\alpha_1[\sigma_{NT}^{\alpha_2}(\rho)] - \alpha_2[\sigma_{NT}^{\alpha_2}(\rho)]\| + o(|\sigma_{NT}^{\alpha_1}(\rho) - \sigma_{NT}^{\alpha_2}(\rho)| + \|\alpha_1 - \alpha_2\|)$$

$$\leqslant \{K_2|\epsilon| + (\tfrac{1}{2} + O(|\epsilon|))L|\epsilon|\}|\sigma_{NT}^{\alpha_1}(\rho) - \sigma_{NT}^{\alpha_2}(\rho)|$$

$$+ (\tfrac{1}{2} + O(|\epsilon|))\|\alpha_1 - \alpha_2\| + o(|\sigma_{NT}^{\alpha_1}(\rho) - \sigma_{NT}^{\alpha_2}(\rho)| + \|\alpha_1 - \alpha_2\|).$$

On the other hand, from

$$\theta(NT; \sigma_{NT}^{\alpha_1}(\rho), \alpha_1[\sigma_{NT}^{\alpha_1}\rho)], \epsilon) - \theta(NT; \sigma_{NT}^{\alpha_2}(\rho), \alpha_2[\sigma_{NT}^{\alpha_2}(\rho)], \epsilon) \equiv 0$$

follows

$$[1 + O(|\epsilon|)][\sigma_{NT}^{\alpha_1}(\rho) - \sigma_{NT}^{\alpha_2}(\rho)] + [U(t) + O(\epsilon)](\alpha_1[\sigma_{NT}^{\alpha_1}(\rho)] - \alpha_2[\sigma_{NT}^{\alpha_2}(\rho)])$$

$$+ o(|\sigma_{NT}^{\alpha_1}(\rho) - \sigma_{NT}^{\alpha_2}(\rho)| + \|\alpha_1[\sigma_{NT}^{\alpha_1}(\rho)] - \alpha_2[\sigma_{NT}^{\alpha_2}(\rho)]\|) \equiv 0,$$

from which we immediately obtain

$$|\sigma_{NT}^{\alpha_1}(\rho) - \sigma_{NT}^{\alpha_2}(\rho)| \leqslant K_3\|\alpha_1 - \alpha_2\|$$

We deduce that

$$|\beta_1 - \beta_2| \leqslant K_4|\epsilon|\,\|\alpha_1 - \alpha_2\| + (\tfrac{1}{2} + O(|\epsilon|))\|\alpha_1 - \alpha_2\| + o(\|\alpha_1 - \alpha_2\|);$$

hence $\|\beta_1 - \beta_2\| \leqslant \frac{2}{3}\|\alpha_1 - \alpha_2\|$ for $|\epsilon|$ sufficiently small, which shows that T_N is a contraction.

It is an open problem to obtain some analogous results for systems in which θ occurs with retardation.

NOTES

General expositions relative to systems with time lag are to be found in [65] and [66]. Results on the stability theory of systems with time lag as well as the fundamental inequality of Section 4.1 are to be found in the monograph [15]. The results of Sections 4.1 and 4.2 have been published in [67–70]. The results of Sections 4.3 and 4.4 have been published in [71], those of Section 4.5 have been partially published in [72], and those of Section 4.6 have been published in a joint paper with V. M. Popov [73] and in [89]. The results of A. Stokes are published in [90]. The results of section 4.8 have been published in [78], those of Sections 4.9 and 4.10 in [74–77], and those of Section 4.11 in [91].

For the case of linear systems with constant coefficients, results have been given by S. N. Šimanov in [79] and [80]. The theory of systems containing a small parameter is to be found in [67] and in [81] and [82]. For quasi-linear systems the results have been stated by S. N. Šimanov in [83]. The results of Section 4.14 have been published in [49] and those relative to the averaging method in [84] and [85]. Theorem 4.35 can be found in [86]. Theorems 4.36 and 4.37 are to be found in [67], Theorems 4.38 and 4.39 in [87], the other results of Section 4.16 in [92] and [93]. Let us note also the results of J. K. Hale, [94] and [95]. For very complete bibliography on differential-functional equations see the papers of Elsgoltz and others, [107] and [108]. For some other questions, see also the book by R. Bellman and K. Cooke [109].

Appendix

A.1. Elements from the Theory of the Fourier Transform

Let f be a function of $L^1(-\infty, \infty)$. We call the Fourier transform of function f the function

$$\phi(\alpha) = \int_{-\infty}^{+\infty} e^{-i\alpha t} f(t)dt, \qquad (\alpha \text{ real}).$$

We state the following properties:

1. The function ϕ is *bounded*, since

$$|\phi(\alpha)| \leqslant \int_{-\infty}^{+\infty} |f(t)|\, dt < +\infty.$$

2. The function ϕ is *continuous*, since

$$|e^{-iht} - 1| = |\cos ht - i \sin ht - 1| = \left| -2\sin^2 \frac{ht}{2} - 2i \sin \frac{ht}{2} \cos \frac{ht}{2} \right|$$

$$= \left| 2 \sin \frac{ht}{2} \right| \left| -\sin \frac{ht}{2} - i \cos \frac{ht}{2} \right| = \left| 2 \sin \frac{ht}{2} \right|,$$

from which

$$|\phi(\alpha + h) - \phi(\alpha)| = \left| \int_{-\infty}^{\infty} e^{-i(\alpha+h)t} f(t)dt - \int_{-\infty}^{\infty} e^{-i\alpha t} f(t)dt \right|$$

$$= \left| \int_{-\infty}^{\infty} e^{-i\alpha t}(e^{-iht} - 1) f(t)dt \right| \leqslant \int_{-\infty}^{\infty} |e^{-iht} - 1|\, |f(t)|\, dt$$

$$\leqslant 2 \int_{-\infty}^{\infty} |f(t)| \left| \sin \frac{ht}{2} \right| dt$$

$$\leqslant 2 \int_{-\infty}^{-R} |f(t)|\, dt + 2 \int_{-R}^{R} |f(t)| \left| \frac{\sin ht}{2} \right| dt + 2 \int_{R}^{\infty} |f(t)|\, dt$$

$$\leqslant 2 \int_{-\infty}^{-R} |f(t)|\, dt + 2 \int_{R}^{\infty} |f(t)|\, dt + \frac{2|h|R}{2} \int_{-R}^{R} |f(t)|\, dt.$$

For $\epsilon > 0$ there exists an R_0 such that if $R > R_0$ we have

$$\int_{-\infty}^{-R} |f(t)|\, dt < \frac{\epsilon}{6}, \qquad \int_{R}^{\infty} |f(t)|\, dt < \frac{\epsilon}{6}.$$

We fix $R > R_0$ and choose $\delta(\epsilon) = \epsilon/3R\int_{-R}^{R}|f(t)|\,dt$. It follows that if $|h| < \delta(\epsilon)$, then $|h|\,R\int_{-R}^{R}|f(t)|\,dt < \epsilon/3$. Finally, for $|h| < \delta(\epsilon)$ we obtain $|\phi(\alpha + h) - \phi(\alpha)| < \epsilon$; hence ϕ is *uniformly continuous on the whole axis.*

3. If $f \in L^1$ and $itf(t) \in L^1$, then $\phi'(\alpha)$ exists and is the Fourier transform of the function $-itf(t)$:

$$\frac{\phi(\alpha + h) - \phi(\alpha)}{h} = \int_{-\infty}^{\infty} \frac{e^{-i\alpha t}(e^{-iht} - 1)}{h} f(t)dt = \int_{-\infty}^{\infty} e^{-i\alpha t}\,\frac{e^{-iht} - 1}{h} f(t)dt$$

$$= \int_{-\infty}^{\infty} e^{-i\alpha t} f_h(t)dt,$$

where we have set

$$f_h(t) = \frac{e^{-iht} - 1}{h} f(t).$$

We see that

$$\lim_{h\to 0} f_h(t) = -itf(t),$$

$$|f_h(t)| \leqslant \frac{|e^{-iht} - 1|}{|h|}|f(t)| = \frac{2|\sin(ht/2)|}{|h|}|f(t)| \leqslant |t|\,|f(t)| \in L^1;$$

hence $f_h(t) \in L^1$. It follows that we can pass at the limit under the integration sign and we obtain

$$\phi'(\alpha) = -\int_{-\infty}^{\infty} e^{-i\alpha t} itf(t)dt.$$

4. If $f' \in L^1, f \in L^1$, then the Fourier transform of f' is $i\alpha\phi(\alpha)$.

We obviously have

$$f(X) - f(x) = \int_x^X f'(t)dt;$$

hence, since $f' \in L^1$, we will have

$$\lim_{X\to\infty} f(X) = l.$$

However, $f \in L^1$ and from

$$\lim_{X\to\infty} f(X) = l,$$

it follows necessarily that $l = 0$. We can thus write that

$$f(x) = -\int_x^{\infty} f'(t)dt.$$

Further,

$$\int_{-\infty}^{\infty} e^{-i\alpha t} f'(t)dt = \lim_{\substack{x_1 \to \infty \\ x_2 \to \infty}} \int_{-x_1}^{x_2} e^{-i\alpha t} f'(t)dt$$

$$= \lim_{\substack{x_1 \to \infty \\ x_2 \to \infty}} \left\{ e^{-i\alpha t} f(t) \Big|_{-x_1}^{x_2} + i\alpha \int_{-x_1}^{x_2} e^{-i\alpha t} f(t)dt \right\} = i\alpha\phi(\alpha).$$

Definition. Let $f, g \in L^1$. *The function*

$$h(x) = \int_{-\infty}^{\infty} f(x-y)g(y)dy = \int_{-\infty}^{\infty} f(y)g(x-y)dy$$

is said to be the convolution of functions f and g.

Theorem 1. *If $f, g \in L^1$, then h is defined for almost every x, $h \in L^1$, and we have*

$$\int_{-\infty}^{\infty} | h | \, dt \leqslant \int_{-\infty}^{\infty} | f | \, dt \int_{-\infty}^{\infty} | g | \, dt.$$

The Fourier transform of h is the product of the Fourier transform of functions f and g.

Proof. We have

$$\int_{-\infty}^{\infty} |f(x-t)| \, |g(t)| \, dx = |g(t)| \int_{-\infty}^{\infty} |f(x-t)| \, dx = |g(t)| \int_{-\infty}^{\infty} |f(t)| \, dt;$$

hence

$$\left| \int_{-\infty}^{\infty} f(x-t(g(t)dx \right| < L |g(t)| \quad \text{and} \quad \int_{-\infty}^{\infty} f(x \quad t)g(t)dx \in L^1.$$

It follows that

$$\int_{-\infty}^{\infty} dt \int_{-\infty}^{\infty} f(x-t)g(t)dx$$

exists and

$$\int_{-\infty}^{\infty} dt \int_{-\infty}^{\infty} |f(x-t)| \, |g(t)| \, dx < \int_{-\infty}^{\infty} |g(t)| \, dt \int_{-\infty}^{\infty} |f(t)| \, dt.$$

The function f is measurable; hence $f(x-t)$ is measurable in the product space of variables (x, t). The Fubini theorem can be applied and we have

$$\int_{-\infty}^{\infty} dt \int_{-\infty}^{\infty} |f(x-t)| \, |g(t)| \, dx = \int_{-\infty}^{\infty} dx \int_{-\infty}^{\infty} |f(x-t)| \, |g(t)| \, dt \geqslant \int_{-\infty}^{\infty} | h(x)| dx.$$

It follows that h exists almost everywhere (Fubini theorem),

$$\int_{-\infty}^{\infty} dt \int_{-\infty}^{\infty} f(x-t)g(t)dx = \int_{-\infty}^{\infty} dx \int_{-\infty}^{\infty} f(x-t)g(t)dt, \qquad h \in L^1$$

and

$$\int_{-\infty}^{\infty} |h(x)|\, dx \leqslant \int_{-\infty}^{\infty} |g(t)|\, dt \int_{-\infty}^{\infty} |f(t)|\, dt.$$

Further,

$$\begin{aligned}\int_{-\infty}^{\infty} e^{-i\alpha x}h(x)dx &= \int_{-\infty}^{\infty} e^{-i\alpha x}\, dx \int_{-\infty}^{\infty} f(x-y)g(y)dy \\ &= \int_{-\infty}^{\infty} dx \int_{-\infty}^{\infty} e^{-i\alpha(x-y)}f(x-y)e^{-i\alpha y}g(y)dy \\ &= \int_{-\infty}^{\infty} e^{-i\alpha y}g(y)dy \int_{-\infty}^{\infty} e^{-i\alpha(x-y)}f(x-y)dx \\ &= \int_{-\infty}^{\infty} e^{-i\alpha y}g(y)dy \int_{-\infty}^{\infty} e^{-i\alpha t}f(t)dt.\end{aligned}$$

Theorem 2. *Let $f_1, f_2 \in L^1$, $\phi_1(\alpha)$, $\phi_2(\alpha)$ be the corresponding Fourier transforms. Then*

$$\phi_1(y)f_2(y) \in L^1, \qquad \phi_2(y)f_1(y) \in L^1$$

and, in addition,

$$\int_{-\infty}^{\infty} \phi_1 f_2\, dx = \int_{-\infty}^{\infty} \phi_2 f_1\, dy.$$

Proof. The first affirmation is immediate, since ϕ_1 and ϕ_2 are bounded:

$$\begin{aligned}\int_{-\infty}^{\infty} \phi_1(y)f_2(y)dy &= \int_{-\infty}^{\infty} f_2(y)dy \int_{-\infty}^{\infty} e^{-iyx}f_1(x)dx \\ &= \int_{-\infty}^{\infty} dy \int_{-\infty}^{\infty} e^{-ixy}f_1(x)f_2(y)dy = \int_{-\infty}^{\infty} dx \int_{-\infty}^{\infty} e^{-ixy}f_1(x)f_2(y)dy \\ &= \int_{-\infty}^{\infty} f_1(x)dx \int_{-\infty}^{\infty} e^{-ixy}f_2(y)dy = \int_{-\infty}^{\infty} \phi_2(x)f_1(x)dx.\end{aligned}$$

Theorem 3. *Let $f \in L^1 \cap L^2$. Then $\phi \in L^2$ and*

$$\int_{-\infty}^{\infty} |\phi(x)|^2\, dx = 2\pi \int_{-\infty}^{\infty} |f(x)|^2\, dx.$$

Proof. Let $h(x) = \int_{-\infty}^{+\infty} f(x+y)\bar{f}(y)dy$. The integral exists due to the fact that $f \in L^2$. We have

$$|h(x)|^2 \leqslant \int_{-\infty}^{\infty} |f(x+y)|^2\,dy \int_{-\infty}^{\infty} |\bar{f}(y)|^2\,dy \leqslant \left(\int_{-\infty}^{\infty} |f(y)|^2\,dy\right)^2 < \infty;$$

hence h is bounded. The function h is also continuous, since

$$\begin{aligned}|h(x+\delta) - h(x)| &= \left|\int_{-\infty}^{\infty} f(x+\delta+y)\bar{f}(y)dy - \int_{-\infty}^{\infty} f(x+y)\bar{f}(y)dy\right| \\ &= \left|\int_{-\infty}^{\infty} [f(x+\delta+y) - f(x+y)]\,\bar{f}(y)dy\right| \\ &\leqslant \int_{-\infty}^{\infty} |f(x+\delta+y) - f(x+y)|\,|\bar{f}(y)|\,dy \\ &\leqslant \left\{\int_{-\infty}^{\infty} |f(x+y+\delta) - f(x+y)|\,dy \int_{-\infty}^{\infty} |\bar{f}(y)|^2\,dy\right\}^{1/2}.\end{aligned}$$

We have, however, for the functions of L^2,

$$\int_{-\infty}^{\infty} |f(x+y+\delta) - f(x+y)|^2\,dy = \int_{-\infty}^{\infty} |f(t+\delta) - f(t)|^2\,dt,$$

however small if δ is sufficiently small, from which follows the continuity of function h. Further,

$$h(x) = \int_{-\infty}^{\infty} f(x+y)\bar{f}(y)dy = \int_{-\infty}^{\infty} f(x-z)\bar{f}(-z)dz = \int_{-\infty}^{\infty} f(x-z)g(z)dz,$$

where we have denoted $g(z) = \bar{f}(-z)$. It follows that h is the convolution of the functions f and g; hence the Fourier transform of h exists and coincides with the product of the transforms of the functions f and g.

The Fourier transform of g is computed in the following way:

$$\int_{-\infty}^{\infty} e^{-i\alpha t}g(t)dt = \int_{-\infty}^{\infty} e^{-i\alpha t}\bar{f}(-t)dt = \int_{-\infty}^{\infty} e^{i\alpha s}\bar{f}(s)ds = \bar{\phi}(\alpha).$$

It follows that the Fourier transform of the function h is

$$\phi(\alpha)\bar{\phi}(\alpha) = |\phi(\alpha)|^2.$$

Let $\gamma(x) = e^{-\epsilon x^2}$. We have

$$\gamma'(x) = -2\epsilon x e^{-\epsilon x^2} = 2\epsilon i i x \gamma(x).$$

We write

$$\psi(\alpha) = \int_{-\infty}^{\infty} e^{-i\alpha t}\gamma(t)dt.$$

On the basis of properties 3 and 4 we have

$$i\alpha\psi(\alpha) = \int_{-\infty}^{\infty} e^{-i\alpha t}\gamma'(t)dt = 2\epsilon i \int_{-\infty}^{\infty} e^{-i\alpha t} it\gamma(t)dt = -2\epsilon i\psi'(\alpha).$$

It follows that

$$\psi'(\alpha) = -\frac{\alpha}{2\epsilon}\psi(\alpha), \qquad \frac{\psi'(\alpha)}{\psi(\alpha)} = -\frac{\alpha}{2\epsilon};$$

hence

$$\psi(\alpha) = Ce^{-\alpha^2/4\epsilon}; \qquad C = \psi(0) = \int_{-\infty}^{\infty} e^{-\epsilon t^2}\, dt = \frac{1}{\sqrt{\epsilon}}\int_{-\infty}^{\infty} e^{-y^2}\, dy = \sqrt{\frac{\pi}{\epsilon}}.$$

It follows that

$$\psi(\alpha) = \sqrt{\frac{\pi}{\epsilon}}\, e^{-\alpha^2/4\epsilon}.$$

We apply Theorem 2 to the functions γ and h. It follows that

$$\int_{-\infty}^{\infty} |\phi(\alpha)|^2 e^{-\epsilon\alpha^2}\, d\alpha = \sqrt{\frac{\pi}{\epsilon}}\int_{-\infty}^{\infty} h(\alpha)e^{-\alpha^2/4\epsilon}\, d\alpha = 2\sqrt{\pi}\int_{-\infty}^{\infty} h(2\sqrt{\epsilon}y)e^{-y^2}\, dy.$$

For $\epsilon \to 0$ we obtain

$$\int_{-\infty}^{\infty} |\phi(\alpha)|^2\, d\alpha = 2\sqrt{\pi}\int_{-\infty}^{\infty} h(0)e^{-y^2}\, dy = 2\sqrt{\pi}h(0)\int_{-\infty}^{\infty} e^{-y^2}\, dy = 2\pi h(0).$$

However,

$$h(0) = \int_{-\infty}^{\infty} f(y)\bar{f}(y)dy = \int_{-\infty}^{\infty} |f(y)|^2\, dy.$$

The theorem is thus proved.

Theorem 4. *Let $f_1, f_2 \in L^1 \cap L^2$ and ϕ_1, ϕ_2 be the Fourier transforms. Then*

$$\int_{-\infty}^{\infty} (f_1\bar{f}_2 + f_2\bar{f}_1)dt = \frac{1}{2\pi}\int_{-\infty}^{\infty} (\phi_1\bar{\phi}_2 + \phi_2\bar{\phi}_1)dt.$$

Proof. On the basis of the preceding theorem,

$$\int_{-\infty}^{\infty} | f_1 + f_2 |^2 \, dt = \frac{1}{2\pi} \int_{-\infty}^{\infty} | \phi_1 + \phi_2 |^2 \, dt,$$

$$\int_{-\infty}^{\infty} (f_1 + f_2)(\bar{f}_1 + \bar{f}_2) dt = \frac{1}{2\pi} \int_{-\infty}^{\infty} (\phi_1 + \phi_2)(\bar{\phi}_1 + \bar{\phi}_2) dt.$$

Consequently,

$$\int_{-\infty}^{\infty} | f_1 |^2 \, dt + \int_{-\infty}^{\infty} | f_2 |^2 \, dt + \int_{-\infty}^{\infty} (f_1 \bar{f}_2 + f_2 \bar{f}_1) dt$$

$$= \frac{1}{2\pi} \int_{-\infty}^{\infty} | \phi_1 |^2 \, dt + \frac{1}{2\pi} \int_{-\infty}^{\infty} | \phi_2 |^2 \, dt + \frac{1}{2\pi} \int_{-\infty}^{\infty} (\phi_1 \bar{\phi}_2 + \phi_2 \bar{\phi}_1) dt.$$

Taking into account the preceding theorem, we obtain the formula in the statement.

Consequence. If f_1 and f_2 are real, the formula becomes

$$2 \int_{-\infty}^{\infty} f_1 f_2 \, dt = \frac{1}{2\pi} \int_{-\infty}^{\infty} (2 \operatorname{Re} \phi_1 \bar{\phi}_2) dt;$$

hence

$$\int_{-\infty}^{\infty} f_1 f_2 \, dt = \frac{1}{2\pi} \int_{-\infty}^{\infty} \operatorname{Re} \phi_1(\alpha) \bar{\phi}_2(\alpha) d\alpha.$$

However,

$$\phi_2(\alpha) = \int_{-\infty}^{\infty} e^{-i\alpha t} f_2(t) dt;$$

hence

$$\bar{\phi}_2(\alpha) = \int_{-\infty}^{\infty} e^{i\alpha t} f_2(t) dt = \phi_2(-\alpha),$$

since f_2 is real.

It follows finally that if f_1 and f_2 are real,

$$\int_{-\infty}^{\infty} f_1 f_2 \, dt = \frac{1}{2\pi} \int_{-\infty}^{\infty} \operatorname{Re} \phi_1(\alpha) \phi_2(-\alpha) d\alpha$$

If the functions f_1 and f_2 are only given in $[0, \infty)$, we extend them by the zero value along $(-\infty, 0)$, and the preceding formula becomes

$$\int_{0}^{\infty} f_1 f_2 \, dt = \frac{1}{2\pi} \int_{-\infty}^{\infty} \operatorname{Re} \phi_1(\alpha) \phi_2(-\alpha) d\alpha.$$

Remark. If f is defined in $[0,\infty)$ and is differentiable, with its derivative in L^1, it follows that

$$\int_0^\infty e^{-i\alpha t}f'(t)dt = e^{-i\alpha t}f(t)\Big|_0^\infty + i\alpha\int_0^\infty e^{-i\alpha t}f(t)dt = -f(0) + i\alpha\phi(\alpha).$$

A.2. The Permutation of the Integration Order in Stieltjes' Integral

We will reproduce a theorem of H. E. Bray [88] relative to the permutation of the integration order in the theory of Stieltjes' integral, which has been repeatedly used in the theory of general systems with time lag.

Theorem. *If $\varphi(s)$ is continuous in $[a, b]$, $\gamma(x)$ with bounded variation in $[c, d]$, $\alpha(x, s)$ continuous in x for $s \in [a, b]$ and with bounded variation with respect to s, uniformly for $x \in [c, d]$, the integrals*

$$\int_c^d \left[\int_a^b \varphi(s)d_s\alpha(x, s)\right] d\gamma(x) \qquad \text{and} \qquad \int_a^b \varphi(s)d_s \int_c^d \alpha(x, s)d\gamma(x)$$

exist and are equal.

Proof. Let

$$\phi(x) = \int_a^b \varphi(s)d_s\alpha(x, s), \qquad \psi(s) = \int_c^d \alpha(x, s)d\gamma(x).$$

It is easy to verify that ψ is of bounded variation and ϕ is continuous. From this follows the existence of the two integrals. The formula

$$\sum_{j=0}^{m}\left[\sum_{i=0}^{n}\varphi(s_i)\{\alpha(x_j, s_{i+1}) - \alpha(x_j, s_i)\}\right](\gamma(x_{j+1}) - \gamma(x_j)]$$
$$= \sum_{i=0}^{n}\varphi(s_i)\left[\sum_{j=0}^{m}\alpha(x_j, s_{i+1})\{\gamma(x_{j+1}) - \gamma(x_j)\} - \sum_{j=0}^{m}\alpha(x_j, s_i)\{\gamma(x_{j+1}) - \gamma(x_j)\}\right]$$

is verified by direct computation.

Let $\epsilon > 0$. For divisions of sufficiently small norm we have

$$\left|\int_c^d \phi(x)d\gamma(x) - \sum_{j=0}^{m}\phi(x_j)\{\gamma(x_{j+1}) - \gamma(x_j)\}\right| < \frac{\epsilon}{4},$$

$$\left|\sum_{j=0}^{m}\phi(x_j)\{\gamma(x_{j+1}) - \gamma(x_j)\}\right.$$
$$\left. - \sum_{j=0}^{m}\left[\sum_{i=0}^{n}\varphi(s_i)\{\alpha(x_j, s_{i+1}) - \alpha(x_j, s_i)\}\right]\{\gamma(x_{j+1}) - \gamma(x_j)\}\right| < \frac{\epsilon}{4}.$$

It follows that

$$\left| \int_c^d \phi(x)d\gamma(x) - \sum_{j=0}^{m} \left[\sum_{j=0}^{n} \varphi(s_i)\{\alpha(x_j, s_{i+1}) - \alpha(x_j, s_i)\} \right] [\gamma(x_{j+1}) - \gamma(x_j)] \right| < \frac{\epsilon}{2}.$$

Likewise, for divisions of small enough norm,

$$\left| \int_a^b \varphi(s)d\psi(s) - \sum_{i=0}^{n'} \varphi(s_i)[\psi(s_{i+1}) - \psi(s_i)] \right| < \frac{\epsilon}{4},$$

$$\left| \sum_{i=0}^{n'} \varphi(s_i)[\psi(s_{i+1}) - \psi(s_i)] - \sum_{i=0}^{n'} \varphi(s_i) \left[\sum_{j=0}^{m'} \alpha(x_j, s_{i+1})\{\gamma(x_{j+1}) - \gamma(x_j)\} \right.\right.$$

$$\left.\left. - \sum_{j=0}^{m'} \alpha(x_j, s_i)\{\gamma(x_{j+1}) - \gamma(x_j)\} \right] \right| < \frac{\epsilon}{4};$$

hence

$$\left| \int_a^b \varphi(s)d\psi(s) - \sum_{i=0}^{n'} \varphi(s_i) \left[\sum_{j=0}^{m'} \alpha(x_j, s_{i+1})\{\gamma(x_{j+1}) - \gamma(x_j)\} \right.\right.$$

$$\left.\left. - \sum_{j=0}^{m'} \alpha(x_j, s_i)\{\gamma(x_{j+1}) - \gamma(x_j)\} \right] \right| < \frac{\epsilon}{2}.$$

Finally, for divisions of small enough norm conveniently chosen,

$$\left| \int_c^d \phi(x)d\gamma(x) - \int_a^b \varphi(s)d\psi(s) \right| < \epsilon;$$

hence

$$\int_c^d \phi(x)d\gamma(x) = \int_a^b \varphi(s)d\psi(s).$$

The theorem is thus proved.

Let us observe that the same computations remain valid in the case when the functions which occur have matrix values for which multiplication is allowed. The formula

$$\int_a^b \left[\int_c^d x(s)d_s\eta(\alpha, s - \alpha) \right] d\alpha = \int_c^d x(s)d_s \int_a^b y(\alpha)\eta(\alpha, s - \alpha)d\alpha$$

is likewise proved in the same way.

Assuming $\eta(\alpha, s) \equiv 0$ for $s \geqslant 0$, there occurs the formula

$$\int_a^b \left[\int_{-A}^{\alpha} x(s)d_s\eta(\alpha, s - \alpha) \right] y(\alpha)d\alpha$$

$$= \int_{-A}^{a} x(s)d_s \int_a^b \eta(\alpha, s - \alpha)y(\alpha)d\alpha + \int_a^b x(s)d_s \int_s^b \eta(\alpha, s - \alpha)y(\alpha)d\alpha.$$

Indeed, taking into account the condition imposed on η we deduce that

$$\int_{\alpha}^{b} x(s)d_s\eta(\alpha, s - \alpha) = 0 \qquad \text{for} \quad a \leqslant \alpha \leqslant b;$$

hence

$$\int_a^b \left[\int_{-A}^{\alpha} x(s)d_s\eta(\alpha, s - \alpha)\right] y(\alpha)d\alpha$$

$$= \int_a^b \left[\int_{-A}^{b} x(s)d_s\eta(\alpha, s - \alpha)\right] y(\alpha)d\alpha = \int_{-A}^{b} x(s)d_s \int_a^b \eta(\alpha, s - \alpha)y(\alpha)d\alpha$$

$$= \int_{-A}^{b} x(s)d_s \int_a^b \eta(\alpha, s - \alpha)y(\alpha)d\alpha + \int_a^b x(s)d_s \int_a^b \eta(\alpha, s - \alpha)y(\alpha)d\alpha$$

$$= \int_{-A}^{b} x(s)d_s \int_a^b \eta(\alpha, s - \alpha)y(\alpha)d\alpha + \int_a^b x(s)d_s \int_a^b \eta(\alpha, s - \alpha)y(\alpha)d\alpha,$$

since for $s \geqslant a$ and $a \leqslant \alpha \leqslant s$ we have $s - \alpha \geqslant 0$ and $\eta(\alpha, s - \alpha) \equiv 0$. The last formula obtained is the one systematically used in the theory of systems with time lag.

References

1. I. G. Petrovsky, "Lectures on Differential Equations" (in Russian). GITTL, Moscow, 1952.
2. V. V. Stepanov, "Differential Equations." (in Russian). GITTL, Moscow, 1950.
3. V. V. Nemyckii and V. V. Stepanov, "Qualitative Theory of Differential Equations" (in Russian), 2 nd ed. GITTL, Moscow, 1949.
4. E. A. Coddington and N. Levinson, "The Theory of Ordinary Differential Equations." McGraw-Hill, New York, 1955.
5. S. Lefschetz, "Differential Equations: Geometric Theory." Wiley (Interscience), New York, 1957.
6. L. S. Pontryagin, "Ordinary Differential Equations" (in Russian). Fizmatizdat, Moscow, 1961.
7. T. Wazewski, Systèmes des équations et des inégalités différentielles ordinaires aux deuxièmes membres monotones et leurs applications. *Ann. Polon. Math.* **XXIII**, 112–166 (1950).
8. A. M. Lyapunov, "General Problem of the Stability of Motion" (in Russian). GIT, Moscow-Leningrad, 1950.
9. I. G. Malkin, "Theory of Stability of Motion" (in Russian). GITTL, Moscow-Leningrad, 1952.
10. J. L. Massera, Contribution to stability theory. *Ann. of Math.* **65**, No. 1, 182–206 (July 1956).
11. K. P. Persidski, Über die Stabilität einer Bewegung nach der ersten Näherung. *Mat. Sb.* **40**, 284–293 (1933).
12. V. V. Rumiantsev, On the stability of a motion in a part of variables. *Vestnik Moskov. Univ. Ser. I Mat. Meh.* **4**, 9–16 (1957).
13. A. Halanay, An generalisation of a theorem of K. P. Persidski (in Rumanian). *Com. Acad. R.P. Romîne* **12**, 1065–1068 (1960).
14. I. G. Malkin, On the reversibility of Lyapunov's theorem on asymptotic stability (in Russian). *Prikl. Mat. Meh.* **18**, 129–138 (1954).
15. N. N. Krasovski, "Some Problems in the Theory of Stability of Motion" (in Russian) [English translation by Stanford Univ. Press, Stanford, California, 1963]. Gos. Fiz. Mat lit, Moscow, 1959.
16. C. Corduneanu, Application of differential inequalities in the theory of stability (in Russian). *An. Sti. Univ. "Al. I. Cuza" Iaşi. Secţ. I.* **VI**, No. 1, 47–58 (1960).
17. I. G. Malkin, Das Existenz-Problem von Lyapunovschen Funktionen. *Izv. Fiz. Mat. Obsč. Kazan* **III**, No. 4, 51–62; **III**, No. 5, 63–84 (1931).
18. I. M. Gel'fand, "Lectures on Linear Algebra" (in Russian). GITTL, Moscow, 1951.
19. W. Hahn, Eine Bemerkung zur zweiten Methode von Ljapunov. *Math. Nachrichten* **14**, 349–354 (1956).
20. R. Bellman, "Stability Theory of Differential Equations." McGraw-Hill, New York, 1953.
21. E. A. Barbasin, On two schemes for the proof of theorems on stability by the first approximation (in Russian). *Dokl. Akad. Nauk SSSR* **111**, 9–11 (1956).

22. A. Halanay, Some remarks about the Asymptotic stability (in Rumanian). *An. Univ. C.I. Parhon Bucureşti. Ser. Sti. Nat.* **9**, 31–38 (1956).
23. A. Halanay, A stability criterium (in Rumanian). *Com. Acad. R.P. Romîne* **IX**, No. 3, 209–214 (1959).
24. N. N. Bautin, "Behaviour of Dynamical Systems near the Boundary of their Region of Stability" (in Russian). GITTL, Moscow, 1949.
25. T. Hacker, Stability of partially controlled motions of an aircraft. *J. Aerospace Sci.* **28**, No. 1, 15–27 (January 1961).
26. V. E. Germaidze and N. N. Krasovskii, On the stability in the case of constantly acting disturbances (in Russian). *Prikl. Mat. Meh.* **21**, No. 6, 769–774, (1957).
27. I. Vrkoč, Integral stability (in Russian). *Czech. Math. J.* **9**(84), 71–128 (1959).
28. Kyuzo Hayashy, On the strong stability and boundedness of solutions of ordinary differential equations. *Mem. Coll. Sci. Univ. Kyoto. Ser. A. Math.* **XXXII**, 2 (1959).
29. N. P. Erugin, Reducible systems (in Russian). *Trudy Mat. Inst. Steklov* **13**, 1–96 (1946).
30. I. M. Gel'fand and V. B. Lidskii, On the structure of the regions of stability of linear canonical systems of differential equations with periodic coefficients (in Russian). *Uspehi Mat. Nauk (N. S.)* **10**, 3–40 (1955). *Ann. Math. Soc. Transl.* **8**, No. 2, 143–182 (1958).
31. M. G. Krein, On the theory of λ-zones of stability of canonical systems of linear differential equations with periodic coefficients. Collected memoirs dedicated to A. Andronov (in Russian). *Izd. Akad. Nauk SSSR*, 413–498 (1955).
32. V. A. Yakubovič, Remarks about some papers on systems of linear differential equations with periodic coefficients. *Prikl. Mat. Meh.* **21**, 707–713 (1957).
33. O. Perron, Die Stabilitätsfrage bei Differentialgleichungen *Math. Z.* **32**, 703–728 (1930).
34. R. Bellman, On an application of a Banach-Steinhaus theorem to the study of the boundedness of solutions of nonlinear differential and difference equations. *Ann. of Math.* **49**, 515–522 (1948).
35. M. Reghis, On the nonuniform stability in general spaces (in Rumanian). *Lucrăr. Şti. Inst. Ped. Timişoara Mat. Fiz.*, 153–169 (1960).
36. A. I. Lurie and V. N. Postnikov, Concerning the theory of stability of regulating systems (in Russian) *Prikl. Mat. Meh.* **8**, 246–248 (1944).
37. A. I. Lurie, "Some Nonlinear Problems of the Theory of Automatic regulation" (in Russian). GITTL, Moscow, 1951.
38. A. M. Letov, "Stability of Nonlinear Regulating Systems" (in Russian), 2nd ed. GIMFL, Moscow, 1962 [English translation by Princeton Univ. Press, Princeton, New Jersey, 1961].
39. V. A. Yakubovič, Stability in the large of the unperturbed motion for the equations of the indirect controls (in Russian). *Vestnik Leningrad. Univ. 19, Ser. Math. Mech. Astr.* **4**, 172–176 (1957).
40. V. A. Yakubovič, On the non linear differential equations of systems of automatic control with a single control organ (in Russian). *Vestnik Leningrad. Univ. 7, Ser. Mat. Meh. Astr.* **2**, 120–153 (1960).
41. S. Lefschetz, An application of the direct method of Liapunov. *Bol. Soc. Mat. Mexicana Sec. Serie* **5**, No. 2, 139–143 (1960).
42. V. M. Popov, Nouveaux criteriums de stabilité pour les systèmes automatiques nonlinéaires. *Rev. d'électrotechnique et d'énergétique. Acad. R. P. Romîne*, **V**. No. 1, 73–88 (1960).
43. V. M. Popov, On the absolute stability of nonlinear control systems (in Russian). *Avtomat. i Telemeh.* **XXII**, No. 8, 961–979 (1961).

44. V. M. Popov, On a critical case of absolute stability (in Russian). *Avtomat. i Telemeh.* **XXIII**, No. 1, 3–24 (1962).
45. V. M. Popov, On the practical stability of control systems which contain an element with nonunivoc nonlinearity (in Russian). *Rev. d'électrotechnique et d'énergétique. Acad. R. P. Romîne* **VI**, No. 1, 81–101 (1959).
46. V. A. Yakubovič, Solutions of some matrix inequalities which are met in the theory of control systems (in Russian). *Dokl. A Nauk SSSR* **143**, No. 6, 1304–1307 (1962).
47. J. L. Massera, The existence of periodic solutions of systems of differential equations. *Duke Math. J.* **17**, 457–475 (1950).
48. A. Halanay, Almost-periodic solutions of nonlinear systems with a small parameter (in Russian). *J. Čist. i Prikl. Mat. Acad. R. P. Romîne* **I**, No. 2, 49–60 (1956).
49. A. Halanay, Periodic and almost periodic solutions of systems of differential equations with delayed argument (in Russian). *Rev. Math. Pures Appl.* **IV**, No. 4, 686–691 (1959).
50. J. L. Massera and J. J. Schäffer, Linear differential equations and functional analysis I. *Ann. of Math.* **67**, No. 3, 517–573 (May 1958).
51. I. Barbălat and A. Halanay, Solutions périodiques des systèmes d'équations différentielles nonlinéaires. *Rev. Math. Pures Appl.* **III**, No. 3, 395–411 (1958).
52. I. G. Malkin, Some Problems in the Theory of Nonlinear Oscillations (in Russian). GITTL, Moscow, 1956.
53. N. N. Bogoliubov, On some statistical methods in mathematical physics (in Russian). *Akad. Nauk Ukrain. R.S.R.* (1945)
54. N. N. Bogoliubov and Y. A. Mitropolski, "Asymptotic Methods in the Theory of Nonlinear Oscillations." GIMFL, Moscow, 1958 [English translation by Gordon and Breach, 1962].
55. A. Halanay, Solutions périodiques des systèmes nonlinéaires à petit paramètre. *Rend. Accad. dei Lincei Sci. Fis. Mat. Naturali, Serie VIII,* **XXII**, 1, 30–32 (1957).
56. I. Berstein and A. Halanay, Index of the singular point and the existence of periodic solutions of systems with a small parameter (in Russian). *Dokl. Akad. Nauk SSSR* **111**, No. 5, 923–925 (1956).
57. F. Browder, On a generalisation of the Schauder fixed-point-theorem. *Duke Math. J.* **26**, No. 2, 291–303 (1959).
58. M. Urabe, Geometric study of nonlinear autonomous system. *Funkcial. Ekvac.* **1**, 1–84 (1958).
59. O. Vejvoda, On the existence and stability of the periodic solution of the second kind of a certain mechanical system. *Czech. Math. S.* **9**(84) 390–415 (1959).
60. L. Cesari, Existence theorems for periodic solutions of nonlinear Lipschitzian differential systems and fixed point theorems. *In* "Contributions to the Theory of Nonlinear Oscillations," Vol. V, pp. 115–172. Princeton, 1960. Univ. Press, Princeton, New Jersey.
61. N. Levinson, Small periodic perturbations of an autonomous system with a stable orbit. *Ann. of Math.* **52**, 729–738 (1950).
62. L. Flatto and N. Levinson, Periodic solutions of singularly perturbed equations. *J. Math. Mech.* **4**, 943–950 (1955).
63. S. K. Hale and G. Seifert, Bounded and almost periodic solutions of singularly perturbed equations. *J. Math. Anal. Appl.* **3**, No. 1, 18–24 (August 1961).
64. N. D. Anosov, On limit cycles of a system of differential equations with a small parameter in the highest derivative (in Russian). *Mat. Sb. N.S.* **50** (92), 299–334 (1960).
65. A. D. Myškis, "Linear Differential Equations with a Delayed Argument (in Russian). GITTL, Moscow, 1951.

66. L. E. Esgoltz, "Qualitative Methods in Mathematical Analysis" (in Russian). GITTL, Moscow, 1955.
67. A. Halanay, Some qualitative questions in the theory of differential equations with a delayed argument (in Russian). *Rev. Math. Pures Appl.* **11**, 127–144 (1957).
68. A. Halanay, Theorems on stability for systems with a delayed argument (in Russian). *Rev. Math. Pures Appl.* **III**, No. 2, 207–216 (1958).
69. A. Halanay, Stability criteriums for systems of differential equations with a delayed argument (in Russian). *Rev. Math. Pures Appl.* **V**, No. 2, 367–374 (1960).
70. A. Halanay, Integral stability for systems of differential equations with a delayed argument (in Russian). *Rev. Math. Pures Appl.* **V**, Nos. 3–4, 541–548 (1960).
71. A. Halanay, The Perron condition in the theory of general systems with retardation (in Russian). *Mathematica* **2** (25), 2, 257–267 (1960).
72. A. Halanay, Differential inequalities with time-lag and an application to a problem of the stability theory for systems with time-lag (in Rumanian). *Com. Acad. R.P. Romaine* **XI**, No. 11, 1305–1310 (1961).
73. V. M. Popov and A. Halanay, On the stability of nonlinear control systems with time-lag (in Russian). *Avtomat. i Telemeh.* **XXIII**, 7 (1962).
74. A. Halanay, Solutions périodiques des systèmes linéaires à argument retardé. *C. R. Acad. Sci. Paris* **249**, 2708–2709 (1959).
75. A. Halanay, Sur les systèmes d'équations différentielles linéaires à argument retardé. *C. R. Acad. Sci. Paris* **250**, 797–798 (1960).
76. A. Halanay, Solutions périodiques des systèmes généraux à retardement. *C. R. Acad. Sci. Paris* **250**, 3557–3559 (1960).
77. A. Halanay, Periodic solutions of linear systems with delay (in Russian). *Rev. Math. Pures Appl.* **VI**, No. 1, 141–158 (1961).
78. A. Halanay, Stability theory of linear periodic systems with delay (in Russian). *Rev. Math. Pures Appl.* **VI**, No. 4, 633–653 (1961).
79. S. N. Šimanov, On the theory of oscillations of quasilinear systems with delay (in Russian). *Prikl. Mat. Meh.* **23**, No. 5, 836–844 (1959).
80. S. N. Šimanov, Almost periodic oscillations of quasilinear systems with time lag in degenerate case (in Russian). *Dokl. Akad. Nauk SSSR* **133**, No. 1, 36–39 (1960).
81. A. Halanay, Periodic solutions of systems with time lag with a small parameter in critical case (in Russian). *Rev. Math. Pures Appl.* **VI**, No. 3, 487–491 (1961).
82. A. Halanay, Autonomous systems with delayed argument and small parameter (in Russian). *Rev. Math. Pures Appl* **VII**, No. 1, 81–89 (1962).
83. S. N. Šimanov, Oscillations of Quasilinear Autonomous Systems with time lag (in Russian). *Izv. Vysš. Uč. Zaved. Radiophysika* **3**, 456–466 (1960).
84. A. Halanay, The method of averaging in equations with delay (in Russian). *Rev. Math. Pures Appl.* **IV**, No. 3, 467–483 (1959).
85. A. Halanay, Almost periodic solutions of systems of differential equations with a delayed argument (in Russian). *Rev. Math. Pures Appl.* **V**, No. 1, 75–79 (1960).
86. A. Halanay, Asymptotic stability and small perturbations of periodic systems of differential equations with a delayed argument (in Russian). *Uspehi Mat. Nauk* **XVII**, No. 1, (103) 231–233 (1962).
87. A. Halanay, Peturbations singulières des systèmes à retardement. *C. R. Acad. Sci. Paris* **253**, 1659–1650 (1961). Singular peturbations of systems with time lag (in Russian). *Rev. Math. Pures Appl.* **VII**, No. 2 (1962).
88. H. E. Bray, Elementary properties of the Stieltjes integral. *Ann. of Math. Series II* **20**, 177–186 (1918–1919).

89. A. Halanay, Absolute stability of some nonlinear control systems with time lag (in Russian). *Avtomat. i Telemeh.* **XXV**, No. 3, 290–301 (1964).
90. A. Stokes, A Floquet theory for functional-differential equations. *Proc. Nat. Acad. Sci. U.S.A.* **48**, No. 8, 1330–1334 (1962).
91. A. Halanay, Almost-periodic solutions of linear systems with time lag (in Russian). *Rev. Math. Pures Appl.* **IX**, No. 1, 71–79 (1964).
92. A. Halanay, Singular perturbations of automonous systems with time lag. *Rev. Math. Pures Appl.* **VII**, No. 4, 627–631 (1962).
93. A. Halanay, Periodic and almost-periodic solutions of some singularly perturbed systems with time lag. *Rev. Math. Pures Appl.* **VIII**, No. 3, 397–403 (1963).
94. J. K. Hale, Linear functional-differential equations with constant coefficients. *Contributions to Differential Equations* **II**, 291–317 (1964).
95. J. K. Hale, Periodic and almost-periodic solutions of functional-differential equations. *Arch. Rational Mech. Anal.* **15**, No. 4, 289–304 (1964).
96. W. Hahn, "Theorie und Anwendung der direkten Methode von Lyapunov." Springer, Berlin, 1959 [English translation by Prentice-Hall, Englewood Cliffs, New Jersey, 1963].
97. J. La Salle and S. Lefschetz, "Stability by Liapunov's Direct Method." Academic Press, New York, 1961.
98. T. Yoshizawa, Liapunov's function and boundedness of solutions. *Funkcial. Ekvac.* **2**, 95–142 (1959).
99. T. Yoshizawa, Stability of sets and perturbed system. *Funkcial. Ekvac.* **5**, 31–69 (1962).
100. R. E. Kalman, Liapunov functions for the problem of Lurie in automatic control. *Proc. Nat. Acad. Sci. U. S. A.* **49**, 2 (1963).
101. V. A. Yakubovič, Absolute stability of nonlinear control systems in critical cases I (in Russian). *Avtomat. i Telemeh.* **XXIV**, No. 3 (1963).
102. V. A. Yakubovič, Absolute stability of nonlinear control systems in critical cases II (in Russian). *Avtomat. i Telemeh.* **XXIV**, No. 6 (1963).
103. M. A. Aizerman and F. R. Gantmacher, "Absolute Stability of Control Systems" (in Russian). Academy of Science of the USSR, 1963.
104. S. Dilliberto, Perturbation theorems for periodic surfaces I, II. Rendiconti Circ. Matem. Palermo, Serie II, T. IX, 1960, 265–299; T. X, 1961, 111–161.
105. L. Cesari, "Asymptotic Behavior and Stability Problems in Ordinary Differential Equations," Ist ed. Springer, Berlin, 1959 (2nd ed; 1963).
106. J. K. Hale, "Oscillations in Nonlinear Systems." McGraw-Hill, New York, 1963.
107. A. M. Zverkin, G. A. Kamenskii, S. B. Norkin, and L. E. Elsgoltz, Differential equations with deviated argument (in Russian). *Uspehi Mat. Nauk* **XVII**, No. 2 (104), 77–164 (1962).
108. A. M. Zverkin, G. A. Kamenskii, S. B. Norkin, and L. E. Elsgoltz, Differential equations with deviated argument II. (in Russian). *Trudy Sem. Teorii Differentialnych Uravnenii Otklaniaiuşcimsia Argumentom.* **I.II**, 3–49 (1963).
109. R. Bellman and K. Cooke, "Differential-Difference Equations." Academic Press, New York, 1963.

Subject Index